DATE DUE

MY 17 '96			
MY 18 96			
SE 9 98			
OC 5 99			
AR 29 99			
AP 2 02			
AP 22 05			
MY 11 05			

DEMCO 38-296

NOBEL PRIZE LIBRARY

FAULKNER

O'NEILL

STEINBECK

Nobel Prize Library

PUBLISHED UNDER THE·SPONSORSHIP OF THE
NOBEL FOUNDATION & THE SWEDISH ACADEMY

William Faulkner

Eugene O'Neill

John Steinbeck

ALEXIS GREGORY, *New York*, AND
CRM PUBLISHING, *Del Mar, California*

CONTENTS

William Faulkner

1949

"For his powerful and

artistically unique contribution

to the modern American novel"

Illustrated by ROBERT J. LEE

PRESENTATION ADDRESS

By GUSTAF HELLSTRÖM

MEMBER

OF THE SWEDISH ACADEMY

W ILLIAM FAULKNER is essentially a regional writer, and as such reminds Swedish readers now and then of two of our own most important
novelists, Selma Lagerlöf and Hjalmar Bergman. Faulkner's Värmland
is the northern part of the state of Mississippi and his Vadköping is
called Jefferson. The parallelism between him and our two fellow
countrymen could be extended and deepened, but time does not allow
such excursions now. The difference—the great difference—between him
and them is that Faulkner's setting is so much darker and more bloody
than that against which Lagerlöf's cavaliers and Bergman's bizarre
figures lived. Faulkner is the great epic writer of the Southern states with
all their background: a glorious past built upon cheap Negro slave labor;
a civil war and a defeat which destroyed the economic basis necessary
for the then existing social structure; a long drawn-out and painful interim
of resentment; and, finally, an industrial and commercial future whose
mechanization and standardization of life are strange and hostile to the
Southerner and to which he has only gradually been able and willing to
adapt himself.

Faulkner's novels are a continuous and ever-deepening description of
this painful process, which he knows intimately and feels intensely, coming as he does from a family which was forced to swallow the bitter
fruits of defeat right down to their worm-eaten cores: impoverishment,
decay, degeneration in its many varied forms. He has been called a re-
actionary. But even if this term is to some extent justified, it is balanced
by the feeling of guilt which becomes clearer and clearer in the dark
fabric at which he labors so untiringly. The price of the gentlemanly en-

[3]

vironment, the chivalry, the courage, and the often extreme individualism was inhumanity. Briefly, Faulkner's dilemma might be expressed thus: he mourns for and, as a writer, exaggerates a way of life which he himself, with his sense of justice and humanity, would never be able to stomach. It is this that makes his regionalism universal. Four bloody years of war brought about the changes in the social structure which it has taken the peoples of Europe, except the Russians, a century and a half to undergo.

It is against a background of war and violence that the fifty-two-year-old writer sets his more important novels. His grandfather held a high command during the Civil War. He himself grew up in the atmosphere created by warlike feats and by the bitterness and the poverty resulting from the never admitted defeat. When he was twenty he entered the Canadian Royal Air Force, crashed twice, and returned home, not as a military hero but as a physically and psychically war-damaged youth with dubious prospects, who for some years faced a precarious existence. He had joined the war because, as his alter ego expressed it in one of his early novels, "one doesn't want to waste a war." But out of the youth who once had been thirsting for sensation and battle, there gradually developed a man whose loathing of violence is expressed more and more passionately and might well be summed up by the Fifth Commandment: Thou shalt not kill. On the other hand, there are things which man must always show himself unwilling to bear: "Some things," says one of his latest characters, "you must always be unable to bear. Injustice and outrage and dishonor and shame. Not for kudos and not for cash—Just refuse to bear them." One might ask how these two maxims can be reconciled or how Faulkner himself envisages a reconciliation between them in times of international lawlessness. It is a question which he leaves open.

The fact is that, as a writer, Faulkner is no more interested in solving problems than he is tempted to indulge in sociological comments on the sudden changes in the economic position of the Southern states. The defeat and the consequences of defeat are merely the soil out of which his epics grow. He is not fascinated by men as a community but by man in the community, the individual as a final unity in himself, curiously unmoved by external conditions. The tragedies of these individuals have nothing in common with Greek tragedy: they are led to their inexorable end by passions caused by inheritance, traditions, and environment, passions which are expressed either in a sudden outburst or in a slow liberation from perhaps generations-old restrictions.

With almost every new work Faulkner penetrates deeper into the human psyche, into man's greatness and powers of self-sacrifice, lust for power, cupidity, spiritual poverty, narrow-mindedness, burlesque obstinacy, anguish, terror, and degenerate aberrations. As a probing psychologist he is the unrivaled master among all living British and American novelists. Neither do any of his colleagues possess his fantastic imaginative powers and his ability to create characters. His subhuman and superhuman figures, tragic or comic in a macabre way, emerge from his mind with a reality that few existing people—even those nearest to us—can give us, and they move in a milieu whose odors of subtropical plants, ladies' perfumes, Negro sweat, and the smell of horses and mules penetrate immediately even into a Scandinavian's warm and cozy den.

As a painter of landscapes he has the hunter's intimate knowledge of his own hunting-ground, the topographer's accuracy, and the impressionist's sensitivity. Moreover—side by side with Joyce and perhaps even more so—Faulkner is the great experimentalist among twentieth-century novelists. Scarcely two of his novels are similar technically. It seems as if by this continuous renewal he wanted to achieve the increased breadth which his limited world, both in geography and in subject matter, cannot give him. The same desire to experiment is shown in his mastery, unrivaled among modern British and American novelists, of the richness of the English language, a richness derived from its different linguistic elements and the periodic changes in style—from the spirit of the Elizabethans down to the scanty but expressive vocabulary of the Negroes of the Southern states.

Nor has anyone since Meredith—except perhaps Joyce—succeeded in framing sentences as infinite and powerful as Atlantic rollers. At the same time, few writers of his own age can rival him in giving a chain of events in a series of short sentences, each of which is like a blow of a hammer, driving the nail into the plank up to the head and securing it immovably. His perfect command over the resources of the language can —and often does—lead him to pile up words and associations which try the reader's patience in an exciting or complicated story. But this profusion has nothing to do with literary flamboyance. Nor does it merely bear witness to the abounding agility of his imagination; in all their richness, every new attribute, every new association is intended to dig deeper into the reality which his imaginative power conjures up.

Faulkner has often been described as a determinist. He himself, however, has never claimed to adhere to any special philosophy of life. Briefly, his view of life may perhaps be summed up in his own words: that the whole thing (perhaps?) signifies nothing. If this were not the case, He or They who set up the whole fabric would have arranged things differently. And yet it must mean something, because man continues to struggle and must continue to struggle until, one day, it is all over. But Faulkner has one belief, or rather one hope: that every man sooner or later receives the punishment he deserves and that self-sacrifice not only brings with it personal happiness but also adds to the sum total of the good deeds of mankind. It is a hope, the latter part of which reminds us of the firm conviction expressed by the Swedish poet Viktor Rydberg in the recitative of the Cantata presented at the Jubilee Degree Conferment at Uppsala in 1877.

Mr. Faulkner—The name of the Southern state in which you were born and reared has long been well known to us Swedes, thanks to two of the closest and dearest friends of your boyhood, Tom Sawyer and Huckleberry Finn. Mark Twain put the Mississippi River on the literary map. Fifty years later you began a series of novels with which you created out of the state of Mississippi one of the landmarks of twentieth-century world literature; novels which with their ever-varying form, their ever-deeper and more intense psychological insight, and their monumental characters—both good and evil—occupy a unique place in modern American and British fiction.

Mr. Faulkner—It is now my privilege to ask you to receive from the hands of His Majesty the King the Nobel Prize in Literature, which the Swedish Academy has awarded you.

ACCEPTANCE SPEECH

By WILLIAM FAULKNER

―――――――

I FEEL THAT THIS AWARD was not made to me as a man, but to my work—a life's work in the agony and sweat of the human spirit, not for glory and least of all for profit, but to create out of the materials of the human spirit something which did not exist before. So this award is only mine in trust. It will not be difficult to find a dedication for the money part of it commensurate with the purpose and significance of its origin. But I would like to do the same with the acclaim too, by using this moment as a pinnacle from which I might be listened to by the young men and women already dedicated to the same anguish and travail, among whom is already that one who will some day stand here where I am standing.

Our tragedy today is a general and universal physical fear so long sustained by now that we can even bear it. There are no longer problems of the spirit. There is only the question: When will I be blown up? Because of this, the young man or woman writing today has forgotten the problems of the human heart in conflict with itself which alone can make good writing because only that is worth writing about, worth the agony and the sweat.

He must learn them again. He must teach himself that the basest of all things is to be afraid; and, teaching himself that, forget it forever, leaving no room in his workshop for anything but the old verities and truths of the heart, the old universal truths lacking which any story is ephemeral and doomed—love and honor and pity and pride and compassion and sacrifice. Until he does so, he labors under a curse. He writes not of love but of lust, of defeats in which nobody loses anything of value, of victories without hope and, worst of all, without pity or compassion. His griefs grieve on no universal bones, leaving no scars. He writes not of the heart but of the glands.

Until he relearns these things, he will write as though he stood among and watched the end of man. I decline to accept the end of man. It is easy enough to say that man is immortal simply because he will endure: that when the last dingdong of doom has clanged and faded from the last worthless rock hanging tideless in the last red and dying evening, that even then there will still be one more sound: that of his puny inexhaustible voice, still talking. I refuse to accept this. I believe that man will not merely endure: he will prevail. He is immortal, not because he alone among creatures has an inexhaustible voice, but because he has a soul, a spirit capable of compassion and sacrifice and endurance. The poet's, the writer's, duty is to write about these things. It is his privilege to help man endure by lifting his heart, by reminding him of the courage and honor and hope and pride and compassion and pity and sacrifice which have been the glory of his past. The poet's voice need not merely be the record of man, it can be one of the props, the pillars to help him endure and prevail.

A ROSE FOR EMILY

By WILLIAM FAULKNER

I

When Miss Emily Grierson died, our whole town went to her funeral: the men through a sort of respectful affection for a fallen monument, the women mostly out of curiosity to see the inside of her house, which no one save an old man-servant—a combined gardener and cook—had seen in at least ten years.

It was a big, squarish frame house that had once been white, decorated with cupolas and spires and scrolled balconies in the heavily lightsome style of the seventies, set on what had once been our most select street. But garages and cotton gins had encroached and obliterated even the august names of that neighborhood; only Miss Emily's house was left, lifting its stubborn and coquettish decay above the cotton wagons and the gasoline pumps—an eyesore among eyesores. And now Miss Emily had gone to join the representatives of those august names where they lay in the cedar-bemused cemetery among the ranked and anonymous graves of Union and Confederate soldiers who fell at the battle of Jefferson.

Alive, Miss Emily had been a tradition, a duty, and a care; a sort of hereditary obligation upon the town, dating from that day in 1894 when Colonel Sartoris, the mayor—he who fathered the edict that no Negro woman should appear on the streets without an apron—remitted her taxes, the dispensation dating from the death of her father on into perpetuity. Not that Miss Emily would have accepted charity. Colonel Sartoris invented an involved tale to the effect that Miss Emily's father had loaned money to the town, which the town, as a matter of business, preferred this way of repaying. Only a man of Colonel Sartoris' generation and thought could have invented it, and only a woman could have believed it.

When the next generation, with its more modern ideas, became mayors and aldermen, this arrangement created some little dissatisfaction. On the first of the year they mailed her a tax notice. February came, and there was no reply. They wrote her a formal letter, asking her to call at the sheriff's office at her convenience. A week later the mayor wrote her himself, offering to call or to send his car for her, and received in reply a note on paper of an archaic shape, in a thin, flowing calligraphy in faded ink, to the effect that she no longer went out at all. The tax notice was also enclosed, without comment.

They called a special meeting of the Board of Aldermen. A deputation waited upon her, knocked at the door through which no visitor had passed since she ceased giving china-painting lessons eight or ten years earlier. They were admitted

[9]

by the old Negro into a dim hall from which a stairway mounted into still more shadow. It smelled of dust and disuse—a close, dank smell. The Negro led them into the parlor. It was furnished in heavy, leather-covered furniture. When the Negro opened the blinds of one window, they could see that the leather was cracked; and when they sat down, a faint dust rose sluggishly about their thighs, spinning with slow motes in the single sunray. On a tarnished gilt easel before the fireplace stood a crayon portrait of Miss Emily's father.

They rose when she entered—a small, fat woman in black, with a thin gold chain descending to her waist and vanishing into her belt, leaning on an ebony cane with a tarnished gold head. Her skeleton was small and spare; perhaps that was why what would have been merely plumpness in another was obesity in her. She looked bloated, like a body long submerged in motionless water, and of that pallid hue. Her eyes, lost in the fatty ridges of her face, looked like two small pieces of coal pressed into a lump of dough as they moved from one face to another while the visitors stated their errand.

She did not ask them to sit. She just stood in the door and listened quietly until the spokesman came to a stumbling halt. Then they could hear the invisible watch ticking at the end of the gold chain.

Her voice was dry and cold. "I have no taxes in Jefferson. Colonel Sartoris explained it to me. Perhaps one of you can gain access to the city records and satisfy yourselves."

"But we have. We are the city authorities, Miss Emily. Didn't you get a notice from the sheriff, signed by him?"

"I received a paper, yes," Miss Emily said. "Perhaps he considers himself the sheriff . . . I have no taxes in Jefferson."

"But there is nothing on the books to show that, you see. We must go by the—"

"See Colonel Sartoris. I have no taxes in Jefferson."

"But, Miss Emily—"

"See Colonel Sartoris." (Colonel Sartoris had been dead almost ten years.) "I have no taxes in Jefferson. Tobe!" The Negro appeared. "Show these gentlemen out."

II

So she vanquished them, horse and foot, just as she had vanquished their fathers thirty years before about the smell. That was two years after her father's death and a short time after her sweetheart— the one we believed would marry her— had deserted her. After her father's death she went out very little; after her sweetheart went away, people hardly saw her at all. A few of the ladies had the temerity to call, but were not received, and the only sign of life about the place was the Negro man—a young man then—going in and out with a market basket.

"Just as if a man—any man—could keep a kitchen properly," the ladies said; so they were not surprised when the smell developed. It was another link between the gross, teeming world and the high and mighty Griersons.

A neighbor, a woman, complained to the mayor, Judge Stevens, eighty years old.

"But what will you have me do about it, madam?" he said.

"Why, send her word to stop it," the woman said. "Isn't there a law?"

"I'm sure that won't be necessary," Judge Stevens said. "It's probably just a snake or a rat that nigger of hers killed in the yard. I'll speak to him about it."

The next day he received two more complaints, one from a man who came in diffident deprecation. "We really must do something about it, Judge. I'd be the last one in the world to bother Miss Emily, but we've got to do something." That night the Board of Aldermen met— three graybeards and one younger man, a member of the rising generation.

"It's simple enough," he said. "Send her word to have her place cleaned up. Give her a certain time to do it in, and if she don't . . ."

"Dammit, sir," Judge Stevens said, "will you accuse a lady to her face of smelling bad?"

So the next night, after midnight, four men crossed Miss Emily's lawn and slunk about the house like burglars, sniffing along the base of the brickwork and at the cellar openings while one of them performed a regular sowing motion with his hand out of a sack slung from his shoulder. They broke open the cellar door and sprinkled lime there, and in all the outbuildings. As they recrossed the lawn, a window that had been dark was lighted and Miss Emily sat in it, the light behind her, and her upright torso motionless as that of an idol. They crept quietly across the lawn and into the shadow of the locusts that lined the street. After a week or two the smell went away.

That was when people had begun to feel really sorry for her. People in our town, remembering how old lady Wyatt, her great-aunt, had gone completely crazy at last, believed that the Griersons held themselves a little too high for what they really were. None of the young men were quite good enough for Miss Emily and such. We had long thought of them as a tableau; Miss Emily a slender figure in white in the background, her father a spraddled silhouette in the foreground, his back to her and clutching a horse-whip, the two of them framed by the back-flung front door. So when she got to be thirty and was still single, we were not pleased exactly, but vindicated; even

with insanity in the family she wouldn't have turned down all of her chances if they had really materialized.

When her father died, it got about that the house was all that was left to her; and in a way, people were glad. At last they could pity Miss Emily. Being left alone, and a pauper, she had become humanized. Now she too would know the old thrill and the old despair of a penny more or less.

The day after his death all the ladies prepared to call at the house and offer condolence and aid, as is our custom. Miss Emily met them at the door, dressed as usual and with no trace of grief on her face. She told them that her father was not dead. She did that for three days, with the ministers calling on her, and the doctors, trying to persuade her to let them dispose of the body. Just as they were about to resort to law and force, she broke down, and they buried her father quickly.

We did not say she was crazy then. We believed she had to do that. We remembered all the young men her father had driven away, and we knew that with nothing left, she would have to cling to that which had robbed her, as people will.

III

She was sick for a long time. When we saw her again, her hair was cut short, making her look like a girl, with a vague resemblance to those angels in colored church windows—sort of tragic and serene.

The town had just let the contracts for paving the sidewalks, and in the summer after her father's death they began the work. The construction company came with niggers and mules and machinery, and a foreman named Homer Barron, a

Yankee—a big, dark, ready man, with a big voice and eyes lighter than his face. The little boys would follow in groups to hear him cuss the niggers, and the niggers singing in time to the rise and fall of picks. Pretty soon he knew everybody in town. Whenever you heard a lot of laughing anywhere about the square, Homer Barron would be in the center of the group. Presently we began to see him and Miss Emily on Sunday afternoons driving in the yellow-wheeled buggy and the matched team of bays from the livery stable.

At first we were glad that Miss Emily would have an interest, because the ladies all said, "Of course a Grierson would not think seriously of a Northerner, a day laborer." But there were still others, older people, who said that even grief could not cause a real lady to forget *noblesse oblige*—without calling it *noblesse oblige*. They just said, "Poor Emily. Her kinsfolk should come to her." She had some kin in Alabama; but years ago her father had fallen out with them over the estate of old lady Wyatt, the crazy woman, and there was no communication between the two families. They had not even been represented at the funeral.

And as soon as the old people said, "Poor Emily," the whispering began. "Do you suppose it's really so?" they said to one another. "Of course it is. What else could . . ." This behind their hands; rustling of craned silk and satin behind jalousies closed upon the sun of Sunday afternoon as the thin, swift clop-clop-clop of the matched team passed: "Poor Emily."

She carried her head high enough—even when we believed that she was fallen. It was as if she demanded more than ever the recognition of her dignity as the last Grierson; as if it had wanted that touch of earthiness to reaffirm her imperviousness. Like when she bought the rat poison, the arsenic. That was over

a year after they had begun to say "Poor Emily," and while the two female cousins were visiting her.

"I want some poison," she said to the druggist. She was over thirty then, still a slight woman, though thinner than usual, with cold, haughty black eyes in a face the flesh of which was strained across the temples and about the eye-sockets as you imagine a lighthouse-keeper's face ought to look. "I want some poison," she said.

"Yes, Miss Emily. What kind? For rats and such? I'd recom—"

"I want the best you have. I don't care what kind."

The druggist named several. "They'll kill anything up to an elephant. But what you want is—"

"Arsenic," Miss Emily said. "Is that a good one?"

"Is . . . arsenic? Yes, ma'am. But what you want—"

"I want arsenic."

The druggist looked down at her. She looked back at him, erect, her face like a strained flag. "Why, of course," the druggist said. "If that's what you want. But the law requires you to tell what you are going to use it for."

Miss Emily just stared at him, her head tilted back in order to look him eye for eye, until he looked away and went and got the arsenic and wrapped it up. The Negro delivery boy brought her the package; the druggist didn't come back. When she opened the package at home there was written on the box, under the skull and bones: "For rats."

IV

So the next day we all said, "She will kill herself"; and we said it would be the best thing. When she had first begun to be seen with Homer Barron, we had said, "She will marry him." Then we said,

"She will persuade him yet," because Homer himself had remarked—he liked men, and it was known that he drank with the younger men in the Elks' Club—that he was not a marrying man. Later we said, "Poor Emily" behind the jalousies as they passed on Sunday afternoon in the glittering buggy, Miss Emily with her head high and Homer Barron with his hat cocked and a cigar in his teeth, reins and whip in a yellow glove.

Then some of the ladies began to say that it was a disgrace to the town and a bad example to the young people. The men did not want to interfere, but at last the ladies forced the Baptist minister—Miss Emily's people were Episcopal—to call upon her. He would never divulge what happened during that interview, but he refused to go back again. The next Sunday they again drove about the streets, and the following day the minister's wife wrote to Miss Emily's relations in Alabama.

So she had blood-kin under her roof again and we sat back to watch developments. At first nothing happened. Then we were sure that they were to be married. We learned that Miss Emily had been to the jeweler's and ordered a man's toilet set in silver, with the letters H. B. on each piece. Two days later we learned that she had bought a complete outfit of men's clothing, including a nightshirt, and we said, "They are married." We were really glad. We were glad because the two female cousins were even more Grierson than Miss Emily had ever been.

So we were not surprised when Homer Barron—the streets had been finished some time since—was gone. We were a little disappointed that there was not a public blowing-off, but we believed that he had gone on to prepare for Miss Emily's coming, or to give her a chance to get rid of the cousins. (By that time it was a cabal, and we were all Miss Emily's allies to help circumvent the cousins.) Sure enough, after another week they departed. And, as we had expected all along, within three days Homer Barron was back in town. A neighbor saw the Negro man admit him at the kitchen door at dusk one evening.

And that was the last we saw of Homer Barron. And of Miss Emily for some time. The Negro man went in and out with the market basket, but the front door remained closed. Now and then we would see her at a window for a moment, as the men did that night when they sprinkled the lime, but for almost six months she did not appear on the streets. Then we knew that this was to be expected too; as if that quality of her father which had thwarted her woman's life so many times had been too virulent and too furious to die.

When we next saw Miss Emily, she had grown fat and her hair was turning gray. During the next few years it grew grayer and grayer until it attained an even pepper-and-salt iron-gray, when it ceased turning. Up to the day of her death at seventy-four it was still that vigorous iron-gray, like the hair of an active man.

From that time on her front door remained closed, save for a period of six or seven years, when she was about forty, during which she gave lessons in china-painting. She fitted up a studio in one of the downstairs rooms, where the daughters and granddaughters of Colonel Sartoris' contemporaries were sent to her with the same regularity and in the same spirit that they were sent to church on Sundays with a twenty-five cent piece for the collection plate. Meanwhile her taxes had been remitted.

Then the newer generation became the backbone and the spirit of the town, and the painting pupils grew up and fell away and did not send their children to her with boxes of color and tedious brushes and pictures cut from the ladies' magazines. The front door closed upon the last one and remained closed for good. When the town got free postal delivery, Miss Emily alone refused to let them fasten the metal numbers above her door and attach a mailbox to it. She would not listen to them.

Daily, monthly, yearly we watched the Negro grow grayer and more stooped, going in and out with the market basket. Each December we sent her a tax notice, which would be returned by the post office a week later, unclaimed. Now and then we would see her in one of the downstairs windows—she had evidently shut up the top floor of the house—like the carven torso of an idol in a niche, looking or not looking at us, we could never tell which. Thus she passed from generation to generation—dear, inescapable, impervious, tranquil, and perverse.

And so she died. Fell ill in the house filled with dust and shadows, with only a doddering Negro man to wait on her. We did not even know she was sick; we had long since given up trying to get any information from the Negro. He talked to no one, probably not even to her, for his voice had grown harsh and rusty, as if from disuse.

She died in one of the downstairs rooms, in a heavy walnut bed with a curtain, her gray head propped on a pillow yellow and moldy with age and lack of sunlight.

V

The Negro met the first of the ladies at the front door and let them in, with their hushed, sibilant voices and their quick, curious glances, and then he disappeared. He walked right through the house and out the back and was not seen again.

The two female cousins came at once. They held the funeral on the second day, with the town coming to look at Miss Emily beneath a mass of bought flowers, with the crayon face of her father musing profoundly above the bier and the ladies sibilant and macabre; and the very old men—some in their brushed Confederate uniforms—on the porch and the lawn, talking of Miss Emily as if she had been a contemporary of theirs, believing that they had danced with her and courted her perhaps, confusing time with its mathematical progression, as the old do, to whom all the past is not a diminishing road but, instead, a huge meadow which no winter ever quite touches, divided from them now by the narrow bottle-neck of the most recent decade of years.

Already we knew that there was one room in that region above stairs which no one had seen in forty years, and which would have to be forced. They waited until Miss Emily was decently in the ground before they opened it.

The violence of breaking down the door seemed to fill this room with pervading dust. A thin, acrid pall as of the tomb seemed to lie everywhere upon this room decked and furnished as for a bridal: upon the valance curtains of faded rose color, upon the rose-shaded lights, upon the dressing table, upon the delicate array of crystal and the man's toilet things backed with tarnished silver, silver so tarnished that the monogram was obscured. Among them lay a collar and tie, as if they had just been removed, which, lifted, left upon the surface a pale crescent in the dust. Upon a chair hung the suit, carefully folded; beneath it the two mute shoes and the discarded socks.

The man himself lay in the bed.

For a long while we just stood there, looking down at the profound and fleshless grin. The body had apparently once lain in the attitude of an embrace, but now the long sleep that outlasts love, that conquers even the grimace of love, had cuckolded him. What was left of him, rotted beneath what was left of the night-shirt, had become inextricable from the bed in which he lay; and upon him and upon the pillow beside him lay that even coating of the patient and biding dust.

Then we noticed that in the second pillow was the indentation of a head. One of us lifted something from it, and leaning forward, that faint and invisible dust dry and acrid in the nostrils, we saw a long strand of iron-gray hair.

AS I LAY DYING

By WILLIAM FAULKNER

DARL

Jewel and I come up from the field, following the path in single file. Although I am fifteen feet ahead of him, anyone watching us from the cottonhouse can see Jewel's frayed and broken straw hat a full head above my own.

The path runs straight as a plumb-line, worn smooth by feet and baked brick-hard by July, between the green rows of laid-by cotton, to the cottonhouse in the center of the field, where it turns and circles the cottonhouse at four soft right angles and goes on across the field again, worn so by feet in fading precision.

The cottonhouse is of rough logs, from between which the chinking has long fallen. Square, with a broken roof set at a single pitch, it leans in empty and shimmering dilapidation in the sunlight, a single broad window in two opposite walls giving onto the approaches of the path. When we reach it I turn and follow the path which circles the house. Jewel, fifteen feet behind me, looking straight ahead, steps in a single stride through the window. Still staring straight ahead, his pale eyes like wood set into his wooden face, he crosses the floor in four strides with the rigid gravity of a cigar store Indian dressed in patched overalls and endued with life from the hips down, and steps in a single stride through the opposite window and into the path again just as I come around the corner. In single file and five feet apart and Jewel now in front, we go on up the path toward the foot of the bluff.

Tull's wagon stands beside the spring, hitched to the rail, the reins wrapped about the seat stanchion. In the wagon bed are two chairs. Jewel stops at the spring and takes the gourd from the willow branch and drinks. I pass him and mount the path, beginning to hear Cash's saw.

When I reach the top he has quit sawing. Standing in a litter of chips, he is fitting two of the boards together. Between the shadow spaces they are yellow as gold, like soft gold, bearing on their flanks in smooth undulations the marks of the adze blade: a good carpenter, Cash is. He holds the two planks on the trestle, fitted along the edges in a quarter of the finished box. He kneels and squints along the edge of them, then he lowers them and takes up the adze. A good carpenter. Addie Bundren could not want a better one, a better box to lie in. It will give her confidence and comfort. I go on to the house, followed by the

Chuck. Chuck. Chuck.

of the adze.

CORA

So I saved out the eggs and baked yesterday. The cakes turned out right well. We

depend a lot on our chickens. They are
good layers, what few we have left after
the possums and such. Snakes too, in the
summer. A snake will break up a hen-
house quicker than anything. So after they
were going to cost so much more than
Mr Tull thought, and after I promised
that the difference in the number of eggs
would make it up, I had to be more careful than ever because it was on my final
say-so we took them. We could have
stocked cheaper chickens, but I gave my
promise as Miss Lawington said when
she advised me to get a good breed,
because Mr Tull himself admits that a
good breed of cows or hogs pays in the
long run. So when we lost so many of
them we couldn't afford to use the eggs
ourselves, because I could not have had
Mr Tull chide me when it was on my say-
so we took them. So when Miss Lawington told me about the cakes I thought
that I could bake them and earn enough
at one time to increase the net value of
the flock the equivalent of two head. And
that by saving the eggs out one at a time,
even the eggs wouldn't be costing anything. And that week they laid so well
that I not only saved out enough eggs
above what we had engaged to sell, to
bake the cakes with, I had saved enough
so that the flour and the sugar and the
stove wood would not be costing anything. So I baked yesterday, more careful
than ever I baked in my life, and the
cakes turned out right well. But when we
got to town this morning Miss Lawington
told me the lady had changed her mind
and was not going to have the party after
all.

"She ought to taken those cakes anyway," Kate says.

"Well," I say, "I reckon she never had
no use for them now."

"She ought to taken them," Kate says.
"But those rich town ladies can change
their minds. Poor folks cant."

Riches is nothing in the face of the
Lord, for He can see into the heart.
"Maybe I can sell them at the bazaar
Saturday," I say. They turned out real
well.

"You cant get two dollars a piece for
them," Kate says.

"Well, it isn't like they cost me anything," I say. I saved them out and
swapped a dozen of them for the sugar
and flour. It isn't like the cakes cost me
anything, as Mr Tull himself realises that
the eggs I saved were over and beyond
what we had engaged to sell, so it was
like we had found the eggs or they had
been given to us.

"She ought to taken those cakes when
she same as gave you her word," Kate
says. The Lord can see into the heart. If
it is His will that some folks has different
ideas of honesty from other folks, it is not
my place to question His decree.

"I reckon she never had any use for
them," I say. They turned out real well,
too.

The quilt is drawn up to her chin, hot
as it is, with only her two hands and her
face outside. She is propped on the pillow, with her head raised so she can see
out the window, and we can hear him
every time he takes up the adze or the
saw. If we were deaf we could almost
watch her face and hear him, see him.
Her face is wasted away so that the
bones draw just under the skin in white
lines. Her eyes are like two candles when
you watch them gutter down into the
sockets of iron candle-sticks. But the
eternal and the everlasting salvation and
grace is not upon her.

"They turned out real nice," I say.
"But not like the cakes Addie used to
bake." You can see that girl's washing
and ironing in the pillow-slip, if ironed it
ever was. Maybe it will reveal her blindness to her, laying there at the mercy and
the ministration of four men and a tom-
boy girl. "There's not a woman in this
section could ever bake with Addie

Bundren," I say. "First thing we know she'll be up and baking again, and then we wont have any sale for ours at all." Under the quilt she makes no more of a hump than a rail would, and the only way you can tell she is breathing is by the sound of the mattress shucks. Even the hair at her cheek does not move, even with that girl standing right over her, fanning her with the fan. While we watch she swaps the fan to the other hand without stopping it.

"Is she sleeping?" Kate whispers.

"She's just watching Cash yonder," the girl says. We can hear the saw in the board. It sounds like snoring. Eula turns on the trunk and looks out the window. Her necklace looks real nice with her red hat. You wouldn't think it only cost twenty-five cents.

"She ought to taken those cakes," Kate says.

I could have used the money real well. But it's not like they cost me anything except the baking. I can tell him that anybody is likely to make a miscue, but it's not all of them that can get out of it without loss, I can tell him. It's not everybody can eat their mistakes, I can tell him.

Someone comes through the hall. It is Darl. He does not look in as he passes the door. Eula watches him as he goes on and passes from sight again toward the back. Her hand rises and touches her beads lightly, and then her hair. When she finds me watching her, her eyes go blank.

DARL

Pa and Vernon are sitting on the back porch. Pa is tilting snuff from the lid of his snuff-box into his lower lip, holding the lip outdrawn between thumb and finger. They look around as I cross the porch and dip the gourd into the water bucket and drink.

"Where's Jewel?" pa says. When I was a boy I first learned how much better water tastes when it has set a while in a cedar bucket. Warmish-cool, with a faint taste like the hot July wind in cedar trees smells. It has to set at least six hours, and be drunk from a gourd. Water should never be drunk from metal.

And at night it is better still. I used to lie on the pallet in the hall, waiting until I could hear them all asleep, so I could get up and go back to the bucket. It would be black, the shelf black, the still surface of the water a round orifice in nothingness, where before I stirred it awake with the dipper I could see maybe a star or two in the bucket, and maybe in the dipper a star or two before I drank. After that I was bigger, older. Then I would wait until they all went to sleep so I could lie with my shirt-tail up, hearing them asleep, feeling myself without touching myself, feeling the cool silence blowing upon my parts and wondering if Cash was yonder in the darkness doing it too, had been doing it perhaps for the last two years before I could have wanted to or could have.

Pa's feet are badly splayed, his toes cramped and bent and warped, with no toenail at all on his little toes, from working so hard in the wet in homemade shoes when he was a boy. Beside his chair his brogans sit. They look as though they had been hacked with a blunt axe out of pig-iron. Vernon has been to town. I have never seen him go to town in overalls. His wife, they say. She taught school too, once.

I fling the dipper dregs to the ground and wipe my mouth on my sleeve. It is going to rain before morning. Maybe before dark. "Down to the barn," I say. "Harnessing the team."

Down there fooling with that horse. He will go on through the barn, into the pasture. The horse will not be in sight: he is up there among the pine seedlings, in the cool. Jewel whistles, once and shrill. The horse snorts, then Jewel sees him, glinting for a gaudy instant among the blue shadows. Jewel whistles again; the horse comes dropping down the slope, stiff-legged, his ears cocking and flicking, his mis-matched eyes rolling, and fetches up twenty feet away, broadside on, watching Jewel over his shoulder in an attitude kittenish and alert.

"Come here, sir," Jewel says. He moves. Moving that quick his coat, bunching, tongues swirling like so many flames. With tossing mane and tail and rolling eye the horse makes another short curvetting rush and stops again, feet bunched, watching Jewel. Jewel walks steadily toward him, his hands at his sides. Save for Jewel's legs they are like two figures carved for a tableau savage in the sun.

When Jewel can almost touch him, the horse stands on his hind legs and slashes down at Jewel. Then Jewel is enclosed by a glittering maze of hooves as by an illusion of wings; among them, beneath the upreared chest, he moves with the flashing limberness of a snake. For an instant before the jerk comes onto his arms he sees his whole body earth-free, horizontal, whipping snake-timber, until he finds the horse's nostrils and touches earth again. Then they are rigid, motionless, terrific, the horse back-thrust on stiffened, quivering legs, with lowered head; Jewel with dug heels, shutting off the horse's wind with one hand, with the other patting the horse's neck in short strokes myriad and caressing, cursing the horse with obscene ferocity.

They stand in rigid terrific hiatus, the horse trembling and groaning. Then Jewel is on the horse's back. He flows upward in a stooping swirl like the lash of a whip, his body in midair shaped to the horse. For another moment the horse stands spraddled, with lowered head, before it bursts into motion. They de-

scend the hill in a series of spine-jolting jumps, Jewel high, leech-like on the withers, to the fence where the horse bunches to a scuttering halt again.

"Well," Jewel says, "You can quit now, if you got a-plenty."

Inside the barn Jewel slides running to the ground before the horse stops. The horse enters the stall, Jewel following. Without looking back the horse kicks at him, slamming a single hoof into the wall with a pistol-like report. Jewel kicks him in the stomach; the horse arches his neck back, crop-toothed; Jewel strikes him across the face with his fist and slides on to the trough and mounts upon it. Clinging to the hay-rack he lowers his head and peers out across the stall tops and through the doorway. The path is empty; from here he cannot even hear Cash sawing. He reaches up and drags down hay in hurried armsful and crams it into the rack.

"Eat," he says. "Get the goddamn stuff out of sight while you got a chance, you pussel-gutted bastard. You sweet son of a bitch," he says.

JEWEL

It's because he stays out there, right under the window, hammering and sawing on that goddamn box. Where she's got to see him. Where every breath she draws is full of his knocking and sawing where she can see him saying See. See what a good one I am making for you. I told him to go somewhere else. I said Good God do you want to see her in it. It's like when he was a little boy and she says if she had some fertilizer she would try to raise some flowers and he taken the bread pan and brought it back from the barn full of dung.

And now them others sitting there, like buzzards. Waiting, fanning themselves.

Because I said If you wouldn't keep on sawing and nailing at it until a man cant sleep even and her hands laying on the quilt like two of them roots dug up and tried to wash and you couldn't get them clean. I can see the fan and Dewey Dell's arm. I said if you'd just let her alone. Sawing and knocking, and keeping the air always moving so fast on her face that when you're tired you cant breathe it, and that goddamn adze going One lick less. One lick less. One lick less until everybody that passes in the road will have to stop and see it and say what a fine carpenter he is. If it had just been me when Cash fell off of that church and if it had just been me when pa laid sick with that load of wood fell on him, it would not be happening with every bastard in the county coming in to stare at her because if there is a God what the hell is He for. It would just be me and her on a high hill and me rolling the rocks down the hill at their faces, picking them up and throwing them down the hill faces and teeth and all by God until she was quiet and not that goddamn adze going One lick less. One lick less and we could be quiet.

DARL

We watch him come around the corner and mount the steps. He does not look at us. "You ready?" he says.

"If you're hitched up," I say. I say "Wait." He stops, looking at pa. Vernon spits, without moving. He spits with decorous and deliberate precision into the pocked dust below the porch. Pa rubs his hands slowly on his knees. He is gazing out beyond the crest of the bluff, out across the land. Jewel watches him a moment, then he goes on to the pail and drinks again.

"I mislike undecision as much as ere a man," pa says.

"It means three dollars," I say. The shirt across pa's hump is faded lighter than the rest of it. There is no sweat stain on his shirt. I have never seen a sweat stain on his shirt. He was sick once from working in the sun when he was twenty-two years old, and he tells people that if he ever sweats, he will die. I suppose he believes it.

"But if she dont last until you get back," he says. "She will be disappointed."

Vernon spits into the dust. But it will rain before morning.

"She's counted on it," pa says. "She'll want to start right away. I know her. I promised her I'd keep the team here and ready, and she's counting on it."

"We'll need that three dollars then, sure," I say. He gazes out over the land, rubbing his hands on his knees. Since he lost his teeth his mouth collapses in slow repetition when he dips. The stubble gives his lower face that appearance that old dogs have. "You'd better make up your mind soon, so we can get there and get a load on before dark," I say.

"Ma aint that sick," Jewel says. "Shut up, Darl."

"That's right," Vernon says. "She seems more like herself today than she has in a week. Time you and Jewel get back, she'll be setting up."

"You ought to know," Jewel says. "You been here often enough looking at her. You or your folks." Vernon looks at him. Jewel's eyes look like pale wood in his high-blooded face. He is a head taller than any of the rest of us, always was. I told them that's why ma always whipped him and petted him more. Because he was peakling around the house more. That's why she named him Jewel I told them.

"Shut up, Jewel," pa says, but as though he is not listening much. He gazes out across the land, rubbing his knees.

"You could borrow the loan of Vernon's team and we could catch up with you," I say. "If she didn't wait for us."

"Ah, shut your goddamn mouth," Jewel says.

"She'll want to go in ourn," pa says. He rubs his knees. "Dont ere a man mislike it more."

"It's laying there, watching Cash whittle on that damn . . ." Jewel says. He says it harshly, savagely, but he does not say the word. Like a little boy in the dark to flail his courage and suddenly aghast into silence by his own noise.

"She wanted that like she wants to go in our own wagon," pa says. "She'll rest easier for knowing it's a good one, and private. She was ever a private woman. You know it well."

"Then let it be private," Jewel says. "But how the hell can you expect it to be—" he looks at the back of pa's head, his eyes like pale wooden eyes.

"Sho," Vernon says, "she'll hold on till it's finished. She'll hold on till everything's ready, till her own good time. And with the roads like they are now, it wont take you no time to get her to town."

"It's fixing up to rain," pa says. "I am a luckless man. I have ever been." He rubs his hands on his knees. "It's that durn doctor, liable to come at any time. I couldn't get word to him till so late. If he was to come tomorrow and tell her the time was nigh, she wouldn't wait. I know her. Wagon or no wagon, she wouldn't wait. Then she'd be upset, and I wouldn't upset her for the living world. With that family burying-ground in Jefferson and them of her blood waiting for her there, she'll be impatient. I promised my word me and the boys would get her there quick as mules could walk it, so she could rest quiet." He rubs his hands on his knees. "No man ever misliked it more."

"If everybody wasn't burning hell to get her there," Jewel says in that harsh, savage voice. "With Cash all day long right under the window, hammering and sawing at that—"

"It was her wish," pa says. "You got no affection nor gentleness for her. You never had. We would be beholden to no man," he says, "me and her. We have never yet been, and she will rest quieter for knowing it and that it was her own blood sawed out the boards and drove the nails. She was ever one to clean up after herself."

"It means three dollars," I say. "Do you want us to go, or not?" Pa rubs his knees. "We'll be back by tomorrow sundown."

"Well . . ." pa says. He looks out over the land, awry-haired, mouthing the snuff slowly against his gums.

"Come on," Jewel says. He goes down the steps. Vernon spits neatly into the dust.

"By sundown, now," pa says. "I would not keep her waiting."

Jewel glances back, then he goes on around the house. I enter the hall, hearing the voices before I reach the door. Tilting a little down the hill, as our house does, a breeze draws through the hall all the time, upslanting. A feather dropped near the front door will rise and brush along the ceiling, slanting backward, until it reaches the down-turning current at the back door: so with voices. As you enter the hall, they sound as though they were speaking out of the air about your head.

CORA

It was the sweetest thing I ever saw. It was like he knew he would never see her again, that Anse Bundren was driving him from his mother's death bed, never to see her in this world again. I always said Darl was different from those others. I always said he was the only one of them that had his mother's nature, had any natural affection. Not that Jewel, the one she labored so to bear and coddled and petted so and him flinging into tantrums or sulking spells, inventing devilment to devil her until I would have frailed him time and time. Not him to come and tell her goodbye. Not him to miss a chance to make that extra three dollars at the price of his mother's goodbye kiss. A Bundren through and through, loving nobody, caring for nothing except how to get something with the least amount of work. Mr Tull says Darl asked them to wait. He said Darl almost begged them on his knees not to force him to leave her in her condition. But nothing would do but Anse and Jewel must make that three dollars. Nobody that knows Anse could have expected different, but to think of that boy, that Jewel, selling all those years of self-denial and down-right partiality—they couldn't fool me: Mr Tull says Mrs Bundren liked Jewel the least of all, but I knew better. I knew she was partial to him, to the same quality in him that let her put up with Anse Bundren when Mr Tull said she ought to poisoned him—for three dollars, denying his dying mother the goodbye kiss.

Why, for the last three weeks I have been coming over every time I could, coming sometimes when I shouldn't have, neglecting my own family and duties so that somebody would be with her in her last moments and she would not have to face the Great Unknown without one familiar face to give her courage. Not that I deserve credit for it: I will expect the same for myself. But thank God it will be the faces of my loved kin, my blood and flesh, for in my husband and children I have been more blessed than most, trials though they have been at times.

She lived, a lonely woman, lonely with her pride, trying to make folks believe different, hiding the fact that they just suffered her, because she was not cold in the coffin before they were carting her forty miles away to bury her, flouting the will of God to do it. Refusing to let her lie in the same earth with those Bundrens.

"But she wanted to go," Mr Tull said. "It was her own wish to lie among her own people."

"Then why didn't she go alive?" I said. "Not one of them would have stopped her, with even that little one almost old enough now to be selfish and stone-hearted like the rest of them."

"It was her own wish," Mr Tull said. "I heard Anse say it was."

"And you would believe Anse, of course," I said. "A man like you would. Dont tell me."

"I'd believe him about something he couldn't expect to make anything off of me by not telling," Mr Tull said.

"Dont tell me," I said. "A woman's place is with her husband and children, alive or dead. Would you expect me to want to go back to Alabama and leave you and the girls when my time comes, that I left of my own will to cast my lot with yours for better and worse, until death and after?"

"Well, folks are different," he said.

I should hope so. I have tried to live right in the sight of God and man, for the honor and comfort of my Christian husband and the love and respect of my Christian children. So that when I lay me down in the consciousness of my duty and reward I will be surrounded by loving faces, carrying the farewell kiss of each of my loved ones into my reward. Not like Addie Bundren dying alone, hiding her pride and her broken heart. Glad to go. Lying there with her head propped up so she could watch Cash building the coffin, having to watch him so he would not skimp on it, like as not, with those men not worrying about anything except if there was time to earn another three dollars before the rain come and the river got too high to get across it. Like as not, if they hadn't decided to make that last load, they would have loaded her into the wagon on a quilt and crossed the river first and then stopped and give her time to die what Christian death they would let her.

Except Darl. It was the sweetest thing I ever saw. Sometimes I lose faith in human nature for a time; I am assailed by doubt. But always the Lord restores my faith and reveals to me His bounteous love for His creatures. Not Jewel, the one she had always cherished, not him. He was after that three extra dollars. It was Darl, the one that folks say is queer, lazy, pottering about the place no better than Anse, with Cash a good carpenter and always more building than he can get around to, and Jewel always doing something that made him some money or got him talked about, and that near-naked girl always standing over Addie with a fan so that every time a body tried to talk to her and cheer her up, would answer for her right quick, like she was trying to keep anybody from coming near her at all.

It was Darl. He come to the door and stood there, looking at his dying mother. He just looked at her, and I felt the bounteous love of the Lord again and His mercy. I saw that with Jewel she had just been pretending, but that it was between her and Darl that the understanding and the true love was. He just looked at her, not even coming in where she could see him and get upset, knowing that Anse was driving him away and he would never see her again. He said nothing, just looking at her.

"What you want, Darl?" Dewey Dell said, not stopping the fan, speaking up quick, keeping even him from her. He didn't answer. He just stood and looked at his dying mother, his heart too full for words.

DEWEY DELL

The first time me and Lafe picked on down the row. Pa dassent sweat because he will catch his death from the sickness so everybody that comes to help us. And Jewel dont care about anything he is not kin to us in caring, not care-kin. And Cash like sawing the long hot sad yellow days up into planks and nailing them to something. And pa thinks because neighbors will always treat one another that way because he has always been too busy letting neighbors do for him to find out. And I did not think that Darl would, that sits at the supper table with his eyes gone further than the food and the lamp, full of the land dug out of his skull and the holes filled with distance beyond the land.

We picked on down the row, the woods getting closer and closer and the secret shade, picking on into the secret shade with my sack and Lafe's sack. Because I said will I or wont I when the sack was half full because I said if the sack is full when we get to the woods it wont be me. I said if it dont mean for me to do it the sack will not be full and I will turn up the next row but if the sack is full, I cannot help it. It will be that I had to do it all the time and I cannot help it. And we picked on toward the secret shade and our eyes would drown together touching on his hands and my hands and I didn't say anything. I said "What are you doing?" and he said "I am picking into your sack." And so it was full when we came to the end of the row and I could not help it.

And so it was because I could not help it. It was then, and then I saw Darl and he knew. He said he knew without the words like he told me that ma is going to die without words, and I knew he knew because if he had said he knew with the words I would not have believed that he had been there and saw us. But he said he did know and I said "Are you going to tell pa are you going to kill him?" without the words I said it and he said "Why?" without the words. And that's why I can talk to him with knowing with hating because he knows.

He stands in the door, looking at her.

"What you want, Darl?" I say.

"She is going to die," he says. And old turkey-buzzard Tull coming to watch her die but I can fool them.

"When is she going to die?" I say.

"Before we get back," he says.

"Then why are you taking Jewel?" I say.

"I want him to help me load," he says.

TULL

Anse keeps on rubbing his knees. His overalls are faded; on one knee a serge patch cut out of a pair of Sunday pants, wore iron-slick. "No man mislikes it more than me," he says.

"A fellow's got to guess ahead now and then," I say. "But, come long and short, it wont be no harm done neither way."

"She'll want to get started right off," he says. "It's far enough to Jefferson at best."

"But the roads is good now," I say. It's fixing to rain tonight, too. His folks buries at New Hope, too, not three miles away. But it's just like him to marry a woman born a day's hard ride away and have her die on him.

He looks out over the land, rubbing his knees. "No man so mislikes it," he says.

"They'll get back in plenty of time," I say. "I wouldn't worry none."

"It means three dollars," he says.

"Might be it wont be no need for them to rush back, noways," I say. "I hope it."

"She's a-going," he says. "Her mind is set on it."

It's a hard life on women, for a fact. Some women. I mind my mammy lived to be seventy and more. Worked every day, rain or shine; never a sick day since her last chap was born until one day she kind of looked around her and then she went and taken that lace-trimmed night gown she had had forty-five years and never wore out of the chest and put it on and laid down on the bed and pulled the covers up and shut her eyes. "You all will have to look out for pa the best you can," she said. "I'm tired."

Anse rubs his hands on his knees. "The Lord giveth," he says. We can hear Cash a-hammering and sawing beyond the corner.

It's true. Never a truer breath was ever breathed. "The Lord giveth," I say.

That boy comes up the hill. He is carrying a fish nigh long as he is. He slings it to the ground and grunts "Hah" and spits over his shoulder like a man. Durn nigh long as he is.

"What's that?" I say. "A hog? Where'd you get it?"

"Down to the bridge," he says. He turns it over, the under side caked over with dust where it is wet, the eye coated over, humped under the dirt.

"Are you aiming to leave it laying there?" Anse says.

"I aim to show it to ma," Vardaman says. He looks toward the door. We can hear the talking, coming out on the draft. Cash too, knocking and hammering at the boards. "There's company in there," he says.

"Just my folks," I say. "They'd enjoy to see it too."

He says nothing, watching the door. Then he looks down at the fish laying in the dust. He turns it over with his foot and prods at the eye-bump with his toe, gouging at it. Anse is looking out over the land. Vardaman looks at Anse's face, then at the door. He turns, going toward the corner of the house, when Anse calls him without looking around.

"You clean that fish," Anse says.

Vardaman stops. "Why cant Dewey Dell clean it?" he says.

"You clean that fish," Anse says.

"Aw, pa," Vardaman says.

"You clean it," Anse says. He dont look around. Vardaman comes back and picks up the fish. It slides out of his hands, smearing wet dirt onto him, and flops down, dirtying itself again, gap-mouthed, goggle-eyed, hiding into the dust like it was ashamed of being dead, like it was in a hurry to get back hid again. Vardaman cusses it. He cusses it like a grown man, standing a-straddle of it. Anse dont look around. Vardaman picks it up again. He goes on around the house, toting it in both arms like a arm-ful of wood, it overlapping him on both ends, head and tail. Durn nigh big as he is.

Anse's wrists dangle out of his sleeves: I never see him with a shirt on that looked like it was his in all my life. They all looked like Jewel might have give him his old ones. Not Jewel, though. He's long-armed, even if he is spindling. Except for the lack of sweat. You could tell they aint been nobody else's but Anse's that way without no mistake. His eyes look like pieces of burnt-out cinder fixed in his face, looking out over the land.

When the shadow touches the steps he says "It's five oclock."

Just as I get up Cora comes to the door and says it's time to get on. Anse reaches for his shoes. "Now, Mr Bundren," Cora says, "dont you get up now." He puts his shoes on, stomping into them, like he does everything, like he is hoping all the time he really cant do

it and can quit trying to. When we go up the hall we can hear them clumping on the floor like they was iron shoes. He comes toward the door where she is, blinking his eyes, kind of looking ahead of hisself before he sees, like he is hoping to find her setting up, in a chair maybe or maybe sweeping, and looks into the door in that surprised way like he looks in and finds her still in bed every time and Dewey Dell still a-fanning her with the fan. He stands there, like he dont aim to move again nor nothing else.

"Well, I reckon we better get on," Cora says. "I got to feed the chickens." It's fixing to rain, too. Clouds like that don't lie, and the cotton making every day the Lord sends. That'll be something else for him. Cash is still trimming at the boards. "If there's ere a thing we can do," Cora says.

"Anse'll let us know," I say.

Anse dont look at us. He looks around, blinking, in that surprised way, like he had wore hisself down being surprised and was even surprised at that. If Cash just works that careful on my barn.

"I told Anse it likely wont be on need," I say. "I so hope it."

"Her mind is set on it," he says. "I reckon she's bound to go."

"It comes to all of us," Cora says. "Let the Lord comfort you."

"About that corn," I say. I tell him again I will help him out if he gets into a tight, with her sick and all. Like most folks around here, I done help him so much already I cant quit now.

"I aimed to get to it today," he says. "Seems like I cant get my mind on nothing."

"Maybe she'll hold out till you are laid-by," I say.

"If God wills it," he says.

"Let Him comfort you," Cora says.

If Cash just works that careful on my barn. He looks up when we pass. "Dont reckon I'll get to you this week," he says.

"'Taint no rush," I say. "Whenever you get around to it."

We get into the wagon. Cora sets the cake box on her lap. It's fixing to rain, sho.

"I dont know what he'll do," Cora says. "I just dont know."

"Poor Anse," I say. "She kept him at work for thirty-odd years. I reckon she is tired."

"And I reckon she'll be behind him for thirty years more," Kate says. "Or if it aint her, he'll get another one before cotton-picking."

"I reckon Cash and Darl can get married now," Eula says.

"That poor boy," Cora says. "The poor little tyke."

"What about Jewel?" Kate says.

"He can, too," Eula says.

"Hmph," Kate says. "I reckon he will. I reckon so. I reckon there's more gals than one around here that dont want to see Jewel tied down. Well, they needn't to worry."

"Why, Kate!" Cora says. The wagon begins to rattle. "The poor little tyke," Cora says.

It's fixing to rain this night. Yes, sir. A rattling wagon is mighty dry weather, for a Birdsell. But that'll be cured. It will for a fact.

"She ought to taken them cakes after she said she would," Kate says.

ANSE

Durn that road. And it fixing to rain, too. I can stand here and same as see it with second-sight, a-shutting down behind them like a wall, shutting down betwixt them and my given promise. I do the best I can, much as I can get my mind on anything, but durn them boys.

A-laying there, right up to my door, where every bad luck that comes and goes is bound to find it. I told Addie it want any luck living on a road when it come by here, and she said, for the world like a woman, "Get up and move, then." But I told her it want no luck in it, because the Lord put roads for travelling: why He laid them down flat on the earth. When He aims for something to be always a-moving, He makes it longways, like a road or a horse or a wagon, but when He aims for something to stay put, He makes it up-and-down ways, like a tree or a man. And so he never aimed for folks to live on a road, because which gets there first, I says, the road or the house? Did you ever know Him to set a road down by a house? I says. No you never, I says, because it's always men cant rest till they gets the house set where everybody that passes in a wagon can spit in the doorway, keeping the folks restless and wanting to get up and go somewheres else when He aimed for them to stay put like a tree or a stand of corn. Because if He'd a aimed for man to be always a-moving and going somewhere else, wouldn't He a put him longways on his belly, like a snake? It stands to reason He would.

Putting it where every bad luck prowling can find it and come straight to my door, charging me taxes on top of it. Making me pay for Cash having to get them carpenter notions when if it hadn't been no road come there, he wouldn't a got them; falling off of churches and lifting no hand in six months and me and Addie slaving and a-slaving, when there's plenty of sawing on this place he could do if he's got to saw.

And Darl too. Talking me out of him, durn them. It aint that I am afraid of work; I always is fed me and mine and kept a roof above us: it's that they would short-hand me just because he tends to his own business, just because he's got his eyes full of the land all the time. I says to them, he was all right at first, with his eyes full of the land, because the land laid up-and-down ways then; it wasn't till that ere road come and switched the land around longways and his eyes still full of the land, that they begun to threaten me out of him, trying to short-hand me with the law.

Making me pay for it. She was well and hale as ere a woman ever were, except for that road. Just laying down, resting herself in her own bed, asking naught of none. "Are you sick, Addie?" I said.

"I am not sick," she said.

"You lay you down and rest you," I said. "I knowed you are not sick. You're just tired. You lay you down and rest."

"I am not sick," she said. "I will get up."

"Lay still and rest," I said. "You are just tired. You can get up tomorrow." And she was laying there, well and hale as ere a woman ever were, except for that road.

"I never sent for you," I said. "I take you to witness I never sent for you."

"I know you didn't," Peabody said. "I bound that. Where is she?"

"She's a-laying down," I said. "She's just a little tired, but she'll—"

"Get outen here, Anse," he said. "Go set on the porch a while."

And now I got to pay for it, me without a tooth in my head, hoping to get ahead enough so I could get my mouth fixed where I could eat God's own victuals as a man should, and her hale and well as ere a woman in the land until that day. Got to pay for being put to the need of that three dollars. Got to pay for the way for them boys to have to go away to earn it. And now I can see same as second sight the rain shutting down betwixt us, a-coming up that road like a durn man, like it want ere a other house to rain on in all the living land.

I have heard men cuss their luck, and right, for they were sinful men. But I do not say it's a curse on me, because I have done no wrong to be cussed by. I am not religious, I reckon. But peace is my heart: I know it is. I have done things but neither better nor worse than them that pretend otherlike, and I know that Old Marster will care for me as for ere a sparrow that falls. But it seems hard that a man in his need could be so flouted by a road.

Vardaman comes around the house, bloody as a hog to his knees, and that ere fish chopped up with the axe like as not, or maybe throwed away for him to lie about the dogs et it. Well, I reckon I aint no call to expect no more of him than of his man-growed brothers. He comes along, watching the house, quiet, and sits on the steps. "Whew," he says, "I'm pure tired."

"Go wash them hands," I say. But couldn't no woman strove harder than Addie to make them right, man and boy: I'll say that for her.

"It was full of blood and guts as a hog," he says. But I just cant seem to get no heart into anything, with this here weather sapping me, too. "Pa," he says, "is ma sick some more?"

"Go wash them hands," I say. But I just cant seem to get no heart into it.

DARL

He has been to town this week: the back of his neck is trimmed close, with a white line between hair and sunburn like a joint of white bone. He has not once looked back.

"Jewel," I say. Back running, tunnelled between the two sets of bobbing mule ears, the road vanishes beneath the wagon as though it were a ribbon and the front axle were a spool. "Do you know she is going to die, Jewel?"

It takes two people to make you, and one people to die. That's how the world is going to end.

I said to Dewey Dell: "You want her to die so you can get to town: is that it?" She wouldn't say what we both knew. "The reason you will not say it is, when you say it, even to yourself, you will know it is true: is that it? But you know it is true now. I can almost tell you the day when you knew it is true. Why wont you say it, even to yourself?" She will not say it. She just keeps on saying Are you going to tell pa? Are you going to kill him? "You cannot believe it is true because you cannot believe that Dewey Dell, Dewey Dell Bundren, could have such bad luck: is that it?"

The sun, an hour above the horizon, is poised like a bloody egg upon a crest of thunderheads; the light has turned copper: in the eye portentous, in the nose sulphurous, smelling of lightning. When Peabody comes, they will have to use the rope. He has pussel-gutted himself eating cold greens. With the rope they will haul him up the path, balloon-like up the sulphurous air.

"Jewel," I say, "do you know that Addie Bundren is going to die? Addie Bundren is going to die?"

PEABODY

When Anse finally sent for me of his own accord, I said "He has wore her out at last." And I said a damn good thing, and at first I would not go because there might be something I could do and I would have to haul her back, by God. I thought maybe they have the same sort of fool ethics in heaven they have in the Medical College and that it was maybe Vernon Tull sending for me again, getting me there in the nick of time, as Vernon always does things, getting the most for Anse's money like he does for his own. But when it got far enough into the day for me to read weather signs I knew it couldn't have been anybody but Anse that sent. I knew that nobody but a luckless man could ever need a doctor in the face of a cyclone. And I knew that if it had finally occurred to Anse himself that he needed one, it was already too late.

When I reach the spring and get down and hitch the team, the sun has gone down behind a bank of black cloud like a topheavy mountain range, like a load of cinders dumped over there, and there is no wind. I could hear Cash sawing for a mile before I got there. Anse is standing at the top of the bluff above the path.

"Where's the horse?" I say.

"Jewel's taken and gone," he says. "Cant nobody else ketch hit. You'll have to walk up, I reckon."

"Me, walk up, weighing two hundred and twenty-five pounds?" I say. "Walk up that durn wall?" He stands there beside a tree. Too bad the Lord made the mistake of giving trees roots and giving the Anse Bundrens He makes feet and legs. If He'd just swapped them, there wouldn't ever be a worry about this country being deforested someday. Or any other country. "What do you aim for me to do?" I say. "Stay here and get blowed clean out of the county when that cloud breaks?" Even with the horse it would take me fifteen minutes to ride up across the pasture to the top of the ridge and reach the house. The path looks like a crooked limb blown against the bluff. Anse has not been in town in twelve years. And how his mother ever got up there to bear him, he being his mother's son.

"Vardaman's gittin the rope," he says.

After a while Vardaman appears with the plowline. He gives the end of it to Anse and comes down the path, uncoiling it.

"You hold it tight," I say. "I done already wrote this visit onto my books, so I'm going to charge you just the same, whether I get there or not."

"I got hit," Anse says. "You kin come on up."

I'll be damned if I can see why I dont quit. A man seventy years old, weighing two hundred and odd pounds, being hauled up and down a damn mountain on a rope. I reckon it's because I must reach the fifty thousand dollar mark of dead accounts on my books before I can quit. "What the hell does your wife mean," I say, "taking sick on top of a durn mountain?"

"I'm right sorry," he says. He let the rope go, just dropped it, and he has turned toward the house. There is a little daylight up here still, of the color of sulphur matches. The boards look like strips of sulphur. Cash does not look back. Vernon Tull says he brings each board up to the window for her to see it and say it is all right. The boy overtakes us. Anse looks back at him. "Where's the rope?" he says.

"It's where you left it," I say. "But never you mind that rope. I got to get back down that bluff. I dont aim for that storm to catch me up here. I'd blow too durn far once I got started."

The girl is standing by the bed, fanning her. When we enter she turns her head and looks at us. She has been dead these ten days. I suppose it's having been a part of Anse for so long that she cannot even make that change, if change it be. I can remember how when I was young I believed death to be a phenomenon of the body; now I know it to be merely a function of the mind—and that of the minds of the ones who suffer the bereavement. The nihilists say it is the end; the fundamentalists, the beginning; when in reality it is no more than a single tenant or family moving out of a tenement or a town.

She looks at us. Only her eyes seem to move. It's like they touch us, not with sight or sense, but like the stream from a hose touches you, the stream at the instant of impact as dissociated from the nozzle as though it had never been there. She does not look at Anse at all. She looks at me, then at the boy. Beneath the quilt she is no more than a bundle of rotten sticks.

"Well, Miss Addie," I say. The girl does not stop the fan. "How are you, sister?" I say. Her head lies gaunt on the pillow, looking at the boy. "You picked out a fine time to get me out here and bring up a storm." Then I send Anse and the boy out. She watches the boy as he leaves the room. She has not moved save her eyes.

He and Anse are on the porch when I come out, the boy sitting on the steps, Anse standing by a post, not even leaning against it, his arms dangling, the hair pushed and matted up on his head like a dipped rooster. He turns his head, blinking at me.

"Why didn't you send for me sooner?" I say.

"Hit was jest one thing and then another," he says. "That ere corn me and the boys was aimin to git up with, and Dewey Dell a-taking good keer of her, and folks comin in, a-offerin to help and sich, till I jest thought . . ."

"Damn the money," I say. "Did you ever hear of me worrying a fellow before he was ready to pay?"

"Hit aint begrudgin the money," he says. "I jest kept a-thinkin . . . She's goin, is she?" The durn little tyke is sitting on the top step, looking smaller than ever in the sulphur-colored light. That's the one trouble with this country: everything, weather, all, hangs on too long. Like our rivers, our land: opaque, slow, violent; shaping and creating the life of man in its implacable and brooding image. "I knowed hit," Anse says. "All the while I made sho. Her mind is sot on hit."

"And a damn good thing, too," I say. "With a trifling—" He sits on the top step, small, motionless in faded overalls. When I came out he looked up at me, then at Anse. But now he has stopped looking at us. He just sits there.

"Have you told her yit?" Anse says.

"What for?" I say. "What the devil for?"

"She'll know hit. I knowed that when she see you she would know hit, same as writing. You wouldn't need to tell her. Her mind—"

Behind us the girl says, "Paw." I look at her, at her face.

"You better go quick," I say.

When we enter the room she is watching the door. She looks at me. Her eyes look like lamps blaring up just before the oil is gone. "She wants you to go out," the girl says.

"Now, Addie," Anse says, "when he come all the way from Jefferson to git you well?" She watches me: I can feel her eyes. It's like she was shoving at me with them. I have seen it before in women. Seen them drive from the room them coming with sympathy and pity, with actual help, and clinging to some trifling animal to whom they never were more than pack-horses. That's what they mean by the love that passeth understanding: that pride, that furious desire to hide that abject nakedness which we bring here with us, carry with us into operating rooms, carry stubbornly and furiously with us into the earth again. I leave the room. Beyond the porch Cash's saw snores steadily into the board. A minute later she calls his name, her voice harsh and strong.

"Cash," she says; "you, Cash!"

DARL

Pa stands beside the bed. From behind his leg Vardaman peers, with his round head and his eyes round and his mouth beginning to open. She looks at pa; all her failing life appears to drain into her eyes, urgent, irremediable. "It's Jewel she wants," Dewey Dell says.

"Why, Addie," pa says, "him and Darl went to make one more load. They thought there was time. That you would wait for them, and that three dollars and all . . ." He stoops laying his hand on hers. For a while yet she looks at him, without reproach, without anything at all, as if her eyes alone are listening to the irrevocable cessation of his voice. Then she raises herself, who has not moved in ten days. Dewey Dell leans down, trying to press her back.

"Ma," she says; "ma."

She is looking out the window, at Cash stooping steadily at the board in the failing light, laboring on toward darkness and into it as though the stroking of the saw illumined its own motion, board and saw engendered.

"You, Cash," she shouts, her voice harsh, strong, and unimpaired. "You, Cash!"

He looks up at the gaunt face framed by the window in the twilight. It is a composite picture of all time since he was a child. He drops the saw and lifts the board for her to see, watching the window in which the face has not moved. He drags a second plank into position and slants the two of them into their final juxtaposition, gesturing toward the ones yet on the ground, shaping with his empty hand in pantomime the finished box. For a while still she looks down at him from the composite picture, neither with censure nor approbation. Then the face disappears.

She lies back and turns her head without so much as glancing at pa. She looks at Vardaman; her eyes, the life in them, rushing suddenly upon them; the two flames glare up for a steady instant. Then they go out as though someone had leaned down and blown upon them.

"Ma," Dewey Dell says; "ma!" Leaning above the bed, her hands lifted a little, the fan still moving like it has for ten days, she begins to keen. Her voice is strong, young, tremulous and clear, rapt with its own timbre and volume, the fan still moving steadily up and down, whispering the useless air. Then she flings herself across Addie Bundren's knees, clutching her, shaking her with the furious strength of the young before sprawling suddenly across the handful of rotten bones that Addie Bundren left, jarring the whole bed into a chattering sibilance of mattress shucks, her arms outflung and the fan in one hand still beating with expiring breath into the quilt.

From behind pa's leg Vardaman peers, his mouth full open and all color draining from his face into his mouth, as though he has by some means fleshed his own teeth in himself, sucking. He begins to move slowly backward from the bed, his eyes round, his pale face fading into the dusk like a piece of paper pasted on a failing wall, and so out of the door.

Pa leans above the bed in the twilight, his humped silhouette partaking of that owl-like quality of awry-feathered, disgruntled outrage within which lurks a wisdom too profound or too inert for even thought.

"Durn them boys," he says.

Jewel, I say. Overhead the day drives level and gray, hiding the sun by a flight of gray spears. In the rain the mules smoke a little, splashed yellow with mud, the off one clinging in sliding lunges to the side of the road above the ditch. The tilted lumber gleams dull yellow, water-soaked and heavy as lead, tilted at a steep angle into the ditch above the broken wheel; about the shattered spokes and about Jewel's ankles a runnel of yellow neither water nor earth swirls, curving with the yellow road neither of earth nor water, down the hill dissolving

into a streaming mass of dark green neither of earth nor sky. Jewel, I say

Cash comes to the door, carrying the saw. Pa stands beside the bed, humped, his arms dangling. He turns his head, his shabby profile, his chin collapsing slowly as he works the snuff against his gums.

"She's gone," Cash says.

"She taken and left us," pa says. Cash does not look at him. "How nigh are you done?" pa says. Cash does not answer. He enters, carrying the saw. "I reckon you better get at it," pa says. "You'll have to do the best you can, with them boys gone off that-a-way." Cash looks down at her face. He is not listening to pa at all. He does not approach the bed. He stops in the middle of the floor, the saw against his leg, his sweating arms powdered lightly with sawdust, his face composed. "If you get in a tight, maybe some of them'll get here tomorrow and help you," pa says. "Vernon could." Cash is not listening. He is looking down at her peaceful, rigid face fading into the dusk as though darkness were a precursor of the ultimate earth, until at last the face seems to float detached upon it, lightly as the reflection of a dead leaf. "There is Christians enough to help you," pa says. Cash is not listening. After a while he turns without looking at pa and leaves the room. Then the saw begins to snore again. "They will help us in our sorrow," pa says.

The sound of the saw is steady, competent, unhurried, stirring the dying light so that at each stroke her face seems to wake a little into an expression of listening and of waiting, as though she were counting the strokes. Pa looks down at the face, at the black sprawl of Dewey Dell's hair, the outflung arms, the clutched fan now motionless on the fading quilt. "I reckon you better get supper on," he says.

Dewey Dell does not move.

"Git up, now, and put supper on," pa says. "We got to keep our strength up. I reckon Doctor Peabody's right hungry, coming all this way. And Cash'll need to eat quick and get back to work so he can finish it in time."

Dewey Dell rises, heaving to her feet. She looks down at the face. It is like a casting of fading bronze upon the pillow, the hands alone still with any semblance of life: a curled, gnarled inertness; a spent yet alert quality from which weariness, exhaustion, travail has not yet departed, as though they doubted even yet the actuality of rest, guarding with horned and penurious alertness the cessation which they know cannot last.

Dewey Dell stoops and slides the quilt from beneath them and draws it up over them to the chin, smoothing it down, drawing it smooth. Then without looking at pa she goes around the bed and leaves the room.

She will go out where Peabody is, where she can stand in the twilight and look at his back with such an expression that, feeling her eyes and turning, he will say: I would not let it grieve me, now. She was old, and sick too. Suffering more than we knew. She couldn't have got well. Vardaman's getting big now, and with you to take good care of them all. I would try not to let it grieve me. I expect you'd better go and get some supper ready. It dont have to be much. But they'll need to eat, and she looking at him, saying You could do so much for me if you just would. If you just knew. I am I and you are you and I know it and you dont know it and you could do so much for me if you just would and if you just would then I could tell you and then nobody would have to know it except you and me and Darl

Pa stands over the bed, dangle-armed, humped, motionless. He raises his hand to his head, scouring his hair, listening to the saw. He comes nearer and rubs his hand, palm and back, on his thigh and lays it on her face and then on the hump of quilt where her hands are. He touches the quilt as he saw Dewey Dell do, trying to smooth it up to the chin, but disarranging it instead. He tries to smooth it again, clumsily, his hand awkward as a claw, smoothing at the wrinkles which he made and which continue to emerge beneath his hand with perverse ubiquity, so that at last he desists, his hand falling to his side and stroking itself again, palm and back, on his thigh. The sound of the saw snores steadily into the room. Pa breathes with a quiet, rasping sound, mouthing the snuff against his gums. "God's will be done," he says. "Now I can get them teeth."

Jewel's hat droops limp about his neck, channelling water onto the soaked towsack tied about his shoulders as, ankle-deep in the running ditch, he pries with a slipping two-by-four, with a piece of rotting log for fulcrum, at the axle. Jewel, I say, she is dead, Jewel. Addie Bundren is dead

VARDAMAN

Then I begin to run. I run toward the back and come to the edge of the porch and stop. Then I begin to cry. I can feel where the fish was in the dust. It is cut up into pieces of not-fish now, not-blood on my hands and overalls. Then it wasn't so. It hadn't happened then. And now she is getting so far ahead I cannot catch her.

The trees look like chickens when they ruffle out into the cool dust on the hot days. If I jump off the porch I will be where the fish was, and it all cut up into not-fish now. I can hear the bed and her face and them and I can feel the floor shake when he walks on it that came and did it. That came and did it when she was all right but he came and did it.

"The fat son of a bitch."

I jump from the porch, running. The top of the barn comes swooping up out of the twilight. If I jump I can go through it like the pink lady in the circus, into the warm smelling, without having to wait. My hands grab at the bushes; beneath my feet the rocks and dirt go rubbling down.

Then I can breathe again, in the warm smelling. I enter the stall, trying to touch him, and then I can cry then I vomit the crying. As soon as he gets through kicking I can and then I can cry, the crying can.

"He kilt her. He kilt her."

The life in him runs under the skin, under my hand, running through the splotches, smelling up into my nose where the sickness is beginning to cry, vomiting the crying, and then I can breathe, vomiting it. It makes a lot of noise. I can smell the life running up from under my hands, up my arms, and then I can leave the stall.

I cannot find it. In the dark, along the dust, the walls I cannot find it. The crying makes a lot of noise. I wish it wouldn't make so much noise. Then I find it in the wagon shed, in the dust, and I run across the lot and into the road, the stick jouncing on my shoulder.

They watch me as I run up, beginning to jerk back, their eyes rolling, snorting, jerking back on the hitch-rein. I strike. I can hear the stick striking; I can see it hitting their heads, the breast-yoke, missing altogether sometimes as they rear and plunge, but I am glad.

"You kilt my maw!"

The stick breaks, they rearing and snorting, their feet popping loud on the ground; loud because it is going to rain and the air is empty for the rain. But it is still long enough. I run this way and that as they rear and jerk at the hitch-rein, striking.

"You kilt her!"

I strike at them, striking, they wheeling in a long lunge, the buggy wheeling onto two wheels and motionless like it is nailed to the ground and the horses motionless like they are nailed by the hind feet to the center of a whirling plate.

I run in the dust. I cannot see, running in the sucking dust where the buggy vanishes tilted on two wheels. I strike, the stick hitting into the ground, bouncing, striking into the dust and then into the air again and the dust sucking on down the road faster than if a car was in it. And then I can cry, looking at the stick. It is broken down to my hand, not longer than stove wood that was a long stick. I throw it away and I can cry. It does not make so much noise now.

The cow is standing in the barn door, chewing. When she sees me come into the lot she lows, her mouth full of flopping green, her tongue flopping.

"I aint-a-goin to milk you. I aint a-goin to do nothing for them."

I hear her turn when I pass. When I turn she is just behind me with her sweet, hot, hard breath.

"Didn't I tell you I wouldn't?"

She nudges me, snuffing. She moans deep inside, her mouth closed. I jerk my hand, cursing her like Jewel does.

"Git, now."

I stoop my hand to the ground and run at her. She jumps back and whirls away and stops, watching me. She moans. She goes on to the path and stands there, looking up the path.

It is dark in the barn, warm, smelling, silent. I can cry quietly, watching the top of the hill.

Cash comes to the hill, limping where he fell off of the church. He looks down at the spring, then up the road and back toward the barn. He comes down the path stiffly and looks at the broken hitch-rein and at the dust in the road and then up the road, where the dust is gone.

"I hope they've got clean past Tull's by now. I so hope hit."

Cash turns and limps up the path.

"Durn him. I showed him. Durn him."

I am not crying now. I am not anything. Dewey Dell comes to the hill and calls me. Vardaman. I am not anything. I am quiet. You, Vardaman. I can cry quiet now, feeling and hearing my tears.

"Then hit want. Hit hadn't happened then. Hit was a-layin right there on the ground. And now she's gittin ready to cook hit."

It is dark. I can hear wood, silence: I know them. But not living sounds, not even him. It is as though the dark were resolving him out of his integrity, into an unrelated scattering of components— snuffings and stampings; smells of cooling flesh and ammoniac hair; an illusion of a co-ordinated whole of splotched hide and strong bones within which, detached and secret and familiar, an *is* different from my *is*. I see him dissolve—legs, a rolling eye, a gaudy splotching like cold flames—and float upon the dark in fading solution; all one yet neither; all either yet none. I can see hearing coil toward him, caressing, shaping his hard shape— fetlock, hip, shoulder and head; smell and sound. I am not afraid.

"Cooked and et. Cooked and et."

DEWEY DELL

He could do so much for me if he just would. He could do everything for me. It's like everything in the world for me is inside a tub full of guts, so that you wonder how there can be any room in it for anything else very important. He is a big tub of guts and I am a little tub of guts and if there is not any room for anything else important in a big tub of guts, how can it be room in a little tub of guts. But I know it is there because God gave women a sign when something has happened bad.

It's because I am alone. If I could just feel it, it would be different, because I would not be alone. But if I were not alone, everybody would know it. And he could do so much for me, and then I would not be alone. Then I could be all right alone.

I would let him come in between me and Lafe, like Darl came in between me and Lafe, and so Lafe is alone too. He is Lafe and I am Dewey Dell, and when mother died I had to go beyond and outside of me and Lafe and Darl to grieve because he could do so much for me and he dont know it. He dont even know it.

From the back porch I cannot see the barn. Then the sound of Cash's sawing comes in from that way. It is like a dog outside the house, going back and forth around the house to whatever door you come to, waiting to come in. He said I worry more than you do and I said You dont know what worry is so I cant worry. I try to but I cant think long enough to worry.

I light the kitchen lamp. The fish, cut into jagged pieces, bleeds quietly in the pan. I put it into the cupboard quick, listening into the hall, hearing. It took her ten days to die; maybe she dont know it is yet. Maybe she wont go until Cash. Or maybe until Jewel. I take the dish of greens from the cupboard and the bread pan from the cold stove, and I stop, watching the door.

"Where's Vardaman?" Cash says. In the lamp his sawdusted arms look like sand.

"I dont know. I aint seen him."

"Peabody's team run away. See if you can find Vardaman. The horse will let him catch him."

"Well. Tell them to come to supper."

I cannot see the barn. I said, I dont know how to worry. I dont know how to cry. I tried, but I cant. After a while the sound of the saw comes around, coming dark along the ground in the dust-dark. Then I can see him, going up and down above the plank.

"You come in to supper," I say. "Tell him." He could do everything for me. And he dont know it. He is his guts and I am my guts. And I am Lafe's guts. That's it. I dont see why he didn't stay in town. We are country people, not as good as town people. I dont see why he didn't. Then I can see the top of the barn. The cow stands at the foot of the path, lowing. When I turn back, Cash is gone.

I carry the buttermilk in. Pa and Cash and he are at the table.

"Where's that big fish Bud caught, sister?" he says.

I set the milk on the table. "I never had no time to cook it."

"Plain turnip greens is mighty spindling eating for a man my size," he says. Cash is eating. About his head the print of his hat is sweated into his hair. His shirt is blotched with sweat. He has not washed his hands and arms.

"You ought to took time," pa says. "Where's Vardaman?"

I go toward the door. "I cant find him."

"Here, sister," he says; "never mind about the fish. It'll save, I reckon. Come on and sit down."

"I aint minding it," I say. "I'm going to milk before it sets in to rain."

Pa helps himself and pushes the dish on. But he does not begin to eat. His hands are halfclosed on either side of his plate, his head bowed a little, his awry hair standing into the lamplight. He looks like right after the maul hits the steer and it's no longer alive and dont yet know that it is dead.

But Cash is eating, and he is too. "You better eat something," he says. He is looking at pa. "Like Cash and me. You'll need it."

"Ay," pa says. He rouses up, like a steer that's been kneeling in a pond and you run at it. "She would not begrudge me it."

When I am out of sight of the house, I go fast. The cow lows at the foot of the bluff. She nuzzles at me, snuffing, blowing her breath in a sweet, hot blast, through my dress, against my hot nakedness, moaning. "You got to wait a little while. Then I'll tend to you." She follows me into the barn where I set the bucket down. She breathes into the bucket, moaning. "I told you. You just got to wait, now. I got more to do than I can tend to." The barn is dark. When I pass, he kicks the wall a single blow. I go on. The broken plank is like a pale plank standing on end. Then I can see the slope, feel the air moving on my face again, slow, pale with lesser dark and with empty seeing, the pine clumps blotched up the tilted slope, secret and waiting.

The cow in silhouette against the door nuzzles at the silhouette of the bucket, moaning.

Then I pass the stall. I have almost passed it. I listen to it saying for a long time before it can say the word and the listening part is afraid that there may not be time to say it. I feel my body, my bones and flesh beginning to part and open upon the alone, and the process of coming unalone is terrible. Lafe. Lafe. "Lafe" Lafe. Lafe. I lean a little forward, one foot advanced with dead walking. I feel the darkness rushing past my breast, past the cow; I begin to rush upon the darkness but the cow stops me and the darkness rushes on upon the sweet blast of her moaning breath, filled with wood and with silence.

"Vardaman. You, Vardaman."

He comes out of the stall. "You durn little sneak! You durn little sneak!"

He does not resist; the last of rushing darkness flees whistling away. "What? I aint done nothing."

"You durn little sneak!" My hands shake him, hard. Maybe I couldn't stop them. I didn't know they could shake so hard. They shake both of us, shaking.

"I never done it," he says. "I never touched them."

My hands stop shaking him, but I still hold him. "What are you doing here? Why didn't you answer when I called you?"

"I aint doing nothing."

"You go on to the house and get your supper."

He draws back. I hold him. "You quit now. You leave me be."

"What were you doing down here? You didn't come down here to sneak after me?"

"I never. I never. You quit, now. I didn't even know you was down here. You leave me be."

I hold him, leaning down to see his face, feel it with my eyes. He is about to cry. "Go on, now. I done put supper on and I'll be there soon as I milk. You better go on before he eats everything up. I hope that team runs clean back to Jefferson."

"He kilt her," he says. He begins to cry.

"Hush."

"She never hurt him and he come and kilt her."

"Hush." He struggles. I hold him. "Hush."

"He kilt her." The cow comes up behind us, moaning. I shake him again.

"You stop it, now. Right this minute. You're fixing to make yourself sick and then you cant go to town. You go on to the house and eat your supper."

"I dont want no supper. I dont want to go to town."

"We'll leave you here, then. Lessen you behave, we will leave you. Go on, now, before that old green-eating tub of guts eats everything up from you." He goes on, disappearing slowly into the hill.

The crest, the trees, the roof of the house stand against the sky. The cow nuzzles at me, moaning. "You'll just have to wait. What you got in you aint nothing to what I got in me, even if you are a woman too." She follows me, moaning. Then the dead, hot, pale air breathes on my face again. He could fix it all right, if he just would. And he dont even know it. He could do everything for me if he just knowed it. The cow breathes upon my hips and back, her breath warm, sweet, stertorous, moaning. The sky lies flat down the slope, upon the secret clumps. Beyond the hill sheet-lightning stains upward and fades. The dead air shapes the dead earth in the dead darkness, further away than seeing shapes the dead earth. It lies dead and warm upon me, touching me naked through my clothes. I said You dont know what worry is. I dont know what it is. I dont know whether I am worrying or not. Whether I can or not. I dont know whether I can cry or not. I dont know whether I have tried to or not. I feel like a wet seed wild in the hot blind earth.

VARDAMAN

When they get it finished they are going to put her in it and then for a long time I couldn't say it. I saw the dark stand up and go whirling away and I said "Are you going to nail her up in it, Cash? Cash? Cash?" I got shut up in the crib the new door it was too heavy for me it went shut I couldn't breathe because the rat was breathing up all the air. I said "Are you going to nail it shut, Cash? Nail it? *Nail* it?"

Pa walks around. His shadow walks around, over Cash going up and down above the saw, at the bleeding plank.

Dewey Dell said we will get some bananas. The train is behind the glass, red on the track. When it runs the track shines on and off. Pa said flour and sugar and coffee costs so much. Because I am a country boy because boys in town. Bicycles. Why do flour and sugar and coffee cost so much when he is a country boy? "Wouldn't you ruther have some bananas instead?" Bananas are gone, eaten. Gone. When it runs on the track shines again. "Why aint I a town boy, pa?" I said. God made me. I did not said to God to made me in the country. If He can make the train, why cant He make them all in the town because flour and sugar and coffee. "Wouldn't you ruther have bananas?"

He walks around. His shadow walks around.

It was not her. I was there, looking. I saw. I thought it was her, but it was not. It was not my mother. She went away when the other one laid down in her bed and drew the quilt up. She went away. "Did she go as far as town?" "She went further than town." "Did all those rabbits and possums go further than town?" God made the rabbits and possums. He made the train. Why must He make a different place for them to go if she is just like the rabbit.

Pa walks around. His shadow does. The saw sounds like it is asleep.

And so if Cash nails the box up, she is not a rabbit. And so if she is not a rabbit I couldn't breathe in the crib and Cash is going to nail it up. And so if she lets him it is not her. I know. I was there. I saw when it did not be her. I saw. They think it is and Cash is going to nail it up.

It was not her because it was laying right yonder in the dirt. And now it's all chopped up. I chopped it up. It's laying in the kitchen in the bleeding pan, waiting to be cooked and et. Then it wasn't and she was, and now it is and she wasn't. And tomorrow it will be cooked and et and she will be him and pa and Cash and Dewey Dell and there wont be

anything in the box and so she can breathe. It was laying right yonder on the ground. I can get Vernon. He was there and he seen it, and with both of us it will be and then it will not be.

TULL

It was nigh to midnight and it had set into rain when he woke us. It had been a misdoubtful night, with the storm making; a night when a fellow looks for most anything to happen before he can get the stock fed and himself to the house and supper et and in bed with the rain starting, and when Peabody's team come up, lathered, with the broke harness dragging and the neck-yoke betwixt the off critter's legs, Cora says "It's Addie Bundren. She's gone at last."

"Peabody mought have been to ere a one of a dozen houses hereabouts," I says. "Besides, how do you know it's Peabody's team?"

"Well, aint it?" she says. "You hitch up, now."

"What for?" I says. "If she is gone, we cant do nothing till morning. And it fixing to storm, too."

"It's my duty," she says. "You put the team in."

But I wouldn't do it. "It stands to reason they'd send for us if they needed us. You dont even know she's gone yet."

"Why, dont you know that's Peabody's team? Do you claim it aint? Well, then." But I wouldn't go. When folks wants a fellow, it's best to wait till they sends for him, I've found. "It's my Christian duty," Cora says. "Will you stand between me and my Christian duty?"

"You can stay there all day tomorrow, if you want," I says.

So when Cora waked me it had set in to rain. Even while I was going to the door with the lamp and it shining on the glass so he could see I am coming, it kept on knocking. Not loud, but steady, like he might have gone to sleep thumping, but I never noticed how low down on the door the knocking was till I opened it and never seen nothing. I held the lamp up, with the rain sparkling across it and Cora back in the hall saying "Who is it, Vernon?" but I couldn't see nobody a-tall at first until I looked down and around the door, lowering the lamp.

He looked like a drownded puppy, in them overalls, without no hat, splashed up to his knees where he had walked them four miles in the mud. "Well, I'll be durned," I says.

"Who is it, Vernon?" Cora says.

He looked at me, his eyes round and black in the middle like when you throw a light in a owl's face. "You mind that ere fish," he says.

"Come in the house," I says. "What is it? Is your maw—"

"Vernon," Cora says.

He stood kind of around behind the door, in the dark. The rain was blowing onto the lamp, hissing on it so I am scared every minute it'll break. "You was there," he says. "You seen it."

Then Cora come to the door. "You come right in outen the rain," she says, pulling him in and him watching me. He looked just like a drownded puppy. "I told you," Cora says. "I told you it was a-happening. You go and hitch."

"But he aint said—" I says.

He looked at me, dripping onto the floor. "He's a-ruining the rug," Cora says. "You go get the team while I take him to the kitchen."

But he hung back, dripping, watching me with them eyes. "You was there. You seen it laying there. Cash is fixing to nail her up, and it was a-laying right there on the ground. You seen it. You seen the mark in the dirt. The rain never come up till after I was a-coming here. So we can get back in time."

I be durn if it didn't give me the creeps, even when I didn't know yet. But Cora did. "You get that team quick as you can," she says. "He's outen his head with grief and worry."

I be durn if it didn't give me the creeps. Now and then a fellow gets to thinking. About all the sorrow and afflictions in this world; how it's liable to strike anywhere, like lightning. I reckon it does take a powerful trust in the Lord to guard a fellow, though sometimes I think that Cora's a mite over-cautious, like she was trying to crowd the other folks away and get in closer than anybody else. But then, when something like this happens, I reckon she is right and you got to keep after it and I reckon I am blessed in having a wife that ever strives for sanctity and well-doing like she says I am.

Now and then a fellow gets to thinking about it. Not often, though. Which is a good thing. For the Lord aimed for him to do and not to spend too much time thinking, because his brain it's like a piece of machinery: it wont stand a whole lot of racking. It's best when it all runs along the same, doing the day's work and not no one part used no more than needful. I have said and I say again, that's ever living thing the matter with Darl: he just thinks by himself too much. Cora's right when she says all he needs is a wife to straighten him out. And when I think about that, I think that if nothing but being married will help a man, he's durn nigh hopeless. But I reckon Cora's right when she says the reason the Lord had to create women is because man dont know his own good when he sees it.

When I come back to the house with the team, they was in the kitchen. She was dressed on top of her nightgown, with a shawl over her head and her umbrella and her bible wrapped up in the oilcloth, and him sitting on a up-turned bucket on the stove-zinc where she had put him, dripping onto the floor. "I cant get nothing outen him except about a fish," she says. "It's a judgment on them. I see the hand of the Lord upon this boy for Anse Bundren's judgment and warning."

"The rain never come up till after I left," he says. "I had done left. I was on the way. And so it was there in the dust. You seen it. Cash is fixing to nail her, but you seen it."

When we got there it was raining hard, and him sitting on the seat between us, wrapped up in Cora's shawl. He hadn't said nothing else, just sitting there with Cora holding the umbrella over him. Now and then Cora would stop singing long enough to say "It's a judgment on Anse Bundren. May it show him the path of sin he is a-trodding." Then she would sing again, and him sitting there between us, leaning forward a little like the mules couldn't go fast enough to suit him.

"It was laying right yonder," he says, "but the rain come up after I taken and left. So I can go and open the windows, because Cash aint nailed her yet."

It was long a-past midnight when we drove the last nail, and almost dust-dawn when I got back home and taken the team out and got back in bed, with Cora's nightcap laying on the other pillow. And be durned if even then it wasn't like I could still hear Cora singing and feel that boy leaning forward between us like he was ahead of the mules, and still see Cash going up and down with that saw, and Anse standing there like a scarecrow, like he was a steer standing knee-deep in a pond and somebody come by and set the pond up on edge and he aint missed it yet.

It was nigh toward daybreak when we drove the last nail and toted it into the house, where she was laying on the bed with the window open and the rain blowing on her again. Twice he did it, and him so dead for sleep that Cora says his face looked like one of these here Christmas masts that had done been buried a while and then dug up, until at last they put her into it and nailed it down so he couldn't open the window on her no more. And the next morning they found him in his shirt tail, laying asleep on the floor like a felled steer, and the top of the box bored clean full of holes and Cash's new auger broke off in the last one. When they taken the lid off they found that two of them had bored on into her face.

If it's a judgment, it aint right. Because the Lord's got more to do than that. He's bound to have. Because the only burden Anse Bundren's ever had is himself. And when folks talks him low, I think to myself he aint that less of a man or he couldn't a bore himself this long.

It aint right. I be durn if it is. Because He said Suffer little children to come unto Me dont make it right, neither. Cora said, "I have bore you what the Lord God sent me. I faced it without fear nor terror because my faith was strong in the Lord, a-bolstering and sustaining me. If you have no son, it's because the Lord has decreed otherwise in His wisdom. And my life is and has ever been a open book to ere a man or woman among His creatures because I trust in my God and my reward."

I reckon she's right. I reckon if there's ere a man or woman anywhere that He could turn it all over to and go away with His mind at rest, it would be Cora. And I reckon she would make a few changes, no matter how He was running it. And I reckon they would be for man's good. Leastways, we would have to like them. Leastways, we might as well go on and make like we did.

DARL

The lantern sits on a stump. Rusted, grease-fouled, its cracked chimney smeared on one side with a soaring smudge of soot, it sheds a feeble and sultry glare upon the trestles and the boards and the adjacent earth. Upon the dark ground the chips look like random smears of soft pale paint on a black canvas. The boards look like long smooth tatters torn from the flat darkness and turned backside out.

Cash labors about the trestles, moving back and forth, lifting and placing the planks with long clattering reverberations in the dead air as though he were lifting and dropping them at the bottom of an invisible well, the sounds ceasing without departing, as if any movement might dislodge them from the immediate air in reverberant repetition. He saws again, his elbow flashing slowly, a thin thread of fire running along the edge of the saw, lost and recovered at the top and bottom of each stroke in unbroken elongation, so that the saw appears to be six feet long, into and out of pa's shabby and aimless silhouette. "Give me that plank," Cash says. "No; the other one." He puts the saw down and comes and picks up the plank he wants, sweeping pa away with the long swinging gleam of the balanced board.

The air smells like sulphur. Upon the impalpable plane of it their shadows form as upon a wall, as though like sound they had not gone very far away in falling but had merely congealed for a moment, immediate and musing. Cash works on, half turned into the feeble light, one thigh and one pole-thin arm braced, his face sloped into the light with a rapt, dynamic immobility above his tireless elbow. Below the sky sheet-lightning slumbers lightly; against it the trees, motionless, are ruffled out to the last twig, swollen, increased as though quick with young.

It begins to rain. The first harsh, sparse, swift drops rush through the leaves and across the ground in a long sigh, as though of relief from intolerable suspense. They are big as buckshot, warm as though fired from a gun; they sweep across the lantern in a vicious hissing. Pa lifts his face, slack-mouthed, the wet black rim of snuff plastered close along the base of his gums; from behind his slack-faced astonishment he muses as though from beyond time, upon the ultimate outrage. Cash looks once at the sky, then at the lantern. The saw has not faltered, the running gleam of its pistoning edge unbroken. "Get something to cover the lantern," he says.

Pa goes to the house. The rain rushes suddenly down, without thunder, without warning of any sort; he is swept onto the porch upon the edge of it and in an instant Cash is wet to the skin. Yet the motion of the saw has not faltered, as though it and the arm functioned in a tranquil conviction that rain was an illusion of the mind. Then he puts down the saw and goes and crouches above the lantern, shielding it with his body, his back shaped lean and scrawny by his wet shirt as though he had been abruptly turned wrongside out, shirt and all.

Pa returns. He is wearing Jewel's raincoat and carrying Dewey Dell's. Squatting over the lantern, Cash reaches back and picks up four sticks and drives them into the earth and takes Dewey Dell's raincoat from pa and spreads it over the sticks, forming a roof above the lantern. Pa watches him. "I dont know what you'll do," he says. "Darl taken his coat with him."

"Get wet," Cash says. He takes up the saw again; again it moves up and down, in and out of that unhurried imperviousness as a piston moves in the oil; soaked, scrawny, tireless, with the lean light body of a boy or an old man. Pa watches him, blinking, his face streaming; again he looks up at the sky with that expression of dumb and brooding outrage and yet of vindication, as though he had expected no less; now and then he stirs, moves, gaunt and streaming, picking up a board or a tool and then laying it down. Vernon Tull is there now, and Cash is wearing Mrs Tull's raincoat and he and Vernon are hunting the saw. After a while they find it in pa's hand.

"Why dont you go on to the house, out of the rain?" Cash says. Pa looks at him, his face streaming slowly. It is as though upon a face carved by a savage caricaturist a monstrous burlesque of all bereavement flowed. "You go on in," Cash says. "Me and Vernon can finish it."

Pa looks at them. The sleeves of Jewel's coat are too short for him. Upon his face the rain streams, slow as cold glycerin. "I dont begrudge her the wetting," he says. He moves again and falls to shifting the planks, picking them up, laying them down again carefully, as though they are glass. He goes to the lantern and pulls at the propped raincoat until he knocks it down and Cash comes and fixes it back.

"You get on to the house," Cash says. He leads pa to the house and returns with the raincoat and folds it and places it beneath the shelter where the lantern sits. Vernon has not stopped. He looks up, still sawing.

"You ought to done that at first," he says. "You knowed it was fixing to rain."

"It's his fever," Cash says. He looks at the board.

"Ay," Vernon says. "He'd a come, anyway."

Cash squints at the board. On the long flank of it the rain crashes steadily, myriad, fluctuant. "I'm going to bevel it," he says.

"It'll take more time," Vernon says. Cash sets the plank on edge; a moment longer Vernon watches him, then he hands him the plane.

Vernon holds the board steady while Cash bevels the edge of it with the tedious and minute care of a jeweler. Mrs Tull comes to the edge of the porch and calls Vernon. "How near are you done?" she says.

Vernon does not look up. "Not long. Some, yet."

She watches Cash stooping at the plank, the turgid savage gleam of the lantern slicking on the raincoat as he moves. "You go down and get some planks off the barn and finish it and come in out of the rain," she says. "You'll both catch your death." Vernon does not move. "Vernon," she says.

"We wont be long," he says. "We'll be done after a spell." Mrs Tull watches them a while. Then she reenters the house.

"If we get in a tight, we could take some of them planks," Vernon says. "I'll help you put them back."

Cash ceases the plane and squints along the plank, wiping it with his palm. "Give me the next one," he says.

Some time toward dawn the rain ceases. But it is not yet day when Cash drives the last nail and stands stiffly up and looks down at the finished coffin, the others watching him. In the lantern light his face is calm, musing; slowly he strokes his hands on his raincoated thighs in a gesture deliberate, final and composed. Then the four of them—Cash and pa and Vernon and Peabody—raise the coffin to their shoulders and turn toward the house. It is light, yet they move slowly; empty, yet they carry it carefully; lifeless, yet they move with hushed precautionary words to one another, speaking of it as though, complete, it now slumbered lightly alive, waiting to come awake. On the dark floor their feet clump awkwardly, as though for a long time they have not walked on floors.

They set it down by the bed. Peabody says quietly: "Let's eat a snack. It's almost daylight. Where's Cash?"

He has returned to the trestles, stooped

again in the lantern's feeble glare as he gathers up his tools and wipes them on a cloth carefully and puts them into the box with its leather sling to go over the shoulder. Then he takes up box, lantern and raincoat and returns to the house, mounting the steps into faint silhouette against the paling east.

In a strange room you must empty yourself for sleep. And before you are emptied for sleep, what are you. And when you are emptied for sleep, you are not. And when you are filled with sleep, you never were. I dont know what I am. I dont know if I am or not. Jewel knows he is, because he does not know that he does not know whether he is or not. He cannot empty himself for sleep because he is not what he is and he is what he is not. Beyond the unlamped wall I can hear the rain shaping the wagon that is ours, the load that is no longer theirs that felled and sawed it nor yet theirs that bought it and which is not ours either, lie on our wagon though it does, since only the wind and the rain shape it only to Jewel and me, that are not asleep. And since sleep is is-not and rain and wind are *was,* it is not. Yet the wagon *is,* because when the wagon is *was,* Addie Bundren will not be. And Jewel *is,* so Addie Bundren must be. And then I must be, or I could not empty myself for sleep in a strange room. And so if I am not emptied yet, I am *is.*

How often have I lain beneath rain on a strange roof, thinking of home.

CASH

I made it on the bevel.
1. There is more surface for the nails to grip.
2. There is twice the gripping-surface to each seam.
3. The water will have to seep into it on a slant. Water moves easiest up and down or straight across.
4. In a house people are upright two thirds of the time. So the seams and joints are made up-and-down. Because the stress is up-and-down.
5. In a bed where people lie down all the time, the joints and seams are made sideways, because the stress is sideways.
6. Except.
7. A body is not square like a crosstie.
8. Animal magnetism.
9. The animal magnetism of a dead body makes the stress come slanting, so the seams and joints of a coffin are made on the bevel.
10. You can see by an old grave that the earth sinks down on the bevel.
11. While in a natural hole it sinks by the center, the stress being up-and-down.
12. So I made it on the bevel.
13. It makes a neater job.

VARDAMAN

My mother is a fish.

TULL

It was ten oclock when I got back, with Peabody's team hitched on to the back of the wagon. They had already dragged the buckboard back from where Quick found it upside down straddle of the ditch about a mile from the spring. It was pulled out of the road at the spring, and about a dozen wagons was already there. It was Quick found it. He said the river was up and still rising. He said it had already covered the highest water-mark on the bridge-piling he had ever seen. "That bridge wont stand a whole lot of water," I said. "Has somebody told Anse about it?"

"I told him," Quick said. "He says he reckons them boys has heard and unloaded and are on the way back by now. He says they can load up and get across."

"He better go on and bury her at New Hope," Armstid said. "That bridge is old. I wouldn't monkey with it."

"His mind is set on taking her to Jefferson," Quick said.

"Then he better get at it soon as he can," Armstid said.

Anse meets us at the door. He has shaved, but not good. There is a long cut on his jaw, and he is wearing his Sunday pants and a white shirt with the neckband buttoned. It is drawn smooth over his hump, making it look bigger than ever, like a white shirt will, and his face is different too. He looks folks in the eye now, dignified, his face tragic and composed, shaking us by the hand as we walk up onto the porch and scrape our shoes, a little stiff in our Sunday clothes, our Sunday clothes rustling, not looking full at him as he meets us.

"The Lord giveth," we say.

"The Lord giveth."

That boy is not there. Peabody told about how he come into the kitchen, hollering, swarming and clawing at Cora when he found her cooking that fish, and how Dewey Dell taken him down to the barn. "My team all right?" Peabody says.

"All right," I tell him. "I give them a bait this morning. Your buggy seems all right too. It aint hurt."

"And no fault of somebody's," he says. "I'd give a nickel to know where that boy was when that team broke away."

"If it's broke anywhere, I'll fix it," I say.

The womenfolks go on into the house. We can hear them, talking and fanning. The fans go whish. whish. whish and them talking, the talking sounding kind of like bees murmuring in a water bucket. The men stop on the porch, talking some, not looking at one another.

"Howdy, Vernon," they say. "Howdy, Tull."

"Looks like more rain."

"It does for a fact."

"Yes, sir. It will rain some more."

"It come up quick."

"And going away slow. It dont fail."

I go around to the back. Cash is filling up the holes he bored in the top of it. He is trimming out plugs for them, one at a time, the wood wet and hard to work. He could cut up a tin can and hide the holes and nobody wouldn't know the difference. Wouldn't mind, anyway. I have seen him spend a hour trimming out a wedge like it was glass he was working, when he could have reached around and picked up a dozen sticks and drove them into the joint and made it do.

When we finished I go back to the front. The men have gone a little piece from the house, sitting on the ends of the boards and on the sawhorses where we made it last night, some sitting and some squatting. Whitfield aint come yet.

They look up at me, their eyes asking.

"It's about," I say. "He's ready to nail."

While they are getting up Anse comes to the door and looks at us and we return to the porch. We scrape our shoes again, careful, waiting for one another to go in first, milling a little at the door. Anse stands inside the door, dignified, composed. He waves us in and leads the way into the room.

They had laid her in it reversed. Cash made it clock-shape, like this

with every joint and seam bevelled and scrubbed with the plane, tight as a drum and neat as a sewing basket, and they had laid her in it head to foot so it wouldn't crush her dress. It was her wedding dress and it had a flare-out bottom, and they had laid her head to foot in it so the dress could spread out, and they had made her a veil out of a mosquito bar so the auger holes in her face wouldn't show.

When we are going out, Whitfield comes. He is wet and muddy to the waist, coming in. "The Lord comfort this house," he says. "I was late because the bridge has gone. I went down to the old ford and swum my horse over, the Lord protecting me. His grace be upon this house."

We go back to the trestles and plank-ends and sit or squat.

"I knowed it would go," Armstid says.

"It's been there a long time, that ere bridge," Quick says.

"The Lord has kept it there, you mean," Uncle Billy says. "I dont know ere a man that's touched hammer to it in twenty-five years."

"How long has it been there, Uncle Billy?" Quick says.

"It was built in . . . let me see . . . It was in the year 1888," Uncle Billy says. "I mind it because the first man to cross it was Peabody coming to my house when Jody was born."

"If I'd a crossed it every time your wife littered since, it'd a been wore out long before this, Billy," Peabody says.

We laugh, suddenly loud, then suddenly quiet again. We look a little aside at one another.

"Lots of folks has crossed it that wont cross no more bridges," Houston says.

"It's a fact," Littlejohn says. "It's so."

"One more aint, no ways," Armstid says. "It'd taken them two-three days to got her to town in the wagon. They'd be gone a week, getting her to Jefferson and back."

"What's Anse so itching to take her to Jefferson for, anyway?" Houston says.

"He promised her," I say. "She wanted it. She come from there. Her mind was set on it."

"And Anse is set on it, too," Quick says.

"Ay," Uncle Billy says. "It's like a man that's let everything slide all his life to get set on something that will make the most trouble for everybody he knows."

"Well, it'll take the Lord to get her over that river now," Peabody says. "Anse cant do it."

"And I reckon He will," Quick says. "He's took care of Anse a long time, now."

"It's a fact," Littlejohn says.

"Too long to quit now," Armstid says.

"I reckon He's like everybody else around here," Uncle Billy says. "He's done it so long now He cant quit."

Cash comes out. He has put on a clean shirt; his hair, wet, is combed smooth down on his brow, smooth and black as if he had painted it onto his head. He squats stiffly among us, we watching him.

"You feeling this weather, aint you?" Armstid says.

Cash says nothing.

"A broke bone always feels it," Littlejohn says. "A fellow with a broke bone can tell it a-coming."

"Lucky Cash got off with just a broke leg," Armstid says. "He might have hurt himself bed-rid. How far'd you fall, Cash?"

"Twenty-eight foot, four and a half inches, about," Cash says. I move over beside him.

"A fellow can sho slip quick on wet planks," Quick says.

"It's too bad," I say. "But you couldn't a holp it."

"It's them durn women," he says. "I made it to balance with her. I made it to her measure and weight."

If it takes wet boards for folks to fall, it's fixing to be lots of falling before this spell is done.

"You couldn't have holp it," I say.

I dont mind the folks falling. It's the cotton and corn I mind.

Neither does Peabody mind the folks falling. How bout it, Doc?

It's a fact. Washed clean outen the ground it will be. Seems like something is always happening to it.

Course it does. That's why it's worth anything. If nothing didn't happen and everybody made a big crop, do you reckon it would be worth the raising?

Well, I be durn if I like to see my work washed outen the ground, work I sweat over.

It's a fact. A fellow wouldn't mind seeing it washed up if he could just turn on the rain himself.

Who is that man can do that? Where is the color of his eyes?

Ay. The Lord made it to grow. It's Hisn to wash up if He sees it fitten so.

"You couldn't have holp it," I say.

"It's them durn women," he says.

In the house the women begin to sing. We hear the first line commence, beginning to swell as they take hold, and we rise and move toward the door, taking off our hats and throwing our chews away. We do not go in. We stop at the steps, clumped, holding our hats between our lax hands in front or behind, standing with one foot advanced and our heads lowered, looking aside, down at our hats in our hands and at the earth or now and then at the sky and at one another's grave, composed face.

The song ends; the voices quaver away with a rich and dying fall. Whitfield begins. His voice is bigger than him. It's like they are not the same. It's like he is one, and his voice is one, swimming on two horses side by side across the ford and coming into the house, the mud-splashed one and the one that never even got wet, triumphant and sad. Somebody in the house begins to cry. It sounds like her eyes and her voice were turned back inside her, listening; we move, shifting to the other leg, meeting one another's eye and making like they hadn't touched.

Whitfield stops at last. The women sing again. In the thick air it's like their voices come out of the air, flowing together and on in the sad, comforting tunes. When they cease it's like they hadn't gone away. It's like they had just disappeared into the air and when we moved we would loose them again out of the air around us, sad and comforting. Then they finish and we put on our hats, our movements stiff, like we hadn't never wore hats before.

On the way home Cora is still singing. "I am bounding toward my God and my reward," she sings, sitting on the wagon, the shawl around her shoulders and the umbrella open over her, though it is not raining.

"She has hern," I say. "Wherever she went, she has her reward in being free of Anse Bundren." *She laid there three days in that box, waiting for Darl and Jewel to come clean back home and get a new wheel and go back to where the wagon was in the ditch. Take my team, Anse, I said.*

We'll wait for ourn, he said. She'll want it so. She was ever a particular woman.

On the third day they got back and they loaded her into the wagon and started and it already too late. You'll have to go all the way round by Samson's bridge. It'll take you a day to get there. Then you'll be forty miles from Jefferson. Take my team, Anse.

We'll wait for ourn. She'll want it so.

It was about a mile from the house we saw him, sitting on the edge of the slough. It hadn't had a fish in it never that I knowed. He looked around at us, his eyes round and calm, his face dirty, the pole across his knees. Cora was still singing.

"This aint no good day to fish," I said.

"You come on home with us and me and you'll go down to the river first thing in the morning and catch some fish."

"It's one in here," he said. "Dewey Dell seen it."

"You come on with us. The river's the best place."

"It's in here," he said. "Dewey Dell seen it."

"I'm bounding toward my God and my reward," Cora sung.

DARL

"It's not your horse that's dead, Jewel," I say. He sits erect on the seat, leaning a little forward, wooden-backed. The brim of his hat has soaked free of the crown in two places, drooping across his wooden face so that, head lowered, he looks through it like through the visor of a helmet, looking long across the valley to where the barn leans against the bluff, shaping the invisible horse. "See them?" I say. High above the house, against the quick thick sky, they hang in narrowing circles. From here they are no more than specks, implacable, patient, portentous. "But it's not your horse that's dead."

"Goddamn you," he says. "Goddamn you."

I cannot love my mother because I have no mother. Jewel's mother is a horse.

Motionless, the tall buzzards hang in soaring circles, the clouds giving them an illusion of retrograde.

Motionless, wooden-backed, wooden-faced, he shapes the horse in a rigid stoop like a hawk, hook-winged. They are waiting for us, ready for the moving of it, waiting for him. He enters the stall and waits until it kicks at him so that he can slip past and mount onto the trough and pause, peering out across the inter-

vening stall-tops toward the empty path, before he reaches into the loft.

"Goddamn him. Goddamn him."

CASH

"It wont balance. If you want it to tote and ride on a balance, we will have—"

"Pick up. Goddamn you, pick up."

"I'm telling you it wont tote and it wont ride on a balance unless—"

"Pick up! Pick up, goddamn your thick-nosed soul to hell, pick up!"

It wont balance. If they want it to tote and ride on a balance, they will have

DARL

He stoops among us above it, two of the eight hands. In his face the blood goes in waves. In between them his flesh is greenish looking, about that smooth, thick, pale green of cow's cud; his face suffocated, furious, his lip lifted upon his teeth. "Pick up!" he says. "Pick up, goddamn your thick-nosed soul!"

He heaves, lifting one whole side so suddenly that we all spring into the lift to catch and balance it before he hurls it completely over. For an instant it resists, as though volitional, as though within it her pole-thin body clings furiously, even though dead, to a sort of modesty, as she would have tried to conceal a soiled garment that she could not prevent her body soiling. Then it breaks free, rising suddenly as though the emaciation of her body had added buoyancy to the planks or as though, seeing that the garment was about to be torn from her, she rushes suddenly after it in a passionate reversal that flouts its own desire and need. Jewel's face goes completely green and I can hear teeth in his breath.

We carry it down the hall, our feet harsh and clumsy on the floor, moving with shuffling steps, and through the door.

"Steady it a minute, now," pa says, letting go. He turns back to shut and lock the door, but Jewel will not wait.

"Come on," he says in that suffocating voice. "Come on."

We lower it carefully down the steps. We move, balancing it as though it were something infinitely precious, our faces averted, breathing through our teeth to keep our nostrils closed. We go down the path, toward the slope.

"We better wait," Cash says. "I tell you it aint balanced now. We'll need another hand on that hill."

"Then turn loose," Jewel says. He will not stop. Cash begins to fall behind, hobbling to keep up, breathing harshly; then he is distanced and Jewel carries the entire front end alone, so that, tilting as the path begins to slant, it begins to rush away from me and slip down the air like a sled upon invisible snow, smoothly evacuating atmosphere in which the sense of it is still shaped.

"Wait, Jewel," I say. But he will not wait. He is almost running now and Cash is left behind. It seems to me that the end which I now carry alone has no weight, as though it coasts like a rushing straw upon the furious tide of Jewel's despair. I am not even touching it when, turning, he lets it overshoot him, swinging, and stops it and sloughs it into the wagon bed in the same motion and looks back at me, his face suffused with fury and despair.

"Goddamn you. Goddamn you."

VARDAMAN

We are going to town. Dewey Dell says it wont be sold because it belongs to Santa Claus and he taken it back with him until next Christmas. Then it will be behind the glass again, shining with waiting.

Pa and Cash are coming down the hill, but Jewel is going to the barn. "Jewel," pa says. Jewel does not stop. "Where you going?" pa says. But Jewel does not stop. "You leave that horse here," pa says. Jewel stops and looks at pa. Jewel's eyes look like marbles. "You leave that horse here," pa says. "We'll all go in the wagon with ma, like she wanted."

But my mother is a fish. Vernon seen it. He was there.

"Jewel's mother is a horse," Darl said.

"Then mine can be a fish, cant it, Darl?" I said.

Jewel is my brother.

"Then mine will have to be a horse, too," I said.

"Why?" Darl said. "If pa is your pa, why does your ma have to be a horse just because Jewel's is?"

"Why does it?" I said. "Why does it, Darl?"

Darl is my brother.

"Then what is your ma, Darl?" I said.

"I haven't got ere one," Darl said. "Because if I had one, it is *was*. And if it is was, it cant be *is*. Can it?"

"No," I said.

"Then I am not," Darl said. "Am I?"

"No," I said.

I am. Darl is my brother.

"But you *are*, Darl," I said.

"I know it," Darl said. "That's why I am not *is*. *Are* is too many for one woman to foal."

Cash is carrying his tool box. Pa looks at him. "I'll stop at Tull's on the way back," Cash says. "Get on that barn roof."

"It aint respectful," pa says. "It's a deliberate flouting of her and of me."

"Do you want him to come all the way back here and carry them up to Tull's afoot?" Darl says. Pa looks at Darl, his mouth chewing. Pa shaves every day now because my mother is a fish.

"It aint right," pa says.

Dewey Dell has the package in her hand. She has the basket with our dinner too.

"What's that?" pa says.

"Mrs Tull's cakes," Dewey Dell says, getting into the wagon. "I'm taking them to town for her."

"It aint right," pa says. "It's a flouting of the dead."

It'll be there. It'll be there come Christmas, she says, shining on the track. She says he wont sell it to no town boys.

DARL

He goes on toward the barn, entering the lot, wooden-backed.

Dewey Dell carries the basket on one arm, in the other hand something wrapped square in a newspaper. Her face is calm and sullen, her eyes brooding and alert; within them I can see Peabody's back like two round peas in two thimbles: perhaps in Peabody's back two of those worms which work surreptitious and steady through you and out the other side and you waking suddenly from sleep or from waking, with on your face an expression sudden, intent, and concerned. She sets the basket into the wagon and climbs in, her leg coming long from beneath her tightening dress: that lever which moves the world; one of that caliper which measures the length and breadth of life. She sits on the seat beside Vardaman and sets the parcel on her lap.

Then he enters the barn. He has not looked back.

"It aint right," pa says. "It's little enough for him to do for her."

"Go on," Cash says. "Leave him stay if he wants. He'll be all right here. Maybe he'll go up to Tull's and stay."

"He'll catch us," I say. "He'll cut across and meet us at Tull's lane."

"He would have rid that horse, too," pa says, "if I hadn't a stopped him. A durn spotted critter wilder than a cattymount. A deliberate flouting of her and of me."

The wagon moves; the mules' ears begin to bob. Behind us, above the house, motionless in tall and soaring circles, they diminish and disappear.

ANSE

I told him not to bring that horse out of respect for his dead ma, because it wouldn't look right, him prancing along on a durn circus animal and her wanting us all to be in the wagon with her that sprung from her flesh and blood, but we hadn't no more than passed Tull's lane when Darl begun to laugh. Setting back there on the plank seat with Cash, with his dead ma laying in her coffin at his feet, laughing. How many times I told him it's doing such things as that that makes folks talk about him, I dont know. I says I got some regard for what folks says about my flesh and blood even if you haven't, even if I have raised such a durn passel of boys, and when you fixes it so folks can say such about you, it's a reflection on your ma, I says, not me: I am a man and I can stand it; it's on your womenfolks, your ma and sister that you should care for, and I turned and looked back at him and him setting there, laughing.

"I dont expect you to have no respect for me," I says. "But with your own ma not cold in her coffin yet."

"Yonder," Cash says, jerking his head toward the lane. The horse is still a right smart piece away, coming up at a good pace, but I dont have to be told who it is. I just looked back at Darl, setting there laughing.

"I done my best," I says. "I tried to do as she would wish it. The Lord will pardon me and excuse the conduct of them He sent me." And Darl setting on the plank seat right above her where she was laying, laughing.

DARL

He comes up the lane fast, yet we are three hundred yards beyond the mouth of it when he turns into the road, the mud flying beneath the flicking drive of the hooves. Then he slows a little, light and erect in the saddle, the horse mincing through the mud.

Tull is in his lot. He looks at us, lifts his hand. We go on, the wagon creaking, the mud whispering on the wheels. Vernon still stands there. He watches Jewel as he passes, the horse moving with a light, high-kneed driving gait, three hundred yards back. We go on, with a motion so soporific, so dreamlike as to be uninferant of progress, as though time and not space were decreasing between us and it.

It turns off at right angles, the wheel-marks of last Sunday healed away now: a smooth, red scoriation curving away into the pines; a white signboard with faded lettering: New Hope Church. 3 mi. It wheels up like a motionless hand lifted above the profound desolation of the ocean; beyond it the red road lies like a spoke of which Addie Bundren is the rim. It wheels past, empty, unscarred, the white signboard turns away its fading and tranquil assertion. Cash looks up the road quietly, his head turning as we pass it like an owl's head, his face composed. Pa looks straight ahead, humped. Dewey Dell looks at the road too, then she looks back at me, her eyes watchful and repudiant, not like that question which was in those of Cash, for a smoldering while. The signboard passes; the unscarred road wheels on. Then Dewey Dell turns her head. The wagon creaks on.

Cash spits over the wheel. "In a couple of days now it'll be smelling," he says.

"You might tell Jewel that," I say.

He is motionless now, sitting the horse at the junction, upright, watching us, no less still than the signboard that lifts its fading capitulation opposite him.

"It aint balanced right for no long ride," Cash says.

"Tell him that, too," I say. The wagon creaks on.

A mile further along he passes us, the horse, arch-necked, reined back to a swift singlefoot. He sits lightly, poised, upright, wooden-faced in the saddle, the broken hat raked at a swaggering angle. He passes us swiftly, without looking at us, the horse driving, its hooves hissing in the mud. A gout of mud, back-flung, plops onto the box. Cash leans forward and takes a tool from his box and removes it carefully. When the road crosses Whiteleaf, the willows leaning near enough, he breaks off a branch and scours at the stain with the wet leaves.

ANSE

It's a hard country on man; it's hard. Eight miles of the sweat of his body washed up outen the Lord's earth, where the Lord Himself told him to put it. Nowhere in this sinful world can a honest, hardworking man profit. It takes them that runs the stores in the towns, doing no sweating, living off of them that sweats. It aint the hardworking man, the farmer. Sometimes I wonder why we keep at it. It's because there is a reward for us above, where they cant take their autos and such. Every man will be equal there and it will be taken from them that have and give to them that have not by the Lord.

But it's a long wait, seems like. It's bad that a fellow must earn the reward of his right-doing by flouting hisself and his dead. We drove all the rest of the day and got to Samson's at dust-dark and then that bridge was gone, too. They hadn't never see the river so high, and it not done raining yet. There was old men that hadn't never see nor hear of it being so in the memory of man. I am the chosen of the Lord, for who He loveth, so doeth He chastiseth. But I be durn if He dont take some curious ways to show it, seems like.

But now I can get them teeth. That will be a comfort. It will.

SAMSON

It was just before sundown. We were sitting on the porch when the wagon came up the road with the five of them in it and the other one on the horse behind. One of them raised his hand, but they was going on past the store without stopping.

"Who's that?" MacCallum says: I cant think of his name: Rafe's twin; that one it was.

"It's Bundren, from down beyond New Hope," Quick says. "There's one of them Snopes horses Jewel's riding."

"I didn't know there was ere a one of them horses left," MacCallum says. "I thought you folks down there finally contrived to give them all away."

"Try and get that one," Quick says. The wagon went on.

"I bet old man Lon never gave it to him," I says.

"No," Quick says. "He bought it from pappy." The wagon went on. "They must not a heard about the bridge," he says.

"What're they doing up here, anyway?" MacCallum says.

"Taking a holiday since he got his wife buried, I reckon," Quick says. "Heading for town, I reckon, with Tull's bridge gone too. I wonder if they aint heard about the bridge."

"They'll have to fly, then," I says. "I dont reckon there's ere a bridge between here and Mouth of Ishatawa."

They had something in the wagon. But Quick had been to the funeral three days ago and we naturally never thought anything about it except that they were heading away from home mighty late and that they hadn't heard about the bridge. "You better holler at them," MacCallum says. Durn it, the name is right on the tip of my tongue. So Quick hollered and they stopped and he went to the wagon and told them.

He come back with them. "They're going to Jefferson," he said. "The bridge at Tull's is gone, too." Like we didn't know it, and his face looked funny, around the nostrils, but they just sat there, Bundren and the girl and the chap on the seat, and Cash and the second one, the one folks talks about, on a plank across the tail-gate, and the other one on that spotted horse. But I reckon they was used to it by then, because when I said to Cash that they'd have to pass by New Hope again and what they'd better do, he just says,

"I reckon we can get there."

I aint much for meddling. Let every man run his own business to suit himself, I say. But after I talked to Rachel about them not having a regular man to fix her and it being July and all, I went back down to the barn and tried to talk to Bundren about it.

"I give her my promise," he says. "Her mind was set on it."

I notice how it takes a lazy man, a man that hates moving, to get set on moving once he does get started off, the same as he was set on staying still, like it aint the moving he hates so much as the starting and the stopping. And like he would be kind of proud of whatever come up to make the moving or the setting still look hard. He set there on the wagon, hunched up, blinking, listening to us tell about how quick the bridge went and how high the water was, and I be durn if he didn't act like he was proud of it, like he had made the river rise himself.

"You say it's higher than you ever see it before?" he says. "God's will be done," he says. "I reckon it wont go down much by morning, neither," he says.

"You better stay here tonight," I says, "and get a early start for New Hope tomorrow morning." I was just sorry for them bone-gaunted mules. I told Rachel, I says, "Well, would you have had me turn them away at dark, eight miles from home? What else could I do," I says. "It wont be but one night, and they'll keep it in the barn, and they'll sholy get started by daylight." And so I says, "You stay here tonight and early tomorrow you can go back to New Hope. I got tools enough, and the boys can go on right after supper and have it dug and ready if they want" and then I found that girl watching me. If her eyes had a been pistols, I wouldn't be talking now. I be dog if they didn't blaze at me. And so when I went down to the barn I come on them, her talking so she never noticed when I come up.

"You promised her," she says. "She wouldn't go until you promised. She thought she could depend on you. If you dont do it, it will be a curse on you."

"Cant no man say I dont aim to keep my word," Bundren says. "My heart is open to ere a man."

"I dont care what your heart is," she says. She was whispering, kind of, talking fast. "You promised her. You've got to. You—" then she seen me and quit, standing there. If they'd been pistols, I wouldn't be talking now. So when I talked to him about it, he says,

"I give her my promise. Her mind is set on it."

"But seems to me she'd rather have her ma buried close by, so she could—"

"It's Addie I give the promise to," he says. "Her mind is set on it."

So I told them to drive it into the barn, because it was threatening rain again, and that supper was about ready. Only they didn't want to come in.

"I thank you," Bundren says. "We wouldn't discommode you. We got a little something in the basket. We can make out."

"Well," I says, "since you are so particular about your womenfolks, I am too. And when folks stops with us at meal time and wont come to the table, my wife takes it as a insult."

So the girl went on to the kitchen to help Rachel. And then Jewel come to me.

"Sho," I says. "Help yourself outen the loft. Feed him when you bait the mules."

"I rather pay you for him," he says.

"What for?" I says. "I wouldn't begrudge no man a bait for his horse."

"I rather pay you," he says; I thought he said extra.

"Extra for what?" I says. "Wont he eat hay and corn?"

"Extra feed," he says. "I feed him a little extra and I dont want him beholden to no man."

"You cant buy no feed from me, boy," I says. "And if he can eat that loft clean, I'll help you load the barn onto the wagon in the morning."

"He aint never been beholden to no man," he says. "I rather pay you for it."

And if I had my rathers, you wouldn't be here a-tall, I wanted to say. But I just says, "Then it's high time he commenced. You cant buy no feed from me."

When Rachel put supper on, her and the girl went and fixed some beds. But wouldn't any of them come in. "She's been dead long enough to get over that sort of foolishness," I says. Because I got just as much respect for the dead as ere a man, but you've got to respect the dead themselves, and a woman that's been dead in a box four days, the best way to respect her is to get her into the ground as quick as you can. But they wouldn't do it.

"It wouldn't be right," Bundren says. "Course, if the boys wants to go to bed, I reckon I can set up with her. I dont begrudge her it."

So when I went back down there they were squatting on the ground around the wagon, all of them. "Let that chap come to the house and get some sleep, anyway," I says. "And you better come too," I says to the girl. I wasn't aiming to interfere with them. And I sholy hadn't done nothing to her that I knowed.

"He's done already asleep," Bundren says. They had done put him to bed in the trough in a empty stall.

"Well, you come on, then," I says to her. But still she never said nothing. They just squatted there. You couldn't hardly see them. "How about you boys?" I says. "You got a full day tomorrow." After a while Cash says,

"I thank you. We can make out."

"We wouldn't be beholden," Bundren says. "I thank you kindly."

So I left them squatting there. I reckon after four days they was used to it. But Rachel wasn't.

"It's a outrage," she says. "A outrage."

"What could he a done?" I says. "He give her his promised word."

"Who's talking about him?" she says. "Who cares about him?" she says, crying. "I just wish that you and him and all the men in the world that torture us alive and flout us dead, dragging us up and down the country—"

"Now, now," I says. "You're upset."

"Dont you touch me!" she says. "Dont you touch me!"

A man cant tell nothing about them. I lived with the same one fifteen years and I be durn if I can. And I imagined a lot of things coming up between us, but I be durn if I ever thought it would be a body four days dead and that a woman. But they make life hard on them, not taking it as it comes up, like a man does.

So I laid there, hearing it commence to rain, thinking about them down there, squatting around the wagon and the rain on the roof, and thinking about Rachel crying there until after a while it was like I could still hear her crying even after she was asleep, and smelling it even when I knowed I couldn't. I couldn't decide even then whether I could or not, or if it wasn't just knowing it was what it was.

So next morning I never went down there. I heard them hitching up and then when I knowed they must be about ready to take out, I went out the front and went down the road toward the bridge until I heard the wagon come out of the lot and go back toward New Hope. And then when I come back to the house, Rachel jumped on me because I wasn't there to make them come in to breakfast. You cant tell about them. Just about when you decide they mean one thing, I be durn if you not only haven't got to change your mind, like as not you got to take a rawhiding for thinking they meant it.

But it was still like I could smell it. And so I decided then that it wasn't smelling it, but it was just knowing it was there, like you will get fooled now and then. But when I went to the barn I knew different. When I walked into the hallway I saw something. It kind of hunkered up when I come in and I thought at first it was one of them got left, then I saw what it was. It was a buzzard. It looked around and saw me and went on down the hall, spraddle-legged, with its wings kind of hunkered out, watching me first over one shoulder and then over the other, like a old baldheaded man. When it got outdoors it begun to fly. It had to fly a long time before it ever got up into the air, with it thick and heavy and full of rain like it was.

If they was bent on going to Jefferson, I reckon they could have gone around up by Mount Vernon, like MacCallum did. He'll get home about day after tomorrow, horseback. Then they'd be just eighteen miles from town. But maybe this bridge being gone too has learned him the Lord's sense and judgment.

That MacCallum. He's been trading with me off and on for twelve years. I have known him from a boy up; know his name as well as I do my own. But be durn if I can say it.

DEWEY DELL

The signboard comes in sight. It is looking out at the road now, because it can wait. New Hope. 3 mi. it will say. New Hope. 3 mi. New Hope. 3 mi. And then the road will begin, curving away into the trees, empty with waiting, saying New Hope three miles.

I heard that my mother is dead. I wish I had time to let her die. I wish I had time to wish I had. It is because in the wild and outraged earth too soon too soon too soon. It's not that I wouldn't and will not it's that it is too soon too soon too soon.

Now it begins to say it. New Hope three miles. New Hope three miles. *That's what they mean by the womb of time: the agony and the despair of spreading bones, the hard girdle in which lie the outraged entrails of events*

Cash's head turns slowly as we approach, his pale empty sad composed and questioning face following the red and empty curve; beside the back wheel Jewel sits the horse, gazing straight ahead.

The land runs out of Darl's eyes; they swim to pinpoints. They begin at my feet and rise along my body to my face, and then my dress is gone: I sit naked on the seat above the unhurrying mules, above the travail. *Suppose I tell him to turn. He will do what I say. Dont you know he will do what I say? Once I waked with a black void rushing under me. I could not see. I saw Vardaman rise and go to the window and strike the knife into the fish, the blood gushing, hissing like steam but I could not see. He'll do as I say. He always does. I can persuade him to anything. You know I can. Suppose I say Turn here.* That was when I died that time. *Suppose I do. We'll go to New Hope. We wont have to go to town.* I rose and took the knife from the streaming fish still hissing and I killed Darl.

When I used to sleep with Vardaman I had a nightmare once I thought I was awake but I couldn't see and couldn't feel I couldn't feel the bed under me and I couldn't think what I was I couldn't think of my name I couldn't even think I am a girl I couldn't even think I nor even think I want to wake up nor remember what was opposite to awake so I could do that I knew that something was passing but I couldn't even think of time then all of a sudden I knew that something was it was wind blowing over me it was like the wind came and blew me back from where it was I was not blowing the room and Vardaman asleep and all of them back under me again and going on like a piece of cool silk dragging across my naked legs.

It blows cool out of the pines, a sad steady sound. New Hope. Was 3 mi. Was 3 mi. I believe in God I believe in God.

"Why didn't we go to New Hope, pa?" Vardaman says. "Mr Samson said we was, but we done passed the road."

Darl says, "Look, Jewel." But he is not looking at me. He is looking at the sky. The buzzard is as still as if he were nailed to it.

We turn into Tull's lane. We pass the barn and go on, the wheels whispering in the mud, passing the green rows of cotton in the wild earth, and Vernon little across the field behind the plow. He lifts his hand as we pass and stands there looking after us for a long while.

"Look, Jewel," Darl says. Jewel sits on his horse like they were both made out of wood, looking straight ahead.

I believe in God, God. God, I believe in God.

TULL

After they passed I taken the mule out and looped up the trace chains and followed. They was setting in the wagon at the end of the levee when I caught up with them. Anse was setting there, looking at the bridge where it was swagged down into the river with just the two ends in sight. He was looking at it like he had believed all the time that folks had been lying to him about it being gone, but like he was hoping all the time it really was. Kind of pleased astonishment he looked, setting on the wagon in his Sunday pants, mumbling his mouth. Looking like a uncurried horse dressed up: I dont know.

The boy was watching the bridge where it was mid-sunk and logs and such drifted up over it and it swagging and shivering like the whole thing would go any minute, big-eyed he was watching it, like he was to a circus. And the gal too. When I come up she looked around at me, her eyes kind of blaring up and going hard like I had made to touch her. Then she looked at Anse again and then back at the water again.

It was nigh up to the levee on both sides, the earth hid except for the tongue of it we was on going out to the bridge and then down into the water, and except for knowing how the road and the bridge used to look, a fellow couldn't tell where was the river and where the land. It was

just a tangle of yellow and the levee not less wider than a knife-back kind of, with us setting in the wagon and on the horse and the mule.

Darl was looking at me, and then Cash turned and looked at me with that look in his eyes like when he was figuring on whether the planks would fit her that night, like he was measuring them inside of him and not asking you to say what you thought and not even letting on he was listening if you did say it, but listening all right. Jewel hadn't moved. He sat there on the horse, leaning a little forward, with that same look on his face when him and Darl passed the house yesterday, coming back to get her.

"If it was just up, we could drive across," Anse says. "We could drive right on across it."

Sometimes a log would get shoved over the jam and float on, rolling and turning, and we could watch it go on to where the ford used to be. It would slow up and whirl crossways and hang out of water for a minute, and you could tell by that that the ford used to be there.

"But that dont show nothing," I say. "It could be a bar of quicksand built up there." We watch the log. Then the gal is looking at me again.

"Mr Whitfield crossed it," she says.

"He was a-horseback," I say. "And three days ago. It's riz five foot since."

"If the bridge was just up," Anse says.

The log bobs up and goes on again. There is a lot of trash and foam, and you can hear the water.

"But it's down," Anse says.

Cash says, "A careful fellow could walk across yonder on the planks and logs."

"But you couldn't tote nothing," I say. "Likely time you set foot on that mess, it'll all go, too. What you think, Darl?"

He is looking at me. He dont say nothing; just looks at me with them queer eyes of hisn that makes folks talk. I always say it aint never been what he done so much or said or anything so much as how he looks at you. It's like he had got into the inside of you, someway. Like somehow you was looking at yourself and your doings outen his eyes. Then I can feel that gal watching me like I had made to touch her. She says something to Anse. ". . . Mr Whitfield . . ." she says.

"I give her my promised word in the presence of the Lord," Anse says. "I reckon it aint no need to worry."

But still he does not start the mules. We set there above the water. Another log bobs up over the jam and goes on; we watch it check up and swing slow for a minute where the ford used to be. Then it goes on.

"It might start falling tonight," I say. "You could lay over one more day."

Then Jewel turns sideways on the horse. He has not moved until then, and he turns and looks at me. His face is kind of green, then it would go red and then green again. "Get to hell on back to your damn plowing," he says. "Who the hell asked you to follow us here?"

"I never meant no harm," I say.

"Shut up, Jewel," Cash says. Jewel looks back at the water, his face gritted, going red and green and then red. "Well," Cash says after a while, "what you want to do?"

Anse dont say nothing. He sets humped up, mumbling his mouth. "If it was just up, we could drive across it," he says.

"Come on," Jewel says, moving the horse.

"Wait," Cash says. He looks at the bridge. We look at him, except Anse and the gal. They are looking at the water. "Dewey Dell and Vardaman and pa better walk across on the bridge," Cash says.

"Vernon can help them," Jewel says.

"And we can hitch his mule ahead of ourn."

"You aint going to take my mule into that water," I say.

Jewel looks at me. His eyes look like pieces of a broken plate. "I'll pay for your damn mule. I'll buy it from you right now."

"My mule aint going into that water," I say.

"Jewel's going to use his horse," Darl says. "Why wont you risk your mule, Vernon?"

"Shut up, Darl," Cash says. "You and Jewel both."

"My mule aint going into that water," I say.

DARL

He sits the horse, glaring at Vernon, his lean face suffused up to and beyond the pale rigidity of his eyes. The summer when he was fifteen, he took a spell of sleeping. One morning when I went to feed the mules the cows were still in the tie-up and then I heard pa go back to the house and call him. When we came on back to the house for breakfast he passed us, carrying the milk buckets, stumbling along like he was drunk, and he was milking when we put the mules in and went on to the field without him. We had been there an hour and still he never showed up. When Dewey Dell came with our lunch, pa sent her back to find Jewel. They found him in the tie-up, sitting on the stool, asleep.

After that, every morning pa would go in and wake him. He would go to sleep at the supper table and soon as supper was finished he would go to bed, and when I came in to bed he would be lying there like a dead man. Yet still pa would have to wake him in the morning. He would get up, but he wouldn't hardly have half sense: he would stand for pa's jawing and complaining without a word and take the milk buckets and go to the barn, and once I found him asleep at the cow, the bucket in place and half full and his hands up to the wrists in the milk and his head against the cow's flank.

After that Dewey Dell had to do the milking. He still got up when pa waked him, going about what we told him to do in that dazed way. It was like he was trying hard to do them; that he was as puzzled as anyone else.

"Are you sick?" ma said. "Dont you feel all right?"

"Yes," Jewel said. "I feel all right."

"He's just lazy, trying me," pa said, and Jewel standing there, asleep on his feet like as not. "Aint you?" he said, waking Jewel up again to answer.

"No," Jewel said.

"You take off and stay in the house today," ma said.

"With that whole bottom piece to be busted out?" pa said. "If you aint sick, what's the matter with you?"

"Nothing," Jewel said. "I'm all right."

"All right?" pa said. "You're asleep on your feet this minute."

"No," Jewel said. "I'm all right."

"I want him to stay at home today," ma said.

"I'll need him," pa said. "It's tight enough, with all of us to do it."

"You'll just have to do the best you can with Cash and Darl," ma said. "I want him to stay in today."

But he wouldn't do it. "I'm all right," he said, going on. But he wasnt all right. Anybody could see it. He was losing flesh, and I have seen him go to sleep chopping; watched the hoe going slower and slower up and down, with less and less of an arc, until it stopped and he leaning on it motionless in the hot shimmer of the sun.

Ma wanted to get the doctor, but pa didn't want to spend the money without it was needful, and Jewel did seem all right except for his thinness and his way of dropping off to sleep at any moment. He ate hearty enough, except for his way of going to sleep in his plate, with a piece of bread halfway to his mouth and his jaws still chewing. But he swore he was all right.

It was ma that got Dewey Dell to do his milking, paid her somehow, and the other jobs around the house that Jewel had been doing before supper she found some way for Dewey Dell and Vardaman to do them. And doing them herself when pa wasn't there. She would fix him special things to eat and hide them for him. And that may have been when I first found it out, that Addie Bundren should be hiding anything she did, who had tried to teach us that deceit was such that, in a world where it was, nothing else could be very bad or very important, not even poverty. And at times when I went in to go to bed she would be sitting in the dark by Jewel where he was asleep. And I knew that she was hating herself for that deceit and hating Jewel because she had to love him so that she had to act the deceit.

One night she was taken sick and when I went to the barn to put the team in and drive to Tull's, I couldn't find the lantern. I remembered noticing it on the nail the night before, but it wasn't there now at midnight. So I hitched in the dark and went on and came back with Mrs Tull just after daylight. And there the lantern was, hanging on the nail where I remembered it and couldn't find it before. And then one morning while Dewey Dell was milking just before sunup, Jewel came into the barn from the back, through the hole in the back wall, with the lantern in his hand.

I told Cash, and Cash and I looked at one another.

"Rutting," Cash said.

"Yes," I said. "But why the lantern? And every night, too. No wonder he's losing flesh. Are you going to say anything to him?"

"Wont do any good," Cash said.

"What he's doing now wont do any good, either."

"I know. But he'll have to learn that himself. Give him time to realise that it'll save, that there'll be just as much more tomorrow, and he'll be all right. I wouldn't tell anybody, I reckon."

"No," I said. "I told Dewey Dell not to. Not ma, anyway."

"No. Not ma."

After that I thought it was right comical: he acting so bewildered and willing and dead for sleep and gaunt as a beanpole, and thinking he was so smart with it. And I wondered who the girl was. I thought of all I knew that it might be, but I couldn't say for sure.

" 'Taint any girl," Cash said. "It's a married woman somewhere. Aint any young girl got that much daring and staying power. That's what I dont like about it."

"Why?" I said. "She'll be safer for him than a girl would. More judgment."

He looked at me, his eyes fumbling, the words fumbling at what he was trying to say. "It aint always the safe things in this world that a fellow . . ."

"You mean, the safe things are not always the best things?"

"Ay; best," he said, fumbling again. "It aint the best things, the things that are good for him . . . A young boy. A fellow kind of hates to see . . . wallowing in somebody else's mire . . ." That's what he was trying to say. When something is new and hard and bright, there ought to be something a little better for it than just being safe, since the safe things are just the things that folks have been doing so long they have worn the edges off and there's nothing to the doing of

them that leaves a man to say, That was not done before and it cannot be done again.

So we didn't tell, not even when after a while he'd appear suddenly in the field beside us and go to work, without having had time to get home and make out he had been in bed all night. He would tell ma that he hadn't been hungry at breakfast or that he had eaten a piece of bread while he was hitching up the team. But Cash and I knew that he hadn't been home at all on those nights and he had come up out of the woods when we got to the field. But we didn't tell. Summer was almost over then; we knew that when the nights began to get cool, she would be done if he wasn't.

But when fall came and the nights began to get longer, the only difference was that he would always be in bed for pa to wake him, getting him up at last in that first state of semi-idiocy like when it first started, worse than when he had stayed out all night.

"She's sure a stayer," I told Cash. "I used to admire her, but I downright respect her now."

"It aint a woman," he said.

"You know," I said. But he was watching me. "What is it, then?"

"That's what I aim to find out," he said.

"You can trail him through the woods all night if you want to," I said. "I'm not."

"I aint trailing him," he said.

"What do you call it, then?"

"I aint trailing him," he said. "I dont mean it that way."

And so a few nights later I heard Jewel get up and climb out the window, and then I heard Cash get up and follow him. The next morning when I went to the barn, Cash was already there, the mules fed, and he was helping Dewey Dell milk. And when I saw him I knew that he knew what it was. Now and then I would catch him watching Jewel with a queer look, like having found out where Jewel went and what he was doing had given him something to really think about at last. But it was not a worried look; it was the kind of look I would see on him when I would find him doing some of Jewel's work around the house, work that pa still thought Jewel was doing and that ma thought Dewey Dell was doing. So I said nothing to him, believing that when he got done digesting it in his mind, he would tell me. But he never did.

One morning—it was November then, five months since it started—Jewel was not in bed and he didn't join us in the field. That was the first time ma learned anything about what had been going on. She sent Vardaman down to find where Jewel was, and after a while she came down too. It was as though, so long as the deceit ran along quiet and monotonous, all of us let ourselves be deceived, abetting it unawares or maybe through cowardice, since all people are cowards and naturally prefer any kind of treachery because it has a bland outside. But now it was like we had all—and by a kind of telepathic agreement of admitted fear—flung the whole thing back like covers on the bed and we all sitting bolt upright in our nakedness, staring at one another and saying "Now is the truth. He hasn't come home. Something has happened to him. We let something happen to him."

Then we saw him. He came up along the ditch and then turned straight across the field, riding the horse. Its mane and tail were going, as though in motion they were carrying out the splotchy pattern of its coat: he looked like he was riding on a big pinwheel, barebacked, with a rope bridle, and no hat on his head. It was a descendant of those Texas ponies Flem Snopes brought here twenty-five years ago and auctioned off for two dol-

lars a head and nobody but old Lon Quick ever caught his and still owned some of the blood because he could never give it away.

He galloped up and stopped, his heels in the horse's ribs and it dancing and swirling like the shape of its mane and tail and the splotches of its coat had nothing whatever to do with the flesh-and-bone horse inside them, and he sat there, looking at us.

"Where did you get that horse?" pa said.

"Bought it," Jewel said. "From Mr Quick."

"Bought it?" pa said. "With what? Did you buy that thing on my word?"

"It was my money," Jewel said. "I earned it. You wont need to worry about it."

"Jewel," ma said; "Jewel."

"It's all right," Cash said. "He earned the money. He cleaned up that forty acres of new ground Quick laid out last spring. He did it single handed, working at night by lantern. I saw him. So I dont reckon that horse cost anybody anything except Jewel. I dont reckon we need worry."

"Jewel," ma said. "Jewel . . ." Then she said: "You come right to the house and go to bed."

"Not yet," Jewel said. "I aint got time. I got to get me a saddle and bridle. Mr Quick says he . . ."

"Jewel," ma said, looking at him. "I'll give—I'll give . . . give . . ." Then she began to cry. She cried hard, not hiding her face, standing there in her faded wrapper, looking at him and him on the horse, looking down at her, his face growing cold and a little sick looking, until he looked away quick and Cash came and touched her.

"You go on to the house," Cash said. "This here ground is too wet for you. You go on, now." She put her hands to her face then and after a while she went on, stumbling a little on the plow-marks. But pretty soon she straightened up and went on. She didn't look back. When she reached the ditch she stopped and called Vardaman. He was looking at the horse, kind of dancing up and down by it.

"Let me ride, Jewel," he said. "Let me ride, Jewel."

Jewel looked at him, then he looked away again, holding the horse reined back. Pa watched him, mumbling his lip.

"So you bought a horse," he said. "You went behind my back and bought a horse. You never consulted me; you know how tight it is for us to make by, yet you bought a horse for me to feed. Taken the work from your flesh and blood and bought a horse with it."

Jewel looked at pa, his eyes paler than ever. "He wont never eat a mouthful of yours," he said. "Not a mouthful. I'll kill him first. Dont you never think it. Dont you never."

"Let me ride, Jewel," Vardaman said. "Let me ride, Jewel." He sounded like a cricket in the grass, a little one. "Let me ride, Jewel."

That night I found ma sitting beside the bed where he was sleeping, in the dark. She cried hard, maybe because she had to cry so quiet; maybe because she felt the same way about tears she did about deceit, hating herself for doing it, hating him because she had to. And then I knew that I knew. I knew that as plain on that day as I knew about Dewey Dell on that day.

TULL

So they finally got Anse to say what he wanted to do, and him and the gal and the boy got out of the wagon. But even when we were on the bridge Anse kept on looking back, like he thought maybe, once he was outen the wagon, the whole thing would kind of blow up and he would find himself back yonder in the field again and her laying up there in the house, waiting to die and it to do all over again.

"You ought to let them taken your mule," he says, and the bridge shaking and swaying under us, going down into the moiling water like it went clean through to the other side of the earth, and the other end coming up outen the water like it wasn't the same bridge a-tall and that them that would walk up outen the water on that side must come from the bottom of the earth. But it was still whole; you could tell that by the way when this end swagged, it didn't look like the other end swagged at all: just like the other trees and the bank yonder were swinging back and forth slow like on a big clock. And them logs scraping and bumping at the sunk part and tilting end-up and shooting clean outen the water and tumbling on toward the ford and the waiting, slick, whirling, and foamy.

"What good would that a done?" I says. "If your team cant find the ford and haul it across, what good would three mules or even ten mules do?"

"I aint asking it of you," he says. "I can always do for me and mine. I aint asking you to risk your mule. It aint your dead; I am not blaming you."

"They ought to went back and laid over until tomorrow," I says. The water was cold. It was thick, like slush ice. Only it kind of lived. One part of you knowed it was just water, the same thing that had been running under this same bridge for a long time, yet when them logs would come spewing up outen it, you were not surprised, like they was a part of water, of the waiting and the threat.

It was like when we was across, up out of the water again and the hard earth under us, that I was surprised. It was like we hadn't expected the bridge to end on the other bank, on something tame like the hard earth again that we had tromped on before this time and knowed well. Like it couldn't be me here, because I'd have had better sense than to done what I just done. And when I looked back and saw the other bank and saw my mule standing there where I used to be and knew that I'd have to get back there someway, I knew it couldn't be, because I just couldn't think of anything that could make me cross that bridge ever even once. Yet here I was, and the fellow that could make himself cross it twice, couldn't be me, not even if Cora told him to.

It was that boy. I said "Here; you better take a holt of my hand" and he waited and held to me. I be durn if it wasn't like he come back and got me; like he was saying They wont nothing hurt you. Like he was saying about a fine place he knowed where Christmas come twice with Thanksgiving and lasts on through the winter and the spring and the summer, and if I just stayed with him I'd be all right too.

When I looked back at my mule it was like he was one of these here spy-glasses and I could look at him standing there and see all the broad land and my house sweated outen it like it was the more the sweat, the broader the land; the more the sweat, the tighter the house because it would take a tight house for Cora, to hold Cora like a jar of milk in the spring: you've got to have a tight jar or you'll need a powerful spring, so if you have a big spring, why then you have the incentive to have tight, wellmade jars, because it is your milk, sour or not, because you would rather have milk that will sour than to have milk that wont, because you are a man.

And him holding to my hand, his hand that hot and confident, so that I was like to say: Look-a-here. Cant you see that mule yonder? He never had no business over here, so he never come, not being nothing but a mule. Because a fellow can

see ever now and then that children have more sense than him. But he dont like to admit it to them until they have beards. After they have a beard, they are too busy because they dont know if they'll ever quite make it back to where they were in sense before they was haired, so you dont mind admitting then to folks that are worrying about the same thing that aint worth the worry that you are yourself.

Then we was over and we stood there, looking at Cash turning the wagon around. We watched them drive back down the road to where the trail turned off into the bottom. After a while the wagon was out of sight.

"We better get on down to the ford and git ready to help," I said.

"I give her my word," Anse says. "It is sacred on me. I know you begrudge it, but she will bless you in heaven."

"Well, they got to finish circumventing the land before they can dare the water," I said. "Come on."

"It's the turning back," he said. "It aint no luck in turning back."

He was standing there, humped, mournful, looking at the empty road beyond the swagging and swaying bridge. And that gal, too, with the lunch basket on one arm and that package under the other. Just going to town. Bent on it. They would risk the fire and the earth and the water and all just to eat a sack of bananas. "You ought to laid over a day," I said. "It would a fell some by morning. It mought not a rained tonight. And it cant get no higher."

"I give my promise," he says. "She is counting on it."

DARL

Before us the thick dark current runs. It talks up to us in a murmur become ceaseless and myriad, the yellow surface dimpled monstrously into fading swirls travelling along the surface for an instant, silent, impermanent and profoundly significant, as though just beneath the surface something huge and alive waked for a moment of lazy alertness out of and into light slumber again.

It clucks and murmurs among the spokes and about the mules' knees, yellow, skummed with flotsam and with thick soiled gouts of foam as though it had sweat, lathering, like a driven horse. Through the undergrowth it goes with a plaintive sound, a musing sound; in it the unwinded cane and saplings lean as before a little gale, swaying without reflections as though suspended on invisible wires from the branches overhead. Above the ceaseless surface they stand—trees, cane, vines—rootless, severed from the earth, spectral above a scene of immense yet circumscribed desolation filled with the voice of the waste and mournful water.

Cash and I sit in the wagon; Jewel sits the horse at the off rear wheel. The horse is trembling, its eye rolling wild and baby-blue in its long pink face, its breathing stertorous like groaning. He sits erect, poised, looking quietly and steadily and quickly this way and that, his face calm, a little pale, alert. Cash's face is also gravely composed; he and I look at one another with long probing looks, looks that plunge unimpeded through one another's eyes and into the ultimate secret place where for an instant Cash and Darl crouch flagrant and unabashed in all the old terror and the old foreboding, alert and secret and without shame. When we speak our voices are quiet, detached.

"I reckon we're still in the road, all right."

"Tull taken and cut them two big whiteoaks. I heard tell how at high water in the old days they used to line up the ford by them trees."

"I reckon he did that two years ago when he was logging down here. I reckon he never thought that anybody would ever use this ford again."

"I reckon not. Yes, it must have been then. He cut a sight of timber outen here then. Payed off that mortgage with it, I hear tell."

"Yes. Yes, I reckon so. I reckon Vernon could have done that."

"That's a fact. Most folks that logs in this here country, they need a durn good farm to support the sawmill. Or maybe a store. But I reckon Vernon could."

"I reckon so. He's a sight."

"Ay. Vernon is. Yes, it must still be here. He never would have got that timber out of here if he hadn't cleaned out that old road. I reckon we are still on it." He looks about quietly, at the position of the trees, leaning this way and that, looking back along the floorless road shaped vaguely high in air by the position of the lopped and felled trees, as if the road too had been soaked free of earth and floated upward, to leave in its spectral tracing a monument to a still more profound desolation than this above which we now sit, talking quietly of old security and old trivial things. Jewel looks at him, then at me, then his face turns in that quiet, constant, questing about the scene, the horse trembling quietly and steadily between his knees.

"He could go on ahead slow and sort of feel it out," I say.

"Yes," Cash says, not looking at me. His face is in profile as he looks forward where Jewel has moved on ahead.

"He cant miss the river," I say. "He couldn't miss seeing it fifty yards ahead."

Cash does not look at me, his face in profile. "If I'd just suspicioned it, I could a come down last week and taken a sight on it."

"The bridge was up then," I say. He does not look at me. "Whitfield crossed it a-horseback."

Jewel looks at us again, his expression sober and alert and subdued. His voice is quiet. "What you want me to do?"

"I ought to come down last week and taken a sight on it," Cash says.

"We couldn't have known," I say. "There wasn't any way for us to know."

"I'll ride on ahead," Jewel says. "You can follow where I am." He lifts the horse. It shrinks, bowed; he leans to it, speaking to it, lifting it forward almost bodily, it setting its feet down with gingerly splashings, trembling, breathing harshly. He speaks to it, murmurs to it. "Go on," he says. "I aint going to let nothing hurt you. Go on, now."

"Jewel," Cash says. Jewel does not look back. He lifts the horse on.

"He can swim," I say. "If he'll just give the horse time, anyhow . . ." When he was born, he had a bad time of it. Ma would sit in the lamp-light, holding him on a pillow on her lap. We would wake and find her so. There would be no sound from them.

"That pillow was longer than him," Cash says. He is leaning a little forward. "I ought to come down last week and sighted. I ought to done it."

"That's right," I say. "Neither his feet nor his head would reach the end of it. You couldn't have known," I say.

"I ought to done it," he says. He lifts the reins. The mules move, into the traces; the wheels murmur alive in the water. He looks back and down at Addie. "It aint on a balance," he says.

At last the trees open; against the open river Jewel sits the horse, half turned, it belly deep now. Across the river we can see Vernon and pa and Vardaman and Dewey Dell. Vernon is waving at us, waving us further downstream.

"We are too high up," Cash says. Vernon is shouting too, but we cannot make out what he says for the noise of the water. It runs steady and deep now, unbroken, without sense of motion until a log comes along, turning slowly. "Watch it," Cash says. We watch it and see it falter and hang for a moment, the current building up behind it in a thick wave, submerging it for an instant before it shoots up and tumbles on.

"There it is," I say.

"Ay," Cash says. "It's there." We look at Vernon again. He is now flapping his arms up and down. We move on downstream, slowly and carefully, watching Vernon. He drops his hands. "This is the place," Cash says.

"Well, goddamn it, let's get across, then," Jewel says. He moves the horse on.

"You wait," Cash says. Jewel stops again.

"Well, by God—" he says. Cash looks at the water, then he looks back at Addie. "It aint on a balance," he says.

"Then go on back to the goddamn bridge and walk across," Jewel says. "You and Darl both. Let me on that wagon."

Cash does not pay him any attention. "It aint on a balance," he says. "Yes, sir. We got to watch it."

"Watch it, hell," Jewel says. "You get out of that wagon and let me have it. By God, if you're afraid to drive it over . . ." His eyes are pale as two bleached chips in his face. Cash is looking at him.

"We'll get it over," he says. "I tell you what you do. You ride on back and walk across the bridge and come down the other bank and meet us with the rope. Vernon'll take your horse home with him and keep it till we get back."

"You go to hell," Jewel says.

"You take the rope and come down the bank and be ready with it," Cash says. "Three cant do no more than two can—one to drive and one to steady it."

"Goddamn you," Jewel says.

"Let Jewel take the end of the rope and cross upstream of us and brace it," I say. "Will you do that, Jewel?"

Jewel watches me, hard. He looks

quick at Cash, then back at me, his eyes alert and hard. "I dont give a damn. Just so we do something. Setting here, not lifting a goddamn hand . . ."

"Let's do that, Cash," I say.

"I reckon we'll have to," Cash says.

The river itself is not a hundred yards across, and pa and Vernon and Vardaman and Dewey Dell are the only things in sight not of that single monotony of desolation leaning with that terrific quality a little from right to left, as though we had reached the place where the motion of the wasted world accelerates just before the final precipice. Yet they appear dwarfed. It is as though the space between us were time: an irrevocable quality. It is as though time, no longer running straight before us in a diminishing line, now runs parallel between us like a looping string, the distance being the doubling accretion of the thread and not the interval between. The mules stand, their fore quarters already sloped a little, their rumps high. They too are breathing now with a deep groaning sound; looking back once, their gaze sweeps across us with in their eyes a wild, sad, profound and despairing quality as though they had already seen in the thick water the shape of the disaster which they could not speak and we could not see.

Cash turns back into the wagon. He lays his hands flat on Addie, rocking her a little. His face is calm, down-sloped, calculant, concerned. He lifts his box of tools and wedges it forward under the seat; together we shove Addie forward, wedging her between the tools and the wagon bed. Then he looks at me.

"No," I say. "I reckon I'll stay. Might take both of us."

From the tool box he takes his coiled rope and carries the end twice around the seat stanchion and passes the end to me without tying it. The other end he pays out to Jewel, who takes a turn about his saddle horn.

He must force the horse down into the current. It moves, highkneed, archnecked, boring and chafing. Jewel sits lightly forward, his knees lifted a little; again his swift alert calm gaze sweeps upon us and on. He lowers the horse into the stream, speaking to it in a soothing murmur. The horse slips, goes under to the saddle, surges to its feet again, the current building up against Jewel's thighs.

"Watch yourself," Cash says.

"I'm on it now," Jewel says. "You can come ahead now."

Cash takes the reins and lowers the team carefully and skillfully into the stream.

I felt the current take us and I knew we were on the ford by that reason, since it was only by means of that slipping contact that we could tell that we were in motion at all. What had once been a flat surface was now a succession of troughs and hillocks lifting and falling about us, shoving at us, teasing at us with light lazy touches in the vain instants of solidity underfoot. Cash looked back at me, and then I knew that we were gone. But I did not realise the reason for the rope until I saw the log. It surged up out of the water and stood for an instant upright upon that surging and heaving desolation like Christ. Get out and let the current take you down to the bend, Cash said. You can make it all right. No, I said, I'd get just as wet that way as this

The log appears suddenly between two hills, as if it had rocketed suddenly from the bottom of the river. Upon the end of it a long gout of foam hangs like the beard of an old man or a goat. When Cash speaks to me I know that he has been watching it all the time, watching it and watching Jewel ten feet ahead of us. "Let the rope go," he says. With his other hand he reaches down and reeves the two turns from the stanchion. "Ride on, Jewel," he says; "see if you can pull us ahead of the log."

Jewel shouts at the horse; again he appears to lift it bodily between his knees. He is just above the top of the ford and the horse has a purchase of some sort for it surges forward, shining wetly half out of the water, crashing on in a succession of lunges. It moves unbelievably fast; by that token Jewel realises at last that the rope is free, for I can see him sawing back on the reins, his head turned, as the log rears in a long sluggish lunge between us, bearing down upon the team. They see it too; for a moment they also shine black out of water. Then the downstream one vanishes, dragging the other with him; the wagon sheers crosswise, poised on the crest of the ford as the log strikes it, tilting it up and on. Cash is half turned, the reins running taut from his hand and disappearing into the water, the other hand reached back upon Addie, holding her jammed over against the high side of the wagon. "Jump clear," he says quietly. "Stay away from the team and dont try to fight it. It'll swing you into the bend all right."

"You come too," I say. Vernon and Vardaman are running along the bank, pa and Dewey Dell stand watching us, Dewey Dell with the basket and the package in her arms. Jewel is trying to fight the horse back. The head of one mule appears, its eyes wide; it looks back at us for an instant, making a sound almost human. The head vanishes again.

"Back, Jewel," Cash shouts. "Back, Jewel." For another instant I see him leaning to the tilting wagon, his arm braced back against Addie and his tools; I see the bearded head of the rearing log strike up again, and beyond it Jewel holding the horse upreared, its head wrenched around, hammering its head with his fist.

I jump from the wagon on the downstream side. Between two hills I see the mules once more. They roll up out of the water in succession, turning completely over, their legs stiffly extended as when they had lost contact with the earth.

VARDAMAN

Cash tried but she fell off and Darl jumped going under he went under and Cash hollering to catch her and I hollering running and hollering and Dewey Dell hollering at me Vardaman you vardaman you vardaman and Vernon passed me because he was seeing her come up and she jumped into the water again and Darl hadn't caught her yet

He came up to see and I hollering catch her Darl catch her and he didn't come back because she was too heavy he had to go on catching at her and I hollering catch her darl catch her darl because in the water she could go faster than a man and Darl had to grabble for her so I knew he could catch her because he is the best grabbler even with the mules in the way again they dived up rolling their feet stiff rolling down again and their backs up now and Darl had to again because in the water she could go faster than a man or woman and I passed Vernon and he wouldn't get in the water and help Darl he wouldn't grabble for her with Darl he knew but he wouldn't help

The mules dived up again diving their legs stiff their stiff legs rolling slow and then Darl again and I hollering catch her darl catch her head her into the bank darl and Vernon wouldn't help and then Darl dodged past the mules where he could he had her under the water coming in to the bank coming in slow because in the water she fought to stay under the water but Darl is strong and he was coming in slow and so I knew he had her because he came slow and I ran down into the water to help and I couldn't stop hollering because Darl was strong and steady holding her under the water even if she did fight he would not let her go he was seeing me and he would hold her and it was all right now it was all right now it was all right

Then he comes up out of the water. He comes a long way up slow before his hands do but he's got to have her got to so I can bear it. Then his hands come up and all of him above the water. I cant stop. I have not got time to try. I will try to when I can but his hands came empty out of the water emptying the water emptying away

"Where is ma, Darl?" I said. "You never got her. You knew she is a fish but you let her get away. You never got her. Darl. Darl. Darl." I began to run along the bank, watching the mules dive up slow again and then down again.

TULL

When I told Cora how Darl jumped out of the wagon and left Cash sitting there trying to save it and the wagon turning over, and Jewel that was almost to the bank fighting that horse back where it had more sense than to go, she says "And you're one of the folks that says Darl is the queer one, the one that aint bright, and him the only one of them that had sense enough to get off that wagon. I notice Anse was too smart to been on it a-tall."

"He couldn't a done no good, if he'd been there," I said. "They was going about it right and they would have made it if it hadn't a been for that log."

"Log, fiddlesticks," Cora said. "It was the hand of God."

"Then how can you say it was foolish?" I said. "Nobody cant guard against the hand of God. It would be sacrilege to try to."

"Then why dare it?" Cora says. "Tell me that."

"Anse didn't," I said. "That's just what you faulted him for."

"His place was there," Cora said. "If he had been a man, he would a been there instead of making his sons do what he dursn't."

"I dont know what you want, then," I said. "One breath you say they was daring the hand of God to try it, and the next breath you jump on Anse because he wasn't with them." Then she begun to sing again, working at the washtub, with that singing look in her face like she had done give up folks and all their foolishness and had done went on ahead of them, marching up the sky, singing.

The wagon hung for a long time while the current built up under it, shoving it off the ford, and Cash leaning more and more, trying to keep the coffin braced so it wouldn't slip down and finish tilting the wagon over. Soon as the wagon got tilted good, to where the current could finish it, the log went on. It headed around the wagon and went on good as a swimming man could have done. It was like it had been sent there to do a job and done it and went on.

When the mules finally kicked loose, it looked for a minute like maybe Cash would get the wagon back. It looked like him and the wagon wasn't moving at all, and just Jewel fighting that horse back to the wagon. Then that boy passed me, running and hollering at Darl and the gal trying to catch him, and then I see the mules come rolling slow up out of the water, their legs spraddled stiff like they had balked upside down, and roll on into the water again.

Then the wagon tilted over and then it and Jewel and the horse was all mixed up together. Cash went outen sight, still holding the coffin braced, and then I couldn't tell anything for the horse lunging and splashing. I thought that Cash had give up then and was swimming for it and I was yelling at Jewel to come on back and then all of a sudden him and the horse went under too and I thought they was all going. I knew that the horse had got dragged off the ford too, and with that wild drowning horse and that wagon and that loose box, it was going to be pretty bad, and there I was, standing knee-deep in the water, yelling at Anse behind me: "See what you done now? See what you done now?"

The horse come up again. It was headed for the bank now, throwing its head up, and then I saw one of them holding to the saddle on the downstream side, so I started running along the bank, trying to catch sight of Cash because he couldn't swim, yelling at Jewel where Cash was like a durn fool, bad as that boy that was on down the bank still hollering at Darl.

So I went down into the water so I could still keep some kind of a grip in the mud, when I saw Jewel. He was middle deep, so I knew he was on the ford, anyway, leaning hard upstream, and then I see the rope, and then I see the water building up where he was holding the wagon snubbed just below the ford.

So it was Cash holding to the horse when it come splashing and scrambling up the bank, moaning and groaning like a natural man. When I come to it it was just kicking Cash loose from his holt on the saddle. His face turned up a second when he was sliding back into the water. It was gray, with his eyes closed and a long swipe of mud across his face. Then he let go and turned over in the water. He looked just like a old bundle of clothes kind of washing up and down against the bank. He looked like he was laying there in the water on his face,

rocking up and down a little, looking at something on the bottom.

We could watch the rope cutting down into the water, and we could feel the weight of the wagon kind of blump and lunge lazy like, like it just as soon as not, and that rope cutting down into the water hard as a iron bar. We could hear the water hissing on it like it was red hot. Like it was a straight iron bar stuck into the bottom and us holding the end of it, and the wagon lazing up and down, kind of pushing and prodding at us like it had come around and got behind us, lazy like, like it just as soon as not when it made up its mind. There was a shoat come by, blowed up like a balloon: one of them spotted shoats of Lon Quick's. It bumped against the rope like it was a iron bar and bumped off and went on, and us watching that rope slanting down into the water. We watched it.

DARL

Cash lies on his back on the earth, his head raised on a rolled garment. His eyes are closed, his face is gray, his hair plastered in a smooth smear across his forehead as though done with a paint brush. His face appears sunken a little, sagging from the bony ridges of eye sockets, nose, gums, as though the wetting had slacked the firmness which had held the skin full; his teeth, set in pale gums, are parted a little as if he had been laughing quietly. He lies pole-thin in his wet clothes, a little pool of vomit at his head and a thread of it running from the corner of his mouth and down his cheek where he couldn't turn his head quick or far enough, until Dewey Dell stoops and wipes it away with the hem of her dress.

Jewel approaches. He has the plane. "Vernon just found the square," he says. He looks down at Cash, dripping too. "Aint he talked none yet?"

"He had his saw and hammer and chalk-line and rule," I say. "I know that."

Jewel lays the square down. Pa watches him. "They cant be far away," pa says. "It all went together. Was there ere a such misfortunate man."

Jewel does not look at pa. "You better call Vardaman back here," he says. He looks at Cash. Then he turns and goes away. "Get him to talk soon as he can," he says, "so he can tell us what else there was."

We return to the river. The wagon is hauled clear, the wheels chocked (carefully: we all helped; it is as though upon the shabby, familiar, inert shape of the wagon there lingered somehow, latent yet still immediate, that violence which had slain the mules that drew it not an hour since) above the edge of the flood. In the wagon bed it lies profoundly, the long pale planks hushed a little with wetting yet still yellow, like gold seen through water, save for two long muddy smears. We pass it and go on to the bank.

One end of the rope is made fast to a tree. At the edge of the stream, knee-deep, Vardaman stands, bent forward a little, watching Vernon with rapt absorption. He has stopped yelling and he is wet to the armpits. Vernon is at the other end of the rope, shoulder-deep in the river, looking back at Vardaman. "Further back than that," he says. "You git back by the tree and hold the rope for me, so it cant slip."

Vardaman backs along the rope, to the tree, moving blindly, watching Vernon. When we come up he looks at us once, his eyes round and a little dazed. Then he looks at Vernon again in that posture of rapt alertness.

"I got the hammer too," Vernon says. "Looks like we ought to done already got that chalk-line. It ought to floated."

"Floated clean away," Jewel says. "We wont get it. We ought to find the saw, though."

"I reckon so," Vernon says. He looks at the water. "That chalk-line, too. What else did he have?"

"He aint talked yet," Jewel says, entering the water. He looks back at me. "You go back and get him roused up to talk," he says.

"Pa's there," I say. I follow Jewel into the water, along the rope. It feels alive in my hand, bellied faintly in a prolonged and resonant arc. Vernon is watching me.

"You better go," he says. "You better be there."

"Let's see what else we can get before it washes on down," I say.

We hold to the rope, the current curling and dimpling about our shoulders. But beneath that false blandness the true force of it leans against us lazily. I had not thought that water in July could be so cold. It is like hands molding and prodding at the very bones. Vernon is still looking back toward the bank.

"Reckon it'll hold us all?" he says. We too look back, following the rigid bar of the rope as it rises from the water to the tree and Vardaman crouched a little beside it, watching us. "Wish my mule wouldn't strike out for home," Vernon says.

"Come on," Jewel says. "Let's get outen here."

We submerge in turn, holding to the rope, being clutched by one another while the cold wall of the water sucks the slanting mud backward and upstream from beneath our feet and we are suspended so, groping along the cold bottom. Even the mud there is not still. It has a chill, scouring quality, as though the earth under us were in motion too. We touch and fumble at one another's extended arms, letting ourselves go cautiously against the rope; or, erect in turn, watch the water suck and boil where one of the other two gropes beneath the surface. Pa has come down to the shore, watching us.

Vernon comes up, streaming, his face sloped down into his pursed blowing mouth. His mouth is bluish, like a circle of weathered rubber. He has the rule.

"He'll be glad of that," I say. "It's right new. He bought it just last month out of the catalogue."

"If we just knowed for sho what else," Vernon says, looking over his shoulder and then turning to face where Jewel had disappeared. "Didn't he go down fore me?" Vernon says.

"I dont know," I say. "I think so. Yes. Yes, he did."

We watch the thick curling surface, streaming away from us in slow whorls.

"Give him a pull on the rope," Vernon says.

"He's on your end of it," I say.

"Aint nobody on my end of it," he says.

"Pull it in," I say. But he has already done that, holding the end above the water; and then we see Jewel. He is ten yards away; he comes up, blowing, and looks at us, tossing his long hair back with a jerk of his head, then he looks toward the bank; we can see him filling his lungs.

"Jewel," Vernon says, not loud, but his voice going full and clear along the water, peremptory yet tactful. "It'll be back here. Better come back."

Jewel dives again. We stand there, leaning back against the current, watching the water where he disappeared, holding the dead rope between us like two men holding the nozzle of a fire hose, waiting for the water. Suddenly Dewey Dell is behind us in the water. "You make him come back," she says. "Jewel!" she says. He comes up again, tossing his hair back from his eyes. He is swimming now, toward the bank, the current sweep-

ing him downstream quartering. "You, Jewel!" Dewey Dell says. We stand holding the rope and see him gain the bank and climb out. As he rises from the water, he stoops and picks up something. He comes back along the bank. He has found the chalk-line. He comes opposite us and stands there, looking about as if he were seeking something. Pa goes on down the bank. He is going back to look at the mules again where their round bodies float and rub quietly together in the slack water within the bend.

"What did you do with the hammer, Vernon?" Jewel says.

"I give it to him," Vernon says, jerking his head at Vardaman. Vardaman is looking after pa. Then he looks at Jewel. "With the square." Vernon is watching Jewel. He moves toward the bank, passing Dewey Dell and me.

"You get on out of here," I say. She says nothing, looking at Jewel and Vernon.

"Where's the hammer?" Jewel says. Vardaman scuttles up the bank and fetches it.

"It's heavier than the saw," Vernon says. Jewel is tying the end of the chalk-line about the hammer shaft.

"Hammer's got the most wood in it," Jewel says. He and Vernon face one another, watching Jewel's hands.

"And flatter, too," Vernon says. "It'd float three to one, almost. Try the plane."

Jewel looks at Vernon. Vernon is tall, too; long and lean, eye to eye they stand in their close wet clothes. Lon Quick could look even at a cloudy sky and tell the time to ten minutes. Big Lon I mean, not little Lon.

"Why dont you get out of the water?" I say.

"It wont float like a saw," Jewel says.

"It'll float nigher to a saw than a hammer will," Vernon says.

"Bet you," Jewel says.

"I wont bet," Vernon says.

They stand there, watching Jewel's still hands.

"Hell," Jewel says. "Get the plane, then."

So they get the plane and tie it to the chalk-line and enter the water again. Pa comes back along the bank. He stops for a while and looks at us, hunched, mournful, like a failing steer or an old tall bird.

Vernon and Jewel return, leaning against the current. "Get out of the way," Jewel says to Dewey Dell. "Get out of the water."

She crowds against me a little so they can pass, Jewel holding the plane high as though it were perishable, the blue string trailing back over his shoulder. They pass us and stop; they fall to arguing quietly about just where the wagon went over.

"Darl ought to know," Vernon says. They look at me.

"I dont know," I says. "I wasn't there that long."

"Hell," Jewel says. They move on, gingerly, leaning against the current, reading the ford with their feet.

"Have you got a holt of the rope?" Vernon says. Jewel does not answer. He glances back at the shore, calculant, then at the water. He flings the plane outward, letting the string run through his fingers, his fingers turning blue where it runs over them. When the line stops, he hands it back to Vernon.

"Better let me go this time," Vernon says. Again Jewel does not answer; we watch him duck beneath the surface.

"Jewel," Dewey Dell whimpers.

"It aint so deep there," Vernon says. He does not look back. He is watching the water where Jewel went under.

When Jewel comes up he has the saw.

When we pass the wagon pa is standing beside it, scrubbing at the two mud smears with a handful of leaves. Against the jungle Jewel's horse looks like a patchwork quilt hung on a line.

Cash has not moved. We stand above him, holding the plane, the saw, the hammer, the square, the rule, the chalk-line, while Dewey Dell squats and lifts Cash's head. "Cash," she says; "Cash."

He opens his eyes, staring profoundly up at our inverted faces.

"If ever was such a misfortunate man," pa says.

"Look, Cash," we say, holding the tools up so he can see; "what else did you have?"

He tries to speak, rolling his head, shutting his eyes.

"Cash," we say; "Cash."

It is to vomit he is turning his head. Dewey Dell wipes his mouth on the wet hem of her dress; then he can speak.

"It's his saw-set," Jewel says. "The new one he bought when he bought the rule." He moves, turning away. Vernon looks up after him, still squatting. Then he rises and follows Jewel down to the water.

"If ever was such a misfortunate man," pa says. He looms tall above us as we squat; he looks like a figure carved clumsily from tough wood by a drunken caricaturist. "It's a trial," he says. "But I dont begrudge her it. No man can say I begrudge her it." Dewey Dell has laid Cash's head back on the folded coat, twisting his head a little to avoid the vomit. Beside him his tools lie. "A fellow might call it lucky it was the same leg he broke when he fell offen that church," pa says. "But I dont begrudge her it."

Jewel and Vernon are in the river again. From here they do not appear to violate the surface at all; it is as though it had severed them both at a single blow, the two torsos moving with infinitesimal and ludicrous care upon the surface. It looks peaceful, like machinery does after you have watched it and listened to it for a long time. As though the clotting which is you had dissolved into the myriad original motion, and seeing and hearing in themselves blind and deaf; fury in itself quiet with stagnation. Squatting, Dewey Dell's wet dress shapes for the dead eyes of three blind men those mammalian ludicrosities which are the horizons and the valleys of the earth.

CASH

It wasn't on a balance. I told them that if they wanted it to tote and ride on a balance, they would have to

CORA

One day we were talking. She had never been pure religious, not even after that summer at the camp meeting when Brother Whitfield wrestled with her spirit, singled her out and strove with the vanity in her mortal heart, and I said to her many a time, "God gave you children to comfort your hard human lot and for a token of His own suffering and love, for in love you conceived and bore them." I said that because she took God's love and her duty to Him too much as a matter of course, and such conduct is not pleasing to Him. I said, "He gave us the gift to raise our voices in His undying praise" because I said there is more rejoicing in heaven over one sinner than over a hundred that never sinned. And she said, "My daily life is an acknowledgment and expiation of my sin" and I said "Who are you, to say what is sin and what is not sin? It is the Lord's part to judge; ours to praise His mercy and His holy name in the hearing of our fellow mortals" because He alone can see into the heart, and just because a woman's life is right in the sight of man, she cant know if there is no sin in her heart without she opens her heart to the Lord and receives His grace. I said, "Just because you have

been a faithful wife is no sign that there is no sin in your heart, and just because your life is hard is no sign that the Lord's grace is absolving you." And she said, "I know my own sin. I know that I deserve my punishment. I do not begrudge it." And I said, "It is out of your vanity that you would judge sin and salvation in the Lord's place. It is our mortal lot to suffer and to raise our voices in praise of Him who judges the sin and offers the salvation through our trials and tribulations time out of mind amen. Not even after Brother Whitfield, a godly man if ever one breathed God's breath, prayed for you and strove as never a man could except him," I said.

Because it is not us that can judge our sins or know what is sin in the Lord's eyes. She has had a hard life, but so does every woman. But you'd think from the way she talked that she knew more about sin and salvation than the Lord God Himself, than them who have strove and labored with the sin in this human world. When the only sin she ever committed was being partial to Jewel that never loved her and was its own punishment, in preference to Darl that was touched by God Himself and considered queer by us mortals and that did love her. I said, "There is your sin. And your punishment too. Jewel is your punishment. But where is your salvation? And life is short enough," I said, "to win eternal grace in. And God is a jealous God. It is His to judge and to mete; not yours."

"I know," she said. "I—" Then she stopped, and I said,

"Know what?"

"Nothing," she said. "He is my cross and he will be my salvation. He will save me from the water and from the fire. Even though I have laid down my life, he will save me."

"How do you know, without you open your heart to Him and lift your voice in His praise?" I said. Then I realised that she did not mean God. I realised that out of the vanity of her heart she had spoken sacrilege. And I went down on my knees right there. I begged her to kneel and open her heart and cast from it the devil of vanity and cast herself upon the mercy of the Lord. But she wouldn't. She just sat there, lost in her vanity and her pride, that had closed her heart to God and set that selfish mortal boy in His place. Kneeling there I prayed for her. I prayed for that poor blind woman as I had never prayed for me and mine.

ADDIE

In the afternoon when school was out and the last one had left with his little dirty snuffling nose, instead of going home I would go down the hill to the spring where I could be quiet and hate them. It would be quiet there then, with the water bubbling up and away and the sun slanting quiet in the trees and the quiet smelling of damp and rotting leaves and new earth; especially in the early spring, for it was worst then.

I could just remember how my father used to say that the reason for living was to get ready to stay dead a long time. And when I would have to look at them day after day, each with his and her secret and selfish thought, and blood strange to each other blood and strange to mine, and think that this seemed to be the only way I could get ready to stay dead, I would hate my father for having ever planted me. I would look forward to the times when they faulted, so I could whip them. When the switch fell I could feel it upon my flesh; when it welted and ridged it was my blood that ran, and I would think with each blow of the switch: Now you are aware of me! Now I am something in your secret and selfish

life, who have marked your blood with my own for ever and ever.

And so I took Anse. I saw him pass the school house three or four times before I learned that he was driving four miles out of his way to do it. I noticed then how he was beginning to hump—a tall man and young—so that he looked already like a tall bird hunched in the cold weather, on the wagon seat. He would pass the school house, the wagon creaking slow, his head turning slow to watch the door of the school house as the wagon passed, until he went on around the curve and out of sight. One day I went to the door and stood there when he passed. When he saw me he looked quickly away and did not look back again.

In the early spring it was worst. Sometimes I thought that I could not bear it, lying in bed at night, with the wild geese going north and their honking coming faint and high and wild out of the wild darkness, and during the day it would seem as though I couldn't wait for the last one to go so I could go down to the spring. And so when I looked up that day and saw Anse standing there in his Sunday clothes, turning his hat round and round in his hands, I said:

"If you've got any womenfolks, why in the world dont they make you get your hair cut?"

"I aint got none," he said. Then he said suddenly, driving his eyes at me like two hounds in a strange yard: "That's what I come to see you about."

"And make you hold your shoulders up," I said. "You haven't got any? But you've got a house. They tell me you've got a house and a good farm. And you live there alone, doing for yourself, do you?" He just looked at me, turning the hat in his hands. "A new house," I said. "Are you going to get married?"

And he said again, holding his eyes to

mine: "That's what I come to see you about."

Later he told me, "I aint got no people. So that wont be no worry to you. I dont reckon you can say the same."

"No. I have people. In Jefferson."

His face fell a little. "Well, I got a little property. I'm forehanded; I got a good honest name. I know how town folks are, but maybe when they talk to me . . ."

"They might listen," I said. "But they'll be hard to talk to." He was watching my face. "They're in the cemetery."

"But your living kin," he said. "They'll be different."

"Will they?" I said. "I dont know. I never had any other kind."

So I took Anse. And when I knew that I had Cash, I knew that living was terrible and that this was the answer to it. That was when I learned that words are no good; that words dont ever fit even what they are trying to say at. When he was born I knew that motherhood was invented by someone who had to have a word for it because the ones that had the children didn't care whether there was a word for it or not. I knew that fear was invented by someone that had never had the fear; pride, who never had the pride. I knew that it had been, not that they had dirty noses, but that we had had to use one another by words like spiders dangling by their mouths from a beam, swinging and twisting and never touching, and that only through the blows of the switch could my blood and their blood flow as one stream. I knew that it had been, not that my aloneness had to be violated over and over each day, but that it had never been violated until Cash came. Not even by Anse in the nights.

He had a word, too. Love, he called it. But I had been used to words for a long time. I knew that that word was like the others: just a shape to fill a lack; that when the right time came, you wouldn't need a word for that anymore than for pride or fear. Cash did not need to say it to me nor I to him, and I would say, Let Anse use it, if he wants to. So that it was Anse or love; love or Anse: it didn't matter.

I would think that even while I lay with him in the dark and Cash asleep in the cradle within the swing of my hand. I would think that if he were to wake and cry, I would suckle him, too. Anse or love: it didn't matter. My aloneness had been violated and then made whole again by the violation: time, Anse, love, what you will, outside the circle.

Then I found that I had Darl. At first I would not believe it. Then I believed that I would kill Anse. It was as though he had tricked me, hidden within a word like within a paper screen and struck me in the back through it. But then I realised that I had been tricked by words older than Anse or love, and that the same word had tricked Anse too, and that my revenge would be that he would never know I was taking revenge. And when Darl was born I asked Anse to promise to take me back to Jefferson when I died, because I knew that father had been right, even when he couldn't have known he was right anymore than I could have known I was wrong.

"Nonsense," Anse said; "you and me aint nigh done chapping yet, with just two."

He did not know that he was dead, then. Sometimes I would lie by him in the dark, hearing the land that was now of my blood and flesh, and I would think: Anse. Why Anse. Why are you Anse. I would think about his name until after a while I could see the word as a shape, a vessel, and I would watch him liquefy and flow into it like cold molasses flowing out of the darkness into the vessel, until the jar stood full and motionless: a significant shape profoundly without life like an empty door frame; and then I would find that I had forgotten the name of the jar. I would think: The shape of my body where I used to be a virgin is in the shape of a   and I couldn't think *Anse,* couldn't remember *Anse.* It was not that I could think of myself as no longer unvirgin, because I was three now. And when I would think *Cash* and *Darl* that way until their names would die and solidify into a shape and then fade away, I would say, All right. It doesn't matter. It doesn't matter what they call them.

And so when Cora Tull would tell me I was not a true mother, I would think how words go straight up in a thin line, quick and harmless, and how terribly doing goes along the earth, clinging to it, so that after a while the two lines are too far apart for the same person to straddle from one to the other; and that sin and love and fear are just sounds that people who never sinned nor loved nor feared have for what they never had and cannot have until they forget the words. Like Cora, who could never even cook.

She would tell me what I owed to my children and to Anse and to God. I gave Anse the children. I did not ask for them. I did not even ask him for what he could have given me: not-Anse. That was my duty to him, to not ask that, and that duty I fulfilled. I would be I; I would let him be the shape and echo of his word. That was more than he asked, because he could not have asked for that and been Anse, using himself so with a word.

And then he died. He did not know he was dead. I would lie by him in the dark, hearing the dark land talking of God's love and His beauty and His sin; hearing the dark voicelessness in which the words are the deeds, and the other words that are not deeds, that are just the gaps in peoples' lacks, coming down like the cries of the geese out of the wild darkness in the old terrible nights, fumbling at the deeds like orphans to whom are pointed out in a crowd two faces and told, That is your father, your mother.

I believed that I had found it. I believed that the reason was the duty to the alive, to the terrible blood, the red bitter flood boiling through the land. I would think of sin as I would think of the clothes we both wore in the world's face, of the circumspection necessary because he was he and I was I; the sin the more utter and terrible since he was the instrument ordained by God who created the sin, to sanctify that sin He had created. While I waited for him in the woods, waiting for him before he saw me, I would think of him as dressed in sin. I would think of him as thinking of me as dressed also in sin, he the more beautiful since the garment which he had exchanged for sin was sanctified. I would think of the sin as garments which we would remove in order to shape and coerce the terrible blood to the forlorn echo of the dead word high in the air. Then I would lay with Anse again—I did not lie to him: I just refused, just as I refused my breast to Cash and Darl after their time was up—hearing the dark land talking the voiceless speech.

I hid nothing. I tried to deceive no one. I would not have cared. I merely took the precautions that he thought necessary for his sake, not for my safety, but just as I wore clothes in the world's face. And I would think then when Cora talked to me, of how the high dead words in time seemed to lose even the significance of their dead sound.

Then it was over. Over in the sense that he was gone and I knew that, see him again though I would, I would never again see him coming swift and secret to me in the woods dressed in sin like a gallant garment already blowing aside with the speed of his secret coming.

But for me it was not over. I mean, over in the sense of beginning and ending, because to me there was no beginning nor ending to anything then. I even held Anse refraining still, not that I was holding him recessional, but as though nothing else had ever been. My children were of me alone, of the wild blood boiling along the earth, of me and of all that lived; of none and of all. Then I found that I had Jewel. When I waked to remember to discover it, he was two months gone.

My father said that the reason for living is getting ready to stay dead. I knew at last what he meant and that he could not have known what he meant himself, because a man cannot know anything about cleaning up the house afterward. And so I have cleaned my house. With Jewel—I lay by the lamp, holding up my own head, watching him cap and suture it before he breathed—the wild blood boiled away and the sound of it ceased. Then there was only the milk, warm and calm, and I lying calm in the slow silence, getting ready to clean my house.

I gave Anse Dewey Dell to negative Jewel. Then I gave him Vardaman to replace the child I had robbed him of. And now he has three children that are his and not mine. And then I could get ready to die.

One day I was talking to Cora. She prayed for me because she believed I was blind to sin, wanting me to kneel and pray too, because people to whom sin is just a matter of words, to them salvation is just words too.

WHITFIELD

When they told me she was dying, all that night I wrestled with Satan, and I emerged victorious. I woke to the enormity of my sin; I saw the true light at last, and I fell on my knees and confessed to God and asked His guidance and received it. "Rise," He said; "repair to that home in which you have put a living lie, among those people with whom you have outraged My Word; confess your sin aloud. It is for them, for that deceived husband, to forgive you: not I."

So I went. I heard that Tull's bridge was gone; I said "Thanks, O Lord, O Mighty Ruler of all"; for by those dangers and difficulties which I should have to surmount I saw that He had not abandoned me; that my reception again into His holy peace and love would be the sweeter for it. "Just let me not perish before I have begged the forgiveness of the man whom I betrayed," I prayed; "let me not be too late; let not the tale of mine and her transgression come from her lips instead of mine. She had sworn then that she would never tell it, but eternity is a fearsome thing to face: have I not wrestled thigh to thigh with Satan myself? let me not have also the sin of her broken vow upon my soul. Let not the waters of Thy Mighty Wrath encompass me until I have cleansed my soul in the presence of them whom I injured."

It was His hand that bore me safely above the flood, that fended from me the dangers of the waters. My horse was frightened, and my own heart failed me as the logs and the uprooted trees bore down upon my littleness. But not my soul: time after time I saw them averted at destruction's final instant, and I lifted my voice above the noise of the flood: "Praise to Thee, O Mighty Lord and King. By this token shall I cleanse my soul and gain again into the fold of Thy undying love."

I knew then that forgiveness was mine. The flood, the danger, behind, and as I rode on across the firm earth again and the scene of my Gethsemane drew closer and closer, I framed the words which I should use. I would enter the house; I would stop her before she had spoken; I would say to her husband: "Anse, I have sinned. Do with me as you will."

It was already as though it were done. My soul felt freer, quieter than it had in years; already I seemed to dwell in abiding peace again as I rode on. To either side I saw His hand; in my heart I could hear His voice: "Courage. I am with thee."

Then I reached Tull's house. His youngest girl came out and called to me as I was passing. She told me that she was already dead.

I have sinned, O Lord. Thou knowest the extent of my remorse and the will of my spirit. But He is merciful; He will accept the will for the deed, Who knew that when I framed the words of my confession it was to Anse I spoke them, even though he was not there. It was He in His infinite wisdom that restrained the tale from her dying lips as she lay surrounded by those who loved and trusted her; mine the travail by water which I sustained by the strength of His hand. Praise to Thee in Thy bounteous and omnipotent love; O praise.

I entered the house of bereavement, the lowly dwelling where another erring mortal lay while her soul faced the awful and irrevocable judgment, peace to her ashes.

"God's grace upon this house," I said.

DARL

On the horse he rode up to Armstid's and *came back on the horse,* leading Armstid's team. We hitched up and laid Cash on top of Addie. When we laid him down he vomited again, but he got his head over the wagon bed in time.

"He taken a lick in the stomach, too," Vernon said.

"The horse may have kicked him in the stomach too," I said. "Did he kick you in the stomach, Cash?"

He tried to say something. Dewey Dell wiped his mouth again.

"What's he say?" Vernon said.

"What is it, Cash?" Dewey Dell said. She leaned down. "His tools," she said. Vernon got them and put them into the wagon. Dewey Dell lifted Cash's head so he could see. We drove on, Dewey Dell and I sitting beside Cash to steady him *and he riding on ahead on the horse.* Vernon stood watching us for a while. Then he turned and went back toward the bridge. He walked gingerly, beginning to flap the wet sleeves of his shirt as though he had just got wet.

He was sitting the horse before the gate. Armstid was waiting at the gate. We stopped *and he got down* and we lifted Cash down and carried him into the house, where Mrs Armstid had the bed ready. We left her and Dewey Dell undressing him.

We followed pa out to the wagon. He went back and got into the wagon and drove on, we following on foot, into the lot. The wetting had helped, because Armstid said, "You're welcome to the house. You can put it there." *He followed, leading the horse, and stood beside the wagon, the reins in his hand.*

"I thank you," pa said. "We'll use in the shed yonder. I know it's a imposition on you."

"You're welcome to the house," Armstid said. *He had that wooden look on his face again; that bold, surly, high-colored rigid look like his face and eyes were two colors of wood, the wrong one pale and the wrong one dark. His shirt was beginning to dry, but it still clung close upon him when he moved.*

"She would appreciate it," pa said.

We took the team out and rolled the wagon back under the shed. One side of the shed was open.

"It wont rain under," Armstid said. "But if you'd rather . . ."

Back of the barn was some rusted sheets of tin roofing. We took two of them and propped them against the open side.

"You're welcome to the house," Armstid said.

"I thank you," pa said. "I'd take it right kind if you'd give them a little snack."

"Sho," Armstid said. "Lula'll have supper ready soon as she gets Cash comfortable." *He had gone back to the horse and he was taking the saddle off, his damp shirt lapping flat to him when he moved.*

Pa wouldn't come in the house.

"Come in and eat," Armstid said. "It's nigh ready."

"I wouldn't crave nothing," pa said. "I thank you."

"You come in and dry and eat," Armstid said. "It'll be all right here."

"It's for her," pa said. "It's for her sake I am taking the food. I got no team, no nothing. But she will be grateful to ere a one of you."

"Sho," Armstid said. "You folks come in and dry."

But after Armstid gave pa a drink, he felt better, and when we went in to see about Cash *he hadn't come in with us. When I looked back he was leading the horse into the barn* he was already talking about getting another team, and by supper time he had good as bought it. *He is down there in the barn, sliding fluidly past the gaudy lunging swirl, into the stall with it. He climbs onto the manger and drags the hay down and leaves the stall and seeks and finds the curry-comb. Then he returns and slips quickly past the single crashing thump and up against the horse, where it cannot overreach. He applies the curry-comb, holding himself within the horse's striking radius with the agility of an acrobat, cursing the horse in a whisper of obscene caress. Its head*

flashes back, tooth-cropped; its eyes roll in the dusk like marbles on a gaudy velvet cloth as he strikes it upon the face with the back of the curry-comb.

ARMSTID

But time I give him another sup of whisky and supper was about ready, he had done already bought a team from somebody, on a credit. Picking and choosing he were by then, saying how he didn't like this span and wouldn't put his money in nothing so-and-so owned, not even a hen coop.

"You might try Snopes," I said. "He's got three-four span. Maybe one of them would suit you."

Then he begun to mumble his mouth, looking at me like it was me that owned the only span of mules in the county and wouldn't sell them to him, when I knew that like as not it would be my team that would ever get them out of the lot at all. Only I dont know what they would do with them, if they had a team. Littlejohn had told me that the levee through Haley bottom had done gone for two miles and that the only way to get to Jefferson would be to go around by Mottson. But that was Anse's business.

"He's a close man to trade with," he says, mumbling his mouth. But when I give him another sup after supper, he cheered up some. He was aiming to go back to the barn and set up with her. Maybe he thought that if he just stayed down there ready to take out, Santa Claus would maybe bring him a span of mules. "But I reckon I can talk him around," he says. "A man'll always help a fellow in a tight, if he's got ere a drop of Christian blood in him."

"Of course you're welcome to the use of mine," I said, me knowing how much he believed that was the reason.

"I thank you," he said. "She'll want to go in ourn," and him knowing how much I believed that was the reason.

After supper Jewel rode over to the Bend to get Peabody. I heard he was to be there today at Varner's. Jewel come back about midnight. Peabody had gone down below Inverness somewhere, but Uncle Billy come back with him, with his satchel of horse-physic. Like he says, a man aint so different from a horse or a mule, come long come short, except a mule or a horse has got a little more sense. "What you been into now, boy?" he says, looking at Cash. "Get me a mattress and a chair and a glass of whisky," he says.

He made Cash drink the whisky, then he run Anse out of the room. "Lucky it was the same leg he broke last summer," Anse says, mournful, mumbling and blinking. "That's something."

We folded the mattress across Cash's legs and set the chair on the mattress and me and Jewel set on the chair and the gal held the lamp and Uncle Billy taken a chew of tobacco and went to work. Cash fought pretty hard for a while, until he fainted. Then he laid still, with big balls of sweat standing on his face like they had started to roll down and then stopped to wait for him.

When he waked up, Uncle Billy had done packed up and left. He kept on trying to say something until the gal leaned down and wiped his mouth. "It's his tools," she said.

"I brought them in," Darl said. "I got them."

He tried to talk again; she leaned down. "He wants to see them," she said. So Darl brought them in where he could see them. They shoved them under the side of the bed, where he could reach his hand and touch them when he felt better. Next morning Anse taken that horse and rode over to the Bend to see Snopes. Him and Jewel stood in the lot talking a while, then Anse got on the horse and rode off. I reckon that was the first time Jewel ever let anybody ride that horse, and until Anse come back he hung around in that swole-up way, watching the road like he was half a mind to take out after Anse and get the horse back.

Along toward nine oclock it begun to get hot. That was when I see the first buzzard. Because of the wetting, I reckon. Anyway it wasn't until well into the day that I see them. Lucky the breeze was setting away from the house, so it wasn't until well into the morning. But soon as I see them it was like I could smell it in the field a mile away from just watching them, and them circling and circling for everybody in the county to see what was in my barn.

I was still a good half a mile from the house when I heard that boy yelling. I thought maybe he might have fell into the well or something, so I whipped up and come into the lot on the lope.

There must have been a dozen of them setting along the ridge-pole of the barn, and that boy was chasing another one around the lot like it was a turkey and it just lifting enough to dodge him and go flopping back to the roof of the shed again where he had found it setting on the coffin. It had got hot then, right, and the breeze had dropped or changed or something, so I went and found Jewel, but Lula come out.

"You got to do something," she said. "It's a outrage."

"That's what I aim to do," I said.

"It's a outrage," she said. "He should be lawed for treating her so."

"He's getting her into the ground the best he can," I said. So I found Jewel and asked him if he didn't want to take one of the mules and go over to the Bend and see about Anse. He didn't say nothing. He just looked at me with his jaws going bone-white and them bone-white eyes of hisn, then he went and begun to call Darl.

"What you fixing to do?" I said.

He didn't answer. Darl come out. "Come on," Jewel said.

"What you aim to do?" Darl said.

"Going to move the wagon," Jewel said over his shoulder.

"Dont be a fool," I said. "I never meant nothing. You couldn't help it." And Darl hung back too, but nothing wouldn't suit Jewel.

"Shut your goddamn mouth," he says.

"It's got to be somewhere," Darl said. "We'll take out soon as pa gets back."

"You wont help me?" Jewel says, them white eyes of hisn kind of blaring and his face shaking like he had a aguer.

"No," Darl said. "I wont. Wait till pa gets back."

So I stood in the door and watched him push and haul at that wagon. It was on a downhill, and once I thought he was fixing to beat out the back end of the shed. Then the dinner bell rung. I called him, but he didn't look around. "Come on to dinner," I said. "Tell that boy." But he didn't answer, so I went on to dinner. The gal went down to get that boy, but she come back without him. About half through dinner we heard him yelling again, running that buzzard out.

"It's a outrage," Lula said; "a outrage."

"He's doing the best he can," I said. "A fellow dont trade with Snopes in thirty minutes. They'll set in the shade all afternoon to dicker."

"Do?" she says. "Do? He's done too much, already."

And I reckon he had. Trouble is, his quitting was just about to start our doing. He couldn't buy no team from nobody, let alone Snopes, withouten he had something to mortgage he didn't know would mortgage yet. And so when I went back to the field I looked at my mules and same as told them goodbye for a spell. And when I come back that evening and the sun shining all day on that shed, I wasn't so sho I would regret it.

He come riding up just as I went out to the porch, where they all was. He looked kind of funny: kind of more hang-dog than common, and kind of proud too. Like he had done something he thought was cute but wasn't so sho now how other folks would take it.

"I got a team," he said.

"You bought a team from Snopes?" I said.

"I reckon Snopes aint the only man in this country that can drive a trade," he said.

"Sho," I said. He was looking at Jewel, with that funny look, but Jewel had done got down from the porch and was going toward the horse. To see what Anse had done to it, I reckon.

"Jewel," Anse says. Jewel looked back. "Come here," Anse says. Jewel come back a little and stopped again.

"What you want?" he said.

"So you got a team from Snopes," I said. "He'll send them over tonight, I reckon? You'll want a early start tomorrow, long as you'll have to go by Mottson."

Then he quit looking like he had been for a while. He got that badgered look like he used to have, mumbling his mouth.

"I do the best I can," he said. "Fore God, if there were ere a man in the living world suffered the trials and floutings I have suffered."

"A fellow that just beat Snopes in a trade ought to feel pretty good," I said. "What did you give him, Anse?"

He didn't look at me. "I give a chattel mortgage on my cultivator and seeder," he said.

"But they aint worth forty dollars.

How far do you aim to get with a forty dollar team?"

They were all watching him now, quiet and steady. Jewel was stopped, halfway back, waiting to go on to the horse. "I give other things," Anse said. He begun to mumble his mouth again, standing there like he was waiting for somebody to hit him and him with his mind already made up not to do nothing about it.

"What other things?" Darl said.

"Hell," I said. "You take my team. You can bring them back. I'll get along someway."

"So that's what you were doing in Cash's clothes last night," Darl said. He said it just like he was reading it outen the paper. Like he never give a durn himself one way or the other. Jewel had come back now, standing there, looking at Anse with them marble eyes of hisn. "Cash aimed to buy that talking machine from Suratt with that money," Darl said.

Anse stood there, mumbling his mouth. Jewel watched him. He aint never blinked yet.

"But that's just eight dollars more," Darl said, in that voice like he was just listening and never give a durn himself. "That still wont buy a team."

Anse looked at Jewel quick, kind of sliding his eyes that way, then he looked down again. "God knows, if there were ere a man," he says. Still they didn't say nothing. They just watched him, waiting, and him sliding his eyes toward their feet and up their legs but no higher. "And the horse," he says.

"What horse?" Jewel said. Anse just stood there. I be durn, if a man cant keep the upper hand of his sons, he ought to run them away from home, no matter how big they are. And if he cant do that, I be durn if he oughtn't to leave himself. I be durn if I wouldn't. "You mean, you tried to swap my horse?" Jewel says.

Anse stands there, dangle-armed. "For fifteen years I aint had a tooth in my head," he says. "God knows it. He knows in fifteen years I aint et the victuals He aimed for man to eat to keep his strength up, and me saving a nickel here and a nickel there so my family wouldn't suffer it, to buy them teeth so I could eat God's appointed food. I give that money. I thought that if I could do without eating, my sons could do without riding. God knows I did."

Jewel stands with his hands on his hips, looking at Anse. Then he looks away. He looked out across the field, his face still as a rock, like it was somebody else talking about somebody else's horse and him not even listening. Then he spit, slow, and said "Hell" and he turned and went on to the gate and unhitched the horse and got on it. It was moving when he come into the saddle and by the time he was on it they was tearing down the road like the Law might have been behind them. They went out of sight that way, the two of them looking like some kind of a spotted cyclone.

"Well," I says. "You take my team," I said. But he wouldn't do it. And they wouldn't even stay, and that boy chasing them buzzards all day in the hot sun until he was nigh as crazy as the rest of them. "Leave Cash here, anyway," I said. But they wouldn't do that. They made a pallet for him with quilts on top of the coffin and laid him on it and set his tools by him, and we put my team in and hauled the wagon about a mile down the road.

"If we'll bother you here," Anse says, "just say so."

"Sho," I said. "It'll be fine here. Safe, too. Now let's go back and eat supper."

"I thank you," Anse said. "We got a little something in the basket. We can make out."

"Where'd you get it?" I said.

"We brought it from home."

"But it'll be stale now," I said. "Come and get some hot victuals."

But they wouldn't come. "I reckon we can make out," Anse said. So I went home and et and taken a basket back to them and tried again to make them come back to the house.

"I thank you," he said. "I reckon we can make out." So I left them there, squatting around a little fire, waiting; God knows what for.

I come on home. I kept thinking about them there, and about that fellow tearing away on that horse. And that would be the last they would see of him. And I be durn if I could blame him. Not for wanting to not give up his horse, but for getting shut of such a durn fool as Anse.

Or that's what I thought then. Because be durn if there aint something about a durn fellow like Anse that seems to make a man have to help him, even when he knows he'll be wanting to kick himself next minute. Because about a hour after breakfast next morning Eustace Grimm that works Snopes' place come up with a span of mules, hunting Anse.

"I thought him and Anse never traded," I said.

"Sho," Eustace said. "All they liked was the horse. Like I said to Mr Snopes, he was letting this team go for fifty dollars, because if his uncle Flem had a just kept them Texas horses when he owned them, Anse wouldn't a never—"

"The horse?" I said. "Anse's boy taken that horse and cleared out last night, probably halfway to Texas by now, and Anse—"

"I didn't know who brung it," Eustace said. "I never see them. I just found the horse in the barn this morning when I went to feed, and I told Mr Snopes and he said to bring the team on over here."

Well, that'll be the last they'll ever see of him now, sho enough. Come Christ-mas time they'll maybe get a postal card from him in Texas, I reckon. And if it hadn't a been Jewel, I reckon it'd a been me; I owe him that much, myself. I be durn if Anse dont conjure a man, some way. I be durn if he aint a sight.

VARDAMAN

Now there are seven of them, in little tall black circles.

"Look, Darl," I say; "see?"

He looks up. We watch them in little tall black circles of not-moving.

"Yesterday there were just four," I say.

There were more than four on the barn.

"Do you know what I would do if he tries to light on the wagon again?" I say.

"What would you do?" Darl says.

"I wouldn't let him light on her," I say. "I wouldn't let him light on Cash, either."

Cash is sick. He is sick on the box. But my mother is a fish.

"We got to get some medicine in Mottson," pa says. "I reckon we'll just have to."

"How do you feel, Cash?" Darl says.

"It dont bother none," Cash says.

"Do you want it propped a little higher?" Darl says.

Cash has a broken leg. He has had two broken legs. He lies on the box with a quilt rolled under his head and a piece of wood under his knee.

"I reckon we ought to left him at Armstid's," pa says.

I haven't got a broken leg and pa hasn't and Darl hasn't and "It's just the bumps," Cash says. "It kind of grinds together a little on a bump. It dont bother none." *Jewel has gone away. He and his horse went away one supper time*

"It's because she wouldn't have us beholden," pa says. "Fore God, I do the best that ere a man" *Is it because Jewel's mother is a horse Darl? I said.*

"Maybe I can draw the ropes a little tighter," Darl says. *That's why Jewel and I were both in the shed and she was in the wagon because the horse lives in the barn and I had to keep on running the buzzard away from*

"If you just would," Cash says. And Dewey Dell hasn't got a broken leg and I haven't. Cash is my brother.

We stop. When Darl loosens the rope Cash begins to sweat again. His teeth look out.

"Hurt?" Darl says.

"I reckon you better put it back," Cash says.

Darl puts the rope back, pulling hard. Cash's teeth look out.

"Hurt?" Darl says.

"It dont bother none," Cash says.

"Do you want pa to drive slower?" Darl says.

"No," Cash says. "Aint no time to hang back. It dont bother none."

"We'll have to get some medicine at Mottson," pa says. "I reckon we'll have to."

"Tell him to go on," Cash says. We go on. Dewey Dell leans back and wipes Cash's face. Cash is my brother. *But Jewel's mother is a horse. My mother is a fish. Darl says that when we come to the water again I might see her and Dewey Dell said, She's in the box; how could she have got out? She got out through the holes I bored, into the water I said, and when we come to the water again I am going to see her. My mother is not in the box. My mother does not smell like that. My mother is a fish*

"Those cakes will be in fine shape by the time we get to Jefferson," Darl says.

Dewey Dell does not look around.

"You better try to sell them in Mottson," Darl says.

"When will we get to Mottson, Darl?" I say.

"Tomorrow," Darl says. "If this team dont rack to pieces. Snopes must have fed them on sawdust."

"Why did he feed them on sawdust, Darl?" I say.

"Look," Darl says. "See?"

Now there are nine of them, tall in little black circles.

When we come to the foot of the hill pa stops and Darl and Dewey Dell and I get out. Cash cant walk because he has a broken leg. "Come up, mules," pa says. The mules walk hard; the wagon creaks. Darl and Dewey Dell and I walk behind the wagon, up the hill. When we come to the top of the hill pa stops and we get back into the wagon.

Now there are ten of them, tall in little tall black circles on the sky.

MOSELEY

I happened to look up, and saw her outside the window, looking in. Not close to the glass, and not looking at anything in particular; just standing there with her head turned this way and her eyes full on me and kind of blank too, like she was waiting for a sign. When I looked up again she was moving toward the door.

She kind of bumbled at the screen door a minute, like they do, and came in. She had on a stiff-brimmed straw hat setting on the top of her head and she was carrying a package wrapped in newspaper: I thought that she had a quarter or a dollar at the most, and that after she stood around a while she would maybe buy a cheap comb or a bottle of nigger toilet water, so I never disturbed her for a minute or so except to notice that she was pretty in a kind of sullen, awkward way, and that she looked a sight better in her gingham dress and her own complexion than she would after she bought whatever she would finally decide on. Or tell what she wanted. I knew that she had already decided before she came in. But you have to let them take their time. So I went on with what I was doing, figuring to let Albert wait on her when he caught up at the fountain, when he came back to me.

"That woman," he said. "You better see what she wants."

"What does she want?" I said.

"I dont know. I cant get anything out of her. You better wait on her."

So I went around the counter. I saw that she was barefooted, standing with her feet flat and easy on the floor, like she was used to it. She was looking at me, hard, holding the package; I saw she had about as black a pair of eyes as ever I saw, and she was a stranger. I never remembered seeing her in Mottson before. "What can I do for you?" I said.

Still she didn't say anything. She stared at me without winking. Then she looked back at the folks at the fountain. Then she looked past me, toward the back of the store.

"Do you want to look at some toilet things?" I said. "Or is it medicine you want?"

"That's it," she said. She looked quick back at the fountain again. So I thought maybe her ma or somebody had sent her in for some of this female dope and she was ashamed to ask for it. I knew she couldn't have a complexion like hers and use it herself, let alone not being much more than old enough to barely know what it was for. It's a shame, the way they poison themselves with it. But a man's got to stock it or go out of business in this country.

"Oh," I said. "What do you use? We have—" She looked at me again, almost like she had said hush, and looked toward the back of the store again.

"I'd liefer go back there," she said.

"All right," I said. You have to humor them. You save time by it. I followed her to the back. She put her hand on the gate. "There's nothing back there but the prescription case," I said. "What do you want?" She stopped and looked at me. It was like she had taken some kind of a lid off her face, her eyes. It was her eyes: kind of dumb and hopeful and sullenly willing to be disappointed all at the same time. But she was in trouble of some sort; I could see that. "What's your trouble?" I said. "Tell me what it is you want. I'm pretty busy." I wasn't meaning to hurry her, but a man just hasn't got the time they have out there.

"It's the female trouble," she said.

"Oh," I said. "Is that all?" I thought maybe she was younger than she looked, and her first one had scared her, or maybe one had been a little abnormal as it will in young women. "Where's your ma?" I said. "Haven't you got one?"

"She's out yonder in the wagon," she said.

"Why not talk to her about it before you take any medicine," I said. "Any woman would have told you about it." She looked at me, and I looked at her again and said, "How old are you?"

"Seventeen," she said.

"Oh," I said. "I thought maybe you were . . ." She was watching me. But then, in the eyes all of them look like they had no age and knew everything in the world, anyhow. "Are you too regular, or not regular enough?"

She quit looking at me but she didn't move. "Yes," she said. "I reckon so. Yes."

"Well, which?" I said. "Dont you know?" It's a crime and a shame; but after all, they'll buy it from somebody. She stood there, not looking at me. "You want something to stop it?" I said. "Is that it?"

"No," she said. "That's it. It's already stopped."

"Well, what—" Her face was lowered a little, still, like they do in all their dealings with a man so he dont ever know just where the lightning will strike next. "You are not married, are you?" I said.

"No."

"Oh," I said. "And how long has it been since it stopped? about five months maybe?"

"It ain't been but two," she said.

"Well, I haven't got anything in my store you want to buy," I said, "unless it's a nipple. And I'd advise you to buy that and go back home and tell your pa, if you have one, and let him make somebody buy you a wedding license. Was that all you wanted?"

But she just stood there, not looking at me.

"I got the money to pay you," she said.

"Is it your own, or did he act enough of a man to give you the money?"

"He give it to me. Ten dollars. He said that would be enough."

"A thousand dollars wouldn't be enough in my store and ten cents wouldn't be enough," I said. "You take my advice and go home and tell your pa or your brothers if you have any or the first man you come to in the road."

But she didn't move. "Lafe said I could get it at the drugstore. He said to tell you me and him wouldn't never tell nobody you sold it to us."

"And I just wish your precious Lafe had come for it himself; that's what I wish. I dont know: I'd have had a little respect for him then. And you can go back and tell him I said so—if he aint halfway to Texas by now, which I dont doubt. Me, a respectable druggist, that's kept store and raised a family and been a church-member for fifty-six years in this town. I'm a good mind to tell your folks myself, if I can just find who they are."

She looked at me now, her eyes and face kind of blank again like when I first saw her through the window. "I didn't know," she said. "He told me I could get something at the drugstore. He said they might not want to sell it to me, but if I had ten dollars and told them I wouldn't never tell nobody . . ."

"He never said this drugstore," I said. "If he did or mentioned my name, I defy him to prove it. I defy him to repeat it or I'll prosecute him to the full extent of the law, and you can tell him so."

"But maybe another drugstore would," she said.

"Then I dont want to know it. Me, that's—" Then I looked at her. But it's a hard life they have; sometimes a man . . . if there can ever be any excuse for sin, which it cant be. And then, life wasn't made to be easy on folks: they wouldn't ever have any reason to be good and die. "Look here," I said. "You get that notion out of your head. The Lord gave you what you have, even if He did use the devil to do it; you let Him take it away from you if it's His will to do so. You go on back to Lafe and you and him take that ten dollars and get married with it."

"Lafe said I could get something at the drugstore," she said.

"Then go and get it," I said. "You wont get it here."

She went out, carrying the package, her feet making a little hissing on the floor. She bumbled again at the door and went out. I could see her through the glass going on down the street.

It was Albert told me about the rest of it. He said the wagon was stopped in front of Grummet's hardware store, with the ladies all scattering up and down the street with handkerchiefs to their noses, and a crowd of hard-nosed men and boys standing around the wagon, listening to the marshal arguing with the man. He was a kind of tall, gaunted man sitting on the wagon, saying it was a public street and he reckoned he had as much right there as anybody, and the marshal telling him he would have to move on; folks couldn't stand it. It had been dead eight days, Albert said. They came from some place out in Yoknapatawpha county, trying to get to Jefferson with it. It must have been like a piece of rotten cheese coming into an ant-hill, in that ramshackle wagon that Albert said folks were scared would fall all to pieces before they could get it out of town, with that home-made box and another fellow with a broken leg lying on a quilt on top of it, and the father and a little boy sitting on the seat and the marshal trying to make them get out of town.

"It's a public street," the man says. "I reckon we can stop to buy something same as airy other man. We got the money to pay for hit, and hit aint airy law that says a man cant spend his money where he wants."

They had stopped to buy some cement. The other son was in Grummet's, trying to make Grummet break a sack and let him have ten cents' worth, and finally Grummet broke the sack to get him out. They wanted the cement to fix the fellow's broken leg, someway.

"Why, you'll kill him," the marshal said. "You'll cause him to lose his leg. You take him on to a doctor, and you get this thing buried soon as you can. Dont you know you're liable to jail for endangering the public health?"

"We're doing the best we can," the father said. Then he told a long tale about how they had to wait for the wagon to come back and how the bridge was washed away and how they went eight miles to another bridge and it was gone too so they came back and swum the ford and the mules got drowned and how they got another team and found that the road was washed out and they

had to come clean around by Mottson, and then the one with the cement came back and told him to shut up.

"We'll be gone in a minute," he told the marshal.

"We never aimed to bother nobody," the father said.

"You take that fellow to a doctor," the marshal told the one with the cement.

"I reckon he's all right," he said.

"It aint that we're hard-hearted," the marshal said. "But I reckon you can tell yourself how it is."

"Sho," the other said. "We'll take out soon as Dewey Dell comes back. She went to deliver a package."

So they stood there with the folks backed off with handkerchiefs to their faces, until in a minute the girl came up with that newspaper package.

"Come on," the one with the cement said, "we've lost too much time." So they got in the wagon and went on. And when I went to supper it still seemed like I could smell it. And the next day I met the marshal and I began to sniff and said,

"Smell anything?"

"I reckon they're in Jefferson by now," he said.

"Or in jail. Well, thank the Lord it's not our jail."

"That's a fact," he said.

DARL

"Here's a place," pa says. He pulls the team up and sits looking at the house. "We could get some water over yonder."

"All right," I say. "You'll have to borrow a bucket from them, Dewey Dell."

"God knows," pa says. "I wouldn't be beholden, God knows."

"If you see a good-sized can, you might bring it," I say. Dewey Dell gets down from the wagon, carrying the package. "You had more trouble than you expected, selling those cakes in Mottson," I say. How do our lives ravel out into the no-wind, no-sound, the weary gestures wearily recapitulant: echoes of old compulsions with no-hand on no-strings: in sunset we fall into furious attitudes, dead gestures of dolls. Cash broke his leg and now the sawdust is running out. He is bleeding to death is Cash.

"I wouldn't be beholden," pa says. "God knows."

"Then make some water yourself," I say. "We can use Cash's hat."

When Dewey Dell comes back the man comes with her. Then he stops and she comes on and he stands there and after a while he goes back to the house and stands on the porch, watching us.

"We better not try to lift him down," pa says. "We can fix it here."

"Do you want to be lifted down, Cash?" I say.

"Wont we get to Jefferson tomorrow?" he says. He is watching us, his eyes interrogatory, intent, and sad. "I can last it out."

"It'll be easier on you," pa says. "It'll keep it from rubbing together."

"I can last it," Cash says. "We'll lose time stopping."

"We done bought the cement, now," pa says.

"I could last it," Cash says. "It aint but one more day. It dont bother to speak of." He looks at us, his eyes wide in his thin gray face, questioning. "It sets up so," he says.

"We done bought it now," pa says.

I mix the cement in the can, stirring the slow water into the pale green thick coils. I bring the can to the wagon where Cash can see. He lies on his back, his thin profile in silhouette, ascetic and profound against the sky. "Does that look about right?" I say.

"You dont want too much water, or it wont work right," he says.

"Is this too much?"

"Maybe if you could get a little sand," he says. "It aint but one more day," he says. "It dont bother me none."

Vardaman goes back down the road to where we crossed the branch and returns with sand. He pours it slowly into the thick coiling in the can. I go to the wagon again.

"Does that look all right?"

"Yes," Cash says. "I could have lasted. It dont bother me none."

We loosen the splints and pour the cement over his leg, slow.

"Watch out for it," Cash says. "Dont get none on it if you can help."

"Yes," I say. Dewey Dell tears a piece of paper from the package and wipes the cement from the top of it as it drips from Cash's leg.

"How does that feel?"

"It feels fine," he says. "It's cold. It feels fine."

"If it'll just help you," pa says. "I asks your forgiveness. I never foreseen it no more than you."

"It feels fine," Cash says.

If you could just ravel out into time. That would be nice. It would be nice if you could just ravel out into time.

We replace the splints, the cords, drawing them tight, the cement in thick pale green slow surges among the cords, Cash watching us quietly with that profound questioning look.

"That'll steady it," I say.

"Ay," Cash says. "I'm obliged."

Then we all turn on the wagon and watch him. He is coming up the road behind us, wooden-backed, wooden-faced, moving only from his hips down. He comes up without a word, with his pale rigid eyes in his high sullen face, and gets into the wagon.

"Here's a hill," pa says. "I reckon you'll have to get out and walk."

VARDAMAN

Darl and Jewel and Dewey Dell and I are walking up the hill, behind the wagon. Jewel came back. He came up the road and got into the wagon. He was walking. Jewel hasn't got a horse anymore. Jewel is my brother. Cash is my brother. Cash has a broken leg. We fixed Cash's leg so it doesn't hurt. Cash is my brother, Jewel is my brother too, but he hasn't got a broken leg.

Now there are five of them, tall in little tall black circles.

"Where do they stay at night, Darl?" I say. "When we stop at night in the barn, where do they stay?"

The hill goes off into the sky. Then the sun comes up from behind the hill and the mules and the wagon and pa walk on the sun. You cannot watch them, walking slow on the sun. In Jefferson it is red on the track behind the glass. The track goes shining round and round. Dewey Dell says so.

Tonight I am going to see where they stay while we are in the barn.

DARL

"Jewel," I say, "whose son are you?"

The breeze was setting up from the barn, so we put her under the apple tree, where the moonlight can dapple the apple tree upon the long slumbering flanks within which now and then she talks in little trickling bursts of secret and murmurous bubbling. I took Vardaman to listen. When we came up the cat leaped down from it and flicked away with silver claw and silver eye into the shadow.

"Your mother was a horse, but who was your father, Jewel?"

"You goddamn lying son of a bitch."

"Dont call me that," I say.

"You goddamn lying son of a bitch."

"Dont you call me that, Jewel." In the tall moonlight his eyes look like spots of white paper pasted on a high small football.

After supper Cash began to sweat a little. "It's getting a little hot," he said. "It was the sun shining on it all day, I reckon."

"You want some water poured on it?" we say. "Maybe that will ease it some."

"I'd be obliged," Cash said. "It was the sun shining on it, I reckon. I ought to thought and kept it covered."

"We ought to thought," we said. "You couldn't have suspicioned."

"I never noticed it getting hot," Cash said. "I ought to minded it."

So we poured the water over it. His leg and foot below the cement looked like they had been boiled. "Does that feel better?" we said.

"I'm obliged," Cash said. "It feels fine."

Dewey Dell wipes his face with the hem of her dress.

"See if you can get some sleep," we say.

"Sho," Cash says. "I'm right obliged. It feels fine now."

Jewel, I say, Who was your father, Jewel?

Goddamn you. Goddamn you.

VARDAMAN

She was under the apple tree and Darl and I go across the moon and the cat jumps down and runs and we can hear her inside the wood.

"Hear?" Darl says. "Put your ear close."

I put my ear close and I can hear her. Only I cant tell what she is saying.

"What is she saying, Darl?" I say. "Who is she talking to?"

"She's talking to God," Darl says. "She is calling on Him to help her."

"What does she want Him to do?" I say.

"She wants Him to hide her away from the sight of man," Darl says.

"Why does she want to hide her away from the sight of man, Darl?"

"So she can lay down her life," Darl says.

"Why does she want to lay down her life, Darl?"

"Listen," Darl says. We hear her. We hear her turn over on her side. "Listen," Darl says.

"She's turned over," I say. "She's looking at me through the wood."

"Yes," Darl says.

"How can she see through the wood, Darl?"

"Come," Darl says. "We must let her be quiet. Come."

"She cant see out there, because the holes are in the top," I say. "How can she see, Darl?"

"Let's go see about Cash," Darl says.

And I saw something Dewey Dell told me not to tell nobody

Cash is sick in his leg. We fixed his leg this afternoon, but he is sick in it again, lying on the bed. We pour water on his leg and then he feels fine.

"I feel fine," Cash says. "I'm obliged to you."

"Try to get some sleep," we say.

"I feel fine," Cash says. "I'm obliged to you."

And I saw something Dewey Dell told me not to tell nobody. It is not about pa and it is not about Cash and it is not about Jewel and it is not about Dewey Dell and it is not about me

Dewey Dell and I are going to sleep on the pallet. It is on the back porch, where we can see the barn, and the moon shines on half of the pallet and we will lie half in the white and half in the black, with the moonlight on our legs. And then I am going to see where they stay at night while we are in the barn. We are not in the barn tonight but I can see the barn and so I am going to find where they stay at night.

We lie on the pallet, with our legs in the moon.

"Look," I say, "my legs look black. Your legs look black, too."

"Go to sleep," Dewey Dell says.

Jefferson is a far piece.

"Dewey Dell."

"What."

"If it's not Christmas now, how will it be there?"

It goes round and round on the shining track. Then the track goes shining round and round.

"Will what be there?"

"That train. In the window."

"You go to sleep. You can see tomorrow if it's there."

Maybe Santa Claus wont know they are town boys.

"Dewey Dell."

"You go to sleep. He aint going to let none of them town boys have it."

It was behind the window, red on the track, the track shining round and round. It made my heart hurt. And then it was pa and Jewel and Darl and Mr Gillespie's boy. Mr Gillespie's boy's legs come down under his nightshirt. When he goes into the moon, his legs fuzz. They go on around the house toward the apple tree.

"What are they going to do, Dewey Dell?"

They went around the house toward the apple tree.

"I can smell her," I say. "Can you smell her, too?"

"Hush," Dewey Dell says. "The wind's changed. Go to sleep."

And so I am going to know where they stay at night soon. They come around the house, going across the yard in the moon, carrying her on their shoulders. They carry her down to the barn, the moon shining flat and quiet on her. Then they come back and go into the house again. While they were in the moon, Mr Gillespie's boy's legs fuzzed. And then I waited and I said Dewey Dell? and then I waited and then I went to find where they stay at night and I saw something that Dewey Dell told me not to tell nobody.

DARL

Against the dark doorway he seems to materialise out of darkness, lean as a race horse in his underclothes in the beginning of the glare. He leaps to the ground with on his face an expression of furious unbelief. He has seen me without even turning his head or his eyes in which the glare swims like two small torches. "Come on," he says, leaping down the slope toward the barn.

For an instant longer he runs silver in the moonlight, then he springs out like a flat figure cut leanly from tin against an abrupt and soundless explosion as the whole loft of the barn takes fire at once, as though it had been stuffed with powder. The front, the conical façade with the square orifice of doorway broken only by the square squat shape of the coffin on the sawhorses like a cubistic bug, comes into relief. Behind me pa and Gillespie and Mack and Dewey Dell and Vardaman emerge from the house.

He pauses at the coffin, stooping, looking at me, his face furious. Overhead the flames sound like thunder; across us rushes a cool draft: there is no heat in it at all yet, and a handful of chaff lifts suddenly and sucks swiftly along the stalls where a horse is screaming. "Quick," I say; "the horses."

He glares a moment longer at me, then at the roof overhead, then he leaps toward the stall where the horse screams. It plunges and kicks, the sound of the crashing blows sucking up into the sound of the flames. They sound like an interminable train crossing an endless trestle. Gillespie and Mack pass me, in knee-length nightshirts, shouting, their voices thin and high and meaningless and at the same time profoundly wild and sad: " . . . cow . . . stall . . . " Gillespie's nightshirt rushes ahead of him on the draft, ballooning about his hairy thighs.

The stall door has swung shut. Jewel thrusts it back with his buttocks and he appears, his back arched, the muscles ridged through his garment as he drags the horse out by its head. In the glare its eyes roll with soft, fleet, wild opaline fire; its muscles bunch and run as it flings its head about, lifting Jewel clear of the ground. He drags it on, slowly, terrifically; again he gives me across his shoulder a single glare furious and brief. Even when they are clear of the barn the horse continues to fight and lash backward toward the doorway until Gillespie passes me, stark-naked, his nightshirt wrapped about the mule's head, and beats the maddened horse on out of the door.

Jewel returns, running; again he looks down at the coffin. But he comes on. "Where's cow?" he cries, passing me. I follow him. In the stall Mack is struggling with the other mule. When its head turns into the glare I can see the wild rolling of its eye too, but it makes no sound. It just stands there, watching Mack over its shoulder, swinging its hind quarters toward him whenever he approaches. He looks back at us, his eyes and mouth three round holes in his face on which the freckles look like English peas on a plate. His voice is thin, high, faraway.

"I cant do nothing . . ." It is as though the sound had been swept from his lips and up and away, speaking back to us from an immense distance of exhaustion. Jewel slides past us; the mule whirls and lashes out, but he has already gained its head. I lean to Mack's ear:

"Nightshirt. Around his head."

Mack stares at me. Then he rips the nightshirt off and flings it over the mule's head, and it becomes docile at once. Jewel is yelling at him: "Cow? Cow?"

"Back," Mack cries. "Last stall."

The cow watches us as we enter. She is backed into the corner, head lowered, still chewing though rapidly. But she makes no move. Jewel has paused, looking up, and suddenly we watch the entire floor to the loft dissolve. It just turns to fire; a faint litter of sparks rains down. He glances about. Back under the trough is a three legged milking stool. He catches it up and swings it into the planking of the rear wall. He splinters a plank, then another, a third; we tear the fragments away. While we are stooping at the opening something charges into us from behind. It is the cow; with a single whistling breath she rushes between us and through the gap and into the outer glare, her tail erect and rigid as a broom nailed upright to the end of her spine.

Jewel turns back into the barn. "Here," I say; "Jewel!" I grasp at him; he strikes my hand down. "You fool," I say, "dont you see you cant make it back yonder?" The hallway looks like a searchlight turned into rain. "Come on," I say, "around this way."

When we are through the gap he begins to run. "Jewel," I say, running. He darts around the corner. When I reach it he has almost reached the next one, running against the glare like that figure cut from tin. Pa and Gillespie and Mack are some distance away, watching the barn, pink against the darkness where for the time the moonlight has been vanquished. "Catch him!" I cry; "stop him!"

When I reach the front, he is struggling with Gillespie; the one lean in underclothes, the other stark naked. They are like two figures in a Greek frieze, isolated out of all reality by the red glare. Before I can reach them he has struck Gillespie to the ground and turned and run back into the barn.

The sound of it has become quite peaceful now, like the sound of the river did. We watch through the dissolving proscenium of the doorway as Jewel runs crouching to the far end of the coffin and stoops to it. For an instant he looks up and out at us through the rain of burning hay like a portiere of flaming beads, and I can see his mouth shape as he calls my name.

"Jewel!" Dewey Dell cries; "Jewel!" It seems to me that I now hear the accumulation of her voice through the last five minutes, and I hear her scuffling and struggling as pa and Mack hold her, screaming "Jewel! Jewel!" But he is no longer looking at us. We see his shoulders strain as he upends the coffin and slides it single-handed from the sawhorses. It looms unbelievably tall, hiding him: I would not have believed that Addie Bundren would have needed that much room to lie comfortable in; for another instant it stands upright while the sparks rain on it in scattering bursts as though they engendered other sparks from the contact. Then it topples forward, gaining momentum, revealing Jewel and the sparks raining on him too in engendering gusts, so that he appears to be enclosed in a thin nimbus of fire. Without stopping it overends and rears again, pauses, then crashes slowly forward and through the curtain. This time Jewel is riding upon it, clinging to it, until it crashes down and flings him forward and clear and Mack leaps forward into a thin smell of scorching meat and slaps at the widening crimson-edged holes that bloom like flowers in his undershirt.

VARDAMAN

When I went to find where they stay at night, I saw something They said, "Where is Darl? Where did Darl go?"

They carried her back under the apple tree.

The barn was still red, but it wasn't a barn now. It was sunk down, and the red went swirling up. The barn went swirling up in little red pieces, against the sky and the stars so that the stars moved backward.

And then Cash was still awake. He turned his head from side to side, with sweat on his face.

"Do you want some more water on it, Cash?" Dewey Dell said.

Cash's leg and foot turned black. We held the lamp and looked at Cash's foot and leg where it was black.

"Your foot looks like a nigger's foot, Cash," I said.

"I reckon we'll have to bust it off," pa said.

"What in the tarnation you put it on there for?" Mr Gillespie said.

"I thought it would steady it some," pa said. "I just aimed to help him."

They got the flat iron and the hammer. Dewey Dell held the lamp. They had to hit it hard. And then Cash went to sleep.

"He's asleep now," I said. "It cant hurt him while he's asleep."

It just cracked. It wouldn't come off.

"It'll take the hide, too," Mr Gillespie said. "Why in the tarnation you put it on there. Didn't none of you think to grease his leg first?"

"I just aimed to help him," pa said. "It was Darl put it on."

"Where is Darl?" they said.

"Didn't none of you have more sense than that?" Mr Gillespie said. "I'd a thought he would, anyway."

Jewel was lying on his face. His back was red. Dewey Dell put the medicine on it. The medicine was made out of butter and soot, to draw out the fire. Then his back was black.

"Does it hurt, Jewel?" I said. "Your back looks like a nigger's, Jewel," I said. Cash's foot and leg looked like a nigger's. Then they broke it off. Cash's leg bled.

"You go on back and lay down," Dewey Dell said. "You ought to be asleep."

"Where is Darl?" they said.

He is out there under the apple tree with her, lying on her. He is there so the cat wont come back. I said, "Are you going to keep the cat away, Darl?"

The moonlight dappled on him too. On her it was still, but on Darl it dappled up and down.

"You needn't to cry," I said. "Jewel got her out. You needn't to cry, Darl."

The barn is still red. It used to be redder than this. Then it went swirling, making the stars run backward without falling. It hurt my heart like the train did.

When I went to find where they stay at night, I saw something that Dewey Dell says I mustn't never tell nobody

DARL

We have been passing the signs for some time now: the drugstores, the clothing stores, the patent medicine and the garages and cafes, and the mile-boards diminishing, becoming more starkly reaccruent: 3 mi. 2 mi. From the crest of a hill, as we get into the wagon again, we can see the smoke low and flat, seemingly unmoving in the unwinded afternoon.

"Is that it, Darl?" Vardaman says. "Is that Jefferson?" He too has lost flesh; like ours, his face has an expression strained, dreamy, and gaunt.

"Yes," I say. He lifts his head and

looks at the sky. High against it they hang in narrowing circles, like the smoke, with an outward semblance of form and purpose, but with no inference of motion, progress or retrograde. We mount the wagon again where Cash lies on the box, the jagged shards of cement cracked about his leg. The shabby mules droop rattling and clanking down the hill.

"We'll have to take him to the doctor," pa says. "I reckon it aint no way around it." The back of Jewel's shirt, where it touches him, stains slow and black with grease. Life was created in the valleys. It blew up onto the hills on the old terrors, the old lusts, the old despairs. That's why you must walk up the hills so you can ride down.

Dewey Dell sits on the seat, the newspaper package on her lap. When we reach the foot of the hill where the road flattens between close walls of trees, she begins to look about quietly from one side of the road to the other. At last she says,

"I got to stop."

Pa looks at her, his shabby profile that of anticipant and disgruntled annoyance. He does not check the team. "What for?"

"I got to go to the bushes," Dewey Dell says.

Pa does not check the team. "Cant you wait till we get to town? It aint over a mile now."

"Stop," Dewey Dell says. "I got to go to the bushes."

Pa stops in the middle of the road and we watch Dewey Dell descend, carrying the package. She does not look back.

"Why not leave your cakes here?" I say. "We'll watch them."

She descends steadily, not looking at us.

"How would she know where to go if she waited till we get to town?" Vardaman says. "Where would you go to do it in town, Dewey Dell?"

She lifts the package down and turns and disappears among the trees and undergrowth.

"Dont be no longer than you can help," pa says. "We aint got no time to waste." She does not answer. After a while we cannot hear her even. "We ought to done like Armstid and Gillespie said and sent word to town and had it dug and ready," he said.

"Why didn't you?" I say. "You could have telephoned."

"What for?" Jewel says. "Who the hell cant dig a hole in the ground?"

A car comes over the hill. It begins to sound the horn, slowing. It runs along the roadside in low gear, the outside wheels in the ditch, and passes us and goes on. Vardaman watches it until it is out of sight.

"How far is it now, Darl?" he says.

"Not far," I say.

"We ought to done it," pa says. "I just never wanted to be beholden to none except her flesh and blood."

"Who the hell cant dig a damn hole in the ground?" Jewel says.

"It aint respectful, talking that way about her grave," pa says. "You all dont know what it is. You never pure loved her, none of you." Jewel does not answer. He sits a little stiffly erect, his body arched away from his shirt. His high-colored jaw juts.

Dewey Dell returns. We watch her emerge from the bushes, carrying the package, and climb into the wagon. She now wears her Sunday dress, her beads, her shoes and stockings.

"I thought I told you to leave them clothes to home," pa says. She does not answer, does not look at us. She sets the package in the wagon and gets in. The wagon moves on.

"How many more hills now, Darl?" Vardaman says.

"Just one," I say. "The next one goes right up into town."

This hill is red sand, bordered on

either hand by negro cabins; against the sky ahead the massed telephone lines run, and the clock on the courthouse lifts among the trees. In the sand the wheels whisper, as though the very earth would hush our entry. We descend as the hill commences to rise.

We follow the wagon, the whispering wheels, passing the cabins where faces come suddenly to the doors, white-eyed. We hear sudden voices, ejaculant. Jewel has been looking from side to side; now his head turns forward and I can see his ears taking on a still deeper tone of furious red. Three negroes walk beside the road ahead of us; ten feet ahead of them a white man walks. When we pass the negroes their heads turn suddenly with that expression of shock and instinctive outrage. "Great God," one says; "what they got in that wagon?"

Jewel whirls. "Son of a bitches," he says. As he does so he is abreast of the white man, who has paused. It is as though Jewel had gone blind for the moment, for it is the white man toward whom he whirls.

"Darl!" Cash says from the wagon. I grasp at Jewel. The white man has fallen back a pace, his face still slack-jawed; then his jaw tightens, claps to. Jewel leans above him, his jaw muscles gone white.

"What did you say?" he says.

"Here," I say. "He dont mean anything, mister. Jewel," I say. When I touch him he swings at the man. I grasp his arm; we struggle. Jewel has never looked at me. He is trying to free his arm. When I see the man again he has an open knife in his hand.

"Hold up, mister," I say; "I've got him. Jewel," I say.

"Thinks because he's a goddamn town fellow," Jewel says, panting, wrenching at me. "Son of a bitch," he says.

The man moves. He begins to edge around me, watching Jewel, the knife low against his flank. "Cant no man call me that," he says. Pa has got down, and Dewey Dell is holding Jewel, pushing at him. I release him and face the man.

"Wait," I say. "He dont mean nothing. He's sick; got burned in a fire last night, and he aint himself."

"Fire or no fire," the man says, "cant no man call me that."

"He thought you said something to him," I say.

"I never said nothing to him. I never see him before."

"Fore God," pa says; "fore God."

"I know," I say. "He never meant anything. He'll take it back."

"Let him take it back, then."

"Put up your knife, and he will."

The man looks at me. He looks at Jewel. Jewel is quiet now.

"Put up your knife," I say.

The man shuts the knife.

"Fore God," pa says. "Fore God."

"Tell him you didn't mean anything, Jewel," I say.

"I thought he said something," Jewel says. "Just because he's—"

"Hush," I say. "Tell him you didn't mean it."

"I didn't mean it," Jewel says.

"He better not," the man says. "Calling me a—"

"Do you think he's afraid to call you that?" I say.

The man looks at me. "I never said that," he said.

"Dont think it, neither," Jewel says.

"Shut up," I say. "Come on. Drive on, pa."

The wagon moves. The man stands watching us. Jewel does not look back. "Jewel would a whipped him," Vardaman says.

We approach the crest, where the street runs, where cars go back and forth; the mules haul the wagon up and onto the crest and the street. Pa stops them. The street runs on ahead, where the square opens and the monument stands before the courthouse. We mount again while the heads turn with that expression which we know; save Jewel. He does not get on, even though the wagon has started again. "Get in, Jewel," I say. "Come on. Let's get away from here." But he does not get in. Instead he sets his foot on the turning hub of the rear wheel, one hand grasping the stanchion, and with the hub turning smoothly under his sole he lifts the other foot and squats there, staring straight ahead, motionless, lean, wooden-backed, as though carved squatting out of the lean wood.

CASH

It wasn't nothing else to do. It was either send him to Jackson, or have Gillespie sue us, because he knowed some way that Darl set fire to it. I dont know how he knowed, but he did. Vardaman see him do it, but he swore he never told nobody but Dewey Dell and that she told him not to tell nobody. But Gillespie knowed it. But he would a suspicioned it sooner or later. He could have done it that night just watching the way Darl acted.

And so pa said, "I reckon there aint nothing else to do," and Jewel said,

"You want to fix him now?"

"Fix him?" pa said.

"Catch him and tie him up," Jewel said. "Goddamn it, do you want to wait until he sets fire to the goddamn team and wagon?"

But there wasn't no use in that. "There aint no use in that," I said. "We can wait till she is underground." A fellow that's going to spend the rest of his life locked up, he ought to be let to have what pleasure he can have before he goes.

"I reckon he ought to be there," pa says. "God knows, it's a trial on me.

Seems like it aint no end to bad luck when once it starts."

Sometimes I aint so sho who's got ere a right to say when a man is crazy and when he aint. Sometimes I think it aint none of us pure crazy and aint none of us pure sane until the balance of us talks him that-a-way. It's like it aint so much what a fellow does, but it's the way the majority of folks is looking at him when he does it.

Because Jewel is too hard on him. Of course it was Jewel's horse was traded to get her that nigh to town, and in a sense it was the value of his horse Darl tried to burn up. But I thought more than once before we crossed the river and after, how it would be God's blessing if He did take her outen our hands and get shut of her in some clean way, and it seemed to me that when Jewel worked so to get her outen the river, he was going against God in a way, and then when Darl seen that it looked like one of us would have to do something, I can almost believe he done right in a way. But I dont reckon nothing excuses setting fire to a man's barn and endangering his stock and destroying his property. That's how I reckon a man is crazy. That's how he cant see eye to eye with other folks. And I reckon they aint nothing else to do with him but what the most folks says is right.

But it's a shame, in a way. Folks seems to get away from the olden right teaching that says to drive the nails down and trim the edges well always like it was for your own use and comfort you were making it. It's like some folks has the smooth, pretty boards to build a courthouse with and others dont have no more than rough lumber fitten to build a chicken coop. But it's better to build a tight chicken coop than a shoddy courthouse, and when they both build shoddy or build well, neither because it's one or tother is going to make a man feel the better nor the worse.

So we went up the street, toward the square, and he said, "We better take Cash to the doctor first. We can leave him there and come back for him." That's it. It's because me and him was born close together, and it nigh ten years before Jewel and Dewey Dell and Vardaman begun to come along. I feel kin to them, all right, but I dont know. And me being the oldest, and thinking already the very thing that he done: I dont know.

Pa was looking at me, then at him, mumbling his mouth.

"Go on," I said. "We'll get it done first."

"She would want us all there," pa says.

"Let's take Cash to the doctor first," Darl said. "She'll wait. She's already waited nine days."

"You all dont know," pa says. "The somebody you was young with and you growed old in her and she growed old in you, seeing the old coming on and it was the one somebody you could hear say it dont matter and know it was the truth outen the hard world and all a man's grief and trials. You all dont know."

"We got the digging to do, too," I said.

"Armstid and Gillespie both told you to send word ahead," Darl said. "Dont you want to go to Peabody's now, Cash?"

"Go on," I said. "It feels right easy now. It's best to get things done in the right place."

"If it was just dug," pa says. "We forgot our spade, too."

"Yes," Darl said. "I'll go to the hardware store. We'll have to buy one."

"It'll cost money," pa says.

"Do you begrudge her it?" Darl says.

"Go on and get a spade," Jewel said. "Here. Give me the money."

But pa didn't stop. "I reckon we can get a spade," he said. "I reckon there are Christians here." So Darl set still and we went on, with Jewel squatting on the tailgate, watching the back of Darl's head. He looked like one of these bull dogs, one of these dogs that dont bark none, squatting against the rope, watching the thing he was waiting to jump at.

He set that way all the time we was in front of Mrs Bundren's house, hearing the music, watching the back of Darl's head with them hard white eyes of hisn.

The music was playing in the house. It was one of them graphophones. It was natural as a music-band.

"Do you want to go to Peabody's?" Darl said. "They can wait here and tell pa, and I'll drive you to Peabody's and come back for them."

"No," I said. It was better to get her underground, now we was this close, just waiting until pa borrowed the shovel. He drove along the street until we could hear the music.

"Maybe they got one here," he said. He pulled up at Mrs Bundren's. It was like he knowed. Sometimes I think that if a working man could see work as far ahead as a lazy man can see laziness. So he stopped there like he knowed, before that little new house, where the music was. We waited there, hearing it. I believe I could have dickered Suratt down to five dollars on that one of his. It's a comfortable thing, music is. "Maybe they got one here," pa says.

"You want Jewel to go," Darl says, "or do you reckon I better?"

"I reckon I better," pa says. He got down and went up the path and around the house to the back. The music stopped, then it started again.

"He'll get it, too," Darl said.

"Ay," I said. It was just like he knowed, like he could see through the walls and into the next ten minutes.

Only it was more than ten minutes. The music stopped and never commenced again for a good spell, where her and pa was talking at the back. We waited in the wagon.

"You let me take you back to Peabody's," Darl said.

"No," I said. "We'll get her underground."

"If he ever gets back," Jewel said. He begun to cuss. He started to get down from the wagon. "I'm going," he said.

Then we saw pa coming back. He had two spades, coming around the house. He laid them in the wagon and got in and we went on. The music never started again. Pa was looking back at the house. He kind of lifted his hand a little and I saw the shade pulled back a little at the window and her face in it.

But the curiousest thing was Dewey Dell. It surprised me. I see all the while how folks could say he was queer, but that was the very reason couldn't nobody hold it personal. It was like he was outside of it too, same as you, and getting mad at it would be kind of like getting mad at a mud-puddle that splashed you when you stepped in it. And then I always kind of had a idea that him and Dewey Dell kind of knowed things betwixt them. If I'd a said it was ere a one of us she liked better than ere a other, I'd a said it was Darl. But when we got it filled and covered and drove out the gate and turned into the lane where them fellows was waiting, when they come out and come on him and he jerked back, it was Dewey Dell that was on him before even Jewel could get at him. And then I believed I knowed how Gillespie knowed about how his barn taken fire.

She hadn't said a word, hadn't even looked at him, but when them fellows told him what they wanted and that they had come to get him and he throwed back, she jumped on him like a wild cat so that one of the fellows had to quit and hold her and her scratching and clawing at him like a wild cat, while the other one and pa and Jewel throwed Darl down and held him lying on his back, looking up at me.

"I thought you would have told me,"

he said. "I never thought you wouldn't have."

"Darl," I said. But he fought again, him and Jewel and the fellow, and the other one holding Dewey Dell and Vardaman yelling and Jewel saying,

"Kill him. Kill the son of a bitch."

It was bad so. It was bad. A fellow cant get away from a shoddy job. He cant do it. I tried to tell him, but he just said, "I thought you'd a told me. It's not that I," he said, then he begun to laugh. The other fellow pulled Jewel off of him and he sat there on the ground, laughing.

I tried to tell him. If I could have just moved, even set up. But I tried to tell him and he quit laughing, looking up at me.

"Do you want me to go?" he said.

"It'll be better for you," I said. "Down there it'll be quiet, with none of the bothering and such. It'll be better for you, Darl," I said.

"Better," he said. He begun to laugh again. "Better," he said. He couldn't hardly say it for laughing. He sat on the ground and us watching him, laughing and laughing. It was bad. It was bad so. I be durn if I could see anything to laugh at. Because there just aint nothing justifies the deliberate destruction of what a man has built with his own sweat and stored the fruit of his sweat into.

But I aint so sho that ere a man has the right to say what is crazy and what aint. It's like there was a fellow in every man that's done a-past the sanity or the insanity, that watches the sane and the insane doings of that man with the same horror and the same astonishment.

PEABODY

I said, "I reckon a man in a tight might let Bill Varner patch him up like a damn mule, but I be damned if the man that'd let Anse Bundren treat him with raw cement aint got more spare legs than I have."

"They just aimed to ease hit some," he said.

"Aimed, hell," I said. "What in hell did Armstid mean by even letting them put you on that wagon again?"

"Hit was gittin right noticeable," he said. "We never had time to wait." I just looked at him. "Hit never bothered me none," he said.

"Dont you lie there and try to tell me you rode six days on a wagon without springs, with a broken leg and it never bothered you."

"It never bothered me much," he said.

"You mean, it never bothered Anse much," I said. "No more than it bothered him to throw that poor devil down in the public street and handcuff him like a damn murderer. Dont tell me. And dont tell me it aint going to bother you to lose sixty-odd square inches of skin to get that concrete off. And dont tell me it aint going to bother you to have to limp around on one short leg for the balance of your life—if you walk at all again. Concrete," I said. "God Amighty, why didn't Anse carry you to the nearest sawmill and stick your leg in the saw? That would have cured it. Then you all could have stuck his head into the saw and cured a whole family . . . Where is Anse, anyway? What's he up to now?"

"He's takin back them spades he borrowed," he said.

"That's right," I said. "Of course he'd have to borrow a spade to bury his wife with. Unless he could borrow a hole in the ground. Too bad you all didn't put him in it too . . . Does that hurt?"

"Not to speak of," he said, and the sweat big as marbles running down his face and his face about the color of blotting paper.

"Course not," I said. "About next summer you can hobble around fine on this leg. Then it wont bother you, not to speak of . . . If you had anything you could call luck, you might say it was lucky this is the same leg you broke before," I said.

"Hit's what paw says," he said.

MACGOWAN

It happened I am back of the prescription case, pouring up some chocolate sauce, when Jody comes back and says, "Say, Skeet, there's a woman up front that wants to see the doctor and when I said What doctor you want to see, she said she wants to see the doctor that works here and when I said There aint any doctor works here, she just stood there, looking back this way."

"What kind of a woman is it?" I says. "Tell her to go upstairs to Alford's office."

"Country woman," he says.

"Send her to the courthouse," I says. "Tell her all the doctors have gone to Memphis to a Barbers' Convention."

"All right," he says, going away. "She looks pretty good for a country girl," he says.

"Wait," I says. He waited and I went and peeped through the crack. But I couldn't tell nothing except she had a good leg against the light. "Is she young, you say?" I says.

"She looks like a pretty hot mamma, for a country girl," he says.

"Take this," I says, giving him the chocolate. I took off my apron and went up there. She looked pretty good. One of them black eyed ones that look like she'd as soon put a knife in you as not if you two-timed her. She looked pretty good. There wasn't nobody else in the store; it was dinner time.

[97]

"What can I do for you?" I says.

"Are you the doctor?" she says.

"Sure," I says. She quit looking at me and was kind of looking around.

"Can we go back yonder?" she says.

It was just a quarter past twelve, but I went and told Jody to kind of watch out and whistle if the old man come in sight, because he never got back before one.

"You better lay off of that," Jody says. "He'll fire your stern out of here so quick you cant wink."

"He dont never get back before one," I says. "You can see him go into the post-office. You keep your eye peeled, now, and give me a whistle."

"What you going to do?" he says.

"You keep your eye out. I'll tell you later."

"Aint you going to give me no seconds on it?" he says.

"What the hell do you think this is?" I says; "a stud-farm? You watch out for him. I'm going into conference."

So I go on to the back. I stopped at the glass and smoothed my hair, then I went behind the prescription case, where she was waiting. She is looking at the medicine cabinet, then she looks at me.

"Now, madam," I says; "what is your trouble?"

"It's the female trouble," she says, watching me. "I got the money," she says.

"Ah," I says. "Have you got female troubles or do you want female troubles? If so, you come to the right doctor." Them country people. Half the time they dont know what they want, and the balance of the time they cant tell it to you. The clock said twenty past twelve.

"No," she says.

"No which?" I says.

"I aint had it," she says. "That's it." She looked at me. "I got the money," she says.

So I knew what she was talking about.

"Oh," I says. "You got something in your belly you wish you didn't have." She looks at me. "You wish you had a little more or a little less, huh?"

"I got the money," she says. "He said I could git something at the drugstore for hit."

"Who said so?" I says.

"He did," she says, looking at me.

"You don't want to call no names," I says. "The one that put the acorn in your belly? He the one that told you?" She dont say nothing. "You aint married, are you?" I says. I never saw no ring. But like as not, they aint heard yet out there that they use rings.

"I got the money," she says. She showed it to me, tied up in her handkerchief: a ten spot.

"I'll swear you have," I says. "He give it to you?"

"Yes," she says.

"Which one?" I says. She looks at me. "Which one of them give it to you?"

"It aint but one," she says. She looks at me.

"Go on," I says. She dont say nothing. The trouble about the cellar is, it aint but one way out and that's back up the inside stairs. The clock says twenty-five to one. "A pretty girl like you," I says.

She looks at me. She begins to tie the money back up in the handkerchief. "Excuse me a minute," I says. I go around the prescription case. "Did you hear about that fellow sprained his ear?" I says. "After that he couldn't even hear a belch."

"You better get her out from back there before the old man comes," Jody says.

"If you'll stay up there in front where he pays you to stay, he wont catch nobody but me," I says.

He goes on, slow, toward the front. "What you doing to her, Skeet?" he says.

"I cant tell you," I says. "It wouldn't

be ethical. You go on up there and watch."

"Say, Skeet," he says.

"Ah, go on," I says. "I aint doing nothing but filling a prescription."

"He may not do nothing about that woman back there, but if he finds you monkeying with that prescription case, he'll kick your stern clean down them cellar stairs."

"My stern has been kicked by bigger bastards than him," I says. "Go back and watch out for him, now."

So I come back. The clock said fifteen to one. She is tying the money in the handkerchief. "You aint the doctor," she says.

"Sure I am," I says. She watches me. "Is it because I look too young, or am I too handsome?" I says. "We used to have a bunch of old water-jointed doctors here," I says; "Jefferson used to be a kind of Old Doctors' Home for them. But business started falling off and folks stayed so well until one day they found out that the women wouldn't never get sick at all. So they run all the old doctors out and got us young good-looking ones that the women would like and then the women begun to get sick again and so business picked up. They're doing that all over the country. Hadn't you heard about it? Maybe it's because you aint never needed a doctor."

"I need one now," she says.

"And you come to the right one," I says. "I already told you that."

"Have you got something for it?" she says. "I got the money."

"Well," I says, "of course a doctor has to learn all sorts of things while he's learning to roll calomel; he cant help himself. But I dont know about your trouble."

"He told me I could get something. He told me I could get it at the drugstore."

"Did he tell you the name of it?" I

says. "You better go back and ask him."

She quit looking at me, kind of turning the handkerchief in her hands. "I got to do something," she says.

"How bad do you want to do something?" I says. She looks at me. "Of course, a doctor learns all sorts of things folks dont think he knows. But he aint supposed to tell all he knows. It's against the law."

Up front Jody says, "Skeet."

"Excuse me a minute," I says. I went up front. "Do you see him?" I says.

"Aint you done yet?" he says. "Maybe you better come up here and watch and let me do that consulting."

"Maybe you'll lay a egg," I says. I come back. She is looking at me. "Of course you realise that I could be put in the penitentiary for doing what you want," I says. "I would lose my license and then I'd have to go to work. You realise that?"

"I aint got but ten dollars," she says. "I could bring the rest next month, maybe."

"Pooh," I says, "ten dollars? You see, I cant put no price on my knowledge and skill. Certainly not for no little paltry sawbuck."

She looks at me. She dont even blink. "What you want, then?"

The clock said four to one. So I decided I better get her out. "You guess three times and then I'll show you," I says.

She dont even blink her eyes. "I got to do something," she says. She looks behind her and around, then she looks toward the front. "Gimme the medicine first," she says.

"You mean, you're ready to right now?" I says. "Here?"

"Gimme the medicine first," she says.

So I took a graduated glass and kind of turned my back to her and picked out a bottle that looked all right, because a man that would keep poison setting around in a unlabelled bottle ought to be in jail, anyway. It smelled like turpentine. I poured some into the glass and give it to her. She smelled it, looking at me across the glass.

"Hit smells like turpentine," she says.

"Sure," I says. "That's just the beginning of the treatment. You come back at ten oclock tonight and I'll give you the rest of it and perform the operation."

"Operation?" she says.

"It wont hurt you. You've had the same operation before. Ever hear about the hair of the dog?"

She looks at me. "Will it work?" she says.

"Sure it'll work. If you come back and get it."

So she drunk whatever it was without batting a eye, and went out. I went up front.

"Didn't you get it?" Jody says.

"Get what?" I says.

"Ah, come on," he says. "I aint going to try to beat your time."

"Oh, her," I says. "She just wanted a little medicine. She's got a bad case of dysentery and she's a little ashamed about mentioning it with a stranger there."

It was my night, anyway, so I helped the old bastard check up and I got his hat on him and got him out of the store by eight-thirty. I went as far as the corner with him and watched him until he passed under two street lamps and went on out of sight. Then I come back to the store and waited until nine-thirty and turned out the front lights and locked the door and left just one light burning at the back, and I went back and put some talcum powder into six capsules and kind of cleared up the cellar and then I was all ready.

She come in just at ten, before the clock had done striking. I let her in and she come in, walking fast. I looked out the door, but there wasn't nobody but a boy in overalls sitting on the curb. "You want something?" I says. He never said nothing, just looking at me. I locked the door and turned off the light and went on back. She was waiting. She didn't look at me now.

"Where is it?" she said.

I gave her the box of capsules. She held the box in her hand, looking at the capsules.

"Are you sure it'll work?" she says.

"Sure," I says. "When you take the rest of the treatment."

"Where do I take it?" she says.

"Down in the cellar," I says.

VARDAMAN

Now it is wider and lighter, but the stores are dark because they have all gone home. The stores are dark, but the lights pass on the windows when we pass. The lights are in the trees around the courthouse. They roost in the trees, but the courthouse is dark. The clock on it looks four ways, because it is not dark. The moon is not dark too. Not very dark. *Darl he went to Jackson is my brother Darl is my brother* Only it was over that way, shining on the track.

"Let's go that way, Dewey Dell," I say.

"What for?" Dewey Dell says. The track went shining around the window, it red on the track. But she said he would not sell it to the town boys. "But it will be there Christmas," Dewey Dell says. "You'll have to wait till then, when he brings it back."

Darl went to Jackson. Lots of people didn't go to Jackson. Darl is my brother. My brother is going to Jackson

While we walk the lights go around, roosting in the trees. On all sides it is the same. They go around the courthouse and then you cannot see them. But you can see them in the black windows beyond. They have all gone home to bed except me and Dewey Dell.

Going on the train to Jackson. My brother

There is a light in the store, far back. In the window are two big glasses of soda water, red and green. Two men could not drink them. Two mules could not. Two cows could not. *Darl*

A man comes to the door. He looks at Dewey Dell.

"You wait out here," Dewey Dell says.

"Why cant I come in?" I say. "I want to come in, too."

"You wait out here," she says.

"All right," I say.

Dewey Dell goes in.

Darl is my brother. Darl went crazy

The walk is harder than sitting on the ground. He is in the open door. He looks at me. "You want something?" he says. His head is slick. Jewel's head is slick sometimes. Cash's head is not slick. *Darl he went to Jackson my brother Darl* In the street he ate a banana. *Wouldn't you rather have bananas? Dewey Dell said. You wait till Christmas. It'll be there then. Then you can see it. So we are going to have some bananas. We are going to have a bag full, me and Dewey Dell.* He locks the door. Dewey Dell is inside. Then the light winks out.

He went to Jackson. He went crazy and went to Jackson both. Lots of people didn't go crazy. Pa and Cash and Jewel and Dewey Dell and me didn't go crazy. We never did go crazy. We didn't go to Jackson either. Darl

I hear the cow a long time, clopping on the street. Then she comes into the square. She goes across the square, her head down   clopping   . She lows. There was nothing in the square before she lowed, but it wasn't empty. Now it is empty after she lowed. She goes on, clopping   . She lows. *My brother is*

Darl. He went to Jackson on the train. He didn't go on the train to go crazy. He went crazy in our wagon. Darl She has been in there a long time. And the cow is gone too. A long time. She has been in there longer than the cow was. But not as long as empty. *Darl is my brother. My brother Darl*

Dewey Dell comes out. She looks at me.

"Let's go around that way now," I say.

She looks at me. "It aint going to work," she says. "That son of a bitch."

"What aint going to work, Dewey Dell?"

"I just know it wont," she says. She is not looking at anything. "I just know it."

"Let's go that way," I say.

"We got to go back to the hotel. It's late. We got to slip back in."

"Cant we go by and see, anyway?"

"Hadn't you rather have bananas? Hadn't you rather?"

"All right." *My brother he went crazy and he went to Jackson too. Jackson is further away than crazy*

"It wont work," Dewey Dell says. "I just know it wont."

"What wont work?" I say. *He had to get on the train to go to Jackson. I have not been on the train, but Darl has been on the train. Darl. Darl is my brother. Darl. Darl*

DARL

Darl has gone to Jackson. They put him on the train, laughing, down the long car laughing, the heads turning like the heads of owls when he passed. "What are you laughing at?" I said.

"Yes yes yes yes yes."

Two men put him on the train. They wore mismatched coats, bulging behind over their right hip pockets. Their necks were shaved to a hairline, as though the recent and simultaneous barbers had had a chalk-line like Cash's. "Is it the pistols you're laughing at?" I said. "Why do you laugh?" I said. "Is it because you hate the sound of laughing?"

They pulled two seats together so Darl could sit by the window to laugh. One of them sat beside him, the other sat on the seat facing him, riding backward. One of them had to ride backward because the state's money has a face to each backside and a backside to each face, and they are riding on the state's money which is incest. A nickel has a woman on one side and a buffalo on the other; two faces and no back. I dont know what that is. Darl had a little spy-glass he got in France at the war. In it it had a woman and a pig with two backs and no face. I know what that is. "Is that why you are laughing, Darl?"

"Yes yes yes yes yes yes."

The wagon stands on the square, hitched, the mules motionless, the reins wrapped about the seat-spring, the back of the wagon toward the courthouse. It looks no different from a hundred other wagons there; Jewel standing beside it and looking up the street like any other man in town that day, yet there is something different, distinctive. There is about it that unmistakable air of definite and imminent departure that trains have, perhaps due to the fact that Dewey Dell and Vardaman on the seat and Cash on a pallet in the wagon bed are eating bananas from a paper bag. "Is that why you are laughing, Darl?"

Darl is our brother, our brother Darl. Our brother Darl in a cage in Jackson where, his grimed hands lying light in the quiet interstices, looking out he foams.

"Yes yes yes yes yes yes yes yes."

DEWEY DELL

When he saw the money I said, "It's not my money, it doesn't belong to me."

"Whose is it, then?"

"It's Cora Tull's money. It's Mrs Tull's. I sold the cakes for it."

"Ten dollars for two cakes?"

"Dont you touch it. It's not mine."

"You never had them cakes. It's a lie. It was them Sunday clothes you had in that package."

"Dont you touch it! If you take it you are a thief."

"My own daughter accuses me of being a thief. My own daughter."

"Pa. Pa."

"I have fed you and sheltered you. I give you love and care, yet my own daughter, the daughter of my dead wife, calls me a thief over her mother's grave."

"It's not mine, I tell you. If it was, God knows you could have it."

"Where did you get ten dollars?"

"Pa. Pa."

"You wont tell me. Did you come by it so shameful you dare not?"

"It's not mine, I tell you. Cant you understand it's not mine?"

"It's not like I wouldn't pay it back. But she calls her own father a thief."

"I cant, I tell you. I tell you it's not my money. God knows you could have it."

"I wouldn't take it. My own born daughter that has et my food for seventeen years, begrudges me the loan of ten dollars."

"It's not mine. I cant."

"Whose is it, then?"

"It was give to me. To buy something with."

"To buy what with?"

"Pa. Pa."

"It's just a loan. God knows, I hate for my blooden children to reproach me. But I give them what was mine without stint. Cheerful I give them, without stint. And now they deny me. Addie. It was lucky for you you died, Addie."

"Pa. Pa."

"God knows it is."

He took the money and went out.

CASH

So when we stopped there to borrow the shovels we heard the graphophone playing in the house, and so when we got done with the shovels pa says, "I reckon I better take them back."

So we went back to the house. "We better take Cash on to Peabody's," Jewel said.

"It wont take but a minute," pa said. He got down from the wagon. The music was not playing now.

"Let Vardaman do it," Jewel said. "He can do it in half the time you can. Or here, you let me—"

"I reckon I better do it," pa says. "Long as it was me that borrowed them."

So we set in the wagon, but the music wasn't playing now. I reckon it's a good thing we aint got ere a one of them. I reckon I wouldn't never get no work done a-tall for listening to it. I dont know if a little music aint about the nicest thing a fellow can have. Seems like when he comes in tired of a night, it aint nothing could rest him like having a little music played and him resting. I have see them that shuts up like a hand-grip, with a handle and all, so a fellow can carry it with him wherever he wants.

"What you reckon he's doing?" Jewel says. "I could a toted them shovels back and forth ten times by now."

"Let him take his time," I said. "He aint as spry as you, remember."

"Why didn't he let me take them back, then? We got to get your leg fixed up so we can start home tomorrow."

"We got plenty of time," I said. "I wonder what them machines costs on the installment."

"Installment of what?" Jewel said. "What you got to buy it with?"

"A fellow cant tell," I said. "I could a bought that one from Suratt for five dollars, I believe."

And so pa come back and we went to Peabody's. While we was there pa said he was going to the barbershop and get a shave. And so that night he said he had some business to tend to, kind of looking away from us while he said it, with his hair combed wet and slick and smelling sweet with perfume, but I said leave him be; I wouldn't mind hearing a little more of that music myself.

And so next morning he was gone again, then he come back and told us to get hitched up and ready to take out and he would meet us and when they was gone he said,

"I dont reckon you got no more money."

"Peabody just give me enough to pay the hotel with," I said. "We dont need nothing else, do we?"

"No," pa said; "no. We dont need nothing." He stood there, not looking at me.

"If it is something we got to have, I reckon maybe Peabody," I said.

"No," he said; "it aint nothing else. You all wait for me at the corner."

So Jewel got the team and come for me and they fixed me a pallet in the wagon and we drove across the square to the corner where pa said, and we was waiting there in the wagon, with Dewey Dell and Vardaman eating bananas, when we see them coming up the street. Pa was coming along with that kind of daresome and hangdog look all at once like when he has been up to something he knows ma aint going to like, carrying a grip in his hand, and Jewel says,

"Who's that?"

Then we see it wasn't the grip that made him look different; it was his face, and Jewel says, "He got them teeth."

It was a fact. It made him look a foot taller, kind of holding his head up, hangdog and proud too, and then we see her behind him, carrying the other grip—a kind of duck-shaped woman all dressed up, with them kind of hard-looking pop eyes like she was daring ere a man to say nothing. And there we set watching them, with Dewey Dell's and Vardaman's mouth half open and half-et bananas in their hands and her coming around from behind pa, looking at us like she dared ere a man. And then I see that the grip she was carrying was one of them little graphophones. It was for a fact, all shut up as pretty as a picture, and everytime a new record would come from the mail order and us setting in the house in the winter, listening to it, I would think what a shame Darl couldn't be to enjoy it too. But it is better so for him. This world is not his world; this life his life.

"It's Cash and Jewel and Vardaman and Dewey Dell," pa says, kind of hang-dog and proud too, with his teeth and all, even if he wouldn't look at us. "Meet Mrs Bundren," he says.

THE LIFE AND WORKS OF
WILLIAM FAULKNER

By JOSEPH BLOTNER

WILLIAM FAULKNER grew up in the provincial milieu of north Mississippi but transformed himself into a citizen of the larger world beyond it. Though he began his literary career in one of the oldest poetic forms, he developed into one of the foremost twentieth-century experimental prose writers. And he treated his own region with unparalleled fidelity while he extracted the universal from the particular.

He was the heir to a family tradition which would prove extraordinarily rich for his fictional purposes, a tradition spanning five generations and perhaps a century and a half before his birth in New Albany, Mississippi, on September 25, 1897. His family knew little of their Scots ancestors other than the legend of a progenitor from one of the four main clan lines who came to the American colonies some time after the battle of Culloden with his tartan and claymore but little else. With a younger brother he landed in South Carolina, fought against the British at Cowpens and Kings Mountain and then moved to western North Carolina where he married and fathered two sons. One of these moved on to Missouri, whence his son, William Cuthbert Falkner, at age fourteen, made his way

south to Ripley, Mississippi, about the year 1839. In him the family talent for action and literature, the proclivity for dreams and for violence, would achieve a spectacular flowering.

This Falkner became a self-made lawyer, writer, planter, soldier, and entrepreneur of impressive persistence and energy. But there was a curse of violence on him; as a young man he twice killed in self-defense. Nevertheless, he built up a profitable practice and plantation before helping to raise a regiment and leading it into battle during the Civil War at the First Battle of Manassas in 1861. Thereafter his military career trailed off in misfortune and frustration. After the war, however, Colonel Falkner was among the first to recover and lead his region in recovery—insofar as one man could. Although he wrote an extremely popular romance entitled *The White Rose of Memphis,* his greatest influence derived from the small local railroad which he expanded with skill and ingenuity before the family curse caught up with him a final time. In the fall of 1889, newly elected to the legislature, he was shot to death by a business rival and longtime enemy. Not long afterward his marble effigy was raised above his grave, looking out—like that of his fictional projection, Colonel John Sartoris—over the railroad he had built.

The Old Colonel's immediate descendants could not match his flair or power. His son, John Wesley Thompson Falkner, called The Young Colonel, earned a law degree and went on to a substantial career as a lawyer, banker, and legislator. His son, Murry C. Falkner, wanted only to work on the family railroad, and when that career was sold out from under him, went on to a series of jobs culminating in the University of Mississippi Business Office. The family had gone from frontier fighter–Gilded Age entrepreneur to college administrator in three generations.

William Cuthbert Falkner had been born to Maud and Murry Falkner while Murry was still working for the railroad. Eight years later, Murry moved to Oxford, where the Young Colonel set him up in business. Billy Falkner and his three brothers, as they came along, enjoyed the kind of early twentieth-century small-town childhood that would seem golden in retrospect. Even schooling fell into a familiar pattern, at least for Billy. After early successes it became a bore and a prison to be escaped from before the end of the high school years. Better read than his classmates, more intelligent than his teachers, he had early drawn pictures and written stories. Now, in adolescence, he turned more and more to verse under the impetus of a dreamy temperament and romantic interest in a girl down the street. Unhappily and briefly employed in his grandfather's bank, he read and imitated Shakespeare, Keats and Shelley, Swinburne and Housman. He showed the work to the girl, Estelle Oldham, and one other appreciative reader: Phil Stone, a brilliant and precocious young man, a few years older but already on his way to two sets of degrees in both art and law from Mississippi and Yale. Stone encouraged him and loaned him books to read, new

work by artists such as Pound and Eliot.

When Falkner lost his sweetheart in a family-arranged marriage to a promising lawyer, Stone again intervened, with an invitation to join him in New Haven. This stay lengthened as Falkner went farther north for pilot training with the R.C.A.F. in Toronto. It was one of his great disappointments that the war ended before he could undergo the course of flight training, let alone battle, but these few months would last him a lifetime in providing not only the lore of the World War and aerial combat but an Anglophilia that would also appear in his work. He had been discharged as a cadet, but he came home sporting the stripes and wings of a second lieutenant: a case of the romantic role-playing he would indulge in all his life, one persona successively giving way to another.

At home, now spelling his name Faulkner, he drifted—dreaming, writing, traveling a little—until he entered the university as a part-time student in the fall of 1919, only to quit it with relief a year later. He had published a poem in *The New Republic,* and when it turned out to be his only sale, his main outlets for poems and literary criticism became the university newspaper and yearbook. He was soon ready again for a change, and in the pattern of alternation between home and away which would increasingly mark his life, he accepted the invitation of Oxford-born writer Stark Young and went to visit him in New York.

It was the fall of 1921 when he took the train north, to work in a bookstore in Lord & Taylor's and to live in a furnished room in Greenwich Village—a shop clerk during business hours, but an aspiring artist like his neighbors on his own time. He wrote some poems and stories but placed none while he grew increasingly tired of selling other people's books to the old ladies the manager always sent to him. Again Stone intervened, this time with a summons to return home to a humdrum job obtained through the influence of friends and family.

He became postmaster of the fourth-class substation at the University of Mississippi. Here he neglected his duties while he entertained his brothers and friends and continued to read Joyce and Synge, Aiken and O'Neill. He translated Verlaine and imitated Eliot, but he also worked at an extended project in a much older tradition. By the time his disregard of his duties brought about his resignation in 1924, he had polished a nineteen-poem cycle combining the conventions of pastoral poetry with a melancholy arising out of meditations upon youth, beauty, love, nature, and mutability. With Phil Stone's financial and clerical help, *The Marble Faun* appeared in late 1924. The sale was extremely limited, but by now the author was occupied with new concerns.

He and Stone had become convinced that if he were to make a reputation, Europe might be the place to do it, as Robert Frost and Ernest Hemingway had demonstrated. Early in 1925 he went to New Orleans, determined to work his passage across if he could. Once there, he enjoyed the hospitality of Sherwood Anderson, the novelist and short story writer. He began to move among the group around Anderson and others associated with an experimental magazine, *The Double Dealer.* Faulkner contributed sketches, short stories, and poems to the magazine and to the *New Orleans Times-Picayune.* The fiction was diverse, ranging from formula stories with surprise endings to Conrad-inspired tales, but a few drew on his home country and foreshadowed character types and situations he would employ later. Admiring Anderson and enjoying his company, luxuriating in the life of the French Quarter where he lived, Faulkner apparently felt little impatience about embarking for Europe. Moreover, he was at work on a

novel, and Anderson encouraged and helped him submit it to his own publisher in New York. By July he was ready to leave—as a passenger on a freighter rather than a seaman—hoping to augment his funds with dispatches from abroad to American papers.

Landing at Genoa, he made his way through northern Italy and Switzerland to Paris, where he found lodgings on the Left Bank. Walking about the city, visiting galleries, writing in the Luxembourg Gardens, he worked on another novel, travel sketches, and other pieces. He made tours outside the city, trips into the provinces and visited England. Back in Paris, he later said, he received notice of the acceptance of his novel and an advance on royalties. Six months after his arrival, he prepared to depart for home, but he had lived in Paris, had seen James Joyce in the flesh, and had come into actual touch with the European culture he had hitherto known only at a distance. He had already begun to mine these experiences for short stories set in Oxford and Naples.

The novel, entitled *Soldiers' Pay,* appeared in late February of 1926. It was a story of postwar disillusionment and death set principally in a small town in Georgia. Both mannered and luxuriant, it had nothing like the success of Hemingway's *The Sun Also Rises,* but this story of the end of a maimed hero belongs to the same general category. It was surprisingly well reviewed but sold slowly.

Now Faulkner turned to his experience in New Orleans for material. Much of the work was satire directed at dilettantes and poseurs grouped about a central figure modeled on Sherwood Anderson. Rather different from the more nearly conventional *Soldiers' Pay,* this story owed something to the brilliant and witty novels Aldous Huxley had been doing. There was also a good deal of literary impressionism in the new book, the prose texture of which was as deliberately poetic as experimental. If word coinages and fantasy scenes suggested Joyce's *Ulysses,* numerous phrases and images alluded directly to Eliot's poems. Not so well reviewed as its predecessor, this novel sold even more slowly when it was published in April, 1927.

There followed a furious spurt of creative activity unmatched by any major American author of this century. Faulkner apparently was alternating at work on a chronicle of an aristocratic family modeled on his own and a long account of the unscrupulous new men who had come into Oxford and Lafayette County (and so many others) in the years after the Civil War. He finally broke off the latter chronicle, which he had been calling *Father Abraham,* and concentrated on the former, taking with him one of the Snopes family from *Father Abraham.* He put him into *Flags in the Dust,* which began with a history of the Sartoris family in Europe and finally focused on its youngest current embodiment. The great grandson of Colonel Sartoris, Bayard was another doomed protagonist, another flier destroyed by the Great War though he had survived the Armistice. The setting was Yoknapatawpha County, and Faulkner later said that it opened up a gold mine of fictional people and situations. It was a long novel, lovingly shaped but an overcrowded many-threaded story. It was rejected by his publisher.

In discouragement Faulkner turned to another body of material which gave him intense personal satisfaction—or, as he would say, moved him deeply. *The Sound and the Fury* was a story of childhood, like other stories he would do about the Compson children. Before long, however, he found that he could not encompass it in a single short story. It became a novella, and before he was finished he would add three more segments of equal length. He was putting to good use the lessons he had learned from the French symbolist poets and from Joseph Conrad and James Joyce. The novel made extensive use of symbolism and particularly sense imagery of several kinds. Like Conrad, Faulkner abandoned conventional chronology and used not one point of view in narration but several. Like Joyce, he employed not only the symbolic method but also the stream-of-consciousness or interior monologue, and in a way quite as spectacularly as Joyce had in *Ulysses.*

Faulkner's narration of significant events in the lives of the Compson family was conveyed to the reader through four voices. The last was his own, when, as omniscient narrator, he tried to pull the material together through a vantage point associated with the Negro servant, Dilsey, who tried to sustain the deteriorating family. But the other three viewpoints were those of the youngest son, the idiot, Benjy; the eldest son, the neurotic and suicidal Quentin; and the middle son, the sadistic Jason. For Benjy, all time planes had the same value, and he shifted from one to another on the spur of free association of external stimuli. Thus he—even more graphically than his brothers—summoned up the past into the present, bringing into clearer relief the tragedy of his adored sister, Caddy, and with it the symptomatic tragedy of the Compson family as well.

During his lifetime William Faulkner would be asked for his favorite work. The one he would mention most consistently would be *The Sound and the Fury.* They had all failed to match the dream, he would say, but this was the one that moved him most, as a mother would care most tenderly for a handicapped child.

The friend who was handling his books in New York wrote Faulkner that he should come north; he thought he had sold *Flags in the Dust* after it had knocked about to a dozen publishers. Faulkner arrived, bringing the Compson manuscript with him. Informed that a publisher would take the novel on condition that it was drastically cut, he responded with anger and hurt, refusing at first to do any cutting himself. While the friend began the cutting, Faulkner worked on to complete *The Sound and the Fury,* living again in Greenwich Village. Before he left the city, *Flags in the Dust* had become *Sartoris.* It would appear in January, 1929, but the publisher did not want *The Sound and the Fury.* Still another new firm took it and published it on October 7 of the same year. The acclaim was immediate, but again, the sales were not overpowering.

His personal life had changed profoundly in June of that year. Estelle Oldham Franklin had returned home previously and divorced her husband. Now, eleven years after the marriage that had separated them, she and "Billy" Faulkner were reunited. The author was suddenly not only husband but stepfather to a ten-year-old girl and her six-year-old brother. He could no longer rely on picking up a few dollars when he needed them by doing housepainting or other odd jobs.

It may have been partly in anticipation of his changed status that he had in January of 1929 begun a book deliberately conceived as a shocker. Combining real and bizarre experiences he had heard about in Oxford and in Memphis, Faulkner wrote a story about a Mississippi coed raped with a corncob by an impotent gangster and then hidden away in a Memphis brothel to provide a murder alibi when he should need it. *Sanctuary* was finished by early summer, and though it showed signs of rapid composition, it still possessed a brutal and sinister power. When he sent *Sanctuary* to New York, his new publisher replied that if he published it they'd both be in jail. Faulkner put it out of his mind.

Returning from his Gulf coast honeymoon in late summer he turned to short stories. Two of his most memorable—"A Rose for Emily" and "Dry September"—date from this period. The first was a study in unfaithful love and necrophilia, told from the point of view of one of the townspeople who would increasingly act as chorus to Faulkner's dramas. The second was one of the most powerful stories of racial mania and lynching ever written. But these and others like them still would not support his new family. So he took a supervisory job on the night shift of the town power plant.

He spent more time writing than supervising, and it probably was not long after he began the work that he started another novel, writing on an overturned wheelbarrow, he would say, to the soothing hum of the dynamo. He would also say that *As I Lay Dying* was a tour de force, written in six weeks on the night shift without changing a word. Actually, a good many words and passages were changed, for Faulkner always revised, sometimes endlessly. He was apparently drawing in part on earlier material that may have dated from the time of *Father Abraham.* From the start, he knew where the book was going, he would say, and the story's steady progress through its 59 short interior monologues appears to bear him out. Rather than telling aspects of the same story over from four different points of view, as in *The Sound and the Fury,* he used more than a dozen narrators to present sequential portions of a macabre family saga. They followed the Bundren family as they suffered fire and flood to take the body of their mother from their hill farm down to Jefferson to bury her with her people. Most of the family had some additional motive for the grotesque journey, and most suffered some material loss before its completion. Though the locale was for the most part back-country Yoknapatawpha County, and though the characters seemed primitives or worse to a number of reviewers, the language was again evocative and, in the case of one of the brothers, consistently poetic.

As I Lay Dying appeared in early October of 1930, almost a year to the day after *The Sound and the Fury*. Its author was gaining critical attention abroad now. Both books were solid critical successes, and with these behind him, it was with shock that one day he received in the mail the proofs of *Sanctuary*. Business conditions had begun looking more threatening than jail to Faulkner's publisher, so he had sent the novel to the printer. Faulkner's shock came from rereading the novel. It was so basely conceived, he said, that he had to rewrite it so that it would not shame the two that had preceded it. He did the rewriting even though it meant paying half the cost of the extra corrections.

The result of the revisions was not to make the story any less explicit or shocking, but rather to render it more coherent and plausible, to demonstrate with intense psychological probing the effects of evil rather than just gratuitous horrors in the Frenchman's Bend section of the county and the red light district of Memphis. *Sanctuary* was closer to *Sartoris* in technique than to the two experimental novels which preceded it. However, it did make consistent use of symbolism and employed one device which Faulkner would develop further in later work. It was the use of two sets of characters in the two locales. The pairs revealed different strata of society and, joined by one or two characters in each area of action, the two worlds were implicitly compared and contrasted.

When the novel was published in February of 1931 it produced shock waves neither publisher nor author had anticipated. It became a *succès de scandale,* offending many reviewers and readers but selling more copies than anything he had previously published. It caused one critic to name him as a progenitor of the novel of violence in America. It also sent the prices of his early first editions soaring and brought his name to the attention of Hollywood studios.

He was still chronically in need of money, however. In June of 1930 he and Estelle had bought the old estate which they renamed Rowan Oak, and had begun a thoroughgoing renovation with a staff of Negro servants from both families who attached themselves to the new household. His publisher's financial condition had so worsened, however, that he saw little of the royalties due him from *Sanctuary*. Magazine sales could not take up the slack and it would be a considerable time before there was any return from a volume of short stories entitled *These 13* which appeared in September, 1931. So reluctantly he prepared to go to Hollywood in the spring of 1932.

Though he was signed by the leading studio, Metro-Goldwyn-Mayer, he disliked California and the motion picture business from the first. He was quick to say that he was not a screenwriter but rather a script-doctor, and it was director-producer Howard Hawks who understood this best. After a series of unsuccessful assignments for the studio, he went to work under the personal direction of Hawks, who had purchased Faulkner's story "Turn About" and made it into a successful war picture. It was the beginning of a relationship that would extend over nearly a quarter of a century.

The money he earned in his brief stay went towards debts, current living expenses, and more renovation for Rowan Oak. It provided the time for him to complete a novel he had reluctantly put aside to go to Hollywood. *Light in August* carried further the technique of using two sets of characters linked by a few others and paired for contrast. One of the major ones here was a woman serene and confident, suggesting a fertility figure out of myth, attuned to the environment in which she moved. The other was a man who remained a stranger wherever he went—ambivalent, hostile, and destructive. Lena Grove and Joe Christmas never saw each other even though they were both in Jefferson on the days of the novel's climactic action. Again subordinate characters served as links, but the two principals never came together, even though he used them to epitomize opposed attributes and they provided him with alternating agents for comedy and tragedy. The subordinate characters—a failed minister, an obsessed spinster, a plain good man—also helped to expand the novel's thematic range as Faulkner treated problems of isolation, the strength of the past, racial mania, and religious fanaticism.

Faulkner continued his extraordinary productivity, which saw the appearance of a book a year. In April of 1933, six months after *Light in August* had appeared, Faulkner's publisher brought out his second (and last) book of verse. *A Green Bough* had been culled from poems Faulkner had accumulated over more than a decade. They were mixed in form and content and generally imitative of the poets he admired. They showed that though he venerated the poet's art as much as ever, his own métier was poetic prose. Another event two months later brought a far deeper joy: the birth of his daughter, Jill. The self-styled harmless vagabond had become a paterfamilias with a plantation house and a growing estate. But the estate was mostly land, for his financial situation—once the Hollywood money was gone—was as precarious as ever.

In 1934 he collected another volume under the title, *Doctor Martino and Other Stories*. He began reworking the material which had gone into a short

story called "Wash," but it would not come right and he put it aside for still another novel which had grown out of a strong personal interest. This was *Pylon*, concerning the contemporary world of barnstorming aviators. Since his return from Hollywood he had been taking flying lessons, and now he employed his personal knowledge of the world of these vagabonds, describing a ménage a trois which would shock many readers, though not as much as *Sanctuary* had done. Faulkner's sympathies were deeply engaged with these people, victims like the ruined wartime aviators who had fascinated him. His scorn was directed toward those who battened on them and toward the corrupt values of the tawdry world epitomized by the New Valois Mardi Gras. The prose again combined the realistic and the impressionistic, with the influence of T. S. Eliot once more clearly discernible. It was comparatively minor Faulkner, but it was received and reviewed with respect which demonstrated that though he was not a truly popular writer, each new work was a literary event.

The financial pressure continued to increase, and it was a particularly disagreeable decision when he saw in late 1935 that he must put aside *Absalom, Absalom!* (as the novel developing from "Wash" would be called) now that he was deeply into it, in order to return to Hollywood once more, this time to 20th Century-Fox. This assignment would continue intermittently for a year and a half, but in spite of it he managed to complete the novel, which was published in October of 1936. It is one of his major works.

This novel took up aspects of the method Faulkner had used in *The Sound and the Fury*. In *Absalom, Absalom!*, however, the past did not simply contribute to the events of the present and an understanding of them. Instead it held the central meaning of the book, with actions in present time providing a final working-out of courses begun long before. The protagonist, Colonel Thomas Sutpen, was long dead when the novel opened. Through the whole of it, however, the principal character in present time, Quentin Compson, struggled toward an understanding of Sutpen's fate: how it came about, the parts played by himself and by his children, and the meaning of that fate as parable. Part of the fascination of this technique—as is sometimes the case in Joseph Conrad (who with Balzac was one of Faulkner's mentors)—lies in the fact that the narration is speculative. Quentin and his friend, Shreve, made the most intelligent surmises they could, but they could only surmise. The reader was thus drawn into the creative process as he speculated with the characters.

Here more than anywhere else Faulkner used the extended flashback. Here too he broke up chronology and showed central events from multiple points of view, providing the reader with a counterpart of the way one often comes to understand people in "real life." More than one critic noted the novel's Greek elements: the operation of something like fate, the effects of *hubris,* and the insistently Greek imagery, replete with references to mythological persons and the use of terms such as strophe and antistrophe.

In the intervals between novels Faulkner continued to work at shorter fiction, sometimes even putting novels aside to try to fashion a story for *The Saturday Evening Post* or another magazine to ease the financial pressure. His stories were more nearly in the classic mold than those of James Joyce, for instance, whether they dealt with the planters, poor whites, or Indians of Yoknapatawpha County. There might be epiphanies, but there was usually plenty of action by memorable characters—action which usually developed, rose to a crescendo, and

declined into a denouement. For more than two years now he had been working at a connected series of stories aimed at the readership of *The Post.* They were stories of two boys—one white and one black—as they underwent initiation in the Civil War period and grew to maturity in the days of Reconstruction. Faulkner rewrote considerable portions of these stories, added new ones, and fused them into a consistent tale by an all-knowing narrator. Published as *The Unvanquished* in February of 1938, this novel achieved respectable sales and considerable praise for the author in the South, where he had been regarded by many as a writer who had made money by describing degenerates and thus exposing his homeland to the ridicule of outsiders. When the book was purchased for a movie, Faulkner used most of the money to buy a farm out in Lafayette County. Therefore, when he felt like it, the persona of the farmer would appear belatedly following those of the war veteran and bohemian artist.

Though the last chapter of the novel, "An Odor of Verbena," was one of the best segments he had ever composed, *The Unvanquished* was nothing like a major effort. His talents were more deeply engaged by the work he now took up, a novel which carried to a kind of logical end the technique of *Light in August.* Now he used two plots and two sets of characters who shared only the same geographical area, and sometimes not even that. *The Wild Palms* was actually two novellas with alternating chapters, so that one read a chapter of "The Wild Palms" and then one of "Old Man." Here the experimentation was structural, for the novellas themselves were written in a conventional way, with one narrator throughout and relatively little reliance on interior monologue. In a sense, form was content. The first and principal story dealt with a couple who sacrificed everything for freedom to love. To counterpoint this theme, the second dealt with a convict who wanted above all to avoid love and return to the safe confinement he preferred. The latter story, set against the great flood of 1927, included some of Faulkner's most impressive prose, evidencing once more the power in working with landscape and the forces of nature which he had employed so successfully in *As I Lay Dying.*

By the time *The Wild Palms* appeared in January of 1939, he had returned to the technique he had used with the stories that made up *The Unvanquished.* His feelings, however, were much different as he approached this new task. He had regarded the other stories as pot-boilers which he tried to redeem. Now, as he began piecing together still other stories, he was returning to the material he had explored in *Father Abraham:* the saga of the Snopes clan, and one which might take as much as three volumes to tell. In the first one, *The Hamlet,* he followed the victory of Flem Snopes in the hamlet of Frenchman's Bend and his departure, at the novel's end, for the larger world to conquer in Jefferson. *The Hamlet* was a virtuoso combination of the poetic, horrific, and comic, although his vision tended to darken as the novel moved toward its close. Here he also displayed something of his past work and taste: his pastoral imagery was put to new uses, far more powerful than it had ever been in *The Marble Faun.* It was April, 1940, when the novel appeared, and it would be far longer than he could have thought before he would get back to the projected trilogy.

He turned instead to another synthesis of magazine stories. To these he added some which had not sold, and then he wrote a long novella entitled "The Bear." The stories explored interrelationships between white and black families of Yoknapatawpha County extending from the years of slavery to the present. The

work was regarded as a novel by Faulkner, autonomous though some of the sections might seem to others. Again, there was considerable humor, but as the work progressed, Faulkner's vision once more seemed to darken. It also expanded, until Ike McCaslin, near the end of "The Bear," saw the fate of his land as emblematic of a large collective human problem. *Go Down, Moses* appeared in May, 1942, and it marked the end of the extraordinary flowering of creative energy which had begun more than a dozen years before.

He was now nearly forty-five, exhausted from work, distracted by World War II, and convinced in moments of depression that his work would never achieve the status it deserved. In July he returned to Hollywood, this time under a long-term contract to Warner Brothers at a salary which made him an object of sympathy to some and contempt to others. This exile would continue for the better part of three years. He abandoned his plans to try to obtain a commission, and for long periods he attempted no sustained work of his own. In late 1944, however, he entered into a partnership with a director and producer to do a screenplay for a picture they would own together. As time went on he began to shift from the screenplay mode to that of the novel. By late 1945, with his publisher's support, he left Hollywood to push on through with this steadily expanding work, the story of Christ's Passion and Death allegorized in the drama of one French squad which led a mutiny in the false armistice of 1918. Fortunately, he could not know that he would struggle with it intermittently for eight more years before he could control all of its intractable ramifications.

By now, when almost all of his books were out of print, the critic Malcolm Cowley was at work editing a collection of Faulkner's short stories and excerpts from the novels. He also provided an introduction which showed their interconnections and revealed something of the scope of their achievement. Faulkner supplied an extended account of the Compson family to be used as an introduction to the Dilsey section of *The Sound and the Fury*. When *The Portable Faulkner* appeared in May, 1946, it revived general interest in his work and started a reassessment in motion.

Balked with his fable, as Faulkner called the World War I novel, he turned to a mode he had long enjoyed. Like his mother and his brother, he was an avid reader of detective stories. *Intruder in the Dust* began, he said, as a story of a man accused of murder who had to exonerate himself while sitting behind bars. As this situation took a firmer hold on Faulkner's imagination, the conventions of the form gave way to deeper exploration of motive and action. There was still mystification, suspense, and solution, but the emphasis gradually shifted from the exoneration of an innocent Negro to the education in human relations of the young white boy who helped free him. And through the boy's uncle, attorney Gavin Stevens, Faulkner was able to convey the views of a Southern moderate on the race question —views often close to his own.

Before the novel appeared in September, 1948, it was purchased by MGM. In print, it sold more than any previous trade edition of a Faulkner book. His days of financial crisis were over.

Fourteen months later Stevens and his nephew, Chick Mallison, appeared in a collection of detective stories entitled *Knight's Gambit*, this time squarely in the detective story genre though with a few glances at world conditions, principally in the title story.

For some time Faulkner and his publishers had talked of another volume of short stories. Now he began to organize one, similar to Cowley's, grouping the stories by locale and subject in a way that emphasized his range as well as continuing themes.

Three months after *Collected Stories of William Faulkner* appeared in August of 1950, the announcement came that the 1949 Nobel Prize for Literature had been awarded to William Faulkner. At first he resolutely resisted pressure to go to Stockholm, but finally, convinced that it was in the national cultural interest for him to go, he gave in. Though his acceptance speech was nearly inaudible, it came to be regarded as one of the best—certainly the most quoted—of Nobel Prize speeches. "I decline to accept the end of man," he said. "I believe that man will not merely endure: he will prevail." To some these were strange sentiments from a man who seemed to have spent most of his career revealing one kind or another of human baseness. But this was a superficial view. In characters such as Dilsey he had exalted the virtues he praised from this rostrum, and in succeeding works including the fable he would provide further embodiments of the virtues which were to him the glory of the race.

Before he returned to the fable, he accomplished an earlier intention by exploring what could happen to a woman like *Sanctuary's* Temple Drake, given the conditions of her life and marriage. The result was a hybrid play-novel, *Requiem for a Nun,* which was not wholly successful from the vantage point of either genre, but which later enjoyed considerable success on the stage, particularly among European critics who saw Faulkner dealing with the human condition in existentialist terms. The book appeared in September of 1951, and with it out of his way, Faulkner returned to the mass of manuscript which had so long resisted his efforts.

By the time he completed *A Fable*, it had evolved into a long, difficult novel with more philosophical exposition than any of his previous works. On the narrative level, the time scheme of the Passion was rigidly adhered to. (He had charted the events on the walls of his study.) And the allegory often had a one-for-one correspondence with events of the New Testament. So the difficulty was not so much stylistic as philosophical or semantic. In the course of the novel Faulkner used three characters to embody different reactions to evil: avoidance, tolerance, and action. Clearly, Faulkner's view was the third: that of the Battalion Runner who had become a disciple of the novel's Christ-figure, the Corporal. Finally it became clear that Faulkner was using the Passion in a secularized form to present his own, humanistic religion, in which the ultimate values were those he enunciated in his Nobel Prize speech: courage and honor and hope and pride and pity and sacrifice. The novel was published in August, 1954, to mixed reviews.

Early in his career reviewers had often objected to the complexity of technique and violence of subject matter; now some found him verbose and wished for the earlier power. Fortunately, he had always paid far less attention to reviews than most writers. And now, no matter how many quarterlies might raise objections, each new work continued to add to his increasing world stature and to demonstrate his continuing intellectual curiosity and passion for experimentation.

His Nobel trip had whetted his appetite for travel once more, and after accepting an invitation to a cultural congress in Paris in 1952 and Brazil in 1954, he agreed to travel to Japan in 1955 under the auspices of the U.S. State Department. Before it was over, he had literally traveled around the world, serving as a cultural emissary out of old-fashioned patriotism in countries as diverse as the Philippines and Iceland. He would later make similar trips to Greece in 1957 and Venezuela in 1961. This concern over the United States in world affairs was paralleled by his growing concern over the Civil Rights crisis and the explosive possibilities he feared. In letters, speeches, and articles he spoke out for a moderate position between the extremes of right and left. As the threat of violence subsided he gradually turned back toward his own work and the completion of the trilogy first envisioned nearly thirty years before.

In *The Town,* of May, 1957, and *The Mansion,* which would appear in November, 1959, he presented a compromise between his experimental and his more nearly conventional styles. He employed more or less straightforward chronologies but shifted the story-telling among a limited number of narrators—chiefly Gavin Stevens, Chick Mallison, and V. K. Ratliff of *The Hamlet*—who not only presented their individual points of view but criticized, corrected, and argued with each other. *The Town* carried the saga through Flem Snopes' depredations in Jefferson, culminating with his presidency of Colonel Sartoris' bank. In *The Mansion* Faulkner would follow the working out of the ultimate retribution.

In early 1957 his life style had undergone a significant change when he and Mrs. Faulkner traveled to Virginia. They had visited Jill and her husband when he was a law student at the University in Charlottesville, but now they settled in for the second semester as William Faulkner became the University's first Writer-in-Residence. It was a highly successful appointment which was renewed for the year 1957–1958. Faulkner bought a home in Charlottesville, where he would retain a connection with the University and grow more and more absorbed with the life of Albemarle County, where he and Mrs. Faulkner moved, just outside the town of Charlottesville. From the first he had resumed the horseback riding which had always attracted him, and soon he had begun to indulge his taste for fox-hunting, riding out almost every day in the season, welcome at not just one hunt but two. In a short time he was invited to wear the colors of the Farmington Hunt, and with them still another Faulkner persona emerged, as the hale, white-haired old man in his sixties renewed himself once more.

But he still had work to do, a novel he had conceived years before, a mellow-retrospective, grandfatherly narrative, told in the first person by Ducius Priest, recalling his initiation into adult life as a young boy in Yoknapatawpha County and environs in the early years of the century. *The Reivers* was successful on all counts when it appeared in May of 1962. It was not a major work in the canon, but one reviewer said that it stood to the rest of his work as *The Tempest* did to the others in the Shakespeare canon.

By now the Faulkners were spending half of each year in Virginia. In the late spring they returned to Oxford and Rowan Oak, planning for their return to Virginia in the fall, but on July 6, 1962, he died of a heart attack in a small hospital north of Oxford.

Looking back at the more than two dozen works he left behind him, one finds his content nearly as complex as his style. One sees that he is interested in man in society and in man alone. That is, he is concerned, like most of the great novelists, with the psychology of the individual and the interaction of groups. He can present the inner workings of the individual mind with a preternatural, at times hallucinatory vividness of the kind one associates with Dostoevsky. The self-lacerating thoughts of Quentin Compson have the terrible immediacy of Rodion Raskolnikov's terrors. And the long sagas of the families—the Compsons and Sartorises, the McCaslins and deSpains, the Snopeses—give a panorama of a country in the way Balzac's *Human Comedy* does. Portions of the novels and stories are set

at the time when the virgin land was owned by the Chickasaws. From there the span continues through the nineteenth century with the sale of the land to the white man. As the Indian debased the land and himself by selling it for money, so the white man commits the evil of slavery and pays with the horror and devastation of the Civil War and its long-drawn-out aftermath.

The historical and sociological processes continue with new entrepreneurs entering the country, just as the "old families" had done as New Men themselves three decades before the war. But these latest new men are far more ruthless. Although the Sartorises, Sutpens, deSpains, and Greniers may have been guilty of the abuses of slavery, at least they adhered to a code which had in it something of the old chivalric regard for values such as honor and pride. But the Snopeses have no scruples to act as a rein upon their desires. As the aristocratic families fall into decadence the Snopeses usurp their power. Their depredations eventually produce their own doom, just as the Chickasaws and the earlier white men have paid for their failures in their turn.

In "The Bear" this cyclical process applies no longer to Yoknapatawpha County alone. By symbolic extension it refers to man's exploitation of the land and his fellows wherever these evils have been committed. It is, in a sense, a kind of reinterpretation of the archetypal story of Adam. God gives man the bounteous earth, but man defiles it and himself, and it is only through atonement and renunciation, says the liberated Ike McCaslin, that the first steps toward expiation can be taken.

In the whole context of his work, one sees that Faulkner adheres to traditional Judaeo-Christian virtues, with an admixture of elements from the old chivalric code, to arrive at a humanistic value system. When Faulkner uses the word God, he uses it in an ambiguous way. Hemingway's best novel, he said, was *The Old Man and the Sea,* for there Hemingway finally discovered God. By this he meant, one assumes, old Santiago's feeling of affinity with all created things, a sense of order in the universe, of a power in that universe greater than the individual, and of the need to live in accordance with a code which emphasizes not only strength and endurance, but humility and compassion as well.

For a final word about Faulkner's content, his view of the world, one should perhaps go a step further. Faulkner often gives the sense that some of his characters are doomed from the start: Caddy Compson, Joe Christmas, Flem Snopes.

Yet his characters are not, as Jean-Paul Sartre once declared, without souls. There is, for most of them, room for choice, for the action of free will. In novels such as *Light in August* he may speak of "The Player" almost like Thomas Hardy positing some malevolent power which persecutes man out of malice, or some force which impersonally crushes him. But Faulkner's noblest characters, though they may err, display this capacity for choice. His world view, one might say, is Shakespearean. As a critic has remarked of the Snopes trilogy, his vision is tragicomic. In the great flux and change and motion of life, man appears in both these aspects, just as he stands forth with an aptitude for baseness as well as for nobility.

Joseph Blotner, professor in the department of English at the University of North Carolina, is the author of the forthcoming official biography of William Faulkner.

THE 1949 PRIZE

By KJELL STRÖMBERG

In 1949 the Swedish Academy was unable to achieve the majority vote required for the award of the Nobel Prize for Literature. This meant announcing its failure to reach a majority decision and remanding its decision to the following year. There was no lack of candidates, simply an inability to agree on one name out of all those nominated by the various qualified sources.

Similar situations had arisen at various times in the past, but on this occasion a storm broke in the press in Sweden and elsewhere. There were repercussions even in the government. The Academy was attacked for incompetence, and critics called either for a complete overhaul of both personnel and bylaws or for the removal of the responsibility for implementing Nobel's will.

In America, *Collier's Magazine* published an article by Irving Wallace, the author of several best sellers which had won no prizes. Mr. Wallace advised the *Collier's* millions of readers that the Nobel Prizes would turn out to be as explosive as the dynamite invented by the founder of the Nobel Foundation because of the scandalous partiality of the award machinery. He accused the Swedes of being as strongly anti-American in literature as they were pro-German in the sciences, as thoroughly anti-Russian as

they were pro-Scandinavian in all fields. Actually, by 1950, after 50 years of activity, the Nobel Institutes had distributed some $6 million to 242 laureates in all categories from 24 different countries. As of that date, Germany led all others with 46 winners as against 45 from the United States and 40 from Great Britain. The Scandinavian countries had won 28 Prizes in all, the same as France, a figure which might be considered proportionately high. But in view of these figures there was really no reason to speak of "scandal" as Mr. Wallace did.

So in 1950, there were two Prizes available. Without going against the bylaws, the Academy could have kept the 1949 Prize and reinvested it in the general fund. Instead the Prize money was awarded to the American novelist William Faulkner, and the 1950 Prize went to Bertrand Russell, the English philosopher. Faulkner had been the leading nominee the year before, but the votes of the Academy were apparently divided in a deadlock among him, Sir Winston Churchill and Pär Lagerkvist, the Swedish poet, novelist and playwright. Two other Americans, Ernest Hemingway and John Steinbeck, had also been entered in the contest, and two Russians were strong contenders—Boris Pasternak and Mikhail Sholokhov, the author of *And Quiet*

Flows the Don. There were besides them a good half-dozen French writers, including François Mauriac and Albert Camus, both of whom were later to win the Prize.

Faulkner had built up a solid reputation in Western Europe, especially in France, well before World War II. Indeed, during the thirties, his prestige in France was well ahead of what it was in his own country. Jean-Paul Sartre and his friends of the Existentialist camp were among the first supporters and interpreters of this new American writer. In Sweden the first translation of a Faulkner book was published in 1944 (*Light in August,* which had come out in America in 1932). Other translations followed in rapid succession, each hailed by the reviewers of the leading Swedish press as a fresh revelation of a new art which was both primitive and refined. To Swedish critics Faulkner seemed to have opened up great new perspectives on the human condition in today's world, in spite of the narrow confines of his own world and the special traits of his black and white characters. The younger postwar generation, which had cut its eyeteeth on Kafka and Joyce, were quickly seduced by this visceral, highly seasoned romanticism, redolent of a doomed civilization.

Dostoevski, Poe and Joyce are the names which are generally evoked to describe Faulkner's literary domain. The Swedish novelist, Gustaf Hellström, a specialist in British and American literature, in reporting on Faulkner to the Academy, observed that Faulkner is a difficult author for the general public and hence has never won the wide foreign readership enjoyed, for example, by Hemingway or Steinbeck, his chief competitors. Because of his fidelity to a carefully defined territory, Faulkner reminded Hellström of two great Swedish novelists, Selma Lagerlöf and Hjalmar Bergmann, who, each in his own way, had also transformed their rural family setting into a vast universal theater lighted by magic and offering the spectacle of a humanity teeming with larger-than-life characters. This time the Swedish Academy was readily convinced by Hellström and the Nobel Prize was awarded to him without any extended discussion "for his powerful and artistically unique contribution to the modern American novel."

Critics in Sweden were exultant at seeing a choice which reflected the preference they had expressed a year before. The press in England and America was much more contained in its comment, which was sporadic and generally brief.

British writers were generally more enthusiastic. In London the *Times* recognized the creative power of this writer from the deep South, but it still had serious reservations about the "oracular style" which clogged his prose and made him hard to read.

Faulkner learned about the award from a friend who had heard the news on the radio. Faulkner was skeptical, but he was soon convinced by the telephone calls which came in from all over America and Europe. He explained to all his well-wishers that he intended to remain a simple farmer. He had no intention of leaving his cottonfields to collect his Prize in a far-off country of which he knew practically nothing. The immediate surge in his royalties and the arrival of requests for translation rights into every conceivable language must have had considerable influence in his change of mind. At the last minute Faulkner decided to fly to Sweden.

In Stockholm the ceremony of the awards was more formal than usual because it was the fiftieth anniversary of the establishment of the Prizes. The flower-decked stage of the great hall of the Concert Palace held not only the prize winners for that year but about 30 laureates from previous years, together with well over 150 special guests. When the stocky Faulkner appeared at the side of the elongated Bertrand Russell, they looked for a moment like Don Quixote and Sancho Panza.

But only for a moment.

Faulkner's acceptance speech, probably his first formal utterance in public, is perhaps the most eloquent and moving of all those made over the years in acknowledging the award.

Translated by Dale McAdoo

Eugene O'Neill

1936

"For the power, honesty,

and deep-felt emotions of his

dramatic works, which embody

an original concept of tragedy"

Illustrated by JEAN-DENIS MALCLES

PRESENTATION ADDRESS

By *PER HALLSTRÖM*

PERMANENT SECRETARY
OF THE SWEDISH ACADEMY

E̲UGENE O'NEILL'S dramatic production has been of a somber character
from the very first, and for him life as a whole quite early came to
signify tragedy. This has been attributed to the bitter experiences of his
youth, more especially to what he underwent as a sailor. The legendary
nimbus that gathers around celebrities in his case took the form of heroic
events created out of his background. With his contempt for publicity,
O'Neill straightway put a stop to all such attempts; there was no glamour
to be derived from his drab hardships and toils. We may indeed conclude
that the stern experiences were not uncongenial to his spirit, tending as
they did to afford release of certain chaotic forces within him.

His pessimism was presumably on the one hand an innate trait of his
being, on the other an offshoot of the literary current of the age, though
possibly it is rather to be interpreted as the reaction of a profound personality to the American optimism of old tradition. Whatever the source
of his pessimism may have been, however, the line of his development
was marked out, and O'Neill became by degrees the uniquely and fiercely
tragic dramatist that the world has come to know. The conception of
life that he presents is not a product of elaborate thinking, but it has the
genuine stamp of something lived through. It is based upon an exceed-
ingly intense, one might say heart-rent, realization of the austerity of
life, side by side with a kind of rapture at the beauty of human destinies
shaped in the struggle against odds.

A primitive sense of tragedy, as we see, lacking moral backing and
achieving no inner victory—merely the bricks and mortar for the temple
of tragedy in the grand and ancient style. By his very primitiveness, how-

ever, this modern tragedian has reached the well-spring of this form of creative art, a naïve and simple belief in fate. At certain stages it has contributed a stream of pulsating life-blood to his work.

That was, however, at a later period. In his earliest dramas O'Neill was a strict and somewhat arid realist; those works we may here pass by. Of more moment was a series of one-act plays, based upon material assembled during his years at sea. They brought to the theater something novel, and hence he attracted attention.

Those plays were not, however, dramatically notable; properly speaking, merely short stories couched in dialogue-form; true works of art, however, of their type, and heart-stirring in their simple, rugged delineation. In one of them, *The Moon of the Caribbees* (1918), he attains poetic heights, partly by the tenderness in depicting the indigence of a sailor's life with its naïve illusions of joy, and partly by the artistic background of the play: dirgelike Negro songs coming from a white coral shore beneath metallically glittering palms and the great moon of the Caribbean Sea. Altogether it is a mystical weave of melancholy, primitive savagery, yearning, lunar effulgence, and oppressive desolateness.

The drama *Anna Christie* (1921) achieves its most striking effect through the description of sailors' life ashore in and about waterfront saloons. The first act is O'Neill's masterpiece in the domain of strict realism, each character being depicted with supreme sureness and mastery. The content is the raising of a fallen Swedish girl to respectable human status by the strong and wholesome influences of the sea; for once pessimism is left out of the picture, the play having what is termed a happy ending.

With his drama *The Hairy Ape* (1922), also concerned with sailors' lives, O'Neill launches into that expressionism which sets its stamp upon his "idea-dramas." The aim of expressionism in literature and the plastic arts is difficult to determine; nor need we discuss it, since for practical purposes a brief description suffices. It endeavors to produce its effects by a sort of mathematical method; it may be said to extract the square root of the complex phenomena of reality, and build with those abstractions a new world on an enormously magnified scale. The procedure is an irksome one and can hardly be said to achieve mathematical exactitude; for a long time, however, it met with great success throughout the world.

The Hairy Ape seeks to present on a monumental scale the rebellious slave of steam power, intoxicated with his force and with superman ideas. Outwardly he is a relapse to primitive man, and he presents himself as a kind of beast, suffering from yearning for genius. The play depicts his tragical discomfiture and ruin on being brought up against cruel society.

Subsequently O'Neill devoted himself for a number of years to a boldly expressionistic treatment of ideas and social questions. The resulting plays have little connection with real life; the poet and dreamer isolates himself, becoming absorbed in feverishly pursued speculation and phantasy.

The Emperor Jones (1920), as an artistic creation, stands rather by itself; through it the playwright first secured any considerable celebrity. The theme embraces the mental breakdown of a Negro despot who rules over a Negro-populated island in the West Indies. The despot perishes on the flight from his glory, hunted in the dead of night by the troll-drums of his pursuers and by recollections of the past shaping themselves as paralyzing visions. These memories stretch back beyond his own life to the dark continent of Africa. Here lies concealed the theory of the individual's unconscious inner life being the carrier of the successive stages in the evolution of the race. As to the rightness of the theory we need form no opinion; the play takes so strong a hold upon our nerves and senses that our attention is entirely absorbed.

The "dramas of ideas" proper are too numerous and too diversified to be included in a brief survey. Their themes derive from contemporary life or from sagas and legends; all are metamorphosed by the author's fancy. They play on emotional chords all tightly strung, give amazing decorative effects, and manifest a never-failing dramatic energy. Practically speaking, everything in human life in the nature of struggle or combat has here been used as a subject for creative treatment, solutions being sought for and tried out of the spiritual or mental riddles presented. One favorite theme is the cleavage of personality that arises when an individual's true character is driven in upon itself by pressure from the world without, having to yield place to a make-believe character, its own live traits being hidden behind a mask. The dramatist's musings are apt to delve so deep that what he evolves has an urge, like deep-sea fauna, to burst asunder on being brought into the light of day. The results he achieves, however, are never without poetry; there is an abundant flow of passionate, pregnant words. The action, too, yields evidence in every case of the never-slumbering energy that is one of O'Neill's greatest gifts.

Underneath O'Neill's fantastic love of experimenting, however, is a hint of a yearning to attain the monumental simplicity characteristic of ancient drama. In his *Desire Under the Elms* (1924) he made an attempt in that direction, drawing his motif from the New England farming community, hardened in the progress of generations into a type of Puritanism that had gradually come to forfeit its idealistic inspiration. The course embarked upon was to be followed with more success in the "Electra" trilogy.

In between appeared *Strange Interlude* (1928), which won high praise and became renowned. It is rightly termed "A Play," for with its broad and loose-knit method of presentation it cannot be regarded as a tragedy; it would rather seem most aptly defined as a psychological novel in scenes. To its subtitle, "Strange Interlude," a direct clue is given in the course of the play: "Life, the present, is the strange interlude between the past and what is to come." The author tries to make his idea clear, as far as possible, by resorting to a peculiar device: on the one hand, the characters speak and reply as the action of the play demands; on the other, they reveal their real natures and their recollections in the form of monologues, inaudible to the other characters upon the stage. Once again, the element of masking!

Regarded as a psychological novel, up to the point at which it becomes too improbable for any psychology, the work is very notable for its wealth of analytical and above all intuitive acumen, and for the profound insight it displays into the inner workings of the human spirit. The training bore fruit in the real tragedy that followed, the author's grandest work: *Mourning Becomes Electra* (1931). Both in the story it unfolds and in the destiny-charged atmosphere enshrouding it, this play keeps close to the tradition of the ancient drama, though in both respects it is adjusted to modern life and to modern lines of thought. The scene of this tragedy of the modern-time house of Atreus is laid in the period of the great Civil War, America's *Iliad*. That choice lends the drama the clear perspective of the past and yet provides it with a background of intellectual life and thought sufficiently close to the present day. The most remarkable feature in the drama is the way in which the element of fate has been further developed. It is based upon up-to-date hypotheses, primarily upon the natural-scientific determinism of the doctrine of heredity, and also upon the Freudian omniscience concerning the unconscious, the nightmare dream of perverse family emotions.

These hypotheses are not, as we know, established beyond dispute, but the all-important point regarding this drama is that its author has embraced and applied them with unflinching consistency, constructing upon their foundation a chain of events as inescapable as if they had been proclaimed by the Sphinx of Thebes herself. Thereby he has achieved a masterly example of constructive ability and elaborate motivation of plot, and one that is surely without a counterpart in the whole range of latter-day drama. This applies especially to the first parts of the trilogy.

Two dramas, wholly different and of a new type for O'Neill, followed. They constitute a characteristic illustration of the way he has of never resting content with a result achieved, no matter what success it may have met with. They also gave evidence of his courage, for in them he launched a challenge to a considerable section of those whose favorable opinions he had won, and even to the dictators of those opinions. Though it may not at the present time be dangerous to defy natural human feelings and conceptions, it is not by any means free from risk to prick the sensitive conscience of critics. In *Ah, Wilderness* (1933) the esteemed writer of tragedies astonished his admirers by presenting them with an idyllic middle-class comedy and carried his audiences with him. In its depiction of the spiritual life of young people the play contains a good deal of poetry, while its gayer scenes display unaffected humor and comedy; it is, moreover, throughout simple and human in its appeal.

In *Days without End* (1934) the dramatist tackled the problem of religion, one that he had until then touched upon only superficially, without identifying himself with it, and merely from the natural scientist's combative standpoint. In this play he showed that he had an eye for the irrational, felt the need of absolute values, and was alive to the danger of spiritual impoverishment in the empty space that will be all that is left over the hard and solid world of rationalism. The form the work took was that of a modern miracle play, and perhaps, as with his tragedies of fate, the temptation to experiment was of great importance in its origination. Strictly observing the conventions of the drama form chosen, he adopted medieval naïveté in his presentation of the struggle of good

[129]

against evil, introducing, however, novel and bold features of stage technique. The principal character he cleaves into two parts, white and black, not only inwardly but also corporeally, each half leading its own independent bodily life—a species of Siamese twins contradicting each other. The result is a variation upon earlier experiments. Notwithstanding the risk attendant upon that venture, the drama is sustained by the author's rare mastery of scenic treatment, while in the spokesman of religion, a Catholic priest, O'Neill has created one of his most lifelike characters. Whether that circumstance may be interpreted as indicating a decisive change in his outlook upon life remains to be seen in the future.

O'Neill's dramatic production has been extraordinarily comprehensive in scope, versatile in character, and abundantly fruitful in new departures; and still its originator is at a stage of vigorous development. Yet in essential matters, he himself has always been the same in the exuberant and unrestrainably lively play of his imagination, in his never-wearying delight in giving shape to the ideas, whether emanating from within or without, that have jostled one another in the depths of his contemplative nature, and, perhaps first and foremost, in his possession of a proudly and ruggedly independent character.

In choosing Eugene O'Neill as the recipient of the 1936 Nobel Prize for Literature, the Swedish Academy can express its appreciation of his peculiar and rare literary gifts and also express their homage to his personality in these words: the Prize has been awarded to him for dramatic works of vital energy, sincerity, and intensity of feeling, stamped with an original conception of tragedy.

ACCEPTANCE SPEECH

By EUGENE O'NEILL

FIRST, I WISH TO EXPRESS again to you my deep regret that circumstances have made it impossible for me to visit Sweden in time for the festival, and to be present at this banquet to tell you in person of my grateful appreciation.

It is difficult to put into anything like adequate words the profound gratitude I feel for the greatest honor that my work could ever hope to attain, the award of the Nobel prize. This highest of distinctions is all the more grateful to me because I feel so deeply that it is not only my work which is being honored, but the work of all my colleagues in America—that this Nobel prize is a symbol of the recognition by Europe of the coming-of-age of the American theater. For my plays are merely, through luck of time and circumstance, the most widely known examples of the work done by American playwrights in the years since the World War—work that has finally made modern American drama in its finest aspects an achievement of which Americans can be justly proud, worthy at last to claim kinship with the modern drama of Europe, from which our original inspiration so surely derives.

This thought of original inspiration brings me to what is, for me, the greatest happiness this occasion affords, and that is the opportunity it gives me to acknowledge, with gratitude and pride, to you and to the people of Sweden, the debt my work owes to that greatest genius of all modern dramatists, your August Strindberg.

It was reading his plays when I first started to write back in the winter of 1913–1914 that, above all else, first gave me the vision of what modern drama could be, and first inspired me with the urge to write for the theater myself. If there is anything of lasting worth in my work, it is due to that original impulse from him, which has continued as my inspiration down all the years since then—to the ambition I received then to follow in the footsteps of his genius as worthily as my talent might permit, and with the same integrity of purpose.

Of course, it will be no news to you in Sweden that my work owes much to the influence of Strindberg. That influence runs clearly through more than a few of my plays and is plain for everyone to see. Neither will it be news for anyone who has ever known me, for I have always stressed it myself. I have never been one of those who are so timidly uncertain of their own contribution that they feel they cannot afford to admit ever having been influenced, lest they be discovered as lacking all originality.

No, I am only too proud of my debt to Strindberg, only too happy to have this opportunity of proclaiming it to his people. For me, he remains, as Nietzsche remains in his sphere, the Master, still to this day more modern than any of us, still our leader. And it is my pride to imagine that perhaps his spirit, musing over this year's Nobel award for literature, may smile with a little satisfaction, and find the follower not too unworthy of his Master.

THE EMPEROR JONES

By EUGENE O'NEILL

CHARACTERS

BRUTUS JONES, *Emperor*

HENRY SMITHERS, *A Cockney Trader*

AN OLD NATIVE WOMAN

LEM, *A Native Chief*

SOLDIERS, *Adherents of Lem*

The Little Formless Fears; Jeff; The Negro Convicts; The Prison Guard; The Planters; The Auctioneer; The Slaves; The Congo Witch-Doctor; The Crocodile God.

The action of the play takes place on an island in the West Indies as yet not self-determined by White Marines. The form of native government is, for the time being, an Empire.

SCENES

Scene I: In the palace of the Emperor Jones. Afternoon.

Scene II: The edge of the Great Forest. Dusk.

Scene III: In the Forest. Night.

Scene IV: In the Forest. Night.

Scene V: In the Forest. Night.

Scene VI: In the Forest. Night.

Scene VII: In the Forest. Night.

Scene VIII: Same as Scene Two—the edge of the Great Forest. Dawn.

SCENE ONE

The audience chamber in the palace of the Emperor—a spacious, high-ceilinged room with bare, white-washed walls. The floor is of white tiles. In the rear, to the left of center, a wide archway giving out on a portico with white pillars. The palace is evidently situated on high ground for beyond the portico nothing can be seen but a vista of distant hills, their summits crowned with thick groves of palm trees. In the right wall, center, a smaller arched doorway leading to the living quarters of the palace. The room is bare of furniture with the exception of one huge chair made of uncut wood which stands at center, its back to rear. This is very apparently the Emperor's throne. It is painted a dazzling, eye-smiting scarlet. There is a brilliant orange cushion on the seat and another smaller one is placed on the floor to serve as a footstool. Strips of matting, dyed scarlet, lead from the foot of the throne to the two entrances.

It is late afternoon but the sunlight still blazes yellowly beyond the portico and there is an oppressive burden of exhausting heat in the air.

As the curtain rises, a native Negro woman sneaks in cautiously from the entrance on the right. She is very old, dressed in cheap calico, bare-footed, a red bandana handkerchief covering all but a few stray wisps of white hair. A bundle bound in colored cloth is carried over her shoulder on the end of a stick. She hesitates beside the doorway, peering back as if in extreme dread of being discovered. Then she begins to glide noiselessly, a step at a time, toward the doorway in the rear. At this moment, SMITHERS appears beneath the portico.

SMITHERS is a tall, stoop-shouldered man about forty. His bald head, perched on a long neck with an enormous Adam's apple, looks like an egg. The tropics have tanned his naturally pasty face with its small, sharp features to a sickly yellow, and native rum has painted his pointed nose to a startling red. His little, washy-blue eyes are red-rimmed and dart about him like a ferret's. His expression is one of unscrupulous meanness, cowardly and dangerous. He is dressed in a worn riding suit of dirty white drill, puttees, spurs, and wears a white cork helmet. A cartridge belt with an automatic revolver is around his waist. He carries a riding whip in his hand. He sees the woman and stops to watch her suspiciously. Then, making up his mind, he steps quickly on tiptoe into the room. The woman, looking back over her shoulder continually, does not see him until it is too late. When she does SMITHERS springs forward and grabs her firmly by the shoulder. She struggles to get away, fiercely but silently.

SMITHERS. (*tightening his grasp—roughly*) Easy! None o' that, me birdie. You can't wiggle out, now I got me 'ooks on yer.

WOMAN. (*seeing the uselessness of struggling, gives way to frantic terror, and sinks to the ground, embracing his knees supplicatingly*) No tell him! No tell him, Mister!

SMITHERS. (*with great curiosity*) Tell 'im? (*Then scornfully*) Oh, you mean 'is bloomin' Majesty. What's the gaime, any'ow? What are you sneakin' away for? Been stealin' a bit, I s'pose. (*He taps her bundle with his riding whip significantly*).

WOMAN. (*shaking her head vehemently*) No, me no steal.

SMITHERS. Bloody liar! But tell me what's up. There's somethin' funny goin' on. I smelled it in the air first thing I got up this mornin'. You blacks are up to some devilment. This palace of 'is is like a bleedin' tomb. Where's all the 'ands? (*The woman keeps sullenly silent.* SMITHERS *raises his whip threateningly*) Ow, yer won't, won't yer? I'll show yer what's what.

WOMAN. (*coweringly*) I tell, Mister. You no hit. They go—all go. (*She makes a sweeping gesture toward the hills in the distance*).

SMITHERS. Run away—to the 'ills?

WOMAN. Yes, Mister. Him Emperor—Great Father (*She touches her forehead to the floor with a quick mechanical jerk*) Him sleep after eat. Then they go—all go. Me old woman. Me left only. Now me go too.

SMITHERS. (*his astonishment giving way to an immense, mean satisfaction*) Ow! So that's the ticket! Well, I know bloody well wot's in the air—when they runs orf to the 'ills. The tom-tom 'll be thumping out there bloomin' soon. (*With extreme vindictiveness*) And I'm bloody glad of it, for one! Serve 'im right! Puttin' on airs, the stinkin' nigger! 'Is Majesty! Gawd blimey! I only 'opes I'm there when they takes 'im out to shoot 'im. (*Suddenly*) 'E's still 'ere all right, ain't 'e?

WOMAN. Him sleep.

SMITHERS. 'E's bound to find out soon as 'e wakes up. 'E's cunnin' enough to know when 'is time's come. (*He goes to the doorway on right and whistles shrilly with his fingers in his mouth. The old woman springs to her feet and runs out of the doorway, rear.* SMITHERS *goes after her, reaching for his revolver*) Stop or I'll shoot! (*Then stopping—indifferently*) Pop orf then, if yer like, yer black cow. (*He stands in the doorway, looking after her*).

(JONES *enters from the right. He is a tall, powerfully-built, full-blooded Negro of middle age. His features are typically negroid, yet there is something decidedly distinctive about his face—an underlying* strength of will, a hardy, self-reliant confidence in himself that inspires respect. His eyes are alive with a keen, cunning intelligence. In manner he is shrewd, suspicious, evasive. He wears a light blue uniform coat, sprayed with brass buttons, heavy gold chevrons on his shoulders, gold braid on the collar, cuffs, etc. His pants are bright red with a light blue stripe down the side. Patent leather laced boots with brass spurs, and a belt with a long-barreled, pearl-handled revolver in a holster complete his make up. Yet there is something not altogether ridiculous about his grandeur. He has a way of carrying it off*).

JONES. (*not seeing anyone—greatly irritated and blinking sleepily—shouts*) Who dare whistle dat way in my palace? Who dare wake up de Emperor? I'll git de hide frayled off some o' you niggers sho'!

SMITHERS. (*showing himself—in a manner half-afraid and half-defiant*) It was me whistled to yer. (*As* JONES *frowns angrily*) I got news for yer.

JONES. (*putting on his suavest manner, which fails to cover up his contempt for the white man*) Oh, it's you, Mister Smithers. (*He sits down on his throne with easy dignity*) What news you got to tell me?

SMITHERS. (*coming close to enjoy his discomfiture*) Don't yer notice nothin' funny today?

JONES. (*coldly*) Funny? No. I ain't perceived nothin' of de kind!

SMITHERS. Then yer ain't so foxy as I thought yer was. Where's all your court? (*sarcastically*) the Generals and the Cabinet Ministers and all?

JONES. (*imperturbably*) Where dey mostly runs to minute I closes my eyes—drinkin' rum and talkin' big down in de town. (*Sarcastically*) How come you don't know dat? Ain't you sousin' with 'em most every day?

SMITHERS. (*stung but pretending in-*

difference—with a wink) That's part of the day's work. I got ter—ain't I—in my business?

JONES. (*contemptuously*) Yo' business!

SMITHERS. (*imprudently enraged*) Gawd blimey, you was glad enough for me ter take yer in on it when you landed here first. You didn' 'ave no 'igh and mighty airs in them days!

JONES. (*his hand going to his revolver like a flash—menacingly*) Talk polite, white man! Talk polite, you heah me! I'm boss heah now, is you fergettin'? (*The Cockney seems about to challenge this last statement with the facts but something in the other's eyes holds and cows him*).

SMITHERS. (*in a cowardly whine*) No 'arm meant, old top.

JONES. (*condescendingly*) I accepts yo' apology. (*Lets his hand fall from his revolver*) No use'n you rakin' up ole times. What I was den is one thing. What I is now 's another. You didn't let me in on yo' crooked work out o' no kind feelin's dat time. I done de dirty work fo' you—and most o' de brain work, too, fo' dat matter—and I was wu'th money to you, dat's de reason.

SMITHERS. Well, blimey, I give yer a start, didn't I?—when no one else would. I wasn't afraid to 'ire you like the rest was—'count of the story about your breakin' jail back in the States.

JONES. No, you didn't have no s'cuse to look down on me fo' dat. You been in jail you'self more'n once.

SMITHERS. (*furiously*) It's a lie! (*Then trying to pass it off by an attempt at scorn*) Garn! Who told yer that fairy tale?

JONES. Dey's some tings I ain't got to be tole. I kin see 'em in folk's eyes. (*Then after a pause—meditatively*) Yes, you sho' give me a start. And it didn't take long from dat time to git dese fool, woods' niggers right where I wanted dem.

(*With pride*) From stowaway to Emperor in two years! Dat's goin' some!

SMITHERS. (*with curiosity*) And I bet you got yer pile o' money 'id safe some place.

JONES. (*with satisfaction*) I sho' has! And it's in a foreign bank where no pusson don't ever git it out but me no matter what come. You didn't s'pose I was holdin' down dis Emperor job for de glory in it, did you? Sho'! De fuss and glory part of it, dat's only to turn de heads o' de low-flung, bush niggers dat's here. Dey wants de big circus show for deir money. I gives it to 'em an' I gits de money. (*With a grin*) De long green, dat's me every time! (*Then rebukingly*) But you ain't got no kick agin me, Smithers. I'se paid you back all you done for me many times. Ain't I pertected you and winked at all de crooked tradin' you been doin' right out in de broad day? Sho' I has—and me makin' laws to stop it at de same time! (*He chuckles*).

SMITHERS. (*grinning*) But, meanin' no 'arm, you been grabbin' right and left yourself, ain't yer? Look at the taxes you've put on 'em! Blimey! You've squeezed 'em dry!

JONES. (*chuckling*) No, dey ain't *all* dry yet. I'se still heah, ain't I?

SMITHERS. (*smiling at his secret thought*) They're dry right now, you'll find out. (*Changing the subject abruptly*) And as for me breakin' laws, you've broke 'em all yerself just as fast as yer made 'em.

JONES. Ain't I de Emperor? De laws don't go for him. (*Judicially*) You heah what I tells you, Smithers. Dere's little stealin' like you does, and dere's big stealin' like I does. For de little stealin' dey gits you in jail soon or late. For de big stealin' dey makes you Emperor and puts you in de Hall o' Fame when you croaks. (*Reminiscently*) If dey's one thing I learns in ten years on de Pullman ca's listenin' to de white quality talk, it's dat same fact. And when I gits a chance to use it I winds up Emperor in two years.

SMITHERS. (*unable to repress the genuine admiration of the small fry for the large*) Yes, yer turned the bleedin' trick, all right. Blimey, I never seen a bloke 'as 'ad the bloomin' luck you 'as.

JONES. (*severely*) Luck? What you mean—luck?

SMITHERS. I suppose you'll say as that swank about the silver bullet ain't luck—and that was what first got the fool blacks on yer side the time of the revolution, wasn't it?

JONES. (*with a laugh*) Oh, dat silver bullet! Sho' was luck. But I makes dat luck, you heah? I loads de dice! Yessuh! When dat murderin' nigger ole Lem hired to kill me takes aim ten feet away and his gun misses fire and I shoots him dead, what you heah me say?

SMITHERS. You said yer'd got a charm so's no lead bullet'd kill yer. You was so strong only a silver bullet could kill yer, you told 'em. Blimey, wasn't that swank for yer—and plain, fat-'eaded luck?

JONES. (*proudly*) I got brains and I uses 'em quick. Dat ain't luck.

SMITHERS. Yer know they wasn't 'ardly liable to get no silver bullets. And it was luck 'e didn't 'it you that time.

JONES. (*laughing*) And dere all dem fool bush niggers was kneelin' down and bumpin' deir heads on de ground like I was a miracle out o' de Bible. Oh, Lawd, from dat time on I has dem all eatin' out of my hand. I cracks de whip and dey jumps through.

SMITHERS. (*with a sniff*) Yankee bluff done it.

JONES. Ain't a man's talkin' big what makes him big—long as he makes folks believe it? Sho', I talks large when I ain't got nothin' to back it up, but I ain't talkin' wild just de same. I knows I kin fool 'em—I *knows* it—and dat's backin' enough fo' my game. And ain't I got to learn deir lingo and teach some of dem English befo' I kin talk to 'em? Ain't dat wuk? You ain't never learned ary word er it, Smithers, in de ten years you been heah, dough you knows it's money in yo' pocket tradin' wid 'em if you does. But you'se too shiftless to take de trouble.

SMITHERS. (*flushing*) Never mind about me. What's this I've 'eard about yer really 'avin' a silver bullet moulded for yourself?

JONES. It's playin' out my bluff. I has de silver bullet moulded and I tells 'em when de time comes I kills myself wid it. I tells 'em dat's 'cause I'm de on'y man in de world big enuff to git me. No use'n deir tryin'. And dey falls down and bumps deir heads. (*He laughs*) I does dat so's I kin take a walk in peace widout no jealous nigger gunnin' at me from behind de trees.

SMITHERS. (*astonished*) Then you 'ad it made—'onest?

JONES. Sho' did. Heah she be. (*He takes out his revolver, breaks it, and takes the silver bullet out of one chamber*) Five lead an' dis silver baby at de last. Don't she shine pretty? (*He holds it in his hand, looking at it admiringly, as if strangely fascinated*).

SMITHERS. Let me see. (*Reaches out his hand for it*).

JONES. (*harshly*) Keep yo' hands whar dey b'long, white man. (*He replaces it in the chamber and puts the revolver back on his hip*).

SMITHERS. (*snarling*) Gawd blimey! Think I'm a bleedin' thief, you would.

JONES. No, 'tain't dat. I knows you'se scared to steal from me. On'y I ain't 'lowin' nary body to touch dis baby. She's my rabbit's foot.

SMITHERS. (*sneering*) A bloomin'

charm, wot? (*Venomously*) Well, you'll need all the bloody charms you 'as before long, s' 'elp me!

JONES. (*judicially*) Oh, I'se good for six months yit 'fore dey gits sick o' my game. Den, when I sees trouble comin', I makes my getaway.

SMITHERS. Ho! You got it all planned, ain't yer?

JONES. I ain't no fool. I knows dis Emperor's time is sho't. Dat why I make hay when de sun shine. Was you thinkin' I'se aimin' to hold down dis job for life? No, suh! What good is gittin' money if you stays back in dis raggedy country? I wants action when I spends. And when I sees dese niggers gittin' up deir nerve to tu'n me out, and I'se got all de money in sight, I resigns on de spot and beats it quick.

SMITHERS. Where to?

JONES. None o' yo' business.

SMITHERS. Not back to the bloody States, I'll lay my oath.

JONES. (*suspiciously*) Why don't I? (*Then with an easy laugh*) You mean 'count of dat story 'bout me breakin' from jail back dere? Dat's all talk.

SMITHERS. (*skeptically*) Ho, yes!

JONES. (*sharply*) You ain't 'sinuatin' I'se a liar, is you?

SMITHERS. (*hastily*) No, Gawd strike me! I was only thinkin' o' the bloody lies you told the blacks 'ere about killin' white men in the States.

JONES. (*angered*) How come dey're lies?

SMITHERS. You'd 'ave been in jail if you 'ad, wouldn't yer then? (*With venom*) And from what I've 'eard, it ain't 'ealthy for a black to kill a white man in the States. They burns 'em in oil, don't they?

JONES. (*with cool deadliness*) You mean lynchin' 'd scare me? Well, I tells you, Smithers, maybe I does kill one white man back dere. Maybe I does. And maybe I kills another right heah 'fore long if he don't look out.

SMITHERS. (*trying to force a laugh*) I was on'y spoofin' yer. Can't yer take a joke? And you was just sayin' you'd never been in jail.

JONES. (*in the same tone—slightly boastful*) Maybe I goes to jail dere for gettin' in an argument wid razors ovah a crap game. Maybe I gits twenty years when dat colored man die. Maybe I gits in 'nother argument wid de prison guard was overseer ovah us when we're wukin' de road. Maybe he hits me wid a whip and I splits his head wid a shovel and runs away and files de chain off my leg and gits away safe. Maybe I does all dat an' maybe I don't. It's a story I tells you so's you knows I'se de kind of man dat if you evah repeats one word of it, I ends yo' stealin' on dis yearth mighty damn quick!

SMITHERS. (*terrified*) Think I'd peach on yer? Not me! Ain't I always been yer friend?

JONES. (*suddenly relaxing*) Sho' you has—and you better be.

SMITHERS. (*recovering his composure —and with it his malice*) And just to show yer I'm yer friend, I'll tell yer that bit o' news I was goin' to.

JONES. Go ahead! Shoot de piece. Must be bad news from de happy way you look.

SMITHERS. (*warningly*) Maybe it's gettin' time for you to resign—with that bloomin' silver bullet, wot? (*He finishes with a mocking grin*).

JONES. (*puzzled*) What's dat you say? Talk plain.

SMITHERS. Ain't noticed any of the guards or servants about the place today, I 'aven't.

JONES. (*carelessly*) Dey're all out in de garden sleepin' under de trees. When I sleeps, dey sneaks a sleep, too, and I pretends I never suspicions it. All I got to do is to ring de bell and dey come flyin', makin' a bluff dey was wukin' all de time.

SMITHERS. (*in the same mocking tone*) Ring the bell now an' you'll bloody well see what I means.

JONES. (*startled to alertness, but preserving the same careless tone*) Sho' I rings. (*He reaches below the throne and pulls out a big, common dinner bell which is painted the same vivid scarlet as the throne. He rings this vigorously— then stops to listen. Then he goes to both doors, rings again, and looks out*).

SMITHERS. (*watching him with malicious satisfaction, after a pause—mockingly*) The bloody ship is sinkin' an' the bleedin' rats 'as slung their 'ooks.

JONES. (*in a sudden fit of anger flings the bell clattering into a corner*) Low-flung, woods' niggers! (*Then catching SMITHERS' eye on him, he controls himself and suddenly bursts into a low chuckling laugh*) Reckon I overplays my hand dis once! A man can't take de pot on a bob-tailed flush all de time. Was I sayin' I'd sit in six months mo'? Well, I'se changed my mind den. I cashes in and resigns de job of Emperor right dis minute.

SMITHERS. (*with real admiration*) Blimey, but you're a cool bird, and no mistake.

JONES. No use'n fussin'. When I knows de game's up I kisses it good-by widout no long waits. Dey've all run off to de hills, ain't dey?

SMITHERS. Yes—every bleedin' man jack of 'em.

JONES. Den de revolution is at de post. And de Emperor better git his feet smokin' up de trail. (*He starts for the door in rear*).

SMITHERS. Goin' out to look for your 'orse? Yer won't find any. They steals the 'orses first thing. Mine was gone when I went for 'im this mornin'. That's wot first give me a suspicion of wot was up.

JONES. (*alarmed for a second, scratches his head, then philosophically*) Well, den I hoofs it. Feet, do yo' duty! (*He pulls out a gold watch and looks at it*) Three-thuty. Sundown's at six-thuty or dereabouts. (*Puts his watch back— with cool confidence*) I got plenty o' time to make it easy.

SMITHERS. Don't be so bloomin' sure of it. They'll be after you 'ot and 'eavy. Ole Lem is at the bottom o' this business an' 'e 'ates you like 'ell. 'E'd rather do for you than eat 'is dinner, 'e would!

JONES. (*scornfully*) Dat fool no-count nigger! Does you think I'se scared o' him? I stands him on his thick head more'n once befo' dis, and I does it again if he comes in my way— (*Fiercely*) And dis time I leave him a dead nigger fo' sho'!

SMITHERS. You'll 'ave to cut through the big forest—an' these blacks 'ere can sniff and follow a trail in the dark like 'ounds. You'd 'ave to 'ustle to get through that forest in twelve hours even if you knew all the bloomin' trails like a native.

JONES. (*with indignant scorn*) Look-a-heah, white man! Does you think I'se a natural bo'n fool? Give me credit fo' havin' some sense, fo' Lawd's sake! Don't you s'pose I'se looked ahead and made sho' of all de chances? I'se gone out in dat big forest, pretendin' to hunt, so many times dat I knows it high an' low like a book. I could go through on dem trails wid my eyes shut. (*With great contempt*) Think dese ign'rent bush niggers dat ain't got brains enuff to know deir own names even can catch Brutus Jones? Huh, I s'pects not! Not on yo' life! Why, man, de white men went after me wid bloodhounds where I come from an' I jes' laughs at 'em. It's a shame to fool dese black trash around heah, dey're so easy. You watch me, man. I'll make dem look sick, I will. I'll be 'cross de plain to de edge of de forest by time dark comes.

Once in de woods in de night dey got a swell chance o' findin' dis baby! Dawn tomorrow I'll be out at de oder side and on de coast whar dat French gunboat is stayin'. She picks me up, takes me to Martinique when she go dar, and dere I is safe wid a mighty big bankroll in my jeans. It's easy as rollin' off a log.

SMITHERS. (*maliciously*) But s'posin' somethin' 'appens wrong an' they do nab yer?

JONES. (*decisively*) Dey don't—dat's de answer.

SMITHERS. But, just for argyment's sake—what'd you do?

JONES. (*frowning*) I'se got five lead bullets in dis gun good enuff fo' common bush niggers—and after dat I got de silver bullet left to cheat 'em out o' gittin' me.

SMITHERS. (*jeeringly*) Ho, I was fergettin' that silver bullet. You'll bump yourself orf in style, won't yer? Blimey!

JONES. (*gloomily*) You kin bet yo' whole roll on one thing, white man. Dis baby plays out his string to de end and when he quits, he quits wid a bang de way he ought. Silver bullet ain't none too good for him when he go, dat's a fac'! (*Then shaking off his nervousness—with a confident laugh*) Sho'! What is I talkin' about? Ain't come to dat yit and I never will—not wid trash niggers like dese yere. (*Boastfully*) Silver bullet bring me luck anyway. I kin outguess, outrun, out-fight, an' outplay de whole lot o' dem all ovah de board any time o' de day er night! You watch me! (*From the distant hills comes the faint, steady thump of a tom-tom, low and vibrating. It starts at a rate exactly corresponding to normal pulse beat—72 to the minute—and continues at a gradually accelerating rate from this point uninterruptedly to the very end of the play*).

(*JONES starts at the sound. A strange look of apprehension creeps into his face

for a moment as he listens. Then he asks, with an attempt to regain his most casual manner) What's dat drum beatin' fo'?

SMITHERS. (*with a mean grin*) For you. That means the bleedin' ceremony 'as started. I've 'eard it before and I knows.

JONES. Cer'mony? What cer'mony?

SMITHERS. The blacks is 'oldin' a bloody meetin', 'avin' a war dance, gettin' their courage worked up b'fore they starts after you.

JONES. Let dem! Dey'll sho' need it!

SMITHERS. And they're there 'oldin' their 'eathen religious service—makin' no end of devil spells and charms to 'elp 'em against your silver bullet. (*He guffaws loudly*) Blimey, but they're balmy as 'ell!

JONES. (*a tiny bit awed and shaken in spite of himself*) Huh! Takes more'n dat to scare dis chicken!

SMITHERS. (*scenting the other's feeling—maliciously*) Ternight when it's pitch black in the forest, they'll 'ave their pet devils and ghosts 'oundin' after you. You'll find yer bloody 'air 'll be standin' on end before termorrow mornin'. (*Seriously*) It's a bleedin' queer place, that stinkin' forest, even in daylight. Yer don't know what might 'appen in there, it's that rotten still. Always sends the cold shivers down my back minute I gets in it.

JONES. (*with a contemptuous sniff*) I ain't no chicken-liver like you is. Trees an' me, we'se friends, and dar's a full moon comin' bring me light. And let dem po' niggers make all de fool spells dey'se a min' to. Does yo' s'pect I'se silly enuff to b'lieve in ghosts an' ha'nts an' all dat ole woman's talk? G'long, white man! You ain't talkin' to me. (*With a chuckle*) Doesn't you know dey's got to do wid a man was member in good standin' o' de Baptist Church? Sho' I was dat when I was porter on de Pullmans, befo' I gits into my little trouble. Let dem try deir heathen tricks. De Baptist Church done pertect me and land dem all in hell. (*Then with more confident satisfaction*) And I'se got little silver bullet o' my own, don't forgit!

SMITHERS. Ho! You 'aven't give much 'eed to your Baptist Church since you been down 'ere. I've 'eard myself you 'ad turned yer coat an' was takin' up with their blarsted witch-doctors, or whatever the 'ell yer calls the swine.

JONES. (*vehemently*) I pretends to! Sho' I pretends! Dat's part o' my game from de fust. If I finds out dem niggers believes dat black is white, den I yells it out louder 'n deir loudest. It don't git me nothin' to do missionary work for de Baptist Church. I'se after de coin, an' I lays my Jesus on de shelf for de time bein'. (*Stops abruptly to look at his watch—alertly*) But I ain't got de time to waste on no more fool talk wid you. I'se gwine away from heah dis secon'. (*He reaches in under the throne and pulls out an expensive Panama hat with a bright multi-colored band and sets it jauntily on his head*) So long, white man! (*With a grin*) See you in jail sometime, maybe!

SMITHERS. Not me, you won't. Well, I wouldn't be in yer bloody boots for no bloomin' money, but 'ere's wishin' yer luck just the same.

JONES. (*contemptuously*) You're de frightenedest man evah I see! I tells you I'se safe's 'f I was in New York City. It takes dem niggers from now to dark to git up de nerve to start somethin'. By dat time, I'se got a head start dey never kotch up wid.

SMITHERS. (*maliciously*) Give my regards to any ghosts yer meets up with.

JONES. (*grinning*) If dat ghost got money, I'll tell him never ha'nt you less'n he wants to lose it.

SMITHERS. (*flattered*) Garn! (*Then curiously*) Ain't yer takin' no luggage with yer?

JONES. I travels light when I wants to move fast. And I got tinned grub buried on de edge o' de forest. (*Boastfully*) Now say dat I don't look ahead an' use my brains! (*With a wide, liberal gesture*) I will all dat's left in de palace to you— and you better grab all you kin sneak away wid befo' dey gits here.

SMITHERS. (*gratefully*) Righto—and thanks ter yer. (*As* JONES *walks toward the door in rear—cautioningly*) Say! Look 'ere, you ain't goin' out that way, are yer?

JONES. Does you think I'd slink out de back door like a common nigger? I'se Emperor yit, ain't I? And de Emperor Jones leaves de way he comes, and dat black trash don't dare stop him—not yit, leastways (*He stops for a moment in the doorway, listening to the far-off but insistent beat of the tom-tom*) Listen to dat roll-call, will you? Must be mighty big drum carry dat far. (*Then with a laugh*) Well, if dey ain't no whole brass band to see me off, I sho' got de drum part of it. So long, white man. (*He puts his hands in his pockets and with studied carelessness, whistling a tune, he saunters out of the doorway and off to the left*).

SMITHERS. (*looks after him with a puzzled admiration*) 'E's got 'is bloomin' nerve with 'im, s'elp me! (*Then angrily*) Ho—the bleedin' nigger—puttin' on 'is bloody airs! I 'opes they nabs 'im an' gives 'im what's what!

CURTAIN

SCENE TWO

The end of the plain where the Great Forest begins. The foreground is sandy, level ground dotted by a few stones and clumps of stunted bushes cowering close against the earth to escape the buffeting of the trade wind. In the rear the forest is a wall of darkness dividing the world.

Only when the eye becomes accustomed to the gloom can the outlines of separate trunks of the nearest trees be made out, enormous pillars of deeper blackness. A somber monotone of wind lost in the leaves moans in the air. Yet this sound serves but to intensify the impression of the forest's relentless immobility, to form a background throwing into relief its brooding, implacable silence.

(JONES *enters from the left, walking rapidly. He stops as he nears the edge of the forest, looks around him quickly, peering into the dark as if searching for some familiar landmark. Then, apparently satisfied that he is where he ought to be, he throws himself on the ground, dog-tired*).

Well, heah I is. In de nick o' time, too! Little mo' an' it'd be blacker'n de ace of spades heahabouts. (*He pulls a bandana handkerchief from his hip pocket and mops off his perspiring face*) Sho'! Gimme air! I'se tuckered out sho' 'nuff. Dat soft Emperor job ain't no trainin' fo' a long hike ovah dat plain in de brilin' sun. (*Then with a chuckle*) Cheer up, nigger, de worst is yet to come. (*He lifts his head and stares at the forest. His chuckle peters out abruptly. In a tone of awe*) My goodness, look at dem woods, will you? Dat no-count Smithers said dey'd be black an' he sho' called de turn. (*Turning away from them quickly and looking down at his feet, he snatches at a chance to change the subject—solicitously*) Feet, you is holdin' up yo' end fine an' I sutinly hopes you ain't blisterin' none. It's time you git a rest. (*He takes off his shoes, his eyes studiously avoiding the forest. He feels of the soles of his feet gingerly*) You is still in de pink—on'y a little mite feverish. Cool yo'selfs. Remember you done got a long journey yit befo' you. (*He sits in a weary attitude, listening to the rhythmic beating of the tom-tom. He grumbles in a loud tone to*

cover up a growing uneasiness*) Bush niggers! Wonder dey wouldn't git sick o' beatin' dat drum. Sound louder, seem like. I wonder if dey's startin' after me? (*He scrambles to his feet, looking back across the plain*) Couldn't see dem now, nohow, if dey was hundred feet away. (*Then shaking himself like a wet dog to get rid of these depressing thoughts*) Sho', dey's miles an' miles behind. What you gittin' fidgety about? (*But he sits down and begins to lace up his shoes in great haste, all the time muttering reassuringly*) You know what? Yo' belly is empty, dat's what's de matter wid you. Come time to eat! Wid nothin' but wind on yo' stumach, o' course you feels jiggedy. Well, we eats right heah an' now soon's I gits dese pesky shoes laced up. (*He finishes lacing up his shoes*) Dere! Now le's see! (*Gets on his hands and knees and searches the ground around him with his eyes*) White stone, white stone, where is you? (*He sees the first white stone and crawls to it—with satisfaction*) Heah you is! I knowed dis was de right place. Box of grub, come to me. (*He turns over the stone and feels in under it—in a tone of dismay*) Ain't heah! Gorry, is I in de right place or isn't I? Dere's 'nother stone. Guess dat's it. (*He scrambles to the next stone and turns it over*) Ain't heah, neither! Grub, whar is you? Ain't heah. Gorry, has I got to go hungry into dem woods—all de night? (*While he is talking he scrambles from one stone to another, turning them over in frantic haste. Finally, he jumps to his feet excitedly*) Is I lost de place? Must have! But how dat happen when I was followin' de trail across de plain in broad daylight? (*Almost plaintively*) I'se hungry, I is! I gotta git my feed. Whar's my strength gonna come from if I doesn't? Gorry, I gotta find dat grub high an' low somehow! Why it come dark so quick like dat? Can't see nothin'. (*He scratches a match on his trousers and*

peers about him. The rate of the beat of the far-off tom-tom increases perceptibly as he does so. He mutters in a bewildered voice) How come all dese white stones come heah when I only remembers one? *(Suddenly, with a frightened gasp, he flings the match on the ground and stamps on it)* Nigger, is you gone crazy mad? Is you lightin' matches to show dem whar you is? Fo' Lawd's sake, use yo' haid. Gorry, I'se got to be careful! *(He stares at the plain behind him apprehensively, his hand on his revolver)* But how come all dese white stones? And whar's dat tin box o' grub I hid all wrapped up in oil cloth?

(While his back is turned, the LITTLE FORMLESS FEARS *creep out from the deeper blackness of the forest. They are black, shapeless, only their glittering little eyes can be seen. If they have any describable form at all it is that of a grub-worm about the size of a creeping child. They move noiselessly, but with deliberate, painful effort, striving to raise themselves on end, failing and sinking prone again.* JONES *turns about to face the forest. He stares up at the tops of the trees, seeking vainly to discover his whereabouts by their conformation).*

Can't tell nothin' from dem trees! Gorry, nothin' 'round heah looks like I evah seed it befo'. I'se done lost de place sho' 'nuff! *(With mournful foreboding)* It's mighty queer! It's mighty queer! *(With sudden forced defiance—in an angry tone)* Woods, is you tryin' to put somethin' ovah on me?

(From the formless creatures on the ground in front of him comes a tiny gale of low mocking laughter like a rustling of leaves. They squirm upward toward him in twisted attitudes. JONES *looks down, leaps backward with a yell of terror, yanking out his revolver as he does so— in a quavering voice)* What's dat? Who's dar? What is you? Git away from me befo' I shoots you up! You don't?—

(He fires. There is a flash, a loud report, then silence broken only by the far-off, quickened throb of the tom-tom. The formless creatures have scurried back into the forest. JONES *remains fixed in his position, listening intently. The sound of the shot, the reassuring feel of the revolver in his hand, have somewhat restored his shaken nerve. He addresses himself with renewed confidence).*

Dey're gone. Dat shot fix 'em. Dey was only little animals—little wild pigs, I reckon. Dey've maybe rooted out yo' grub an' eat it. Sho', you fool nigger, what you think dey is—ha'nts? *(Excitedly)* Gorry, you give de game away when you fire dat shot. Dem niggers heah dat fo' su'tin! Time you beat it in de woods widout no long waits. *(He starts for the forest—hesitates before the plunge—then urging himself in with manful resolution)* Git in, nigger! What you skeered at? Ain't nothin' dere but de trees! Git in! *(He plunges boldly into the forest).*

SCENE THREE

In the forest. The moon has just risen. Its beams, drifting through the canopy of leaves, make a barely perceptible, suffused, eerie glow. A dense low wall of underbrush and creepers is in the nearer foreground, fencing in a small triangular clearing. Beyond this is the massed blackness of the forest like an encompassing barrier. A path is dimly discerned leading down to the clearing from left, rear, and winding away from it again toward the right. As the scene opens nothing can be distinctly made out. Except for the beating of the tom-tom, which is a trifle louder and quicker than at the close of the previous scene, there is silence, broken every few seconds by a queer, clicking sound. Then gradually the figure of the Negro, JEFF, *can be dis-*

cerned crouching on his haunches at the rear of the triangle. He is middle-aged, thin, brown in color, is dressed in a Pullman porter's uniform and cap. He is throwing a pair of dice on the ground before him, picking them up, shaking them, casting them out with the regular, rigid, mechanical movements of an automaton. The heavy, plodding footsteps of someone approaching along the trail from the left are heard and JONES' *voice, pitched on a slightly higher key and strained in a cheery effort to overcome its own tremors.*

De moon's rizen. Does you heah dat, nigger? You gits more light from dis out. No mo' buttin' yo' fool head agin' de trunks an' scratchin' de hide off yo' legs in de bushes. Now you sees whar yo'se gwine. So cheer up! From now on you has a snap. (*He steps just to the rear of the triangular clearing and mops off his face on his sleeve. He has lost his Panama hat. His face is scratched, his brilliant uniform shows several large rents*) What time's it gittin' to be, I wonder? I dassent light no match to find out. Phoo'. It's wa'm an' dat's a fac'! (*Wearily*) How long I been makin' tracks in dese woods? Must be hours an' hours. Seems like fo'evah! Yit can't be, when de moon's jes' riz. Dis am a long night fo' yo', yo' Majesty! (*With a mournful chuckle*) Majesty! Der ain't much majesty 'bout dis baby now. (*With attempted cheerfulness*) Never min'. It's all part o' de game. Dis night come to an end like everything else. And when you gits dar safe and has dat bankroll in yo' hands you laughs at all dis. (*He starts to whistle but checks himself abruptly*) What yo' whistlin' for, you po' dope! Want all de worl' to heah you? (*He stops talking to listen*) Heah dat ole drum! Sho' gits nearer from de sound. Dey's packin' it along wid 'em. Time fo' me to move. (*He takes a step forward, then*

stops—*worriedly*) What's dat odder queer clickety sound I heah? Dere it is! Sound close! Sound like—sound like— Fo' God sake, sound like some nigger was shootin' crap! (*Frightenedly*) I better beat it quick when I gits dem notions. (*He walks quickly into the clear space—then stands transfixed as he sees* JEFF—*in a terrified gasp*) Who dar? Who dat? Is dat you, Jeff? (*Starting toward the other, forgetful for a moment of his surroundings and really believing it is a living man that he sees—in a tone of happy relief*) Jeff! I'se sho' mighty glad to see you! Dey tol' me you done died from dat razor cut I gives you. (*Stopping suddenly, bewilderedly*) But how you come to be heah, nigger? (*He stares fascinatedly at the other who continues mechanical play with the dice.* JONES' *eyes begin to roll wildly. He stutters*) Ain't you gwine—look up—can't you speak to me? Is you—is you—a ha'nt? (*He jerks out his revolver in a frenzy of terrified rage*) Nigger, I kills you dead once. Has I got to kill you ag'in? You take it den. (*He fires. When the smoke clears away* JEFF *has disappeared.* JONES *stands trembling—then with a certain reassurance*) He's gone, anyway. Ha'nt or not ha'nt, dat shot fix him. (*The beat of the far-off tom-tom is perceptibly louder and more rapid.* JONES *becomes conscious of it—with a start, looking back over his shoulder*) Dey's gittin' near! Dey's comin' fast! And heah I is shootin' shots to let 'em know jes' whar I is! Oh, Gorry, I'se got to run. (*Forgetting the path he plunges wildly into the underbrush in the rear and disappears in the shadow*).

SCENE FOUR

In the forest. A wide dirt road runs diagonally from right, front, to left, rear. Rising sheer on both sides the forest walls it in. The moon is now up. Under its light the road glimmers ghastly and unreal. It is as if the forest had stood aside momentarily to let the road pass through and accomplish its veiled purpose. This done, the forest will fold in upon itself again and the road will be no more. JONES *stumbles in from the forest on the right. His uniform is ragged and torn. He looks about him with numbed surprise when he sees the road, his eyes blinking in the bright moonlight. He flops down exhaustedly and pants heavily for a while. Then with sudden anger.*

I'm meltin' wid heat! Runnin' an' runnin' an' runnin'! Damn dis heah coat! Like a straitjacket! (*He tears off his coat and flings it away from him, revealing himself stripped to the waist*) Dere! Dat's better! Now I kin breathe! (*Looking down at his feet, the spurs catch his eye*) And to hell wid dese high-fangled spurs. Dey're what's been a-trippin' me up an' breakin' my neck. (*He unstraps them and flings them away disgustedly*) Dere! I gits rid o' dem frippety Emperor trappin's an' I travels lighter. Lawd! I'se tired! (*After a pause, listening to the insistent beat of the tom-tom in the distance*) I must 'a' put some distance between myself an' dem—runnin' like dat—and yit—dat damn drum sounds jes' de same—nearer, even. Well, I guess I a'most holds my lead anyhow. Dey won't never catch up. (*With a sigh*) If on'y my fool legs stands up. Oh, I'se sorry I evah went in for dis. Dat Emperor job is sho' hard to shake. (*He looks around him suspiciously*) How'd dis road evah git heah? Good level road, too. I never remembers seein' it befo'! (*Shaking his head apprehensively*) Dese woods is sho' full o' de queerest things at night. (*With a sudden terror*) Lawd God, don't let me see no more o' dem ha'nts! Dey gits my goat! (*Then trying to talk himself into confidence*) Ha'nts! You fool nigger, dey

ain't no such things! Don't de Baptist parson tell you dat many time? Is you civilized, or is you like dese ign'rent black niggers heah? Sho'! Dat was all in yo' own head. Wasn't nothin' dere. Wasn't no Jeff! Know what? You jus' get seein' dem things 'cause yo' belly's empty and you's sick wid hunger inside. Hunger 'fects yo' head and yo' eyes. Any fool know dat. (*Then pleading fervently*) But bless God, I don't come across no more o' dem, whatever dey is! (*Then cautiously*) Rest! Don't talk! Rest! You needs it. Den you gits on yo' way again. (*Looking at the moon*) Night's half gone a'most. You hits de coast in de mawning! Den you's all safe.

(*From the right forward a small gang of Negroes enter. They are dressed in striped convict suits, their heads are shaven, one leg drags limpingly, shackled to a heavy ball and chain. Some carry picks, the others shovels. They are followed by a white man dressed in the uniform of a prison guard. A Winchester rifle is slung across his shoulders and he carries a heavy whip. At a signal from the* GUARD *they stop on the road opposite where* JONES *is sitting.* JONES, *who has been staring up at the sky, unmindful of their noiseless approach, suddenly looks down and sees them. His eyes pop out, he tries to get to his feet and fly, but sinks back, too numbed by fright to move. His voice catches in a choking prayer*).

Lawd Jesus!

(*The* PRISON GUARD *cracks his whip—noiselessly—and at that signal all the convicts start to work on the road. They swing their picks, they shovel, but not a sound comes from their labor. Their movements, like those of* JEFF *in the preceding scene, are those of automatons,—rigid, slow, and mechanical. The* PRISON GUARD *points sternly at* JONES *with his whip, motions him to take his place among the other shovelers.* JONES *gets to his feet in a hypnotized stupor. He mumbles subserviently).*

Yes, suh! Yes, suh! I'se comin'.

(As he shuffles, dragging one foot, over to his place, he curses under his breath with rage and hatred).

God damn yo' soul, I gits even wid you yit, sometime.

(As if there were a shovel in his hands he goes through weary, mechanical gestures of digging up dirt, and throwing it to the roadside. Suddenly the GUARD *approaches him angrily, threateningly. He raises his whip and lashes* JONES *viciously across the shoulders with it.* JONES *winces with pain and cowers abjectly. The* GUARD *turns his back on him and walks away contemptuously. Instantly* JONES *straightens up. With arms upraised as if his shovel were a club in his hands he springs murderously at the unsuspecting* GUARD. *In the act of crashing down his shovel on the white man's skull,* JONES *suddenly becomes aware that his hands are empty. He cries despairingly).*

Whar's my shovel? Gimme my shovel 'til I splits his damn head! *(Appealing to his fellow convicts)* Gimme a shovel, one o' you, fo' God's sake!

(They stand fixed in motionless attitudes, their eyes on the ground. The GUARD *seems to wait expectantly, his back turned to the attacker.* JONES *bellows with baffled, terrified rage, tugging frantically at his revolver).*

I kills you, you white debil, if it's de last thing I evah does! Ghost or debil, I kill you agin!

(He frees the revolver and fires point blank at the GUARD'S *back. Instantly the walls of the forest close in from both sides, the road and the figures of the convict gang are blotted out in an enshrouding darkness. The only sounds are a crashing in the underbrush as* JONES *leaps away in mad flight and the throbbing of the tom-tom still far distant, but*

increased in volume of sound and rapidity of beat).

SCENE FIVE

A large circular clearing, enclosed by the serried ranks of gigantic trunks of tall trees whose tops are lost to view. In the center is a big dead stump worn by time into a curious resemblance to an auction block. The moon floods the clearing with a clear light. JONES *forces his way in through the forest on the left. He looks wildly about the clearing with hunted, fearful glances. His pants are in tatters, his shoes cut and misshapen, flapping about his feet. He slinks cautiously to the stump in the center and sits down in a tense position, ready for instant flight. Then he holds his head in his hands and rocks back and forth, moaning to himself miserably.*

Oh, Lawd, Lawd! Oh, Lawd, Lawd! *(Suddenly he throws himself on his knees and raises his clasped hands to the sky—in a voice of agonized pleading)* Lawd Jesus, heah my prayer! I'se a po' sinner, a po' sinner! I knows I done wrong, I knows it! When I cotches Jeff cheatin' wid loaded dice my anger overcomes me and I kills him dead! Lawd, I done wrong! When dat guard hits me wid de whip, my anger overcomes me, and I kills him dead. Lawd, I done wrong! And down heah whar dese fool bush niggers raises me up to the seat o' de mighty, I steals all I could grab. Lawd, I done wrong! I knows it! I'se sorry! Forgive me, Lawd! Forgive dis po' sinner! *(Then beseeching terrifiedly)* And keep dem away, Lawd! Keep dem away from me! And stop dat drum soundin' in my ears! Dat begin to sound ha'nted, too. *(He gets to his feet, evidently slightly reassured by his prayer—with attempted confidence)* De Lawd'll preserve me from dem ha'nts after dis. *(Sits down on the stump again)*

I ain't skeered o' real men. Let dem come. But dem odders—(*He shudders—then looks down at his feet, working his toes inside the shoes—with a groan*) Oh, my po' feet! Dem shoes ain't no use no more 'ceptin' to hurt. I'se better off widout dem. (*He unlaces them and pulls them off—holds the wrecks of the shoes in his hands and regards them mournfully*) You was real, A-one patin' leather, too. Look at you now. Emperor, you'se gittin' mighty low!

(*He sighs dejectedly and remains with bowed shoulders, staring down at the shoes in his hands as if reluctant to throw them away. While his attention is thus occupied, a crowd of figures silently enter the clearing from all sides. All are dressed in Southern costumes of the period of the fifties of the last century. There are middle-aged men who are evidently well-to-do planters. There is one spruce, authoritative individual—the* AUCTIONEER. *There is a crowd of curious spectators, chiefly young belles and dandies who have come to the slave-market for diversion. All exchange courtly greetings in dumb show and chat silently together. There is something stiff, rigid, unreal, marionettish about their movements. They group themselves about the stump. Finally a batch of slaves is led in from the left by an attendant—three men of different ages, two women, one with a baby in her arms, nursing. They are placed to the left of the stump, beside* JONES.

The white planters look them over appraisingly as if they were cattle, and exchange judgments on each. The dandies point with their fingers and make witty remarks. The belles titter bewitchingly. All this in silence save for the ominous throb of the tom-tom. The AUCTIONEER *holds up his hand, taking his place at the stump. The groups strain forward attentively. He touches* JONES *on the shoulder peremptorily, motioning for him to stand on the stump—the auction block.*

JONES *looks up, sees the figures on all sides, looks wildly for some opening to escape, sees none, screams and leaps madly to the top of the stump to get as far away from them as possible. He stands there, cowering, paralyzed with horror. The* AUCTIONEER *begins his silent spiel. He points to* JONES, *appeals to the planters to see for themselves. Here is a good field hand, sound in wind and limb as they can see. Very strong still in spite of his being middle-aged. Look at that back. Look at those shoulders. Look at the muscles in his arms and his sturdy legs. Capable of any amount of hard labor. Moreover, of a good disposition, intelligent and tractable. Will any gentleman start the bidding? The* PLANTERS *raise their fingers, make their bids. They are apparently all eager to possess* JONES. *The bidding is lively, the crowd interested. While this has been going on,* JONES *has been seized by the courage of desperation. He dares to look down and around him. Over his face abject terror gives way to mystification, to gradual realization—stutteringly*).

What you all doin', white folks? What's all dis? What you all lookin' at me fo'? What you doin' wid me, anyhow? (*Suddenly convulsed with raging hatred and fear*) Is dis a auction? Is you sellin' me like dey uster befo' de war? (*Jerking out his revolver just as the* AUCTIONEER *knocks him down to one of the planters—glaring from him to the purchaser*) And *you* sells me? And *you* buys me? I shows you I'se a free nigger, damn yo' souls! (*He fires at the* AUCTIONEER *and at the* PLANTER *with such rapidity that the two shots are almost simultaneous. As if this were a signal the walls of the forest fold in. Only blackness remains and silence broken by* JONES *as he rushes off, crying with fear—and by the quickened, ever louder beat of the tom-tom*)

SCENE SIX

A cleared space in the forest. The limbs of the trees meet over it forming a low ceiling about five feet from the ground. The interlocked ropes of creepers reaching upward to entwine the tree trunks give an arched appearance to the sides. The space thus enclosed is like the dark, noisome hold of some ancient vessel. The moonlight is almost completely shut out and only a vague wan light filters through. There is the noise of someone approaching from the left, stumbling and crawling through the undergrowth. JONES' *voice is heard between chattering moans.*

Oh, Lawd, what I gwine do now? Ain't got no bullet left on'y de silver one. If mo' o' dem ha'nts come after me, how I gwine skeer dem away? Oh, Lawd, on'y de silver one left—an' I gotta save dat fo' luck. If I shoots dat one I'm a goner sho'! Lawd, it's black heah! Whar's de moon? Oh, Lawd, don't dis night evah come to an end! (*By the sounds, he is feeling his way cautiously forward*) Dere! Dis feels like a clear space. I gotta lie down an' rest. I don't care if dem niggers does cotch me. I gotta rest.

(*He is well forward now where his figure can be dimly made out. His pants have been so torn away that what is left of them is no better than a breech cloth. He flings himself full length, face downward on the ground, panting with exhaustion. Gradually it seems to grow lighter in the enclosed space and two rows of seated figures can be seen behind* JONES. *They are sitting in crumpled, despairing attitudes, hunched, facing one another with their backs touching the forest walls as if they were shackled to them. All are Negroes, naked save for loin cloths. At first they are silent and motionless. Then they begin to sway slowly forward toward each and back again in unison, as if they were laxly letting themselves follow the long roll of a ship at sea. At the same time, a low, melancholy murmur rises among them, increasing gradually by rhythmic degrees which seem to be directed and controlled by the throb of the tom-tom in the distance, to a long, tremulous wail of despair that reaches a certain pitch, unbearably acute, then falls by slow gradations of tone into silence and is taken up again.* JONES *starts, looks up, sees the figures and throws himself down again to shut out the sight. A shudder of terror shakes his whole body as the wail rises up about him again. But the next time, his voice, as if under some uncanny compulsion, starts with the others. As their chorus lifts he rises to a sitting posture similar to the others, swaying back and forth. His voice reaches the highest pitch of sorrow, of desolation. The light fades out, the other voices cease, and only darkness is left.* JONES *can be heard scrambling to his feet and running off, his voice sinking down the scale and receding as he moves farther and farther away in the forest. The tom-tom beats louder, quicker, with a more insistent, triumphant pulsation*).

SCENE SEVEN

The foot of a gigantic tree by the edge of a great river. A rough structure of boulders, like an altar, is by the tree. The raised river bank is in the nearer background. Beyond this the surface of the river spreads out, brilliant and unruffled in the moonlight, blotted out and merged into a veil of bluish mist in the distance. JONES' *voice is heard from the left rising and falling in the long, despairing wail of the chained slaves, to the rhythmic beat of the tom-tom. As his voice sinks into silence, he enters the open space. The ex-*

pression of his face is fixed and stony, his eyes have an obsessed glare, he moves with a strange deliberation like a sleep-walker or one in a trance. He looks around at the tree, the rough stone altar, the moonlit surface of the river beyond, and passes his hand over his head with a vague gesture of puzzled bewilderment. Then, as if in obedience to some obscure impulse, he sinks into a kneeling, devotional posture before the altar. Then he seems to come to himself partly, to have an uncertain realization of what he is doing, for he straightens up and stares about him horrifiedly—in an incoherent mumble.

What—what is I doin'? What is—dis place? Seems like I know dat tree—an' dem stones—an' de river. I remember—seems like I been heah befo'. (*Tremblingly*) Oh, Gorry, I'se skeered in dis place! I'se skeered. Oh, Lawd, pertect dis sinner!

(*Crawling away from the altar, he cowers close to the ground, his face hidden, his shoulders heaving with sobs of hysterical fright. From behind the trunk of the tree, as if he had sprung out of it, the figure of the* CONGO WITCH-DOCTOR *appears. He is wizened and old, naked except for the fur of some small animal tied about his waist, its bushy tail hanging down in front. His body is stained all over a bright red. Antelope horns are on each side of his head, branching upward. In one hand he carries a bone rattle, in the other a charm stick with a bunch of white cockatoo feathers tied to the end. A great number of glass beads and bone ornaments are about his neck, ears, wrists, and ankles. He struts noiselessly with a queer prancing step to a position in the clear ground between* JONES *and the altar. Then with a preliminary, summoning stamp of his foot on the earth, he begins to dance and to chant. As if in response to his sum-*mons the beating of the tom-tom grows to a fierce, exultant boom whose throbs seem to fill the air with vibrating rhythm.* JONES *looks up, starts to spring to his feet, reaches a half-kneeling, half-squatting position and remains rigidly fixed there, paralyzed with awed fascination by this new apparition. The* WITCH-DOCTOR *sways, stamping with his foot, his bone rattle clicking the time. His voice rises and falls in a weird, monotonous croon, without articulate word divisions. Gradually his dance becomes clearly one of a narrative in pantomime, his croon is an incantation, a charm to allay the fierceness of some implacable deity demanding sacrifice. He flees, he is pursued by devils, he hides, he flees again. Ever wilder and wilder becomes his flight, nearer and nearer draws the pursuing evil, more and more the spirit of terror gains possession of him. His croon, rising to intensity, is punctuated by shrill cries.* JONES *has become completely hypnotized. His voice joins in the incantation, in the cries, he beats time with his hands and sways his body to and fro from the waist. The whole spirit and meaning of the dance has entered into him, has become his spirit. Finally the theme of the pantomime halts on a howl of despair, and is taken up again in a note of savage hope. There is a salvation. The forces of evil demand sacrifice. They must be appeased. The* WITCH-DOCTOR *points with his wand to the sacred tree, to the river beyond, to the altar, and finally to* JONES *with a ferocious command.* JONES *seems to sense the meaning of this. It is he who must offer himself for sacrifice. He beats his forehead abjectly to the ground, moaning hysterically*).

Mercy, Oh, Lawd! Mercy! Mercy on dis po' sinner.

(*The* WITCH-DOCTOR *springs to the river bank. He stretches out his arms and calls to some God within its depths. Then he starts backward slowly, his arms re-*

maining out. A huge head of a crocodile appears over the bank and its eyes, glittering greenly, fasten upon JONES. *He stares into them fascinatedly. The* WITCH-DOCTOR *prances up to him, touches him with his wand, motions with hideous command toward the waiting monster.* JONES *squirms on his belly nearer and nearer, moaning continually).*

Mercy, Lawd! Mercy!

(The crocodile heaves more of his enormous hulk onto the land. JONES *squirms toward him. The* WITCH-DOCTOR'S *voice shrills out in furious exultation, the tom-tom beats madly.* JONES *cries out in a fierce, exhausted spasm of anguished pleading).*

Lawd, save me! Lawd Jesus, heah my prayer!

(Immediately, in answer to his prayer, comes the thought of the one bullet left him. He snatches at his hip, shouting defiantly).

De silver bullet! You don't git me yit!

(He fires at the green eyes in front of him. The head of the crocodile sinks back behind the river bank, the WITCH-DOCTOR *springs behind the sacred tree and disappears.* JONES *lies with his face to the ground, his arms outstretched, whimpering with fear as the throb of the tom-tom fills the silence about him with a somber pulsation a baffled but revengeful power).*

SCENE EIGHT

Dawn. Same as Scene Two, the dividing line of forest and plain. The nearest tree trunks are dimly revealed but the forest behind them is still a mass of glooming shadow. The tom-tom seems on the very spot, so loud and continuously vibrating are its beats. LEM *enters from the left, followed by a small squad of his soldiers, and by the Cockney trader,* SMITHERS. LEM *is a heavy-set, ape-faced old savage of the extreme African type, dressed only in a loin cloth. A revolver and cartridge belt are about his waist. His soldiers are in different degrees of rag-concealed nakedness. All wear broad palm-leaf hats. Each one carries a rifle.* SMITHERS *is the same as in Scene One. One of the soldiers, evidently a tracker, is peering about keenly on the ground. He points to the spot where* JONES *entered the forest.* LEM *and* SMITHERS *come to look.*

SMITHERS. *(after a glance, turns away in disgust)* That's where 'e went in right enough. Much good it'll do yer. 'E's miles orf by this an' safe to the Coast, damn 's 'ide! I tole yer yer'd lose 'im, didn't I?—wastin' the 'ole bloomin' night beatin' yer bloody drum and castin' yer silly spells! Gawd blimey, wot a pack!

LEM. *(gutturally)* We cotch him. *(He makes a motion to his soldiers who squat down on their haunches in a semicircle).*

SMITHERS. *(exasperatedly)* Well, ain't yer goin' in an' 'unt 'im in the woods? What the 'ell's the good of waitin'?

LEM. *(imperturbably—squatting down himself)* We cotch him.

SMITHERS. *(turning away from him contemptuously)* Aw! Garn! 'E's a better man than the lot o' you put together. I 'ates the sight o' 'im but I'll say that for 'im. *(A sound comes from the forest. The soldiers jump to their feet, cocking their rifles alertly.* LEM *remains sitting with an imperturbable expression, but listening intently. He makes a quick signal with his hand. His followers creep quickly into the forest, scattering so that each enters at a different spot).*

SMITHERS. You ain't thinkin' that would be 'im, I 'ope?

LEM. *(calmly)* We cotch him.

SMITHERS. Blarsted fat 'eads! *(Then after a second's thought—wonderingly)* Still an' all, it might 'appen. If 'e lost 'is bloody way in these stinkin' woods 'e'd likely turn in a circle without 'is knowin' it.

LEM. (*peremptorily*) *Sssh!* (*The reports of several rifles sound from the forest, followed a second later by savage, exultant yells. The beating of the tom-tom abruptly ceases.* LEM *looks up at the white man with a grin of satisfaction*) We cotch him. Him dead.

SMITHERS. (*with a snarl*) 'Ow d'yer know it's 'im an' 'ow d'yer know 'e's dead?

LEM. My mens dey got um silver bullets. Lead bullet no kill him. He got um strong charm. I cook um money, make um silver bullet, make um strong charm, too.

SMITHERS. (*astonished*) So that's wot you was up to all night, wot? You was scared to put after 'im till you'd moulded silver bullets, eh?

LEM. (*simply stating a fact*) Yes. Him got strong charm. Lead no good.

SMITHERS. (*slapping his thigh and guffawing*) Haw-haw! If yer don't beat all 'ell! (*Then recovering himself—scornfully*) I'll bet yer it ain't 'im they shot at all, yer bleedin' looney!

LEM. (*calmly*) Dey come bring him now. (*The soldiers come out of the forest, carrying* JONES' *limp body. He is dead. They carry him to* LEM, *who examines his body with great satisfaction.* SMITHERS *leans over his shoulder—in a tone of frightened awe*) Well, they did for yer right enough, Jonesey, me lad! Dead as a 'erring! (*Mockingly*) Where's yer 'igh an' mighty airs now, yer bloomin' Majesty? (*Then with a grin*) Silver bullets! Gawd blimey, but yer died in the 'eighth o' style, any'ow!

CURTAIN

HOMECOMING

By EUGENE O'NEILL

CHARACTERS

BRIGADIER-GENERAL EZRA MANNON

CHRISTINE, *his wife*

LAVINIA, *their daughter*

CAPTAIN ADAM BRANT, *of the clipper "Flying Trades"*

CAPTAIN PETER NILES, *U.S. Artillery*

HAZEL NILES, *his sister*

SETH BECKWITH

AMOS AMES

LOUISA, *his wife*

MINNIE, *her cousin*

SCENES

ACT ONE: Exterior of the Mannon house in New England—April, 1865.

ACT TWO: Ezra Mannon's study in the house—no time has elapsed.

ACT THREE: The same as Act One—exterior of the house—a night a week later.

ACT FOUR: A bedroom in the house—later the same night.

ACT ONE

SCENE—*Exterior of the Mannon house
on a late afternoon in April, 1865. At
front is the driveway which leads up to
the house from the two entrances on the
street. Behind the driveway the white
Grecian temple portico with its six tall
columns extends across the stage. A big
pine tree is on the lawn at the edge of the
drive before the right corner of the
house. Its trunk is a black column in
striking contrast to the white columns of
the portico. By the edge of the drive, left
front, is a thick clump of lilacs and
syringas. A bench is placed on the lawn
at front of this shrubbery which partly
screens anyone sitting on it from the
front of the house.*

*It is shortly before sunset and the soft
light of the declining sun shines directly
on the front of the house, shimmering in
a luminous mist on the white portico and
the gray stone wall behind, intensifying
the whiteness of the columns, the somber
grayness of the wall, the green of the
open shutters, the green of the lawn and
shrubbery, the black and green of the
pine tree. The white columns cast black
bars of shadow on the gray wall behind
them. The windows of the lower floor
reflect the sun's rays in a resentful glare.
The temple portico is like an incongruous
white mask fixed on the house to hide its
somber gray ugliness.*

*In the distance, from the town, a band
is heard playing "John Brown's Body."
Borne on the light puffs of wind this
music is at times quite loud, then sinks
into faintness as the wind dies.*

*From the left rear, a man's voice is
heard singing the chanty "Shenandoah"—a song that more than any other
holds in it the brooding rhythm of the
sea. The voice grows quickly nearer. It is*
thin and aged, the wraith of what must
once have been a good baritone.*

"*Oh, Shenandoah, I long to hear you
A-way, my rolling river
Oh, Shenandoah, I can't get near you
Way-ay, I'm bound away
Across the wide Missouri.*"

The singer, SETH BECKWITH, *finishes
the last line as he enters from around the
corner of the house. Closely following
him are* AMOS AMES, *his wife* LOUISA, *and
her cousin* MINNIE.

SETH BECKWITH, *the Mannons' gardener and man of all work, is an old man
of seventy-five with white hair and beard,
tall, rawboned and stoop-shouldered, his
joints stiffened by rheumatism, but still
sound and hale. He has a gaunt face that
in repose gives one the strange impression of a life-like mask. It is set in a grim
expression, but his small, sharp eyes still
peer at life with a shrewd prying avidity
and his loose mouth has a strong suggestion of ribald humor. He wears his earth-
stained working clothes.*

AMOS AMES, *carpenter by trade but
now taking a holiday and dressed in his
Sunday best, as are his wife and her
cousin, is a fat man in his fifties. In
character he is the townsfolk type of
garrulous gossip-monger who is at the
same time devoid of evil intent, scandal
being for him merely the subject most
popular with his audience.*

His wife, LOUISA, *is taller and stouter
than he and about the same age. Of a
similar scandal-bearing type, her tongue
is sharpened by malice.*

Her cousin, MINNIE, *is a plump little
woman of forty, of the meek, eager-
listener type, with a small round face,
round stupid eyes, and a round mouth
pursed out to drink in gossip.*

These last three are types of townsfolk

*rather than individuals, a chorus repre-
senting the town come to look and listen
and spy on the rich and exclusive
Mannons.*

Led by SETH, *they come forward as far
as the lilac clump and stand staring at
the house.* SETH, *in a mood of aged play-
fulness, is trying to make an impression
on* MINNIE. *His singing has been for her
benefit. He nudges her with his elbow,
grinning.*

SETH. How's that fur singin' fur an old
feller? I used to be noted fur my
chanties. (*Seeing she is paying no attention to him but is staring with open-
mouthed awe at the house, he turns to*
AMES—*jubilantly*) By jingo, Amos, if
that news is true, there won't be a sober
man in town tonight! It's our patriotic
duty to celebrate!

AMES. (*with a grin*) We'd ought to,
that's sartin!

LOUISA. You ain't goin' to git Amos
drunk tonight, surrender or no surrender!
An old reprobate, that's what you be!

SETH. (*pleased*) Old nothin'! On'y
seventy-five! My old man lived to be
ninety! Licker can't kill the Beckwiths!
(*He and* AMES *laugh.* LOUISA *smiles in
spite of herself.* MINNIE *is oblivious, still
staring at the house*).

MINNIE. My sakes! What a purty
house!

SETH. Wal, I promised Amos I'd help
show ye the sights when you came to
visit him. 'Taint everyone can git to see
the Mannon place close to. They're strict
about trespassin'.

MINNIE. My! They must be rich!
How'd they make their money?

SETH. Ezra's made a pile, and before
him, his father, Abe Mannon, he inherited some and made a pile more in
shippin'. Started one of the fust Western
Ocean packet lines.

MINNIE. Ezra's the General, ain't he?

SETH. (*proudly*) Ayeh. The best
fighter in the hull of Grant's army!

MINNIE. What kind is he?

SETH. (*boastfully expanding*) He's
able, Ezra is! Folks think he's cold-
blooded and uppish, 'cause he's never got
much to say to 'em. But that's only the
Mannons' way. They've been top dog
around here for near on two hundred
years and don't let folks fergit it.

MINNIE. How'd he come to jine the
army if he's so rich?

SETH. Oh, he'd been a soldier afore
this war. His paw made him go to West
P'int. He went to the Mexican war and
come out a major. Abe died that same
year and Ezra give up the army and took
holt of the shippin' business here. But he
didn't stop there. He learned law on the
side and got made a judge. Went in fur
politics and got 'lected mayor. He was
mayor when this war broke out but he
resigned to once and jined the army
again. And now he's riz to be General.
Oh, he's able, Ezra is!

AMES. Ayeh. This town's real proud of
Ezra.

LOUISA. Which is more'n you kin say
fur his wife. Folks all hates her! She ain't
the Mannon kind. French and Dutch
descended, she is. Furrin lookin' and
queer. Her father's a doctor in New
York, but he can't be much of a one
'cause she didn't bring no money when
Ezra married her.

SETH. (*his face growing grim—sharply*)
Never mind her. We ain't talkin' 'bout
her. (*Then abruptly changing the subject*) Wal, I've got to see Vinnie. I'm
goin' round by the kitchen. You wait
here. And if Ezra's wife starts to run you
off fur trespassin', you tell her I got
permission from Vinnie to show you
round. (*He goes off around the corner of
the house, left. The three stare about
them gawkily, awed and uncomfortable.
They talk in low voices*).

LOUISA. Seth is so proud of his durned old Mannons! I couldn't help givin' him a dig about Ezra's wife.

AMES. Wal, don't matter much. He's allus hated her.

LOUISA. Ssshh! Someone's comin' out. Let's get back here! (*They crowd to the rear of the bench by the lilac clump and peer through the leaves as the front door is opened and* CHRISTINE MANNON *comes out to the edge of the portico at the top of the steps.* LOUISA *prods her cousin and whispers excitedly*) That's her! (CHRISTINE MANNON *is a tall striking-looking woman of forty but she appears younger. She has a fine, voluptuous figure and she moves with a flowing animal grace. She wears a green satin dress, smartly cut and expensive, which brings out the peculiar color of her thick curly hair, partly a copper brown, partly a bronze gold, each shade distinct and yet blending with the other. Her face is unusual, handsome rather than beautiful. One is struck at once by the strange impression it gives in repose of being not living flesh but a wonderfully life-like pale mask, in which only the deep-set eyes, of a dark violet blue, are alive. Her black eyebrows meet in a pronounced straight line above her strong nose. Her chin is heavy, her mouth large and sensual, the lower lip full, the upper a thin bow, shadowed by a line of hair. She stands and listens defensively, as if the music held some meaning that threatened her. But at once she shrugs her shoulders with disdain and comes down the steps and walks off toward the flower garden, passing behind the lilac clump without having noticed* AMES *and the women*).

MINNIE. (*in an awed whisper*) My! She's awful handsome, ain't she?

LOUISA. Too furrin lookin' fur my taste.

MINNIE. Ayeh. There's somethin' queer lookin' about her face.

AMES. Secret lookin'—'s if it was a mask she'd put on. That's the Mannon look. They all has it. They grow it on their wives. Seth's growed it on too, didn't you notice—from bein' with 'em all his life. They don't want folks to guess their secrets.

MINNIE. (*breathlessly eager*) Secrets?

LOUISA. The Mannons got skeletons in their closets same as others! Worse ones. (*Lowering her voice almost to a whisper—to her husband*) Tell Minnie about old Abe Mannon's brother David marryin' that French Canuck nurse girl he'd got into trouble.

AMES. Ssshh! Shet up, can't you? Here's Seth comin'. (*But he whispers quickly to* MINNIE) That happened way back when I was a youngster. I'll tell you later. (SETH *has appeared from around the left corner of the house and now joins them*).

SETH. That durned nigger cook is allus askin' me to fetch wood fur her! You'd think I was her slave! That's what we get fur freein' 'em! (*Then briskly*) Wal, come along, folks. I'll show you the peach orchard and then we'll go to my greenhouse. I couldn't find Vinnie. (*They are about to start when the front door of the house is opened and* LAVINIA *comes out to the top of the steps where her mother had stood. She is twenty-three but looks considerably older. Tall like her mother, her body is thin, flat-breasted and angular, and its unattractiveness is accentuated by her plain black dress. Her movements are stiff and she carries herself with a wooden, square-shouldered, military bearing. She has a flat dry voice and a habit of snapping out her words like an officer giving orders. But in spite of these dissimilarities, one is immediately struck by her facial resemblance to her mother. She has the same peculiar shade of copper-gold hair, the same pallor and dark violet-blue eyes, the black eyebrows meeting in a straight line above her nose, the same sensual mouth, the same heavy jaw. Above all, one is struck by the same strange, life-like mask impression her face gives in repose. But it is evident* LAVINIA *does all in her power to emphasize the dissimilarity rather than the resemblance to her parent. She wears her hair pulled tightly back, as if to conceal its natural curliness, and there is not a touch of feminine allurement to her severely plain get-up. Her head is the same size as her mother's, but on her thin body it looks too large and heavy).*

SETH. (*seeing her*) There she be now. (*He starts for the steps—then sees she has not noticed their presence, and stops and stands waiting, struck by something in her manner. She is looking off right, watching her mother as she strolls through the garden to the greenhouse. Her eyes are bleak and hard with an intense, bitter enmity. Then her mother evidently disappears in the greenhouse, for* LAVINIA *turns her head, still oblivious to* SETH *and his friends, and looks off left, her attention caught by the band, the music of which, borne on a freshening breeze, has suddenly become louder. It is still playing "John Brown's Body."* LAVINIA *listens, as her mother had a moment before, but her reaction is the direct opposite to what her mother's had been. Her eyes light up with a grim satisfaction, and an expression of strange vindictive triumph comes into her face).*

LOUISA. (*in a quick whisper to* MINNIE) That's Lavinia!

MINNIE. She looks like her mother in face—queer lookin'—but she ain't purty like her.

SETH. You git along to the orchard, folks. I'll jine you there. (*They walk back around the left of the house and disappear. He goes to* LAVINIA *eagerly*) Say, I got fine news fur you, Vinnie. The telegraph feller says Lee is a goner sure this time! They're only waitin' now fur the news to be made official. You can count on your paw comin' home!

LAVINIA. (*grimly*) I hope so. It's time.

SETH. (*with a keen glance at her—slowly*) Ayeh.

LAVINIA. (*turning on him sharply*) What do you mean, Seth?

SETH. (*avoiding her eyes—evasively*) Nothin'—'cept what you mean. (LAVINIA *stares at him. He avoids her eyes—then heavily casual*) Where was you gallivantin' night afore last and all yesterday?

LAVINIA. (*again starts—then slowly as* Peter's house.

SETH. Ayeh. There's where Hannah said you'd told her you was goin'. That's funny now—'cause I seen Peter upstreet yesterday and he asked me where you was keepin' yourself.

LAVINIA. (*again starts—then slowly as if admitting a secret understanding between them*) I went to New York, Seth.

SETH. Ayeh. That's where I thought you'd gone, mebbe. (*Then with deep sympathy*) It's durned hard on you, Vinnie. It's a durned shame.

LAVINIA. (*stiffening—curtly*) I don't know what you're talking about.

SETH. (*nods comprehendingly*) All right, Vinnie. Just as you say. (*He pauses—then after hesitating frowningly for a moment, blurts out*) There's somethin' been on my mind lately I want to warn you about. It's got to do with what's worryin' you—that is, if there's anythin' in it.

LAVINIA. (*stiffly*) There's nothing worrying me. (*Then sharply*) Warn me? About what?

SETH. Mebbe it's nothin'—and then again mebbe I'm right, and if I'm right, then you'd ought t'be warned. It's to do with that Captain Brant.

LAVINIA. (*starts again but keeps her tone cold and collected*) What about him?

SETH. Somethin' I calc'late no one'd notice 'specially 'ceptin' me, because— (*Then hastily as he sees someone coming up the drive*) Here's Peter and Hazel comin'. I'll tell you later, Vinnie. I ain't got time now anyways. Those folks are waitin' for me.

LAVINIA. I'll be sitting here. You come back afterwards. (*Then her cold disciplined mask breaking for a moment—tensely*) Oh, why do Peter and Hazel have to come now? I don't want to see anyone! (*She starts as if to go into the house*).

SETH. You run in. I'll git rid of 'em fur you.

LAVINIA. (*recovering herself—curtly*) No. I'll see them. (SETH *goes back around the corner of the house, left. A moment later* HAZEL *and* PETER NILES *enter along the drive from left, front.* HAZEL *is a pretty, healthy girl of nineteen, with dark hair and eyes. Her features are small but clearly modelled. She has a strong chin and a capable, smiling mouth. One gets a sure impression of her character at a glance—frank, innocent, amiable and good—not in a negative but in a positive, self-possessed way. Her brother,* PETER, *is very like her in character—straightforward, guileless and good-natured. He is a heavily built young fellow of twenty-two, awkward in movement and hesitating in speech. His face is broad, plain, with a snubby nose, curly brown hair, fine gray eyes and a big mouth. He wears the uniform of an artillery captain in the Union Army*).

LAVINIA. (*with forced cordiality*) Good afternoon. How are you? (*She and* HAZEL *kiss and she shakes hands with* PETER).

HAZEL. Oh, we're all right. But how are you, Vinnie, that's the question? Seems as if we hadn't seen you in ages! You haven't been sick, I hope!

LAVINIA. Well—if you call a pesky cold sick.

PETER. Gosh, that's too bad! All over it now?

LAVINIA. Yes—almost. Do sit down, won't you? (HAZEL *sits at left of bench,*

LAVINIA *beside her in the middle.* PETER *sits gingerly on the right edge so that there is an open space between him and* LAVINIA).

HAZEL. Peter can stay a while if you want him to, but I just dropped in for a second to find out if you'd had any more news from Orin.

LAVINIA. Not since the letter I showed you.

HAZEL. But that was ages ago! And I haven't had a letter in months. I guess he must have met another girl some place and given me the go by. (*She forces a smile but her tone is really hurt*).

PETER. Orin not writing doesn't mean anything. He never was much of a hand for letters.

HAZEL. I know that, but—you don't think he's been wounded, do you, Vinnie?

LAVINIA. Of course not. Father would have let us know.

PETER. Sure he would. Don't be foolish, Hazel! (*Then after a little pause*) Orin ought be home before long now. You've heard the good news, of course, Vinnie?

HAZEL. Peter won't have to go back. Isn't that fine?

PETER. My wound is healed and I've got orders to leave tomorrow but they'll be cancelled, I guess. (*Grinning*) I won't pretend I'm the sort of hero that wants to go back, either! I've had enough!

HAZEL. (*impulsively*) Oh, it will be so good to see Orin again. (*Then embarrassed, forces a self-conscious laugh and gets up and kisses* LAVINIA) Well, I must run. I've got to meet Emily. Good-bye, Vinnie. Do take care of yourself and come to see us soon. (*With a teasing glance at her brother*) And be kind to Peter. He's nice—when he's asleep. And he has something he's just dying to ask you!

PETER. (*horribly embarrassed*) Darn you! (HAZEL *laughs and goes off down the drive, left front.* PETER *fidgets, his eyes on the ground.* LAVINIA *watches him. Since* HAZEL'S *teasing statement, she has visibly withdrawn into herself and is on the defensive. Finally* PETER *looks up and blurts out awkwardly)* Hazel feels bad about Orin not writing. Do you think he really—loves her?

LAVINIA. (*stiffening—brusquely*) I don't know anything about love! I don't want to know anything! (*Intensely*) I hate love!

PETER. (*crushed by this but trying bravely to joke*) Gosh, then, if that's the mood you're in, I guess I better not ask—something I'd made up my mind to ask you today.

LAVINIA. It's what you asked me a year ago when you were home on leave, isn't it?

PETER. And you said wait till the war was over. Well, it's over now.

LAVINIA. (*slowly*) I can't marry anyone, Peter. I've got to stay home. Father needs me.

PETER. He's got your mother.

LAVINIA. (*sharply*) He needs me more! (*A pause. Then she turns pityingly and puts her hand on his shoulder*) I'm sorry, Peter.

PETER. (*gruffly*) Oh, that's all right.

LAVINIA. I know it's what girls always say in books, but I do love you as a brother, Peter. I wouldn't lose you as a brother for anything. We've been like that ever since we were little and started playing together—you and Orin and Hazel and I. So please don't let this come between us.

PETER. 'Course it won't. What do you think I am? (*Doggedly*) Besides, I'm not giving up hope but what you'll change your mind in time. That is, unless it's because you love someone else—

LAVINIA. (*snatching her hand back*) Don't be stupid, Peter!

PETER. But how about this mysterious clipper captain that's been calling?

LAVINIA. (*angrily*) Do you think I care anything about that—that—!

PETER. Don't get mad. I only meant, folks say he's courting you.

LAVINIA. Folks say more than their prayers!

PETER. Then you don't—care for him?

LAVINIA. (*intensely*) I hate the sight of him!

PETER. Gosh! I'm glad to hear you say that, Vinnie. I was afraid—I imagined girls all liked him. He's such a darned romantic-looking cuss. Looks more like a gambler or a poet than a ship captain. I got a look as he was coming out of your gate—I guess it was the last time he was here. Funny, too. He reminded me of someone. But I couldn't place who it was.

LAVINIA. (*startled, glances at him uneasily*) No one around here, that's sure. He comes from out West. Grandfather Hamel happened to meet him in New York and took a fancy to him, and Mother met him at Grandfather's house.

PETER. Who is he, anyway, Vinnie?

LAVINIA. I don't know much about him in spite of what you think. Oh, he did tell me the story of his life to make himself out romantic, but I didn't pay much attention. He went to sea when he was young and was in California for the Gold Rush. He's sailed all over the world—he lived on a South Sea island once, so he says.

PETER. (*grumpily*) He seems to have had plenty of romantic experience, if you can believe him!

LAVINIA. (*bitterly*) That's his trade—being romantic! (*Then agitatedly*) But I don't want to talk any more about him. (*She gets up and walks toward right to conceal her agitation, keeping her back turned to* PETER).

PETER. (*with a grin*) Well, I don't either. I can think of more interesting subjects. (CHRISTINE MANNON *appears from left, between the clump of lilacs* and the house. *She is carrying a big bunch of flowers.* LAVINIA *senses her presence and whirls around. For a moment, mother and daughter stare into each other's eyes. In their whole tense attitudes is clearly revealed the bitter antagonism between them. But* CHRISTINE *quickly recovers herself and her air resumes its disdainful aloofness*).

CHRISTINE. Ah, here you are at last! (*Then she sees* PETER, *who is visibly embarrassed by her presence*) Why, good afternoon, Peter, I didn't see you at first.

PETER. Good afternoon, Mrs. Mannon. I was just passing and dropped in for a second. I guess I better run along now, Vinnie.

LAVINIA. (*with an obvious eagerness to get him off—quickly*) All right. Good-bye, Peter.

PETER. Good-bye. Good-bye, Mrs. Mannon.

CHRISTINE. Good-bye, Peter. (*He disappears from the drive, left.* CHRISTINE *comes forward*) I must say you treat your one devoted swain pretty rudely. (LAVINIA *doesn't reply.* CHRISTINE *goes on coolly*) I was wondering when I was going to see you. When I returned from New York last night you seemed to have gone to bed.

LAVINIA. I had gone to bed.

CHRISTINE. You usually read long after that. I tried your door—but you had locked yourself in. When you kept yourself locked in all day I was sure you were intentionally avoiding me. But Annie said you had a headache. (*While she has been speaking she has come toward* LAVINIA *until she is now within arm's reach of her. The facial resemblance, as they stand there, is extraordinary.* CHRISTINE *stares at her coolly, but one senses an uneasy wariness beneath her pose*) Did you have a headache?

LAVINIA. No. I wanted to be alone—to think over things.

CHRISTINE. What things, if I may ask?

(*Then, as if she were afraid of an answer to this question, she abruptly changes the subject*) Who are those people I saw wandering about the grounds?

LAVINIA. Some friends of Seth's.

CHRISTINE. Because they know that lazy old sot, does it give them the privilege of trespassing?

LAVINIA. I gave Seth permission to show them around.

CHRISTINE. And since when have you the right without consulting me?

LAVINIA. I couldn't very well consult you when Seth asked me. You had gone to New York—(*She pauses a second—then adds slowly, staring fixedly at her mother*) to see Grandfather. Is he feeling any better? He seems to have been sick so much this past year.

CHRISTINE. (*casually, avoiding her eyes*) Yes. He's much better now. He'll soon be going the rounds to his patients again, he hopes. (*As if anxious to change the subject, looking at the flowers she carries*) I've been to the greenhouse to pick these. I felt our tomb needed a little brightening. (*She nods scornfully toward the house*) Each time I come back after being away it appears more like a sepulchre! The "whited" one of the Bible—pagan temple front stuck like a mask on Puritan gray ugliness! It was just like old Abe Mannon to build such a monstrosity—as a temple for his hatred. (*Then with a little mocking laugh*) Forgive me, Vinnie. I forgot you liked it. And you ought to. It suits your temperament. (LAVINIA *stares at her but remains silent.* CHRISTINE *glances at her flowers again and turns toward the house*) I must put these in water. (*She moves a few steps toward the house—then turns again—with a studied casualness*) By the way, before I forget, I happened to run into Captain Brant on the street in New York. He said he was coming up here today to take over his ship and asked me if he might drop in to see you. I told him he could—and stay to supper with us. (*Without looking at* LAVINIA, *who is staring at her with a face grown grim and hard*) Doesn't that please you, Vinnie? Or do you remain true to your one and only beau, Peter?

LAVINIA. Is that why you picked the flowers—because he is coming? (*Her mother does not answer. She goes on with a threatening undercurrent in her voice*) You have heard the news, I suppose? It means Father will be home soon!

CHRISTINE. (*without looking at her— coolly*) We've had so many rumors lately. This report hasn't been confirmed yet, has it? I haven't heard the fort firing a salute.

LAVINIA. You will before long!

CHRISTINE. I'm sure I hope so as much as you.

LAVINIA. You can say that!

CHRISTINE. (*concealing her alarm— coldly*) What do you mean? You will kindly not take that tone with me, please! (*Cuttingly*) If you are determined to quarrel, let us go into the house. We might be overheard out here. (*She turns and sees* SETH *who has just come to the corner of the house, left, and is standing there watching them*) See. There is your old crony doing his best to listen now! (*Moving to the steps*) I am going in and rest a while. (*She walks up the steps*).

LAVINIA. (*harshly*) I've got to have a talk with you, Mother—before long!

CHRISTINE. (*turning defiantly*) Whenever you wish. Tonight after the Captain leaves you, if you like. But what is it you want to talk about?

LAVINIA. You'll know soon enough!

CHRISTINE. (*staring at her with a questioning dread—forcing a scornful smile*) You always make such a mystery of things, Vinnie. (*She goes into the house and closes the door behind her.* SETH *comes forward from where he had withdrawn around the corner of the house.* LAVINIA *makes a motion for him to fol-*

low her, and goes and sits on the bench at left. A pause. She stares straight ahead, her face frozen, her eyes hard. He regards her understandingly*).

LAVINIA. (*abruptly*) Well? What is it about Captain Brant you want to warn me against? (*Then as if she felt she must defend her question from some suspicion that she knows is in his mind*) I want to know all I can about him because—he seems to be calling to court me.

SETH. (*managing to convey his entire disbelief of this statement in one word*) Ayeh.

LAVINIA. (*sharply*) You say that as if you didn't believe me.

SETH. I believe anything you tell me to believe. I ain't been with the Mannons for sixty years without learning that. (*A pause. Then he asks slowly*) Ain't you noticed this Brant reminds you of someone in looks?

LAVINIA. (*struck by this*) Yes. I have —ever since I first saw him—but I've never been able to place who— Who do you mean?

SETH. Your Paw, ain't it, Vinnie?

LAVINIA. (*startled—agitatedly*) Father? No! It can't be! (*Then as if the conviction were forcing itself on her in spite of herself*) Yes! He does—something about his face—that must be why I've had the strange feeling I've known him before— why I've felt—(*Then tensely as if she were about to break down*) Oh! I won't believe it! You must be mistaken, Seth! That would be too—!

SETH. He ain't only like your Paw. He's like Orin, too—and all the Mannons I've known.

LAVINIA. (*frightenedly*) But why—why should he—?

SETH. More speshully he calls to my mind your Grandpaw's brother, David. How much do you know about David Mannon, Vinnie? I know his name's never been allowed to be spoke among Mannons since the day he left—but

[161]

you've likely heard gossip, ain't you—even if it all happened before you was born.

LAVINIA. I've heard that he loved the Canuck nurse girl who was taking care of Father's little sister who died, and had to marry her because she was going to have a baby; and that Grandfather put them both out of the house and then afterwards tore it down and built this one because he wouldn't live where his brother had disgraced the family. But what has that old scandal got to do with—

SETH. Wait. Right after they was throwed out they married and went away. There was talk they'd gone out West, but no one knew nothin' about 'em afterwards—'ceptin' your Grandpaw let out to me one time she'd had the baby—a boy. He was cussin' it. (*Then impressively*) It's about her baby I've been thinkin', Vinnie.

LAVINIA. (*a look of appalled comprehension growing on her face*) Oh!

SETH. How old is that Brant, Vinnie?

LAVINIA. Thirty-six, I think.

SETH. Ayeh! That'd make it right. And here's another funny thing—his name. Brant's sort of queer fur a name. I ain't never heard tell of it before. Sounds made up to me—like short for somethin' else. Remember what that Canuck girl's name was, do you, Vinnie? Marie Brantôme! See what I'm drivin' at?

LAVINIA. (*agitatedly, fighting against a growing conviction*) But—don't be stupid, Seth—his name would be Mannon and he'd be only too proud of it.

SETH. He'd have good reason not to use the name of Mannon when he came callin' here, wouldn't he? If your Paw ever guessed—!

LAVINIA. (*breaking out violently*) No! It can't be! God wouldn't let it! It would be too horrible—on top of—! I won't even think of it, do you hear? Why did you have to tell me?

SETH. (*calmingly*) There now! Don't take on, Vinnie. No need gettin' riled at me. (*He waits—then goes on insistently*) All I'm drivin' at is that it's durned funny—his looks and the name—and you'd ought fur your Paw's sake to make sartin.

LAVINIA. How can I make certain?

SETH. Catch him off guard sometime and put it up to him strong—as if you knowed it—and see if mebbe he don't give himself away. (*He starts to go—looks down the drive at left*) Looks like him comin' up the drive now, Vinnie. There's somethin' about his walk calls back David Mannon, too. If I didn't know it was him I'd think it was David's ghost comin' home. (*He turns away abruptly*) Wal, calc'late I better git back to work. (*He walks around the left corner of the house. A pause. Then* CAPTAIN ADAM BRANT *enters from the drive, left, front. He starts on seeing* LAVINIA *but immediately puts on his most polite, winning air. One is struck at a glance by the peculiar quality his face in repose has of being a life-like mask rather than living flesh. He has a broad, low forehead, framed by coal-black straight hair which he wears noticeably long, pushed back carelessly from his forehead as a poet's might be. He has a big aquiline nose, bushy eyebrows, swarthy complexion, hazel eyes. His wide mouth is sensual and moody—a mouth that can be strong and weak by turns. He wears a mustache, but his heavy cleft chin is clean-shaven. In figure he is tall, broad-shouldered and powerful. He gives the impression of being always on the offensive or defensive, always fighting life. He is dressed with an almost foppish extravagance, with touches of studied carelessness, as if a romantic Byronic appearance were the ideal in mind. There is little of the obvious ship captain about him, except his big, strong hands and his deep voice*).

[162]

BRANT. (*bowing with an exaggerated politeness*) Good afternoon. (*Coming and taking her hand which she forces herself to hold out to him*) Hope you don't mind my walking in on you without ceremony. Your mother told me—

LAVINIA. I know. She had to go out for a while and she said I was to keep you company until she returned.

BRANT. (*gallantly*) Well, I'm in good luck, then. I hope she doesn't hurry back to stand watch over us. I haven't had a chance to be alone with you since—that night we went walking in the moonlight, do you remember? (*He has kept her hand and he drops his voice to a low, lover-like tone.* LAVINIA *cannot repress a start, agitatedly snatching her hand from his and turning away from him*).

LAVINIA. (*regaining command of herself—slowly*) What do you think of the news of Lee surrendering, Captain? We expect my father home very soon now. (*At something in her tone he stares at her suspiciously, but she is looking straight before her*) Why don't you sit down?

BRANT. Thank you. (*He sits on the bench at her right. He has become wary now, feeling something strange in her attitude but not able to make her out— casually*) Yes, you must be very happy at the prospect of seeing your father again. Your mother has told me how close you've always been to him.

LAVINIA. Did she? (*Then with intensity*) I love Father better than anyone in the world. There is nothing I wouldn't do—to protect him from hurt!

BRANT. (*watching her carefully—keeping his casual tone*) You care more for him than for your mother?

LAVINIA. Yes.

BRANT. Well, I suppose that's the usual way of it. A daughter feels closer to her father and a son to his mother. But I should think you ought to be a born exception to that rule.

LAVINIA. Why?

BRANT. You're so like your mother in some ways. Your face is the dead image of hers. And look at your hair. You won't meet hair like yours and hers again in a month of Sundays. I only know of one other woman who had it. You'll think it strange when I tell you. It was my mother.

LAVINIA. (*with a start*) Ah!

BRANT. (*dropping his voice to a reverent, hushed tone*) Yes, she had beautiful hair like your mother's, that hung down to her knees, and big, deep, sad eyes that were blue as the Caribbean Sea!

LAVINIA. (*harshly*) What do looks amount to? I'm not a bit like her! Everybody knows I take after Father!

BRANT. (*brought back with a shock, astonished at her tone*) But—you're not angry at me for saying that, are you? (*Then filled with uneasiness and resolving he must establish himself on an intimate footing with her again—with engaging bluntness*) You're puzzling today, Miss Lavinia. You'll excuse me if I come out with it bluntly. I've lived most of my life at sea and in camps and I'm used to straight speaking. What are you holding against me? If I've done anything to offend you, I swear it wasn't meant. (*She is silent, staring before her with hard eyes, rigidly upright. He appraises her with a calculating look, then goes on*) I wouldn't have bad feeling come between us for the world. I may only be flattering myself, but I thought you liked me. Have you forgotten that night walking along the shore?

LAVINIA. (*in a cold, hard voice*) I haven't forgotten. Did Mother tell you you could kiss me?

BRANT. What—what do you mean? (*But he at once attributes the question to her naïveté—laughingly*) Oh! I see! But, come now, Lavinia, you can't mean, can you, I should have asked her permission?

[163]

LAVINIA. Shouldn't you?

BRANT. (*again uneasy—trying to joke it off*) Well, I wasn't brought up that strictly and, should or shouldn't, at any rate, I didn't—and it wasn't the less sweet for that! (*Then at something in her face he hurriedly goes off on another tack*) I'm afraid I gabbed too much that night. Maybe I bored you with my talk of clipper ships and my love for them?

LAVINIA. (*dryly*) "Tall, white clippers," you called them. You said they were like beautiful, pale women to you. You said you loved them more than you'd ever loved a woman. Is that true, Captain?

BRANT. (*with forced gallantry*) Aye. But I meant, before I met you. (*Then thinking he has at last hit on the cause of her changed attitude toward him—with a laugh*) So that's what you're holding against me, is it? Well, I might have guessed. Women are jealous of ships. They always suspect the sea. They know they're three of a kind when it comes to a man! (*He laughs again but less certainly this time, as he regards her grim, set expression*) Yes, I might have seen you didn't appear much taken by my sea gamming that night. I suppose clippers are too old a story to the daughter of a ship builder. But unless I'm much mistaken, you were interested when I told you of the islands in the South Seas where I was shipwrecked my first voyage at sea.

LAVINIA. (*in a dry, brittle tone*) I remember your admiration for the naked native women. You said they had found the secret of happiness because they had never heard that love can be a sin.

BRANT. (*surprised—sizing her up puzzledly*) So you remember that, do you? (*Then romantically*) Aye! And they live in as near the Garden of Paradise before sin was discovered as you'll find on this earth! Unless you've seen it, you can't picture the green beauty of their land set in the blue of the sea! The clouds like down on the mountain tops, the sun drowsing in your blood, and always the surf on the barrier reef singing a croon in your ears like a lullaby! The Blessed Isles, I'd call them! You can forget there all men's dirty dreams of greed and power!

LAVINIA. And their dirty dreams—of love?

BRANT. (*startled again—staring at her uneasily*) Why do you say that? What do you mean, Lavinia?

LAVINIA. Nothing. I was only thinking—of your Blessed Isles.

BRANT. (*uncertainly*) Oh! But you said—(*Then with a confused, stupid persistence he comes closer to her, dropping his voice again to his love-making tone*) Whenever I remember those islands now, I will always think of you, as you walked beside me that night with your hair blowing in the sea wind and the moonlight in your eyes! (*He tries to take her hand, but at his touch she pulls away and springs to her feet*).

LAVINIA. (*with cold fury*) Don't you touch me! Don't you dare—! You liar! You—! (*Then as he starts back in confusion, she seizes this opportunity to follow* SETH's *advice—staring at him with deliberately insulting scorn*) But I suppose it would be foolish to expect anything but cheap romantic lies from the son of a low Canuck nurse girl!

BRANT. (*stunned*) What's that? (*Then rage at the insult to his mother overcoming all prudence—springs to his feet threateningly*) Belay, damn you!—or I'll forget you're a woman—no Mannon can insult her while I—

LAVINIA. (*appalled now she knows the truth*) So—it is true— You are her son! Oh!

BRANT. (*fighting to control himself—with harsh defiance*) And what if I am? I'm proud to be! My only shame is my dirty Mannon blood! So that's why you couldn't stand my touching you just now, is it? You're too good for the son of a servant, eh? By God, you were glad enough before—!

LAVINIA. (*fiercely*) It's not true! I was only leading you on to find out things!

BRANT. Oh, no! It's only since you suspected who I was! I suppose your father has stuffed you with his lies about my mother! But, by God, you'll hear the truth of it, now you know who I am— And you'll see if you or any Mannon has the right to look down on her!

LAVINIA. I don't want to hear—(*She starts to go toward the house*).

BRANT. (*grabbing her by the arm—tauntingly*) You're a coward, are you, like all Mannons, when it comes to facing the truth about themselves? (*She turns on him defiantly. He drops her arm and goes on harshly*) I'll bet he never told you your grandfather, Abe Mannon, as well as his brother, loved my mother!

LAVINIA. It's a lie!

BRANT. It's the truth. It was his jealous revenge made him disown my father and cheat him out of his share of the business they'd inherited!

LAVINIA. He didn't cheat him! He bought him out!

BRANT. Forced him to sell for one-tenth its worth, you mean! He knew my father and mother were starving! But the money didn't last my father long! He'd taken to drink. He was a coward—like all Mannons—once he felt the world looked down on him. He skulked and avoided people. He grew ashamed of my mother—and me. He sank down and down and my mother worked and supported him. I can remember when men from the corner saloon would drag him home and he'd fall in the door, a sodden carcass. One night when I was seven he came home crazy drunk and hit my mother in the face. It was the first time he'd ever struck her. It made me blind mad. I hit at him with the poker and cut his head. My mother pulled me back and

gave me a hiding. Then she cried over him. She'd never stopped loving him.

LAVINIA. Why do you tell me this? I told you once I don't want to hear—

BRANT. (*grimly*) You'll see the point of it damned soon! (*Unheeding—as if the scene were still before his eyes*) For days after, he sat and stared at nothing. One time when we were alone he asked me to forgive him hitting her. But I hated him and I wouldn't forgive him. Then one night he went out and he didn't come back. The next morning they found him hanging in a barn!

LAVINIA. (*with a shudder*) Oh!

BRANT. (*savagely*) The only decent thing he ever did!

LAVINIA. You're lying! No Mannon would ever—

BRANT. Oh, wouldn't they? They are all fine, honorable gentlemen, you think! Then listen a bit and you'll hear something about another of them! (*Then going on bitterly with his story*) My mother sewed for a living and sent me to school. She was very strict with me. She blamed me for his killing himself. But she was bound she'd made a gentleman of me—like he was!—if it took her last cent and her last strap! (*With a grim smile*) She didn't succeed, as you notice! At seventeen I ran away to sea—and forgot I had a mother, except I took part of her name—Brant was short and easy on ships—and I wouldn't wear the name of Mannon. I forgot her until two years ago when I came back from the East. Oh, I'd written to her now and then and sent her money when I happened to have any. But I'd forgotten her just the same—and when I got to New York I found her dying—of sickness and starvation! And I found out that when she'd been laid up, not able to work, not knowing where to reach me, she'd sunk her last shred of pride and written to your father asking for a loan. He never answered her. And I came too late. She died in my arms. (*With vindictive passion*) He could have saved her—and he deliberately let her die! He's as guilty of murder as anyone he ever sent to the rope when he was a judge!

LAVINIA. (*springing to her feet—furiously*) You dare say that about Father! If he were here—

BRANT. I wish to God he was! I'd tell him what I tell you now—that I swore on my mother's body I'd revenge her death on him.

LAVINIA. (*with cold deadly intensity*) And I suppose you boast that now you've done so, don't you?—in the vilest, most cowardly way—like the son of a servant you are!

BRANT. (*again thrown off guard—furiously*) Belay, I told you, with that kind of talk!

LAVINIA. She is only your means of revenge on Father, is that it?

BRANT. (*stunned—stammers in guilty confusion*) What?—She?—Who?—I don't know what you're talking about!

LAVINIA. Then you soon will know! And so will she! I've found out all I wanted to from you. I'm going in to talk to her now. You wait here until I call you!

BRANT. (*furious at her tone*) No! Be damned if you can order me about as if I was your servant!

LAVINIA. (*icily*) If you have any consideration for her, you'll do as I say and not force me to write my father. (*She turns her back on him and walks to the steps woodenly erect and square-shouldered*).

BRANT. (*desperately now—with a grotesque catching at his lover's manner*) I don't know what you mean, Lavinia. I swear before God it is only you I—(*She turns at the top of the steps at this and stares at him with such a passion of hatred that he is silenced. Her lips move as if she were going to speak, but she fights back the words, turns stiffly and*

goes into the house and closes the door behind her*)

CURTAIN

ACT TWO

SCENE—*In the house—*EZRA MANNON'S *study. No time has elapsed.*

The study is a large room with a stiff, austere atmosphere. The furniture is old colonial. The walls are plain plastered surfaces tinted a dull gray with a flat white trim. At rear, right, is a door leading to the hall. On the right wall is a painting of George Washington in a gilt frame, flanked by smaller portraits of Alexander Hamilton and John Marshall. At rear, center, is an open fireplace. At left of fireplace, a bookcase filled with law books. Above the fireplace, in a plain frame, is a large portrait of EZRA MANNON *himself, painted ten years previously. One is at once struck by the startling likeness between him and* ADAM BRANT. *He is a tall man in his early forties, with a spare, wiry frame, seated stiffly in an armchair, his hands on the arms, wearing his black judge's robe. His face is handsome in a stern, aloof fashion. It is cold and emotionless and has the same strange semblance of a life-like mask that we have already seen in the faces of his wife and daughter and* BRANT.

On the left are two windows. Between them a desk. A large table with an armchair on either side, right and left, stands at left center, front. At right center is another chair. There are hooked rugs on the floor.

Outside the sun is beginning to set and its glow fills the room with a golden mist. As the action progresses this becomes brighter, then turns to crimson, which darkens to somberness at the end.

LAVINIA *is discovered standing by the*

[166]

table. She is fighting to control herself, but her face is torn by a look of stricken anguish. She turns slowly to her father's portrait and for a moment stares at it fixedly. Then she goes to it and puts her hand over one of his hands with a loving, protecting gesture.

LAVINIA. Poor Father! (*She hears a noise in the hall and moves hastily away. The door from the hall is opened and* CHRISTINE *enters. She is uneasy underneath, but affects a scornful indignation*).

CHRISTINE. Really, this unconfirmed report must have turned your head—otherwise I'd find it difficult to understand your sending Annie to disturb me when you knew I was resting.

LAVINIA. I told you I had to talk to you.

CHRISTINE. (*looking around the room with aversion*) But why in this musty room, of all places?

LAVINIA. (*indicating the portrait—quietly*) Because it's Father's room.

CHRISTINE. (*starts, looks at the portrait and quickly drops her eyes.* LAVINIA *goes to the door and closes it.* CHRISTINE *says with forced scorn*) More mystery?

LAVINIA. You better sit down. (CHRISTINE *sits in the chair at rear center.* LAVINIA *goes back to her father's chair at left of table*).

CHRISTINE. Well—if you're quite ready, perhaps you will explain.

LAVINIA. I suppose Annie told you I'd been to visit Hazel and Peter while you were away.

CHRISTINE. Yes. I thought it peculiar. You never visit anyone overnight. Why did you suddenly take that notion?

LAVINIA. I didn't.

CHRISTINE. You didn't visit them?

LAVINIA. No.

CHRISTINE. Then where did you go?

LAVINIA. (*accusingly*) To New York! (CHRISTINE *starts.* LAVINIA *hurries on a bit incoherently*) I've suspected something—lately—the excuse you've made

for all your trips there the past year, that Grandfather was sick— (*As* CHRISTINE *is about to protest indignantly*) Oh! I know he has been—and you've stayed at his house—but I've suspected lately that wasn't the real reason—and now I can prove it isn't! Because I waited outside Grandfather's house and followed you. I saw you meet Brant!

CHRISTINE. (*alarmed but concealing it—coolly*) Well, what if you did? I told you myself I ran into him by accident—

LAVINIA. You went to his room!

CHRISTINE. (*shaken*) He asked me to meet a friend of his—a lady. It was her house we went to.

LAVINIA. I asked the woman in the basement. He had hired the room under another name, but she recognized his description. And yours too. She said you had come there often in the past year.

CHRISTINE. (*desperately*) It was the first time I had ever been there. He insisted on my going. He said he had to talk to me about you. He wanted my help to approach your father—

LAVINIA. (*furiously*) How can you lie like that? How can you be so vile as to try to use me to hide your adultery?

CHRISTINE. (*springing up—with weak indignation*) Vinnie!

LAVINIA. Your adultery, I said!

CHRISTINE. No!

LAVINIA. Stop lying, I tell you! I went upstairs! I heard you telling him—"I love you, Adam"—and kissing him! (*with a cold bitter fury*) You vile—! You're shameless and evil! Even if you are my mother, I say it! (CHRISTINE *stares at her, overwhelmed by this onslaught, her poise shattered for the moment. She tries to keep her voice indifferent but it trembles a little*).

CHRISTINE. I—I knew you hated me, Vinnie—but not as bitterly as that! (*Then with a return of her defiant coolness*) Very well! I love Adam Brant. What are you going to do?

LAVINIA. How you say that—without any shame! You don't give one thought to Father—who is so good—who trusts you! Oh, how could you do this to Father? How could you?

CHRISTINE. (*with strident intensity*) You would understand if you were the wife of a man you hated!

LAVINIA. (*horrified—with a glance at the portrait*) Don't! Don't say that—before him! I won't listen!

CHRISTINE. (*grabbing her by the arm*) You will listen! I'm talking to you as a woman now, not as mother to daughter! That relationship has no meaning between us! You've called me vile and shameless! Well, I want you to know that's what I've felt about myself for over twenty years, giving my body to a man I—

LAVINIA. (*trying to break away from her, half putting her hands up to her ears*) Stop telling me such things! Let me go! (*She breaks away, shrinking from her mother with a look of sick repulsion. A pause. She stammers*) You—then you've always hated Father?

CHRISTINE. (*bitterly*) No. I loved him once—before I married him—incredible as that seems now! He was handsome in his lieutenant's uniform! He was silent and mysterious and romantic! But marriage soon turned his romance into—disgust!

LAVINIA. (*wincing again—stammers harshly*) So I was born of your disgust! I've always guessed that, Mother—ever since I was little—when I used to come to you—with love—but you would always push me away! I've felt it ever since I can remember—your disgust! (*Then with a flare-up of bitter hatred*) Oh, I hate you! It's only right I should hate you!

CHRISTINE. (*shaken—defensively*) I tried to love you. I told myself it wasn't human not to love my own child, born of

my body. But I never could make myself feel you were born of any body but his! You were always my wedding night to me—and my honeymoon!

LAVINIA. Stop saying that! How can you be so—! (*Then suddenly—with a strange jealous bitterness*) You've loved Orin! Why didn't you hate him, too?

CHRISTINE. Because by then I had forced myself to become resigned in order to live! And most of the time I was carrying him, your father was with the army in Mexico. I had forgotten him. And when Orin was born he seemed my child, only mine, and I loved him for that! (*Bitterly*) I loved him until he let you and your father nag him into the war, in spite of my begging him not to leave me alone. (*Staring at* LAVINIA *with hatred*) I know his leaving me was your doing principally, Vinnie!

LAVINIA. (*sternly*) It was his duty as a Mannon to go! He'd have been sorry the rest of his life if he hadn't! I love him better than you! I was thinking of him!

CHRISTINE. Well, I hope you realize I never would have fallen in love with Adam if I'd had Orin with me. When he had gone there was nothing left—but hate and a desire to be revenged—and a longing for love! And it was then I met Adam. I saw he loved me—

LAVINIA. (*with taunting scorn*) He doesn't love you! You're only his revenge on Father! Do you know who he really is? He's the son of that low nurse girl Grandfather put out of our house!

CHRISTINE. (*concealing a start—coolly*) So you've found that out? Were you hoping it would be a crushing surprise to me? I've known it all along. He told me when he said he loved me.

LAVINIA. Oh! And I suppose knowing who he was gave you all the more satisfaction—to add that disgrace!

CHRISTINE. (*cuttingly*) Will you kindly come to the point and tell me what you intend doing? I suppose you'll hardly let your father get in the door before you tell him!

LAVINIA. (*suddenly becoming rigid and cold again—slowly*) No. Not unless you force me to. (*Then as she sees her mother's astonishment—grimly*) I don't wonder you're surprised! You know you deserve the worst punishment you could get. And Father would disown you publicly, no matter how much the scandal cost him!

CHRISTINE. I realize that. I know him even better than you do!

LAVINIA. And I'd like to see you punished for your wickedness! So please understand this isn't for your sake. It's for Father's. He hasn't been well lately. I'm not going to have him hurt! It's my first duty to protect him from you!

CHRISTINE. I know better than to expect any generosity on my account.

LAVINIA. I won't tell him, provided you give up Brant and never see him again—and promise to be a dutiful wife to Father and make up for the wrong you've done him!

CHRISTINE. (*stares at her daughter—a pause—then she laughs dryly*) What a fraud you are, with your talk of your father and your duty! Oh, I'm not denying you want to save his pride—and I know how anxious you are to keep the family from more scandal! But all the same, that's not your real reason for sparing me!

LAVINIA. (*confused—guiltily*) It is!

CHRISTINE. You wanted Adam Brant yourself!

LAVINIA. That's a lie!

CHRISTINE. And now you know you can't have him, you're determined that at least you'll take him from me!

LAVINIA. No!

CHRISTINE. But if you told your father, I'd have to go away with Adam. He'd be mine still. You can't bear that thought, even at the price of my disgrace, can you?

LAVINIA. It's your evil mind!

CHRISTINE. I know you, Vinnie! I've watched you ever since you were little, trying to do exactly what you're doing now! You've tried to become the wife of your father and the mother of Orin! You've always schemed to steal my place!

LAVINIA. (*wildly*) No! It's you who have stolen all love from me since the time I was born! (*Then her manner becoming threatening*) But I don't want to listen to any more of your lies and excuses! I want to know right now whether you're going to do what I told you or not!

CHRISTINE. Suppose I refuse! Suppose I go off openly with Adam! Where will you and your father and the family name be after that scandal? And what if I were disgraced myself? I'd have the man I love, at least!

LAVINIA. (*grimly*) Not for long! Father would use all his influence and get Brant blacklisted so he'd lose his command and never get another! You know how much the "Flying Trades" means to him. And Father would never divorce you. You could never marry. You'd be an anchor around his neck. Don't forget you're five years older than he is! He'll still be in his prime when you're an old woman with all your looks gone! He'd grow to hate the sight of you!

CHRISTINE. (*stung beyond bearing— makes a threatening move as if to strike her daughter's face*) You devil! You mean little—! (*But* LAVINIA *stares back coldly into her eyes and she controls herself and drops her hand*).

LAVINIA. I wouldn't call names if I were you! There is one you deserve!

CHRISTINE. (*turning away—her voice still trembling*) I'm a fool to let you make me lose my temper—over your jealous spite! (*A pause.* LAVINIA *stares at* her. CHRISTINE *seems considering something. A sinister expression comes to her face. Then she turns back to* LAVINIA— *coldly*) But you wanted my answer, didn't you? Well, I agree to do as you said. I promise you I'll never see Adam again after he calls this evening. Are you satisfied?

LAVINIA. (*stares at her with cold suspicion*) You seem to take giving him up pretty easily!

CHRISTINE. (*hastily*) Do you think I'll ever give you the satisfaction of seeing me grieve? Oh, no, Vinnie! You'll never have a chance to gloat!

LAVINIA. (*still suspiciously—with a touch of scorn*) If I loved anyone—!

CHRISTINE. (*tauntingly*) If? I think you do love him—as much as you can love! (*With a sudden flurry of jealousy*) You little fool! Don't you know I made him flirt with you, so you wouldn't be suspicious?

LAVINIA. (*gives a little shudder—then fiercely*) He didn't fool me! I saw what a liar he was! I just led him on—to find out things! I always hated him! (CHRISTINE *smiles mockingly and turns away, as if to go out of the room.* LAVINIA'S *manner becomes threatening again*) Wait! I don't trust you! I know you're thinking already how you can fool me and break the promise you've just made! But you better not try it! I'll be watching you every minute! And I won't be the only one! I wrote to Father and Orin as soon as I got back from New York!

CHRISTINE. (*startled*) About Adam?

LAVINIA. Only enough so they'd be suspicious and watch you too. I said a Captain Brant had been calling and folks had begun to gossip.

CHRISTINE. Ah! I see what it's going to mean—that you'll always have this to hold over me and I'll be under your thumb for the rest of my life! (*She cannot restrain her rage—threateningly*)

Take care, Vinnie! You'll be responsible if—! (*She checks herself abruptly*).

LAVINIA. (*suspiciously*) If what?

CHRISTINE. (*quickly*) Nothing. I only meant if I went off with Adam. But of course you know I won't do that. You know there's nothing I can do now—but obey your orders!

LAVINIA. (*continues to stare at her suspiciously—grimly*) You ought to see it's your duty to Father, not my orders—if you had any honor or decency! (*Then brusquely*) Brant is waiting outside. You can tell him what you've got to do—and tell him if he ever dares come here again—! (*Forcing back her anger*) And see that you get rid of him right now! I'm going upstreet to get the latest news. I won't be gone more than a half-hour and I want him out of the house by the time I get back, do you hear? If he isn't, I'll write Father again. I won't even wait for him to come home! (*She turns her back on her mother and marches out the door, square-shouldered and stiff, without a backward glance.* CHRISTINE *looks after her, waiting until she hears the side door of the house close after her. Then she turns and stands in tense calculating thought. Her face has become like a sinister evil mask. Finally, as if making up her mind irrevocably, she comes to the table, tears off a slip of paper and writes two words on it. She tucks this paper in the sleeve of her dress and goes to the open window and calls*).

CHRISTINE. Adam! (*She moves toward the door to wait for him. Her eyes are caught by the eyes of her husband in the portrait over the fireplace. She stares at him with hatred and addresses him vindictively, half under her breath*) You can thank Vinnie, Ezra! (*She goes to the door and reaches it just as* BRANT *appears from the hall. She takes his hand and draws him into the room, closing the door behind him. One is immediately struck by the resemblance between his face and that of the portrait of* EZRA MANNON).

BRANT. (*glancing uneasily at her, as they come to the center of the room*) She knows—?

CHRISTINE. Yes. She followed me to New York. And she's found out who you are too, Adam.

BRANT. (*with a grim smile*) I know. She got that out of me—the proof of it, at any rate. Before I knew what was up I'd given myself away.

CHRISTINE. She must have noticed your resemblance to Orin. I was afraid that might start her thinking.

BRANT. (*sees the portrait for the first time. Instantly his body shifts to a fighting tenseness. It is as if he were going to spring at the figure in the painting. He says slowly*) That, I take it, is General Mannon?

CHRISTINE. Judge Mannon then. Don't forget he used to be a judge. He won't forget it.

BRANT. (*his eyes still fixed on the portrait—comes and sits in* MANNON'S *chair on the left of table. Unconsciously he takes the same attitude as* MANNON, *sitting erect, his hands on the arms of the chair—slowly*) Does Orin by any chance resemble his father?

CHRISTINE. (*stares at him—agitatedly*) No! Of course not! What put such a stupid idea in your head?

BRANT. It would be damned queer if you fell in love with me because I recalled Ezra Mannon to you!

CHRISTINE. (*going to him and putting an arm around his shoulder*) No, no, I tell you! It was Orin you made me think of! It was Orin!

BRANT. I remember that night we were introduced and I heard the name Mrs. Ezra Mannon! By God, how I hated you then for being his! I thought, by God, I'll take her from him and that'll be part of

my revenge! And out of that hatred my love came! It's damned queer, isn't it?

CHRISTINE. (*hugging him to her*) Are you going to let him take me from you now, Adam?

BRANT. (*passionately*) You ask that!

CHRISTINE. You swear you won't—no matter what you must do?

BRANT. By God, I swear it!

CHRISTINE. (*kisses him*) Remember that oath! (*She glances at the portrait—then turns back to* BRANT *with a little shiver—nervously*) What made you sit there? It's his chair. I've so often seen him sitting there— (*Forcing a little laugh*) Your silly talk about resemblances— Don't sit there. Come. Bring that chair over here. (*She moves to the chair at right center. He brings the chair at right of table close to hers*).

BRANT. We've got to decide what we must do. The time for skulking and lying is over—and by God I'm glad of it! It's a coward's game I have no stomach for! (*He has placed the chair beside hers. She is staring at the portrait*) Why don't you sit down, Christine?

CHRISTINE. (*slowly*) I was thinking— perhaps we had better go to the sitting-room (*Then defiantly*) No! I've been afraid of you long enough, Ezra! (*She sits down*).

BRANT. I felt there was something wrong the moment I saw her. I tried my damnedest to put her off the course by giving her some softsoap—as you'd told me to do to blind her. (*Frowning*) That was a mistake, Christine. It made her pay too much attention to me—and opened her eyes!

CHRISTINE. Oh, I know I've made one blunder after another. It's as if love drove me on to do everything I shouldn't. I never should have brought you to this house. Seeing you in New York should have been enough for me. But I loved you too much. I wanted you every possible moment we could steal! And I simply couldn't believe that he ever would come home. I prayed that he should be killed in the war so intensely that I finally believed it would surely happen! (*With savage intensity*) Oh, if he were only dead!

BRANT. That chance is finished now.

CHRISTINE. (*slowly—without looking at him*) Yes—in that way.

BRANT. (*stares at her*) What do you mean? (*She remains silent. He changes the subject uneasily*) There's only one thing to do! When he comes home I'll wait for him and not give Vinnie the satisfaction of telling him. I'll tell him myself. (*Vindictively*) By God! I'd give my soul to see his face when he knows you love Marie Brantôme's son! And then I'll take you away openly and laugh at him! And if he tries to stop me—! (*He stops and glances with savage hatred at the portrait*).

CHRISTINE. What would you do then?

BRANT. If ever I laid hands on him, I'd kill him!

CHRISTINE. And then? You would be hanged for murder! And where would I be? There would be nothing left for me but to kill myself!

BRANT. If I could catch him alone, where no one would interfere, and let the best man come out alive—as I've often seen it done in the West!

CHRISTINE. This isn't the West.

BRANT. I could insult him on the street before everyone and make him fight me! I could let him shoot first and then kill him in self-defense.

CHRISTINE. (*scornfully*) Do you imagine you could force him to fight a duel with you? Don't you know duelling is illegal? Oh, no! He'd simply feel bound to do his duty as a former judge and have you arrested! (*She adds calculatingly, seeing he is boiling inside*) It would be a poor revenge for your mother's death to let him make you a laughing stock!

BRANT. But when I take you off, the laugh will be on him! You can come on the "Flying Trades."

CHRISTINE. (*calculatingly reproachful*) I don't think you'd propose that, Adam, if you stopped thinking of your revenge for a moment and thought of me! Don't you realize he would never divorce me, out of spite? What would I be in the world's eyes? My life would be ruined and I would ruin yours! You'd grow to hate me!

BRANT. (*passionately*) Don't talk like that! It's a lie and you know it!

CHRISTINE. (*with bitter yearning*) If I could only believe that, Adam! But I'll grow old so soon! And I'm afraid of time! (*Then abruptly changing tone*) As for my sailing on your ship, you'll find you won't have a ship! He'll see to it you lose this command and get you blacklisted so you'll have no chance of getting another.

BRANT. (*angrily*) Aye! He can do that if he sets about it. There are twice as many skippers as ships these days.

CHRISTINE. (*calculatingly—without looking at him*) If he had only been killed, we could be married now and I would bring you my share of the Mannon estate. That would only be justice. It's yours by right. It's what his father stole from yours.

BRANT. That's true enough, damn him!

CHRISTINE. You wouldn't have to worry about commands or owners' favors then. You could buy your own ship and be your own master!

BRANT. (*yearningly*) That's always been my dream—some day to own my own clipper! And Clark and Dawson would be willing to sell the "Flying Trades." (*Then forgetting everything in his enthusiasm*) You've seen her, Christine. She's as beautiful a ship as you're a woman. Aye, the two of you are like sisters. If she was mine, I'd take you on a honeymoon then! To China—and on the voyage back, we'd stop at the South Pacific Islands I've told you about. By God, there's the right place for love and a honeymoon!

CHRISTINE. (*slowly*) Yes—but Ezra is alive!

BRANT. (*brought back to earth—gloomily*) I know it's only a dream.

CHRISTINE. (*turning to stare at him—slowly*) You can have your dream—and I can have mine. There is a way. (*Then turning away again*) You remember my telling you he had written complaining of pains about his heart?

BRANT. You're surely not hoping—

CHRISTINE. No. He said it was nothing serious. But I've let it be known that he has heart trouble. I went to see our old family doctor and told him about Ezra's letter. I pretended to be dreadfully worried, until I got him worried too. He's the town's worst old gossip. I'm sure everyone knows about Ezra's weak heart by this time.

BRANT. What are you driving at, Christine?

CHRISTINE. Something I've been thinking of ever since I realized he might soon come home. And now that Vinnie—but even if we didn't have to consider her, it'd be the only way! I couldn't fool him long. He's a strange, hidden man. His silence always creeps into my thoughts. Even if he never spoke, I would feel what was in his mind and some night, lying beside him, it would drive me mad and I'd have to kill his silence by screaming out the truth! (*She has been staring before her—now she suddenly turns on* BRANT—*slowly*) If he died suddenly now, no one would think it was anything but heart failure. I've been reading a book in Father's medical library. I saw it there one day a few weeks ago—it was as if some fate in me forced me to see it! (*She reaches in the sleeve of her dress and takes out the slip of paper she had written on*) I've written something here.

I want you to get it for me. (*His fingers close on it mechanically. He stares at it with a strange stupid dread. She hurries on so as not to give him time for reflection*) The work on the "Flying Trades" is all finished, isn't it? You sail to Boston tomorrow, to wait for cargo?

BRANT. (*dully*) Aye.

CHRISTINE. Get this at some druggist's down by the waterfront the minute you reach there. You can make up some story about a sick dog on your ship. As soon as you get it, mail it to me here. I'll be on the lookout, so Vinnie will never know it came. Then you must wait on the "Flying Trades" until you hear from me or I come to you—afterward!

BRANT. (*dully*) But how can you do it —so no one will suspect?

CHRISTINE. He's taking medicine. I'll give him his medicine. Oh, I've planned it carefully.

BRANT. But—if he dies suddenly, won't Vinnie—

CHRISTINE. There'll be no reason for her to suspect. She's worried already about his heart. Besides, she may hate me, but she would never think—

BRANT. Orin will be coming home, too.

CHRISTINE. Orin will believe anything I want him to. As for the people here, they'd never dream of such a thing in the Mannon house! And the sooner I do it, the less suspicion there'll be! They will think the excitement of coming home and the reaction were too much for his weak heart! Doctor Blake will think so. I'll see that's what he thinks.

BRANT. (*harshly*) Poison! It's a coward's trick!

CHRISTINE. (*with fierce scorn now, seeing the necessity of goading him*) Do you think you would be braver to give me up to him and let him take away your ship?

BRANT. No!

CHRISTINE. Didn't you say you wanted to kill him?

BRANT. Aye! But I'd give him his chance!

CHRISTINE. Did he give your mother her chance?

BRANT. (*aroused*) No, damn him!

CHRISTINE. Then what makes you suddenly so scrupulous about his death? (*With a sneer*) It must be the Mannon in you coming out! Are you going to prove, the first time your love is put to a real test, that you're a weak coward like your father?

BRANT. Christine! If it was any man said that to me—!

CHRISTINE. (*passionately*) Have you thought of this side of his homecoming— that he's coming back to my bed? If you love me as much as you claim, I should think that would rid you of any scruples! If it was a question of some woman taking you from me, I wouldn't have qualms about which was or wasn't the way to kill her! (*More tauntingly*) But perhaps your love has been only a lie you told me—to take the sneaking revenge on him of being a backstairs lover! Perhaps—

BRANT. (*stung, grabbing her by the shoulders—fiercely*) Stop it! I'll do anything you want! You know it! (*then with a change to somber grimness—putting the paper in his pocket*) And you're right. I'm a damn fool to have any feeling about how Ezra Mannon dies!

CHRISTINE. (*a look of exultant satisfaction comes to her face as she sees he is definitely won over now. She throws her arms around him and kisses him passionately*) Ah! Now you're the man I love again, not a hypocritical Mannon! Promise me, no more cowardly romantic scruples! Promise me!

BRANT. I promise. (*The boom of a cannon sounds from the fort that guards the harbor. He and* CHRISTINE *start frightenedly and stand staring at each other. Another boom comes, reverberating, rattling the windows.* CHRISTINE *recovers herself*).

CHRISTINE. You hear? That's the salute to his homecoming! (*She kisses him— with fierce insistence*) Remember your mother's death! Remember your dream of your own ship! Above all, remember you'll have me!—all your own—your wife! (*Then urgently*) And now you must go! She'll be coming back—and you're not good at hiding your thoughts. (*Urging him toward the door*) Hurry! I don't want you to meet her! (*The cannon at the fort keep booming at regular intervals until the end of the scene.* BRANT *goes out in the hall and a moment later the front door is heard closing after him.* CHRISTINE *hurries from the door to the window and watches him from behind the curtains as he goes down the drive. She is in a state of tense, exultant excitement. Then, as if an idea had suddenly come to her, she speaks to his retreating figure with a strange sinister air of elation*) You'll never dare leave me now, Adam—for your ships or your sea or your naked Island girls—when I grow old and ugly! (*She turns back from the window. Her eyes are caught by the eyes of her husband in the portrait and for a moment she stares back into them, as if fascinated. Then she jerks her glance away and, with a little shudder she cannot repress, turns and walks quickly from the room and closes the door behind her*).

CURTAIN

ACT THREE

SCENE—*The same as Act One, Scene One—exterior of the Mannon house. It is around nine o'clock of a night a week later. The light of a half moon falls on the house, giving it an unreal, detached, eerie quality. The pure white temple front seems more than ever like an incongruous mask fixed on the somber,*

*stone house. All the shutters are closed.
The white columns of the portico cast
black bars of shadow on the gray wall
behind them. The trunk of the pine at
right is an ebony pillar, its branches a
mass of shade.*

LAVINIA *is sitting on the top of the
steps to the portico. She is dressed, as
before, severely in black. Her thin figure,
seated stiffly upright, arms against her
sides, the legs close together, the shoulders square, the head upright, is like that
of an Egyptian statue. She is staring
straight before her. The sound of* SETH'S
*thin, aged baritone mournfully singing
the chanty "Shenandoah" is heard from
down the drive, off right front. He is approaching the house and the song draws
quickly nearer:*

*"Oh, Shenandoah, I long to hear you
A-way, my rolling river.
Oh, Shenandoah, I can't get near you
Way-ay, I'm bound away
Across the wide Missouri.*

*"Oh, Shenandoah, I love your daughter
A-way, my rolling river."*

*He enters right front. He is a bit drunk
but holding his liquor well. He walks up
by the lilacs starting the next line "Oh,
Shenandoah"—then suddenly sees* LAVINIA
*on the steps and stops abruptly, a bit
sheepish.*

LAVINIA. (*disapprovingly*) This is the
second time this week I've caught you
coming home like this.

SETH. (*unabashed, approaches the
steps—with a grin*) I'm aimin' to do my
patriotic duty, Vinnie. The first time was
celebratin' Lee's surrender and this time
is drownin' my sorrow for the President
gittin' shot! And the third'll be when
your Paw gits home!

LAVINIA. Father might arrive tonight.

SETH. Gosh, Vinnie, I never calc'lated
he could git here so soon!

LAVINIA. Evidently you didn't. He'd
give you fits if he caught you drunk. Oh,
I don't believe he'll come, but it's possible
he might.

SETH. (*is evidently trying to pull himself together. He suddenly leans over
toward her and, lowering his voice, asks
soberly*) Did you find out anything about
that Brant?

LAVINIA. (*sharply*) Yes. There's no
connection. It was just a silly idea of
yours.

SETH. (*stares at her—then understandingly*) Wal, if you want it left that way,
I'll leave it that way. (*A pause. He continues to stand looking at her, while she
stares in front of her*).

LAVINIA. (*in a low voice*) What was
that Marie Brantôme like, Seth?

SETH. Marie? She was always laughin'
and singin'—frisky and full of life—with
something free and wild about her like an
animile. Purty she was, too! (*Then he
adds*) Hair just the color of your Maw's
and yourn she had.

LAVINIA. I know.

SETH. Oh, everyone took to Marie—
couldn't help it. Even your Paw. He was
only a boy then, but he was crazy about
her, too, like a youngster would be. His
mother was stern with him, while Marie,
she made a fuss over him and petted him.

LAVINIA. Father, too!

SETH. Ayeh—but he hated her worse
than anyone when it got found out she
was his Uncle David's fancy woman.

LAVINIA. (*in a low voice, as if to herself, staring at the house*) It's all so
strange! It frightens me! (*She checks
herself abruptly—turns to* SETH, *curtly*) I
don't believe that about Father. You've
had too much whiskey. Go to bed and
sleep it off. (*She walks up the steps
again*).

SETH. (*gazes at her with understanding*) Ayeh. (*Then warningly, making a
surreptitious signal as he sees the front
door opening behind her*) Ssstt! (CHRIS-

TINE *appears outlined in the light from the hall. She is dressed in a gown of green velvet that sets off her hair. The light behind her glows along the edges of the dress and in the color of her hair. She closes the door and comes into the moonlight at the edge of the steps, standing above and a little to the right of* LAVINIA. *The moonlight, falling full on them, accentuates strangely the resemblance between their faces and at the same time the hostile dissimilarity in body and dress.* LAVINIA *does not turn or give any sign of knowing her mother is behind her. There is a second's uncomfortable silence.* SETH *moves off left)* Wal, I'll trot along! (*He disappears around the corner of the house. There is a pause. Then* CHRISTINE *speaks in a dry mocking tone*).

CHRISTINE. What are you moongazing at? Puritan maidens shouldn't peer too inquisitively into Spring! Isn't beauty an abomination and love a vile thing? (*She laughs with bitter mockery—then tauntingly*) Why don't you marry Peter? You don't want to be left an old maid, do you?

LAVINIA. (*quietly*) You needn't hope to get rid of me that way. I'm not marrying anyone. I've got my duty to Father.

CHRISTINE. Duty! How often I've heard that word in this house! Well, you can't say I didn't do mine all these years. But there comes an end.

LAVINIA. (*grimly*) And there comes another end—and you must do your duty again!

CHRISTINE. (*starts as if to retort defiantly—then says calmly*) Yes, I realize that.

LAVINIA. (*after a pause—suspiciously*) What's going on at the bottom of your mind? I know you're plotting something!

CHRISTINE. (*controlling a start*) Don't be stupid, please!

LAVINIA. Are you planning how you can see Adam again? You better not!

CHRISTINE. (*calmly*) I'm not so foolish. I said good-bye once. Do you think I want to make it harder for myself?

LAVINIA. Has it been hard for you? I'd never guess it—and I've been watching you.

CHRISTINE. I warned you you would have no chance to gloat! (*After a pause*) When do you expect your father home? You want me to play my part well when he comes, don't you?—for his sake. I'd like to be forewarned.

LAVINIA. His letter said he wouldn't wait until his brigade was disbanded but would try to get leave at once. He might arrive tonight—or tomorrow—or the next day. I don't know.

CHRISTINE. You think he might come tonight? (*Then with a mocking smile*) So he's the beau you're waiting for in the spring moonlight! (*Then after a pause*) But the night train got in long ago.

LAVINIA. (*glances down the drive, left front—then starts to her feet excitedly*) Here's someone! (CHRISTINE *slowly rises. There is the sound of footsteps. A moment later* EZRA MANNON *enters from left, front. He stops short in the shadow for a second and stands, erect and stiff, as if at attention, staring at his house, his wife and daughter. He is a tall, spare, big-boned man of fifty, dressed in the uniform of a Brigadier-General. One is immediately struck by the mask-like look of his face in repose, more pronounced in him than in the others. He is exactly like the portrait in his study, which we have seen in Act Two, except that his face is more lined and lean and the hair and beard are grizzled. His movements are exact and wooden and he has a mannerism of standing and sitting in stiff, posed attitudes that suggest the statues of military heroes. When he speaks, his deep voice has a hollow repressed quality, as if he were continually withholding emotion from it. His air is brusque and authoritative.*)

LAVINIA. (*seeing the man's figure stop in the shadow—calls excitedly*) Who's that?

MANNON. (*stepping forward into the moonlight*) It's I.

LAVINIA. (*with a cry of joy*) Father! (*She runs to him and throws her arms around him and kisses him*) Oh, Father! (*She bursts into tears and hides her face against his shoulder*).

MANNON. (*embarrassed—patting her head—gruffly*) Come! I thought I'd taught you never to cry.

LAVINIA. (*obediently forcing back her tears*) I'm sorry, Father—but I'm so happy!

MANNON. (*awkwardly moved*) Tears are queer tokens of happiness! But I appreciate your—your feeling.

CHRISTINE. (*has slowly descended the steps, her eyes fixed on him—tensely*) Is it really you, Ezra? We had just given up hope of your coming tonight.

MANNON. (*going stiffly to meet her*) Train was late. The railroad is jammed up. Everybody has got leave. (*He meets her at the foot of the steps and kisses her with a chill dignity—formally*) I am glad to see you, Christine. You are looking well. (*He steps back and stares at her— then in a voice that betrays a deep under-current of suppressed feeling*) You have changed, somehow. You are prettier than ever— But you always were pretty.

CHRISTINE. (*forcing a light tone*) Compliments from one's husband! How gallant you've become, Ezra! (*Then solicitously*) You must be terribly tired. Wouldn't you like to sit here on the steps for a while? The moonlight is so beautiful.

LAVINIA. (*who has been hovering about jealously, now manages to worm herself between them—sharply*) No. It's too damp out here. And Father must be hungry. (*Taking his arm*) Come inside with me and I'll get you something to eat. You poor dear! You must be starved.

MANNON. (*really revelling in his daughter's coddling but embarrassed before his wife—pulling his arm back— brusquely*) No, thanks! I would rather rest here for a spell. Sit down, Vinnie. (CHRISTINE *sits on the top step at center; he sits on the middle step at right;* LAVINIA *on the lowest step at left. While they are doing this he keeps on talking in his abrupt sentences, as if he were trying to cover up some hidden uneasiness*) I've got leave for a few days. Then I must go back and disband my brigade. Peace ought to be signed soon. The President's assassination is a frightful calamity. But it can't change the course of events.

LAVINIA. Poor man! It's dreadful he should die just at his moment of victory.

MANNON. Yes! (*Then after a pause— somberly*) All victory ends in the defeat of death. That's sure. But does defeat end in the victory of death? That's what I wonder! (*They both stare at him,* LAVINIA *in surprise,* CHRISTINE *in uneasy wonder. A pause*).

CHRISTINE. Where is Orin? Couldn't you get leave for him too?

MANNON. (*hesitates—then brusquely*) I've been keeping it from you. Orin was wounded.

LAVINIA. Wounded! You don't mean— badly hurt?

CHRISTINE. (*half starting to her feet impulsively—with more of angry bitter-ness than grief*) I knew it! I knew when you forced him into your horrible war—! (*Then sinking back—tensely*) You needn't trouble to break the news gradu-ally, Ezra. Orin is dead, isn't he?

LAVINIA. Don't say that! It isn't true, is it, Father?

MANNON. (*curtly—a trace of jealousy in his tone*) Of course it isn't! If your mother would permit me to finish instead of jumping at conclusions about her baby—! (*With a grim, proud satisfac-tion*) He's no baby now. I've made a man of him. He did one of the bravest things I've seen in the war. He was wounded in the head—a close shave but it turned out only a scratch. But he got brain fever from the shock. He's all right now. He was in a rundown condition, they say at the hospital. I never guessed it. Nerves. I wouldn't notice nerves. He's always been restless. (*Half turning to* CHRISTINE) He gets that from you.

CHRISTINE. When will he be well enough to come home?

MANNON. Soon. The doctor advised a few more days' rest. He's still weak. He was out of his head for a long time. Acted as if he were a little boy again. Seemed to think you were with him. That is, he kept talking to "Mother."

CHRISTINE. (*with a tense intake of breath*) Ah!

LAVINIA. (*pityingly—with a tinge of scorn in her voice*) Poor Orin!

MANNON. I don't want you to baby him when he comes home, Christine. It would be bad for him to get tied to your apron strings again.

CHRISTINE. You needn't worry. That passed—when he left me. (*Another pause. Then* LAVINIA *speaks*).

LAVINIA. How is the trouble with your heart, Father? I've been so afraid you might be making it out less serious than it really was to keep us from worrying.

MANNON. (*gruffly*) If it was serious, I'd tell you, so you'd be prepared. If you'd seen as much of death as I have in the past four years, you wouldn't be afraid of it. (*Suddenly jumping to his feet—brusquely*) Let's change the subject! I've had my fill of death. What I want now is to forget it. (*He turns and paces up and down to the right of steps.* LAVINIA *watches him worriedly*) All I know is the pain is like a knife. It puts me out of commission while it lasts. The doctor gave me orders to avoid worry or any over-exertion or excitement.

CHRISTINE. (*staring at him*) You don't look well. But probably that's because you're so tired. You must go to bed soon, Ezra.

MANNON. (*comes to a stop in his pacing directly before her and looks into her eyes—a pause—then he says in a voice that he tries to make ordinary*) Yes, I want to—soon.

LAVINIA. (*who has been watching him jealously—suddenly pulling him by the arm—with a childish volubility*) No! Not yet! Please, Father! You've only just come! We've hardly talked at all! (*Defiantly to her mother*) How can you tell him he looks tired? He looks as well as I've ever seen him. (*Then to her father with a vindictive look at* Christine) We've so much to tell you. All about Captain Brant. (*If she had expected her mother to flinch at this, she is disappointed.* CHRISTINE *is prepared and remains unmoved beneath the searching, suspicious glance Mannon now directs at her*).

MANNON. Vinnie wrote me you'd had company. I never heard of him. What business had he here?

CHRISTINE. (*with an easy smile*) You had better ask Vinnie! He's her latest beau! She even went walking in the moonlight with him!

LAVINIA. (*with a gasp at being defied so brazenly*) Oh!

MANNON. (*now jealous and suspicious of his daughter*) I notice you didn't mention that in your letter, young lady!

LAVINIA. I only went walking once with him—and that was before—(*She checks herself abruptly*).

MANNON. Before what?

LAVINIA. Before I knew he's the kind who chases after every woman he sees.

MANNON. (*angrily to* CHRISTINE) A fine guest to receive in my absence!

LAVINIA. I believe he even thought Mother was flirting with him. That's why I felt it my duty to write you. You know how folks in town gossip, Father. I thought you ought to warn Mother she was foolish to allow him to come here.

MANNON. Foolish! It was downright—!

CHRISTINE. (*coldly*) I would prefer not to discuss this until we are alone, Ezra—if you don't mind! And I think Vinnie is extremely inconsiderate the moment you're home—to annoy you with such ridiculous nonsense! (*She turns to* LAVINIA) I think you've done enough mischief. Will you kindly leave us?

LAVINIA. No.

MANNON. (*sharply*) Stop your squabbling, both of you! I hoped you had grown out of that nonsense! I won't have it in my house!

LAVINIA. (*obediently*) Yes, Father.

MANNON. It must be your bedtime, Vinnie.

LAVINIA. Yes, Father. (*She comes and kisses him—excitedly*) Oh, I'm so happy you're here! Don't let Mother make you believe I— You're the only man I'll ever love! I'm going to stay with you!

MANNON. (*patting her hair—with gruff tenderness*) I hope so. I want you to remain my little girl—for a while longer, at least. (*Then suddenly catching* CHRISTINE's *scornful glance—pushes* LAVINIA *away—brusquely*) March now!

LAVINIA. Yes, Father. (*She goes up the steps past her mother without a look. Behind her mother, in the portico, she stops and turns*) Don't let anything worry you, Father. I'll always take care of you (*She goes in.* MANNON *looks at his wife who stares before her. He clears his throat as if about to say something—then starts pacing self-consciously up and down at the right of steps*).

CHRISTINE. (*forcing a gentle tone*) Sit down, Ezra. You will only make yourself more tired, keeping on your feet. (*He sits awkwardly two steps below her, on her left, turned sideways to face her. She asks with disarming simplicity*) Now

please tell me just what it is you suspect me of?

MANNON. (*taken aback*) What makes you think I suspect you?

CHRISTINE. Everything! I've felt your distrust from the moment you came. Your eyes have been probing me, as if you were a judge again and I were the prisoner.

MANNON. (*guiltily*) I—?

CHRISTINE. And all on account of a stupid letter Vinnie had no business to write. It seems to me a late day, when I am an old woman with grown-up children, to accuse me of flirting with a stupid ship captain!

MANNON. (*impressed and relieved—placatingly*) There's no question of accusing you of that. I only think you've been foolish to give the gossips a chance to be malicious.

CHRISTINE. Are you sure that's all you have in your heart against me?

MANNON. Yes! Of course! What else? (*Patting her hand embarrassedly*) We'll say no more about it. (*Then he adds gruffly*) But I'd like you to explain how this Brant happened—

CHRISTINE. I'm only too glad to! I met him at Father's. Father has taken a fancy to him for some reason. So when he called here I couldn't be rude, could I? I hinted that his visits weren't welcome, but men of his type don't understand hints. But he's only been here four times in all, I think. And as for there having been gossip, that's nonsense! The only talk has been that he came to court Vinnie! You can ask anyone in town.

MANNON. Damn his impudence! It was your duty to tell him flatly he wasn't wanted!

CHRISTINE. (*forcing a contrite air*) Well, I must confess I didn't mind his coming as much as I might have—for one reason. He always brought me news of Father. Father's been sick for the past year, as I wrote you. (*Then with a twitch of the lips, as if she were restraining a derisive smile*) You can't realize what a strain I've been under—worrying about Father and Orin and—you.

MANNON. (*deeply moved, turns to her and takes her hand in both of his—awkwardly*) Christine—I deeply regret—having been unjust. (*He kisses her hand impulsively—then embarrassed by this show of emotion, adds in a gruff, joking tone*) Afraid old Johnny Reb would pick me off, were you?

CHRISTINE. (*controlling a wild impulse to burst into derisive laughter*) Do you need to ask that? (*A pause. He stares at her, fascinated and stirred*).

MANNON. (*finally blurts out*) I've dreamed of coming home to you, Christine! (*Leans toward her, his voice trembling with desire and a feeling of strangeness and awe—touching her hair with an awkward caress*) You're beautiful! You look more beautiful than ever—and strange to me. I don't know you. You're younger. I feel like an old man beside you. Only your hair is the same—your strange beautiful hair I always—

CHRISTINE. (*with a start of repulsion, shrinking from his hand*) Don't! (*Then as he turns away, hurt and resentful at this rebuff—hastily*) I'm sorry, Ezra. I didn't mean—I—I'm nervous tonight. (MANNON *paces to the right and stands looking at the trees.* CHRISTINE *stares at his back with hatred. She sighs with affected weariness and leans back and closes her eyes*).

CHRISTINE. I'm tired, Ezra.

MANNON. (*blurts out*) I shouldn't have bothered you with that foolishness about Brant tonight. (*He forces a strained smile*) But I was jealous a mite, to tell you the truth. (*He forces himself to turn and, seeing her eyes are shut, suddenly comes and leans over her awkwardly, as if to kiss her, then is stopped by some strangeness he feels about her still face*).

CHRISTINE. (*feeling his desire and instinctively shrinking—without opening her eyes*) Why do you look at me like that?

MANNON. (*turns away guiltily*) Like what? (*Uneasily*) How do you know? Your eyes are shut. (*Then, as if some burden of depression were on him that he had to throw off, he blurts out heavily*) I can't get used to home yet. It's so lonely. I've got used to the feel of camps with thousands of men around me at night—a sense of protection, maybe! (*Suddenly uneasy again*) Don't keep your eyes shut like that! Don't be so still! (*Then, as she opens her eyes—with an explosive appeal*) God, I want to talk to you, Christine! I've got to explain some things—inside me—to my wife—try to, anyway! (*He sits down beside her*) Shut your eyes again! I can talk better. It has always been hard for me to talk—about feelings. I never could when you looked at me. Your eyes were always so—so full of silence! That is, since we've been married. Not before, when I was courting you. They used to speak then. They made me talk—because they answered.

CHRISTINE. (*her eyes closed—tensely*) Don't talk, Ezra.

MANNON. (*as if he had determined, once started, to go on doggedly without heeding any interruption*) It was seeing death all the time in this war got me to thinking these things. Death was so common, it didn't mean anything. That freed me to think of life. Queer, isn't it? Death made me think of life. Before that life had only made me think of death!

CHRISTINE. (*without opening her eyes*) Why are you talking of death?

MANNON. That's always been the Mannons' way of thinking. They went to the white meeting-house on Sabbaths and meditated on death. Life was a dying. Being born was starting to die. Death was being born. (*Shaking his head with a dogged bewilderment*) How in hell people ever got such notions! That white meeting-house. It stuck in my mind—clean-scrubbed and whitewashed—a temple of death! But in this war I've seen too many white walls splattered with blood that counted no more than dirty water. I've seen dead men scattered about, no more important than rubbish to be got rid of. That made the white meeting-house seem meaningless—making so much solemn fuss over death!

CHRISTINE. (*opens her eyes and stares at him with a strange terror*) What has this talk of death to do with me?

MANNON. (*avoiding her glance—insistently*) Shut your eyes again. Listen and you'll know. (*She shuts her eyes. He plods on with a note of desperation in his voice*) I thought about my life—lying awake nights—and about your life. In the middle of battle I'd think maybe in a minute I'll be dead. But my life as just me ending, that didn't appear worth a thought one way or another. But listen, me as your husband being killed that seemed queer and wrong—like something dying that had never lived. Then all the years we've been man and wife would rise up in my mind and I would try to look at them. But nothing was clear except that there'd always been some barrier between us—a wall hiding us from each other! I would try to make up my mind exactly what that wall was but I never could discover. (*With a clumsy appealing gesture*) Do you know?

CHRISTINE. (*tensely*) I don't know what you're talking about.

MANNON. But you've known it was there! Don't lie, Christine! (*He looks at her still face and closed eyes, imploring her to reassure him—then blunders on doggedly*) Maybe you've always known you didn't love me. I call to mind the Mexican War. I could see you wanted me to go. I had a feeling you'd grown to hate me. Did you? (*She doesn't answer*) That was why I went. I was hoping I might get

killed. Maybe you were hoping that too. Were you?

CHRISTINE. (*stammers*) No, no, I— What makes you say such things?

MANNON. When I came back you had turned to your new baby, Orin. I was hardly alive for you any more. I saw that. I tried not to hate Orin. I turned to Vinnie, but a daughter's not a wife. Then I made up my mind I'd do my work in the world and leave you alone in your life and not care. That's why the shipping wasn't enough—why I became a judge and a mayor and such vain truck, and why folks in town look on me as so able! Ha! Able for what? Not for what I wanted most in life! Not for your love! No! Able only to keep my mind from thinking of what I'd lost! (*He stares at her—then asks pleadingly*) For you did love me before we were married. You won't deny that, will you?

CHRISTINE. (*desperately*) I don't deny anything!

MANNON. (*drawing himself up with a stern pride and dignity and surrendering himself like a commander against hopeless odds*) All right, then. I came home to surrender to you—what's inside me. I love you. I loved you then, and all the years between, and I love you now.

CHRISTINE. (*distractedly*) Ezra! Please!

MANNON. I want that said! Maybe you have forgotten it. I wouldn't blame you. I guess I haven't said it or showed it much—ever. Something queer in me keeps me mum about the things I'd like most to say—keeps me hiding the things I'd like to show. Something keeps me sitting numb in my own heart—like a statue of a dead man in a town square. (*Suddenly he reaches over and takes her hand*) I want to find what that wall is marriage put between us! You've got to help me smash it down! We have twenty good years still before us! I've been thinking of what we could do to get back to each other. I've a notion if we'd leave the children and go off on a voyage together—to the other side of the world— find some island where we could be alone a while. You'll find I have changed, Christine. I'm sick of death! I want life! Maybe you could love me now! (*In a note of final desperate pleading*) I've got to make you love me!

CHRISTINE. (*pulls her hand away from him and springs to her feet wildly*) For God's sake, stop talking. I don't know what you're saying. Leave me alone! What must be, must be! You make me weak! (*Then abruptly*) It's getting late.

MANNON. (*terribly wounded, withdrawn into his stiff soldier armor—takes out his watch mechanically*) Yes—six past eleven. Time to turn in. (*He ascends two steps, his face toward the door. He says bitterly*) You tell me to stop talking! By God, that's funny!

CHRISTINE. (*collected now and calculating—takes hold of his arm, seductively*) I meant—what is the good of words? There is no wall between us. I love you.

MANNON. (*grabs her by the shoulders and stares into her face*) Christine! I'd give my soul to believe that—but—I'm afraid! (*She kisses him. He presses her fiercely in his arms—passionately*) Christine! (*The door behind him is opened and* LAVINIA *appears at the edge of the portico behind and above him. She wears slippers over her bare feet and has a dark dressing-gown over her night dress. She shrinks back from their embrace with aversion. They separate, startled*).

MANNON. (*embarrassed—irritably*) Thought you'd gone to bed, young lady!

LAVINIA. (*woodenly*) I didn't feel sleepy. I thought I'd walk a little. It's such a fine night.

CHRISTINE. We are just going to bed. Your father is tired. (*She moves up, past her daughter, taking* MANNON'S *hand, leading him after her to the door*).

MANNON. No time for a walk, if you ask me. See you turn in soon.

LAVINIA. Yes, Father.

MANNON. Good night. (*The door closes behind them.* LAVINIA *stands staring before her—then walks stiffly down the steps and stands again. Light appears between the chinks of the shutters in the bedroom on the second floor to the left. She looks up*).

LAVINIA. (*in an anguish of jealous hatred*) I hate you! You steal even Father's love from me again! You stole all love from me when I was born! (*Then almost with a sob, hiding her face in her hands*) Oh, Mother! Why have you done this to me? What harm had I done you? (*Then looking up at the window again— with passionate disgust*) Father, how can you love that shameless harlot? (*Then frenziedly*) I can't bear it! I won't! It's my duty to tell him about her! I will! (*She calls desperately*) Father! Father! (*The shutter of the bedroom is pushed open and* MANNON *leans out*).

MANNON. (*sharply*) What is it? Don't shout like that!

LAVINIA. (*stammers lamely*) I—I remembered I forgot to say good night, Father.

MANNON. (*exasperated*) Good heavens! What— (*Then gently*) Oh—all right— good night, Vinnie. Get to bed soon, like a good girl.

LAVINIA. Yes, Father. Good night. (*He goes back in the bedroom and pulls the shutter closed. She stands staring fascinatedly up at the window, wringing her hands in a pitiful desperation*).

CURTAIN

ACT FOUR

SCENE—EZRA MANNON'S *bedroom. A big four-poster bed is at rear, center, the foot front, the head against the rear wall. A small stand, with a candle on it, is by the head of the bed on the left. To the left of the stand is a door leading into* CHRISTINE'S *room. The door is open. In the left wall are two windows. At left, front, is a table with a lamp on it and a chair beside it. In the right wall, front, is a door leading to the hall. Further back, against the wall, is a bureau.*

None of these details can be discerned at first because the room is in darkness, except for what moonlight filters feebly through the shutters. It is around dawn of the following morning.

CHRISTINE'S *form can be made out, a pale ghost in the darkness, as she slips slowly and stealthily from the bed. She tiptoes to the table, left front, and picks up a light-colored dressing-gown that is flung over the chair and puts it on. She stands listening for some sound from the bed. A pause. Then* MANNON'S *voice comes suddenly from the bed, dull and lifeless.*

MANNON. Christine.

CHRISTINE. (*starts violently—in a strained voice*) Yes.

MANNON. Must be near daybreak, isn't it?

CHRISTINE. Yes. It is beginning to get gray.

MANNON. What made you jump when I spoke? Is my voice so strange to you?

CHRISTINE. I thought you were asleep.

MANNON. I haven't been able to sleep. I've been lying here thinking. What makes you so uneasy?

CHRISTINE. I haven't been able to sleep either.

MANNON. You slunk out of bed so quietly.

CHRISTINE. I didn't want to wake you.

MANNON. (*bitterly*) Couldn't you bear it—lying close to me?

CHRISTINE. I didn't want to disturb you by tossing around.

MANNON. We'd better light the light and talk a while.

CHRISTINE. (*with dread*) I don't want to talk! I prefer the dark.

MANNON. I want to see you. (*He takes matches from the stand by the bed and lights the candle on it.* CHRISTINE *hastily sits down in the chair by the table, pushing it so she sits facing left, front, with her face turned three-quarters away from him. He pushes his back up against the head of the bed in a half-sitting position. His face, with the flickering candle light on its side, has a grim, bitter expression*) You like the dark where you can't see your old man of a husband, is that it?

CHRISTINE. I wish you wouldn't talk like that, Ezra. If you are going to say stupid things, I'll go in my own room. (*She gets to her feet but keeps her face turned away from him*).

MANNON. Wait! (*Then a note of pleading in his voice*) Don't go. I don't want to be alone. (*She sits again in the same position as before. He goes on humbly*) I didn't mean to say those things. I guess there's bitterness inside me—my own cussedness, maybe—and sometimes it gets out before I can stop it.

CHRISTINE. You have always been bitter.

MANNON. Before we married?

CHRISTINE. I don't remember.

MANNON. You don't want to remember you ever loved me!

CHRISTINE. (*tensely*) I don't want to talk of the past! (*Abruptly changing the subject*) Did you hear Vinnie the first part of the night? She was pacing up and down before the house like a sentry guarding you. She didn't go to bed until two. I heard the clock strike.

MANNON. There is one who loves me, at least! (*Then after a pause*) I feel strange, Christine.

CHRISTINE. You mean—your heart? You don't think you are going to be—taken ill, do you?

MANNON. (*harshly*) No! (*A pause—then accusingly*) Is that what you're waiting for? Is that why you were so willing to give yourself tonight? Were you hoping—?

CHRISTINE. (*springing up*) Ezra! Stop talking like that! I can't stand it! (*She moves as if to go into her own room*).

MANNON. Wait! I'm sorry I said that. (*Then, as she sits down again, he goes on gloomily*) It isn't my heart. It's something uneasy troubling my mind—as if something in me was listening, watching, waiting for something to happen.

CHRISTINE. Waiting for what to happen?

MANNON. I don't know. (*A pause— then he goes on somberly*) This house is not my house. This is not my room nor my bed. They are empty—waiting for someone to move in! And you are not my wife! You are waiting for something!

CHRISTINE. (*beginning to snap under the strain—jumps to her feet again*) What would I be waiting for?

MANNON. For death—to set you free!

CHRISTINE. Leave me alone! Stop nagging at me with your crazy suspicions! (*Then anger and hatred come into her voice*) Not your wife! You acted as if I were your wife—your property—not so long ago!

MANNON. (*with bitter scorn*) Your body? What are bodies to me? I've seen too many rotting in the sun to make grass greener! Ashes to ashes, dirt to dirt! Is that your notion of love? Do you think I married a body? (*Then, as if all the bitterness and hurt in him had suddenly burst its dam*) You were lying to me tonight as you've always lied! You were only pretending love! You let me take you as if you were a nigger slave I'd bought at auction! You made me appear a lustful beast in my own eyes!—as you've always done since our first marriage night! I would feel cleaner now if I had gone to a brothel! I would feel more honor between myself and life!

CHRISTINE. (*in a stifled voice*) Look out, Ezra! I won't stand—

MANNON. (*with a harsh laugh*) And I had hoped my homecoming would mark a new beginning—new love between us! I told you my secret feelings. I tore my insides out for you—thinking you'd understand! By God, I'm an old fool!

CHRISTINE. (*her voice grown strident*) Did you think you could make me weak—make me forget all the years? Oh, no, Ezra! It's too late! (*Then her voice changes, as if she had suddenly resolved on a course of action, and becomes deliberately taunting*) You want the truth? You've guessed it! You've used me, you've given me children, but I've never once been yours! I never could be! And whose fault is it? I loved you when I married you! I wanted to give myself! But you made me so I couldn't give! You filled me with disgust!

MANNON. (*furiously*) You say that to me! (*Then trying to calm himself—stammers*) No! Be quiet! We mustn't fight! I mustn't lose my temper! It will bring on—!

CHRISTINE. (*goading him with calculating cruelty*) Oh, no! You needn't adopt that pitiful tone! You wanted the truth and you're going to hear it now!

MANNON. (*frightened—almost pleading*) Be quiet, Christine!

CHRISTINE. I've lied about everything! I lied about Captain Brant! He is Marie Brantôme's son! And it was I he came to see, not Vinnie! I made him come!

MANNON. (*seized with fury*) You dared—! You—! The son of that—!

CHRISTINE. Yes, I dared! And all my trips to New York weren't to visit Father but to be with Adam! He's gentle and tender, he's everything you've never been. He's what I've longed for all these years with you—a lover! I love him! So now you know the truth!

MANNON. (*in a frenzy—struggling to*

get out of bed) You—you whore—I'll kill you! (*Suddenly he falls back, groaning, doubled up on his left side, with intense pain*).

CHRISTINE. (*with savage satisfaction*) Ah! (*She hurries through the doorway into her room and immediately returns with a small box in her hand. He is facing away from her door, and, even if the intense pain left him any perception, he could not notice her departure and return, she moves so silently*).

MANNON. (*gaspingly*) Quick—medicine!

CHRISTINE. (*turned away from him, takes a pellet from the box, asking tensely as she does so*) Where is your medicine?

MANNON. On the stand! Hurry!

CHRISTINE. Wait. I have it now. (*She pretends to take something from the stand by the head of the bed—then holds out the pellet and a glass of water which is on the stand*) Here. (*He turns to her groaning and opens his mouth. She puts the pellet on his tongue and presses the glass of water to his lips*) Now drink.

MANNON. (*takes a swallow of water— then suddenly a wild look of terror comes over his face. He gasps*) That's not—my medicine! (*She shrinks back to the table, the hand with the box held out behind her, as if seeking a hiding place. Her fingers release the box on the table top and she brings her hand in front of her as if instinctively impelled to prove to him she has nothing. His eyes are fixed on her in a terrible accusing glare. He tries to call for help but his voice fades to a wheezy whisper*) Help! Vinnie! (*He falls back in a coma, breathing stertorously.* CHRISTINE *stares at him fascinatedly—then starts with terror as she hears a noise from the hall and frantically snatches up the box from the table and holds it behind her back, turning to face the door as it opens and* LAVINIA *appears in the doorway. She is dressed as*

at the end of Act Three, in nightgown, wrapper and slippers. She stands, dazed and frightened and hesitating, as if she had just awakened).

LAVINIA. I had a horrible dream—I thought I heard Father calling me—it woke me up—

CHRISTINE. (*trembling with guilty terror—stammers*) He just had—an attack.

LAVINIA. (*hurries to the bed*) Father! (*She puts her arms around him*) He's fainted!

CHRISTINE. No. He's all right now. Let him sleep. (*At this moment* MANNON, *with a last dying effort, straightens up in a sitting position in* LAVINIA'S *arms, his eyes glaring at his wife, and manages to raise his arm and point an accusing finger at her*).

MANNON. (*gasps*) She's guilty—not medicine! (*He falls back limply*).

LAVINIA. Father! (*Frightenedly she feels for his pulse, puts her ear against his chest to listen for a heartbeat*).

CHRISTINE. Let him alone. He's asleep.

LAVINIA. He's dead!

CHRISTINE. (*repeats mechanically*) Dead? (*Then in a strange flat tone*) I hope—he rests in peace.

LAVINIA. (*turning on her with hatred*) Don't you dare pretend—! You wanted him to die! You— (*She stops and stares at her mother with a horrified suspicion—then harshly accusing*) Why did he point at you like that? Why did he say you were guilty? Answer me!

CHRISTINE. (*stammers*) I told him— Adam was my lover.

LAVINIA. (*aghast*) You told him that— when you knew his heart—! Oh! You did it on purpose! You murdered him!

CHRISTINE. No—it was your fault— you made him suspicious—he kept talking of love and death—he forced me to tell him! (*Her voice becomes thick, as if she were drowsy and fighting off sleep. Her eyes half close*).

LAVINIA. (*grabbing her by the shoul-*

[185]

ders—*fiercely*) Listen! Look at me! He said "not medicine"! What did he mean?

CHRISTINE. (*keeping the hand with the poison pressed against her back*) I—I don't know.

LAVINIA. You do know! What was it? Tell me!

CHRISTINE. (*with a last effort of will manages · to draw herself up and speak with a simulation of outraged feeling*) Are you accusing your mother of—

LAVINIA. Yes! I—! (*Then distractedly*) No—you can't be that evil!

CHRISTINE. (*her strength gone—swaying weakly*) I don't know what—you're talking about. (*She edges away from* LAVINIA *toward her bedroom door, the hand with the poison stretched out behind her—weakly*) I—feel faint. I must go—and lie down. I—(*She turns as if to run into the room, takes a tottering step—then her knees suddenly buckle under her and she falls in a dead faint at the foot of the bed. As her hand strikes the floor the fingers relax and the box slips out onto one of the hooked rugs*).

LAVINIA. (*does not notice this. Startled by* CHRISTINE'S *collapse, she automatically bends on one knee beside her and hastily feels for her pulse. Then satisfied she has only fainted, her anguished hatred immediately returns and she speaks with strident denunciation*) You murdered him just the same—by telling him! I suppose you think you'll be free to marry Adam now! But you won't! Not while I'm alive! I'll make you pay for your crime! I'll find a way to punish you! (*She is starting to her feet when her eyes fall on the little box on the rug. Immediately she snatches it up and stares at it, the look of suspicion changing to a dreadful, horrified certainty. Then with a shuddering cry she shrinks back along the side of the bed, the box clutched in her hand, and sinks on her knees by the head of the bed, and flings her arms around the dead man. With anguished beseeching*) Father! Don't leave me alone! Come back to me! Tell me what to do!

CURTAIN

THE LIFE AND WORKS OF

EUGENE O'NEILL

By JOHN GASSNER

WHEN EUGENE O'NEILL received the Nobel Prize for Literature in 1936, he was in his forty-eighth year and appeared to have concluded his career. More than thirty-five short and long plays by him had been produced in the United States, and they had won him important awards in his own country and an international reputation. A long period of absence from the theater followed his last new work, *Days without End,* which opened in New York on January 8, 1934, and O'Neill did not return to the theater with a new play until the Theater Guild production of *The Iceman Cometh* in 1946. But another decade of absence from the New York stage ensued when his next play, *The Moon for the Misbegotten,* was withdrawn from a trial tour in the midwest by O'Neill and the Theater Guild management. Ten years elapsed before another new play by him, *Long Day's Journey into Night,* reached New York. In the meantime, O'Neill, stricken with illness, had died in Boston on November 27, 1953. His renewed career as a dramatist, mainly posthumous, was concluded by this more or less autobiographical drama and three other new pieces, *A Touch of the Poet, More Stately Mansions,* and the one-act play *Hughie.* O'Neill, who performed many other feats

of endurance in the theater, happened to have two careers in it rather than the customary single career.

O'Neill also attracted attention with *two* styles of theater rather than one, since he was adept equally in the styles of realism and expressionism; and he was equally effective in short, one-act plays and in works twice the normal length of modern plays.

In all his work, O'Neill was a modern dramatist in search of an esthetic and spiritual center. Indeed, his work embodied the ideas and conflicts of the first half of the twentieth century, assimilated its advances in dramatic art, and expressed its uneasy aspirations toward tragic vision and tragic art. His impressiveness as a dramatist is the result of his determined effort to trace a thread of meaning in a universe virtually emptied of meaning by a century of scientific and sociological thought. He did not, it is true, find any comforting meaning in the world or in man's life, but the important thing is that he had the integrity to acknowledge his failure and the persistence to dramatize it with insight into human nature. O'Neill's experiments were not a trifler's whims or opportunist's calculations following the latest fashions in the theater; they manifest, rather, a unity of outlook and purpose rarely exhibited by a modern playwright.

Eugene Gladstone O'Neill was born in 1888 in the very heart of the theatrical district of New York known as Broadway. He was the son of the matinee idol and successful actor-manager James O'Neill, who amassed a fortune touring in a melodrama based on Alexandre Dumas's famous romantic novel *The Count of Monte Cristo*. O'Neill, the playwright who took so many successful liberties with dramatic form, was entirely at home in the theater, and at times he also acted in his father's theatrical company. But it became distressingly evident to his father that young O'Neill was a rebel who would be more inclined to revolt against the romantic tradition than to preserve it. O'Neill was born into a tragically disturbed family (his mother suffered from drug addiction and his elder brother was a confirmed alcoholic) and had an unstable childhood, touring the United States with his parents and receiving an irregular education in different private boarding schools. Encouraged by his irresponsible brother, he was inducted into the bohemian life of the theatrical world of New York at a tender age. After a year at Princeton University, from which he was suspended in 1907 for a student prank, he contracted a secret and short-lived marriage, and ultimately gave vent to his restless spirit by going to sea.

In 1909 he went prospecting for gold in Central America with a mining engineer. Having contracted malaria in the course of this fruitless expedition, he returned to his family and, for a brief period, joined his father's company as an actor and assistant manager. Growing restless again, he shipped to Buenos Aires on a Norwegian vessel. In Argentina he found employment for a time with American companies that were located in the area: an electric company, a packing plant, and the Singer Sewing Machine Company. Tiring of clerical employment, he worked on a cattleboat, traveling from Buenos Aires to South Africa tending mules. On his return to South America, he lapsed into a state of destitution that ended when he joined a British vessel bound for New York. There he promptly relapsed into a life of dissipation on the waterfront, frequenting a disreputable tavern, Jimmy the Priest's, a place he was to recall in the setting for two of his plays, *Anna Christie* and *The Iceman Cometh*. He was still attracted to the sea, however, and he became an able seaman on the American Line and made a voyage to Southampton, England, before finally deciding to settle down to a less adventurous mode of life.

Again, he joined his father's company for a time and played a small part in *The Count of Monte Cristo*. But he was always restless. He went to New London, Connecticut, where his family had a summer home, and joined the local newspaper, the *New London Telegraph*, as a reporter. For a time he wrote a humorous column and contributed poetry to the newspaper, but his good intentions and journalistic career were abruptly terminated. His health, undermined by his intemperate mode of life, gave out and he succumbed to tuberculosis for which he had to be hospitalized in 1912. A term of six months in a sanatorium, however, proved to be doubly beneficial: it arrested the disease and made an avid reader and introspective artist of O'Neill. During his convalescence, he read widely, falling under the influence of the Greek tragic poets and Strindberg. He began to write plays in 1913, and in 1914 he attended a course in playwriting at Harvard given by the famous professor, George Pierce Baker. A year later, he joined an avant-garde group of writers and artists in Greenwich Village who established themselves as an amateur theatrical company and called themselves the Provincetown Players. They started their first season in the summer of 1915 on an abandoned wharf in the artist's summer colony of Provincetown, on Cape Cod, Massachusetts. In addition to acting, O'Neill began to write short plays for this group, and he soon became their foremost playwright as well as one of their directors when they moved to a small theater in Greenwich Village.

The importance of O'Neill's early association with the Provincetown Players cannot be exaggerated. It was here he found an outlet for his personal rebellion because he was able to associate himself with an enterprise created by artists who were in rebellion against materialistic American society and the consequent commercialism of the professional theater. His natural rebelliousness, which had turned him against his father's old-fashioned theatricality as well as conventional values, now found an essential outlet. In writing for the Provincetown Players and having his early plays performed before a small public of interested intellectuals, he avoided the necessity of conforming to the popular taste to which his father had catered all his life. He felt free to deal with the life he had come to know during his years of restless wandering—a life of poverty, dissipation, loneliness, and desperation among common men and among outcasts from respectable society. As a result, in his early short plays about the seafaring life, especially those collected under the title of *S.S. Glencairn and Other Plays,* he became the first American "naturalist," this while the general public in America was still expecting from its playwrights discreet pictures of reality that would offend no one.

His early plays evoked a vigorous poetry of naturalism compounded of the atmosphere of the sea and the moods of the desperate men who seek the seafaring

life as an outlet for their romantic longings or as a way to escape from a life of failure on land. For O'Neill, moreover, the sea actually became a symbol of Man lost in a vast, unfeeling universe and of the conspiracy of Nature against Man. Had he started his career thirty years later—in 1945 rather than 1915—he might have been enrolled in the ranks of the Existentialist writers and been considered the Sartre of the American stage. But O'Neill became a significant figure in America because his early work was a natural synthesis of both the naturalistic and the poetic strivings of the modern theater.

At first, this synthesis was apparent in his one-act plays, short, slice-of-life dramas dealing with the miseries, delusions, and obsessions of men adrift in the world. These plays, like most of those of the avant-garde movement of the period, were relatively inexpensive to produce and easy for amateurs to perform. The S.S. Glencairn cycle of sea pieces, beginning with the Provincetown Players' production of his atmospheric drama of the death of a common seaman, *Bound East for Cardiff,* in the summer of 1916, and other short pieces made him the undisputed master of the one-act play in America. *Ile,* first presented by the Provincetown Players on November 30, 1917, is most respresentative of his early style. It exemplifies his taste for tragic irony, his characteristic concern with destructive obsessiveness that resembles the *hubris* of classic tragedy, and his fascination with the sea as a mystery, a symbol, and a seduction.

The same interests soon appeared in a richer context when O'Neill began to write his early full-length plays. He gave his sense of tragic irony full scope in the first of these, *Beyond the Horizon,* produced in New York in 1920. A country lad, who longs to go to sea, attracts a farm girl with his romantic personality and is condemned by marriage to a routine life for which he is unfit. His practical-minded brother, who is his rival in love, departs for strange lands for which he has no particular liking. Blinded by the sexual instinct, the brothers make the wrong choices in life and destroy their chances of happiness.

In *Anna Christie,* first produced under a different title in 1920, and successfully revived a year later, it is the sea that is blamed for the combination of circumstances that made a prostitute of the heroine. And in *Diff'rent,* also produced in 1920, fate plays an ironic trick on a New England girl who rejected her sea-captain lover because he was not chaste enough to satisfy her puritanical principles; having doomed herself to a life of lonely spinsterhood, she succumbs to the wiles of a designing young rascal thirty-three years later.

In one way or another, the characters in these works and in other early plays, such as *The First Man* and *Welded,* entangled themselves and were further entangled by their circumstances in lives of frustration and unhappiness. In *The First Man* (1922), a scientist destroys his prospects of happiness by resenting the intrusion of a child into his life; and in *Welded* (1924), a play written under the influence of Strindberg but steeped in personal experience, a man and woman are consumed with resentment of each other while feeling such a strong attachment for each other that they cannot live apart. In these and other works, O'Neill employed realistic characterization and naturalistic dialogue.

His determination to probe into human unhappiness and bewilderment carried him to a climax of naturalistic tragedy in *Desire under the Elms,* produced in the fall of 1924 with sensational effect. This work is a tragedy of passion involving the third wife of a New England farmer and his son by his deceased

second wife. O'Neill, who belonged to a generation of severely critical Victorian, especially Puritan, morality, contrasted the passions of his characters with the hardness and lovelessness of Calvinist morality; and he was especially concerned with the Freudian theme of sexual frustration. The son, Eben, who betrays his tyrannical father, Ezra Cabot, is engaged in an Oedipal conflict with him; and the young stepmother, Abbie, who married Ezra for his money, becomes tragically involved with her stepson when her suppressed hunger for love turns into reckless passion.

Desire under the Elms set forth O'Neill's critical view of his milieu and his interest in Freudian psychology as well as his tragic sense of life. In this intense play he strained the boundaries of naturalistic drama until the play verged on melodrama, when Abbie strangles her child by Eben in order to convince him that she had given herself to him out of love rather than out of a desire to deprive him of his heritage by producing a new heir to his father's farm. In this play, as in his earlier naturalistic plays, O'Neill also strained toward poetry, with symbols of fertility such as two huge elm trees hovering over the farmhouse and the enveloping atmosphere of loneliness and lust.

By 1924 it was already quite evident that O'Neill was not bound by realistic convention, and that he felt strongly impelled to express his sense of poetry and fatality with radical departures from naturalistic dramaturgy. To follow his efforts in expressionist drama we must go back four years, when the Provincetown Players produced *The Emperor Jones,* on November 3, 1920. Greatly influenced by the expressionist experiments of Strindberg, two of which (*The Spook Sonata* and *The Dream Play*) O'Neill actually helped to produce in New York, he became a pioneer of expressionistic theater in the United States. Not only was he adept in the use of expressionist techniques of dream-distortion and hallucinatory fantasy, but he was convinced that he could, by these means, recover imaginative power for modern drama, which had been made arid and cramped by nineteenth-century realism.

He began to entertain a theory of dramatic art that would carry him, even in his short plays, far from commonplace values and ordinary plot-making. Characteristically, he preferred the atmospheric and static one-act play *The Moon of the Caribbees* (1918) to his earlier *In the Zone,* because "the spirit of the sea . . . is in this latter play the hero," and he noted that the central character of both plays, Smitty, was differently related to reality: "Smitty in the stuffy, greasepaint atmosphere of *In the Zone* is magnified into a hero who attracts our sentimental sympathy. In *The Moon* [of the *Caribbees*], posed against a background of that beauty [of the spectacle of the sea under moonlight], sad because it is eternal, which is one of the revealing moods of the sea's truth, his silhouetted gestures of self-pity are reduced to their proper insignificance, his thin whine of weakness is lost in the silence which it was mean enough to disturb, we get the perspective to judge him."

In *The Emperor Jones,* O'Neill intensified the fears of a Negro ex-convict, who had made himself the ruler of a West Indian island, into a nightmare of guilt and superstition. Fleeing from the native islanders in revolt against his tyranny, Jones loses himself in the tropical jungle of the island and recapitulates, in part, the primal fears of the human race itself. Employing brief, explosive scenes and reducing the dialogue to increasingly frenzied monologues as Jones loses his way in the jungle through which he expects to escape to the seacoast, O'Neill created a tour de force in dramatic art.

Combined with haunting visual effects and with the mounting excitement of the native tom-toms, this dramatization of atavistic terrors and of the panic that overcomes a man whose ignorance has been no deterrent to arrogance demonstrated a close relationship between O'Neill's theatrical genius and his philosophical intentions.

It proved no less effective when O'Neill returned to this tragic theme in *The Hairy Ape* (1922), in which the unsuccessful efforts of a brutish steamship stoker to assert himself as a human being acquired a more than private significance. All mankind was symbolized by the stoker Yank, who lingered in a limbo between animal and human existence. He became, as O'Neill declared in a newspaper article (*New York Herald-Tribune* of November 16, 1924), "a symbol of man, who has lost his old harmony with nature, the harmony which he used to have as an animal and has not yet acquired in a spiritual way." O'Neill was partial to the symbolic meaning of the play, declaring that it alone distinguished *The Hairy Ape* from an ordinary kind of drama. "The subject," O'Neill maintained, "is the same ancient one . . . man and his struggle with his own fate. The struggle used to be with the gods, but is now with himself, his own past, his attempt to belong."

Fully launched upon a career of experimentation, confident that he could make demands upon the American public never before made upon it by an American writer, O'Neill continued his search for new dramatic forms. He returned to the expressionist technique of expressive distortion in *All God's Chillun Got Wings,* produced at the Provincetown Playhouse in 1924. The subject was the problem of love and marriage between a bewildered white girl and an intellectual Negro; and the play became a *succès de scandale* in New York because the theme of intermarriage between the white and black races was denounced by bigots as offensive or subversive. The production of *All God's Chillun Got Wings,* in which the chief character was impersonated by the famous Negro actor and singer Paul Robeson, was a moving experience of human relations and inner tensions, and the sociological interest of the work was secondary rather than primary. The playwright's expressionistic treatment of some scenes also deepened the sense of tragedy instead of making the play argumentative. When the young wife goes mad and the husband is unsuccessful in his search for a career they are presented as victims of irrational fate and inherited anxieties and fears. When their marriage proves disastrous, the author blames "fate" rather than society. When the young wife, Ella, recovers from a seizure of madness during which she tried to kill her husband, she asks, like a child, "Will God forgive me, Jim?", and Jim replies, "Maybe He can forgive what you've done to me; and maybe He can forgive Himself."

O'Neill experimented next with masks in one of his most piquant, if not altogether satisfying, plays *The Great God Brown.* He had used masks in a dramatic arrangement of Coleridge's narrative poem *The Ancient Mariner* for the Provincetown Players; and the potentialities of this device must have occurred to him even earlier, while he was steeping himself in Greek tragedy during his convalescence period. His use of masks in *The Great God Brown* was as original as it was effective in representing the divided personalities of his main characters. It remains to be noted that O'Neill employed symbolism in this work consciously, if not indeed so consciously that he succumbed to over-elaboration.

He was less ambitious in conceiving *Marco Millions,* written in 1925, but first produced by the Theater Guild in 1928. It dealt with middle-class obtuseness and insensitivity; the smugness of the Venetian traveler Marco Polo re-created in the image of an American business man was contrasted with the exotic atmosphere and romantic possibilities of the East, to which Marco Polo had failed to respond. But *Strange Interlude,* also produced by the Theater Guild in 1928, showed its author making a determined effort to cover more ground and at the same time to penetrate it more deeply than most modern playwrights. In order to recount the life story of a woman, Nina, who represents the eternal feminine in *Strange Interlude,* O'Neill wrote a nine-act work in which he gave her and the male characters with whom her fate is involved two levels of dialogue—that is, the speech heard by the other characters and the speech they address to themselves alone.

O'Neill took the old Elizabethan device of the "aside" and elaborated it into interior monologues of variable length to express the inner thoughts of the characters. Performed by a remarkable Theater Guild cast led by Lynn Fontanne in the role of Nina, the play described the search of a woman for fulfillment after she loses her idealized young lover in World War I. Thereafter, her strong drive for life precipitates her into many roles as wife, mistress, and mother, and involves her with men who fulfill her needs only partially in their separate relation to her as father-confidant, husband-lover, and son. Her life was shown in this ample work as a succession of efforts to complete herself with the help, and even at the expense, of other peoples' lives. Although repetitious, since many of the asides were not dramatically necessary, and somewhat too schematic in assigning narrow limits to the men in Nina's life, *Strange Interlude* was an impressive drama that conveyed Freudian insights into the psychology of sex and possessed the comprehensiveness of a modern "stream-of-consciousness" novel.

After two plays that failed, *Lazarus Laughs* and *Dynamo*, O'Neill came up in 1931 with his most triumphant experiment, *Mourning Becomes Electra*. Instead of treating a universal theme abstractly, he treated it concretely, giving it a specific locale and idiom by recasting Greek tragedy as modern psychological drama replete with Freudian interpretations. The familiar legend of the murder of Agamemnon by his wife and the vengeance of her children, Electra and Orestes, against their mother and her lover became the story of an American merchant-prince, Ezra Mannon, murdered by his wife Christine on his return from the Civil War in 1865. *Mourning Becomes Electra* was a shattering drama of sexual conflict between husband and wife, of the son Orin's (Orestes) and the daughter Lavinia's (Electra) Oedipus complex, and the incestuous desire of the brother for the sister. O'Neill also reversed his tactics by reducing the formalism of Greek tragedy, amputating the classic chorus and dispensing with masks. Nevertheless, this exceptional long work was no ordinary realistic reduction of high tragedy but a work of noble dimensions, tragic dignity, austere remoteness, and unobtrusively formal structure.

Mourning Becomes Electra, produced by the Theater Guild in New York on October 26, 1931, became the outstanding American drama in the opinion of American and European critics, and it is believed to have been equaled, or perhaps surpassed, by only one other play—another by O'Neill, his *Long Day's Journey into Night*, posthumously produced a quarter of a century later. More than any other work, it was *Mourning Becomes Electra* that won the Nobel Prize for its author.

Ah, Wilderness!, a genial and optimistic comedy which opened in New York in October 1933, was an idealized recollection of life at the turn of the century, when the author had been an adolescent. It was a warm and tenderly amusing family picture, in the foreground of which stood an attractively impulsive young son and a benignly understanding father, who was quite unlike any other father in an O'Neill play. It seemed as if the leading dramatist of family conflict and tragic excess in the American theater had become reconciled with his past and with an untragic conception of life. It also seemed that O'Neill no longer found it essential to depart from middle-class drama and shatter the conventions of the realistic theater in an effort to express the cosmic anguish which he was inclined to identify with human fate.

Following a long but not unproductive period of retirement from public view between 1934 to 1946 O'Neill characterized human history as a total failure in a press interview on the occasion of the first production of his new play, *The Iceman Cometh*, in the fall of 1946. In the plays he wrote during his absence from Broadway, O'Neill returned to realistic style and dramaturgy, but he was no less austere in his view of humanity than in his early expressionistic dramas. O'Neill, despite the sunny interval indicated by *Ah, Wilderness!*, remained loyal to his fundamentally tragic view of life. In *The Iceman Cometh*, a long and grimly ironic drama, he collected a number of life's failures in a disreputable tavern, and showed them subsisting entirely on self-deception. Reminiscent of Maxim Gorki's naturalistic masterpiece *The Lower Depths*, this first new work by O'Neill was more nihilistic than Gorki's play, which looked forward to a future for free men; the most intelligent character in O'Neill's drama looked forward only to the release of death while his fellow derelicts slunk back into their sodden dreams after a brief sortie into the outside world.

A Moon for the Misbegotten, first produced in 1947, was apparently the last play to be completed by its author, who was severely incapacitated by disease during his last years. Wretchedness such as the hopelessness that permeated this drama of an alcoholic idler and a grotesquely large farm girl has rarely been seen in the American theater. *A Touch of the Poet,* first staged in Sweden in 1957, and a year later in New York, revolved around an Irish pretender to aristocracy trapped in New England, and was another study of failure and self-deception. It was the first play of a projected but uncompleted and partially destroyed cycle of family dramas which had the overall theme of failure in every generation of the materialistic American family founded by the Irish pretender. Another play belonging to this cycle, *More Stately Mansions,* had its world premiere at the Royal Dramatic Theater of Stockholm in the fall of 1962.

The most celebrated of O'Neill's posthumously published plays, as mentioned earlier, was *Long Day's Journey into Night,* produced in the fall of 1956. Here the playwright depicted with unmitigated realism the main characters who bear a resemblance to the playwright as a young man, his alcoholic brother, his drug-addicted mother, and his actor-manager father.

It must be noted, however, that in all these works, and especially in this loosely autobiographical masterpiece which summarizes some of the private tensions that shaped O'Neill's somber art, there is a transcendence of as well as a representation of reality. The stasis of *The Iceman Cometh* is akin to a long stupor interrupted by an explosion, and each character can stand for all befuddled mankind in general. The grotesque romance of *A Moon for the Misbegotten* adds a nightmare version of romantic irony to a play that would be wearingly overwrought and sentimental but for its author's mordant yet perversely lyrical view of humanity. In *A Touch of the Poet,* self-deception has a tarnished grandeur, and it is as if the nobler part of a man has died when he finally renounces his fiercely preserved pretensions and shoots the horse that has been the symbolic evidence of his claim to status as a gentleman and an officer in the British army. And in *Long Day's Journey into Night,* for all its laboriousness, O'Neill managed to weave into one richly textured web of tragic reconciliation—that is, of compassion and understanding—the many threads of experience he had spun in the plays with which he had impressed the world.

O'Neill died in Boston in 1953. His greatness as a twentieth-century dramatist resides in the tangled filaments of passion to be found in his plays. In the fierce domestic conflicts of hemmed-in lives, the attachments of men and women that made love look like hate and hate like love, the anxiously maintained masquerades and agonized unmaskings of troubled or obsessed characters, the feeling of alienation and the search for some meaning in existence, the sense of doom accompanied by affirmations of human dignity and, at times, by tragic exaltation. In these and related elements of O'Neill's work will be found some of the twentieth century's most strenuous efforts to regain for the theater in wholly modern terms the status of universal art that the drama possessed in centuries more favorable to dramatic poetry and high tragedy.

John Gassner was a professor at Yale University's School of Drama, a personal friend of O'Neill, and one of the United States' outstanding theater critics.

THE 1936 PRIZE

By KJELL STRÖMBERG

IN 1935, the members of the Swedish Academy were unable to agree on a choice for the Nobel Prize for Literature. The prize was not awarded that year, and the money remained invested in the Nobel Institute's funds. Although exceptional, this procedure was perfectly in order because the Academy is not required to make the award more than once every five years. However, this was the first time since 1918, the final year of World War I, that an annual award was passed up and the Swedish press was severely critical. There was certainly no lack of qualified candidates. These included G. K. Chesterton, H. G. Wells, Benedetto Croce, Miguel de Unamuno, Georges Duhamel, Jules Romains, Paul Valéry, and Roger Martin du Gard, as well as some other less prominent names. Two noteworthy new candidates appeared in 1936, both famous explorers in the realm of the unconscious. They were Sigmund Freud, the inventor of psychoanalysis, and Ludwig Klages, his bitter adversary, an acknowledged defender of Nazi racial doctrine in Germany. But, it was an American writer, Eugene O'Neill, twice before a candidate, who was awarded the prize in 1936.

By this time, O'Neill was almost universally recognized as the greatest American dramatist. He was the only one who had found an audience in Europe. We can safely conjecture that O'Neill would surely have won a majority of the votes of the members of the Academy in 1935 if the report prepared for the committee had not been so lukewarm in its conclusions. The writer of the report was Per Hallström, president of the Nobel Committee and permanent secretary of the Academy. A favorable vote for O'Neill in 1935 would have constituted a formal disavowal of the president. A bit of maneuvering was needed—particularly since this was not the first time that a strong minority found itself in disagreement with Hallström. The O'Neill faction was reluctant to yield. The result was a postponement of the award, a procedure too difficult to make public.

Hallström's conclusions, which had injected such great confusion into the voting, can be summarized in his own words.

[O'Neill] is unquestionably a remarkable dramatist in his impulsive power, but he quickly exhausts his audience's interest by his obsessions, by his complicated plots, and by his technical tricks, which rarely come off. He has great gaps in his general culture and an almost total lack of taste, which does not make him particularly well known in his own country. His psychology is monotonous, although we must concede that his imagination conjures up a full roster of characters.

He plays, however, on a single chord, which he tightens to the breaking point. He has strength of character and temperament, often to an impressive degree, but it is not enough to enlist us in that chorus of praise which we hear from his fellow countrymen. In considering the proposal to honor him with a Nobel prize, we must bear in mind that although many speak for him, many more speak against him. In casting the account of his voluminous production, we find a good number of more or less impressive attempts, but scarcely a single work that is wholly successful. We may well ask whether the value of certain parts of his work which are truly dramatic is sufficient to counterbalance the faults of many other parts. He has, moreover, turned out such a quantity of inferior work that we wonder whether in his case a measure of grace for the redemption of his sins is even to be considered.

This extremely severe judgment is all the more astonishing when we consider that practically all of the principal works —*Anna Christie, Strange Interlude, Desire under the Elms,* and *Mourning Becomes Electra*—had already been brilliantly staged by the Royal Dramatic Theater of Stockholm before their author was proposed for the prize and before any one of his works had been produced in other European theaters. The better informed critics in Sweden viewed O'Neill's work as a rebirth of Elizabethan or even Greek tragedy in modern dress. Swedish critics also recognized in O'Neill a dramatic genius of the calibre of Sweden's own Strindberg.

So in 1936 Per Hallström relented and O'Neill was awarded this prize. At the presentation ceremony Hallström praised the laureate whom he had previously criticized. Unfortunately O'Neill was ill in the United States, and could not be in Stockholm for the award. The American consul in Sweden accepted the prize on his behalf. O'Neill was cited, in the official presentations, for "the power, honesty, and deep-felt emotions of his dramatic works, which embody an original concept of tragedy."

The award of the Nobel prize to O'Neill was universally approved on the two continents where his plays had consistently met the enthusiasm of both critics and public. The decision was welcomed with particular warmth in America, especially since considerable resentment had greeted the earlier award of the prize to Sinclair Lewis in 1930. In those days, the creator of Babbitt was still considered, by many "right-thinking" Americans, a shameless detractor of the American way of life. An editorial in the *New York Times* remarked on this, while stressing that no one should be tempted to suspect some secret motive behind the Academy's choice of O'Neill. He deserved the prize if only because for years he had been the outstanding playwright in America. The editorial went on to explain that the negative attitude at the time of Lewis's award was based on the suspicion that it had been given as a backhanded way of attacking America. It also recalled that, at the time, Lewis had speculated on what would happen to the guardians of good taste and conduct in America if O'Neill were ever to be so honored. "Both Sinclair Lewis and we ourselves have learned much since then, and the decision to award the prize to O'Neill is greeted with a universal satisfaction as proof of the respect and admiration that he and other American writers enjoy abroad."

O'Neill's Nobel diploma, medal, and check were delivered to the writer by the Swedish consul in San Francisco, where he was in the hospital recovering from an appendicitis operation. The check, the dramatist commented, was barely enough to cover the taxes he owed.

O'Neill, whose health grew constantly worse, never succeeded in visiting Sweden as he had hoped to do, but his widow showed her gratitude to the country which had done so much for her husband. After his death, it was learned that he had left important manuscripts to his wife with the provision that they were not to be published until twenty-five years after his death, and then for the benefit of his son. But O'Neill's son died shortly after his father, and Mrs. O'Neill was free to dispose of the literary estate. Through Dag Hammarskjöld, then Secretary-General of the United Nations and a member of the Swedish Academy, it was arranged for Karl-Ragnar Gierow, the administrator of the Royal Dramatic Theater of Stockholm, to inspect this rich legacy and to select any items he wished for his theater. Gierow went immediately to New York, where he selected *Long Day's Journey into Night,* which had its world premiere in Stockholm in February 1956. At least half a dozen other plays in various degrees of completion are still at Gierow's disposal, and he has since turned his capable and meticulous hand to the task of preparing them for the Royal Dramatic Theater.

Translated by Dale McAdoo

John Steinbeck

1962

"For his realistic as well as

imaginative writings, distinguished

by a sympathetic humor

and a keen social perception"

Illustrated by FONTANAROSA

PRESENTATION ADDRESS

By ANDERS ÖSTERLING

PERMANENT SECRETARY
OF THE SWEDISH ACADEMY

JOHN STEINBECK, the author awarded this year's Nobel Prize for Literature, was born in the little town of Salinas, California, a few miles from the Pacific coast near the fertile Salinas Valley. This locality forms the background for many of his descriptions of the common man's everyday life. He was raised in moderate circumstances, yet he was on equal terms with the workers' families in this rather diversified area. While studying at Stanford University, he often had to earn his living by working on the ranches. He left Stanford without graduating and, in 1925, went to New York as a free-lance writer. After bitter years of struggling to exist, he returned to California, where he found a home in a lonely cottage by the sea. There he continued his writing.

Although he had already written several books by 1935, he achieved his first popular success in that year with *Tortilla Flat*. He offered his readers spicy and comic tales about a gang of *paisanos*, asocial individuals who, in their wild revels, are almost caricatures of King Arthur's Knights of the Round Table. It has been said that in the United States this book came as a welcome antidote to the gloom of the then-prevailing depression. The laugh was now on Steinbeck's side.

But he had no mind to be an unoffending comforter and entertainer. The topics he chose were serious and denunciatory, as for example the bitter strikes on California's fruit and cotton plantations which he depicted in his novel *In Dubious Battle* (1936). The power of his literary style increased steadily during these years. The little masterpiece *Of*

Mice and Men (1937), which is the story of Lennie, the imbecile giant who out of tenderness alone squeezes the life out of every living creature that comes into his hands, was followed by those incomparable short stories which he collected in the volume *The Long Valley* (1938). The way had now been paved for the great work that is principally associated with Steinbeck's name, the epic chronicle *The Grapes of Wrath* (1939). This is the story of the emigration to California which was forced upon a group of people from Oklahoma through unemployment and abuse of power. This tragic episode in the social history of the United States inspired in Steinbeck a poignant description of the experiences of one particular farmer and his family during their endless, heartbreaking journey to a new home.

In this brief presentation it is not possible to dwell at any length on individual works which Steinbeck later produced. If at times the critics have seemed to note certain signs of flagging powers, of repetitions that might point to a decrease in vitality, Steinbeck belied their fears most emphatically with *The Winter of Our Discontent* (1961), a novel published last year. Here he attained the same standard which he set in *The Grapes of Wrath*. Again he holds his position as an independent expounder of the truth with an unbiased instinct for what is genuinely American, be it good or bad.

In this recent novel, the central figure is the head of a family who has come down in the world. After serving in the war, he fails at whatever he tries until at last he is employed in the simple work of a grocery store clerk in the New England town of his forefathers. He is an honest man and he does not complain without due cause, although he is constantly exposed to temptation when he sees the means by which material success must be purchased. However, such means require both hard scrupulousness and moral obduracy, qualities he cannot muster without risking his personal integrity. Tellingly displayed in his sensitive conscience, irradiated like a prism, is a whole body of questions which bear on the nation's welfare problems. This is done without any theorizing, using concrete, or even trivial, everyday situations, which are nonetheless convincing when described with all of Steinbeck's vigorous and realistic verve. Even with his insistence on the factual, there are harmonic tones of daydreaming, fumbling speculations around the eternal theme of life and death.

Steinbeck's latest book is an account of his experiences during a three-month tour of forty American states (*Travels with Charley,* 1962). He traveled in a small truck equipped with a cabin where he slept and kept his stores. He traveled incognito, his only companion being a black poodle. We see here what a very experienced observer and *raisonneur* he is. In a series of admirable explorations into local color, he rediscovers his country and its people. In its informal way this book is also a forceful criticism of society. The traveler in Rosinante—the name which he gave his truck—shows a slight tendency to praise the old at the expense of the new, even though it is quite obvious that he is on guard against the temptation. "I wonder why progress so often looks like destruction," he says in one place when he sees the bulldozers flattening out the verdant forest of Seattle to make room for the feverishly expanding residential areas and the skyscrapers. It is, in any case, a most topical reflection, valid also outside America.

Among the masters of modern American literature who have already been awarded this prize—from Sinclair Lewis to Ernest Hemingway—Steinbeck more than holds his own, independent in position and achievement. There is in him a strain of grim humor which to some extent redeems his often cruel and crude motif. His sympathies always go out to the oppressed, to the misfits and the distressed; he likes to contrast the simple joy of life with the brutal and cynical craving for money. But in him we find the American temperament also in his great feeling for nature, for the tilled soil, the wasteland, the mountains, and the ocean coasts, all an inexhaustible source of inspiration to Steinbeck in the midst of, and beyond, the world of human beings.

The Swedish Academy's reason for awarding the prize to John Steinbeck reads, "For his realistic as well as imaginative writings, distinguished by a sympathetic humor and a keen social perception."

Dear Mr. Steinbeck—You are not a stranger to the Swedish public any more than to that of your own country and of the whole world. With your most distinctive works you have become a teacher of good will and charity, a defender of human values, which can well be said to correspond to the proper idea of the Nobel prize. In expressing the congratulations of the Swedish Academy, I now ask you to receive this year's Nobel Prize for Literature from the hands of His Majesty the King.

ACCEPTANCE SPEECH

By JOHN STEINBECK

I THANK THE SWEDISH ACADEMY for finding my work worthy of this highest honor.

In my heart there may be doubt that I deserve the Nobel award over other men of letters whom I hold in respect and reverence—but there is no question of my pleasure and pride in having it for myself.

It is customary for the recipient of this award to offer personal or scholarly comment on the nature and the direction of literature. At this particular time, however, I think it would be well to consider the high duties and the responsibilities of the makers of literature.

Such is the prestige of the Nobel award and this place where I stand that I am impelled, not to squeak like a grateful and apologetic mouse, but to roar like a lion out of pride in my profession and in the great and good men who have practiced it through the ages.

Literature was not promulgated by a pale and emasculated critical priesthood singing their litanies in empty churches—nor is it a game for the cloistered elect, the tinhorn mendicants of low calorie despair.

Literature is as old as speech. It grew out of human need for it, and it has not changed except to become more needed.

The skalds, the bards, the writers are not separate and exclusive. From the beginning, their functions, their duties, their responsibilities have been decreed by our species.

Humanity has been passing through a gray and desolate time of confusion. My great predecessor, William Faulkner, speaking here, referred to it as a tragedy of universal fear so long sustained that there were no longer problems of the spirit, so that only the human heart in conflict with itself seemed worth writing about.

Faulkner, more than most men, was aware of human strength as well as of human weakness. He knew that the understanding and the resolution of fear are a large part of the writer's reason for being.

This is not new. The ancient commission of the writer has not changed.

He is charged with exposing our many grievous faults and failures, with dredging up to the light our dark and dangerous dreams for the purpose of improvement.

Furthermore, the writer is delegated to declare and to celebrate man's proven capacity for greatness of heart and spirit—for gallantry in defeat—for courage, compassion, and love. In the endless war against weakness and despair, these are the bright rally-flags of hope and of emulation.

I hold that a writer who does not passionately believe in the perfectibility of man, has no dedication nor any membership in literature.

The present universal fear has been the result of a forward surge in our knowledge and manipulation of certain dangerous factors in the physical world.

It is true that other phases of understanding have not yet caught up with this great step, but there is no reason to presume that they cannot or will not draw abreast. Indeed it is a part of the writer's responsibility to make sure that they do.

With humanity's long proud history of standing firm against natural enemies, sometimes in the face of almost certain defeat and extinctions, we would be cowardly and stupid to leave the field on the eve of our greatest potential victory.

Understandably, I have been reading the life of Alfred Nobel—a solitary man, the books say, a thoughtful man. He perfected the release of explosive forces capable of creative good or of destructive evil, but lacking choice, ungoverned by conscience or judgment.

Nobel saw some of the cruel and bloody misuses of his inventions. He may even have foreseen the end result of his probing—access to ultimate violence—to final destruction. Some say that he became cynical, but I do not believe this. I think he strove to invent a control, a safety valve. I think he found it finally only in the human mind and the human spirit. To me, his thinking is clearly indicated in the categories of these awards.

They are offered for increased and continuing knowledge of man and of his world—for understanding and communication, which are the functions of literature. And they are offered for demonstrations of the capacity for peace—the culmination of all the others.

Less than fifty years after his death, the door of nature was unlocked and we were offered the dreadful burden of choice.

We have usurped many of the powers we once ascribed to God.

Fearful and unprepared, we have assumed lordship over the life or death of the whole world—of all living things.

The danger and the glory and the choice rest finally in man. The test of his perfectibility is at hand.

Having taken Godlike power, we must seek in ourselves for the responsibility and the wisdom we once prayed some deity might have.

Man himself has become our greatest hazard and our only hope.

So that today, St. John the Apostle may well be paraphrased: In the end is the Word, and the Word is Man—and the Word is with Men.

Innumerable force of Spirits armed,
That durst dislike his reign, and, me preferring,
His utmost power with adverse power opposed
In dubious battle on the plains of Heaven
And shook his throne. What though the field be lost?
All is not lost—the unconquerable will,
And study of revenge, immortal hate,
And courage never to submit or yield:
And what is else not to be overcome?

—PARADISE LOST

The persons and places in this book are fictitious

IN DUBIOUS BATTLE

By JOHN STEINBECK

1

At last it was evening. The lights in the street outside came on, and the Neon restaurant sign on the corner jerked on and off, exploding its hard red light in the air. Into Jim Nolan's room the sign threw a soft red light. For two hours Jim had been sitting in a small, hard rocking-chair, his feet up on the white bedspread. Now that it was quite dark, he brought his feet down to the floor and slapped the sleeping legs. For a moment he sat quietly while waves of itching rolled up and down his calves; then he stood up and reached for the unshaded light. The furnished room lighted up—the big white bed with its chalk-white spread, the golden-oak bureau, the clean red carpet worn through to a brown warp.

Jim stepped to the washstand in the corner and washed his hands and combed water through his hair with his fingers. Looking into the mirror fastened across the corner of the room above the wash-stand, he peered into his own small grey eyes for a moment. From an inside pocket he took a comb fitted with a pocket clip and combed his straight brown hair, and parted it neatly on the side. He wore a dark suit and a grey flannel shirt, open at the throat. With a

towel he dried the soap and dropped the thin bar into a paper bag that stood open on the bed. A Gillette razor was in the bag, four pairs of new socks and an-other grey flannel shirt. He glanced about the room and then twisted the mouth of the bag closed. For a moment more he looked casually into the mirror, then turned off the light and went out the door.

He walked down narrow, uncarpeted stairs and knocked at a door beside the front entrance. It opened a little. A woman looked at him and then opened the door wider—a large blonde woman with a dark mole beside her mouth.

She smiled at him. "*Mis*-ter Nolan," she said.

"I'm going away," said Jim.

"But you'll be back, you'll want me to hold your room?"

"No. I've got to go away for good. I got a letter telling me."

"You didn't get no letters here," said the woman suspiciously.

"No, where I work. I won't be back. I'm paid a week in advance."

Her smile faded slowly. Her expression seemed to slip toward anger without any great change. "You should of give me a week's notice," she said sharply. "That's the rule. I got to keep that advance be-cause you didn't give me no notice."

"I know," Jim said. "That's all right. I didn't know how long I could stay."

The smile was back on the landlady's face. "You been a good quiet roomer," she said, "even if you ain't been here long. If you're ever around again, come right straight here. I'll find a place for you. I got sailors that come to me every time they're in port. And I find room for them. They wouldn't go no place else."

"I'll remember, Mrs. Meer. I left the key in the door."

"Light turned out?"

"Yes."

"Well, I won't go up till tomorrow morning. Will you come in and have a little nip?"

"No, thank you. I've got to be going."

Her eyes narrowed wisely. "You ain't in trouble? I could maybe help you."

"No," Jim said. "Nobody's after me. I'm just taking a new job. Well, good night, Mrs. Meer."

She held out a powdered hand. Jim shifted his paper bag and took her hand for a moment, and felt the soft flesh give under his fingers.

"Don't forget," she said. "I can always find room. People come back to me year after year, sailors and drummers."

"I'll remember. Good night."

She looked after him until he was out the front door and down the cement steps to the sidewalk.

He walked to the corner and looked at the clock in a jeweller's window—seven-thirty. He set out walking rapidly eastward, through a district of department stores and specialty shops, and then through the wholesale produce district, quiet now in the evening, the narrow streets deserted, the depot entrances closed with wooden bars and wire netting. He came at last to an old street of three-storey brick buildings. Pawn-shops and second-hand tool dealers occupied the ground floors, while failing dentists and lawyers had offices in the upper two

flights. Jim looked at each doorway until he found the number he wanted. He went in a dark entrance and climbed the narrow stairs, rubber-treaded, the edges guarded with strips of brass. A little night light burned at the head of the steps, but only one door in the long hall showed a light through its frosted glass. Jim walked to it, looked at the "Sixteen" on the glass, and knocked.

A sharp voice called, "Come in."

Jim opened the door and stepped into a small, bare office containing a desk, a metal filing cabinet, an army cot and two straight chairs. On the desk sat an electric cooking plate, on which a little tin coffee-pot bubbled and steamed. A man looked solemnly over the desk at Jim. He glanced at a card in front of him. "Jim Nolan?" he asked.

"Yes." Jim looked closely at him, a small man, neatly dressed in a dark suit. His thick hair was combed straight down on each side from the top in a vain attempt to cover a white scar half an inch wide that lay horizontally over the right ear. The eyes were sharp and black, quick nervous eyes that moved constantly about—from Jim to the card, and up to a wall calendar, and to an alarm clock, and back to Jim. The nose was large, thick at the bridge and narrow at the point. The mouth might at one time have been full and soft, but habitual muscular tension had drawn it close and made a deep line on each lip. Although the man could not have been over forty, his face bore heavy parenthetical lines of resistance to attack. His hands were as nervous as his eyes, large hands, almost too big for his body, long fingers with spatulate ends, and flat, thick nails. The hands moved about on the desk like the exploring hands of a blind man, feeling the edges of paper, following the corner of the desk, touching in turn each button on his vest. The right hand went to the electric plate and pulled out the plug.

Jim closed the door quietly and stepped to the desk. "I was told to come here," he said.

Suddenly the man stood up and pushed his right hand across. "I'm Harry Nilson. I have your application here." Jim shook hands. "Sit down, Jim." The nervous voice was soft, but made soft by an effort.

Jim pulled the extra chair close and sat down by the desk. Harry opened a desk-drawer, took out an open can of milk, the holes plugged with matches, a cup of sugar and two thick mugs. "Will you have a cup of coffee?"

"Sure," said Jim.

Nilson poured the black coffee into the mugs. He said, "Now here's the way we work on applications, Jim. Your card went into the membership committee. I have to talk to you and make a report. The committee passes on the report and then the membership votes on you. So you see, if I question you pretty deep, I just have to." He poured milk into his coffee, and then he looked up, and his eyes smiled for a second.

"Sure, I know," said Jim. "I've heard you're more select than the Union League Club."

"By God, we have to be!" He shoved the sugar bowl at Jim, then suddenly, "Why do you want to join the Party?"

Jim stirred his coffee. His face wrinkled up in concentration. He looked down into his lap. "Well—I could give you a lot of little reasons. Mainly, it's this: My whole family has been ruined by this system. My old man, my father, was slugged so much in labor trouble that he went punch-drunk. He got an idea that he'd like to dynamite a slaughter-house where he used to work. Well, he caught a charge of buckshot in the chest from a riot gun."

Harry interrupted, "Was your father Roy Nolan?"

"Yeah. Killed three years ago."

"Jesus!" Harry said. "He had a reputation for being the toughest mug in the country. I've heard he could lick five cops with his bare hands."

Jim grinned. "I guess he could, but every time he went out he met six. He always got the hell beat out of him. He used to come home all covered with blood. He'd sit beside the cook stove. We had to let him alone then. Couldn't even speak to him or he'd cry. When my mother washed him later, he'd whine like a dog." He paused. "You know he was a sticker in the slaughter-house. Used to drink warm blood to keep up his strength."

Nilson looked quickly at him, and then away. He bent the corner of the application card and creased it down with his thumb nail. "Your mother is alive?" he asked softly.

Jim's eyes narrowed. "She died a month ago," he said. "I was in jail. Thirty days for vagrancy. Word came in she was dying. They let me go home with a cop. There wasn't anything the matter with her. She wouldn't talk at all. She was a Catholic, only my old man wouldn't let her go to church. He hated churches. She just stared at me. I asked her if she wanted a priest, but she didn't answer me, just stared. 'Bout four o'clock in the morning she died. Didn't seem like dying at all. I didn't go to the funeral. I guess they would've let me. I didn't want to. I guess she just didn't want to live. I guess she didn't care if she went to hell, either."

Harry started nervously. "Drink your coffee and have some more. You act half asleep. You don't take anything, do you?"

"You mean dope? No, I don't even drink."

Nilson pulled out a piece of paper and made a few notes on it. "How'd you happen to get vagged?"

Jim said fiercely, "I worked in Tulman's Department Store. Head of the wrapping department. I was out to a picture show one night, and coming home I saw a crowd in Lincoln Square. I stopped to see what it was all about. There was a guy in the middle of the park talking. I climbed up on the pedestal of that statue of Senator Morgan so I could see better. And then I heard the sirens. I was watching the riot squad come in from the other side. Well, a squad came up from behind, too. Cop slugged me from behind, right in the back of the neck. When I came to I was already booked for vagrancy. I was rumdum for a long time. Got hit right here." Jim put his fingers on the back of his neck at the base of his skull. "Well, I told 'em I wasn't a vagrant and had a job, and told 'em to call up Mr. Webb, he's manager at Tulman's. So they did. Webb asked where I was picked up, and the sergeant said 'at a radical meeting,' and then Webb said he never heard of me. So I got the rap."

Nilson plugged in the hot plate again. The coffee started rumbling in the pot. "You look half drunk, Jim. What's the matter with you?"

"I don't know. I feel dead. Everything in the past is gone. I checked out of my rooming house before I came here. I still had a week paid for. I don't want to go back to any of it again. I want to be finished with it."

Nilson poured the coffee cups full. "Look, Jim, I want to give you a picture of what it's like to be a Party member. You'll get a chance to vote on every decision, but once the vote's in, you'll have to obey. When we have money we try to give field workers twenty dollars a month to eat on. I don't remember a time when we ever had the money. Now listen to the work: In the field you'll have to work alongside the men, and you'll have to do the Party work after that, sometimes six-teen, eighteen hours a day. You'll have to get your food where you can. Do you think you could do that?"

"Yes."

Nilson touched the desk here and there with his fingertips. "Even the people you're trying to help will hate you most of the time. Do you know that?"

"Yes."

"Well, why do you want to join, then?"

Jim's grey eyes half closed in perplexity. At last he said, "In the jail there were some Party men. They talked to me. Everything's been a mess, all my life. Their lives weren't messes. They were working toward something. I want to work toward something. I feel dead. I thought I might get alive again."

Nilson nodded. "I see. You're God-damn right I see. How long did you go to school?"

"Second year in high-school. Then I went to work."

"But you talk as though you had more school than that."

Jim smiled. "I've read a lot. My old man didn't want me to read. He said I'd desert my own people. But I read anyway. One day I met a man in the park. He made lists of things for me to read. Oh, I've read a hell of a lot. He made lists like Plato's *Republic,* and the *Utopia,* and Bellamy, and like Herodotus and Gibbon and Macaulay and Carlyle and Prescott, and like Spinoza and Hegel and Kant and Nietzsche and Schopenhauer. He even made me read *Das Kapital.* He was a crank, he said. He said he wanted to know things without believing them. He liked to group books that all aimed in the same direction."

Harry Nilson was quiet for a while. Then he said, "You see why we have to be so careful. We only have two punishments, reprimand and expulsion. You've got to want to belong to the Party pretty badly. I'm going to recommend you, 'cause I think you're a good man; you might get voted down, though."

"Thanks," said Jim.

"Now listen, have you any relatives who might suffer if you use your right name?"

"I've an uncle, Theodore Nolan. He's a mechanic. Nolan's an awful common name."

"Yeah, I guess it is common. Have you any money?"

"About three dollars. I had some, but I spent it for the funeral."

"Well, where you going to stay?"

"I don't know. I cut off from everything. I wanted to start new. I didn't want to have anything hanging over."

Nilson looked around at the cot. "I live in this office," he said. "I eat and sleep and work here. If you want to sleep on the floor, you can stay here for a few days."

Jim smiled with pleasure. "I'd like that. The bunks in jail weren't any softer than your floor."

"Well, have you had any dinner?"

"No. I forgot it."

Nilson spoke irritably. "If you think I'm chiseling, go ahead," he said. "I haven't any money. You have three dollars."

Jim laughed. "Come on, we'll get dried herrings and cheese and bread. And we'll get stuff for a stew tomorrow. I can make a pretty good stew."

Harry Nilson poured the last of the coffee into the mugs. "You're waking up, Jim. You're looking better. But you don't know what you're getting into. I can tell you about it, but it won't mean anything until you go through it."

Jim looked evenly at him. "Did you ever work at a job where, when you got enough skill to get a raise in pay, you were fired and a new man put in? Did you ever work in a place where they

talked about loyalty to the firm, and loyalty meant spying on the people around you? Hell, I've got nothing to lose."

"Nothing except hatred," Harry said quietly. "You're going to be surprised when you see that you stop hating people. I don't know why it is, but that's what usually happens."

2

All during the day Jim had been restive. Harry Nilson, working on a long report, had turned on him several times in exasperation. "Look," he said finally, "you can go down to the spot alone if you want. There's no reason why you can't. But in an hour I'll go down with you. I've got to finish this thing."

"I wonder if I ought to change my name," said Jim. "I wonder if changing your name would have any effect on you."

Nilson turned back to his report. "You get some tough assignments and go to jail enough and change your name a few times, and a name won't mean any more to you than a number."

Jim stood by the window and looked out. A brick wall was opposite, bounding the other side of a narrow vacant lot between two buildings. A crowd of boys played handball against the building. Their yells came faintly through the closed window.

"I used to play in lots when I was a kid," Jim said. "Seems to me we fought most of the time. I wonder if the kids fight as much as they used to."

Harry did not pause in his writing. "Sure they do," he said. "I look out and see 'em down there. Sure they fight."

"I used to have a sister," Jim went on. "She could lick nearly everybody in the lot. She was the best marble shot I ever saw. Honest, Harry, I've seen her split an agate at ten feet, with her knuckles down, too."

Harry looked up. "I didn't know you had a sister. What happened to her?"

"I don't know," said Jim.

"You don't know?"

"No. It was funny—I don't mean funny. It was one of those things that happen."

"What do you mean, you don't know what happened to her?" Harry laid his pencil down.

"Well, I can tell you about it," said Jim. "Her name was May. She was a year older than I was. We always slept in the kitchen. Each had a cot. When May was about fourteen and I was thirteen, she hung a sheet across the corner to make a kind of a little closet to dress and undress behind. She got giggly, too. Used to sit on the steps downstairs with a lot of other girls, and giggle when boys went by. She had yellow hair. She was kind of pretty, I guess. Well, one evening I came home from playing ball over on Twenty-third and Fulton—used to be a vacant lot, there's a bank there now. I climbed up to our flat. My mother said, 'Did you see May down on the steps?' I said I hadn't. Pretty soon my old man came home from work. He said, 'Where's May?' My mother said, 'She hasn't come in yet.'

"It's funny how this whole thing stands out, Harry. I remember every bit of it, what everybody said, and how everybody looked.

"We waited dinner a while, but pretty soon my old man stuck out his chin and got mad. 'Put on the food,' he said. 'May's getting too smart. She thinks she's too big to get licked.'

"My mother had light blue eyes. I remember they looked like white stones. Well, after dinner my old man sat in his chair by the stove. And he got madder and madder. My mother sat beside him. I went to bed. I could see my mother turn her head from my father and move her lips. I guess she was praying. She was a Catholic, but my father hated churches. Every little while he'd growl out what he'd do to May when she did come home.

"About eleven o'clock both of 'em went into the bedroom, but they left the light burning in the kitchen. I could hear them talking for a long time. Two or three times in the night I woke up and saw my mother looking out from the bedroom. Her eyes looked just like white stones."

Jim turned from the window and sat down on the cot. Harry was digging his pencil into the desk top. Jim said, "When I woke up the next morning it was sunshiny outside, and that light was still burning. It gives you a funny, lonely feeling to see a light burning in the daytime. Pretty soon my mother came out of the bedroom and started a fire in the stove. Her face was stiff, and her eyes didn't move much. Then my father came out. He acted just as though he'd been hit between the eyes—slugged. He couldn't get a word out. Just before he went to work, he said, 'I think I'll stop in at the precinct station. She might of got run over.'

"Well, I went to school, and right after school I came home. My mother told me to ask all the girls if they'd seen May. By that time the news had got around that May was gone. They said they hadn't seen May at all. They were all shivery about it. Then my father came home. He'd been to the police station on the way home, too. He said, 'The cops took a description. They said they'd keep their eyes peeled.'

"That night was just like the one before. My old man and my mother sitting side by side, only my father didn't do any talking that second night. They left the light on all night again. The next day my old man went back to the station house. Well, the cops sent a dick to question the kids on the block, and a cop came and talked to my mother. Finally they said they'd keep their eyes open. And that was all. We never heard of her again, ever."

Harry stabbed the desk and broke his pencil point. "Was she going around with any older boys she might've run off with?"

"I don't know. The girls said not, and they would have known."

"But haven't you an idea of what might have happened to her?"

"No. She just disappeared one day, just dropped out of sight. The same thing happened to Bertha Riley two years later —just dropped out."

Jim felt with his hand along the line of his jaw. "It might have been my imagination, but it seemed to me that my mother was quieter even than before. She moved kind of like a machine, and she hardly ever said anything. Her eyes got a kind of a dead look, too. But it made my old man mad. He had to fight everything with his fists. He went to work and beat hell out of the foreman at the Monel packing house. Then he did ninety days for assault."

Harry stared out the window. Suddenly he put down his pencil and stood up. "Come on!" he said. "I'm going to take you down to the house and get rid of you. I've got to get that report out. I'll do it when I get back."

Jim walked to the radiator and picked off two pairs of damp socks. He rolled them up and put them in his paper bag. "I'll dry them down at the other place," he said.

Harry put on his hat, and folded the report and put it in his pocket. "Every once in a while the cops go through this place," he explained. "I don't leave any-

thing around." He locked the office door as he went out.

They walked through the business center of the city, and past blocks of apartment houses. At last they came to a district of old houses, each in its own yard. Harry turned into a driveway. "Here we are. It's in back of this house." They followed the gravelled drive, and in back came to a tiny cottage, newly painted. Harry walked to the door and opened it, and motioned Jim inside.

The cottage contained one large room and a kitchenette. In the big room there were six steel cots, made up with army blankets. Three men were in the room, two lying on cots and one large man, with the face of a scholarly prizefighter, pecking slowly at a typewriter.

He looked up quickly when Harry opened the door, and then stood up and came forward smiling. "Hello, Harry," he said. "What's on your mind?"

"This is Jim Nolan," Harry explained. "Remember? His name came up the other night. Jim, this is Mac. He knows more about field work than anybody in the state."

Mac grinned. "Glad to see you, Jim," he said.

Harry, turning to go, said, "Take care of him, Mac. Put him to work. I've got to get out a report." He waved to the two who were lying down. " 'Bye, boys."

When the door was closed, Jim looked about the room. The wallboarded walls were bare. Only one chair was in the room, and that stood in front of the typewriter. From the kitchenette came an odor of boiling corned beef. He looked back at Mac, at his broad shoulders and long arms, at his face, wide between the cheekbones with flat planes under the eyes like those of a Swede. Mac's lips were dry and cracked. He looked at Jim as closely as he was being inspected.

Suddenly he said, "Too bad we're not

dogs, we could get that all over with. We'd either be friends or fighting by now. Harry said you were O.K., and Harry knows. Come on, meet the boys. This pale one here is Dick, a bedroom radical. We get many a cake because of Dick."

The pale, dark-haired boy on the bed grinned and held out his hand.

Mac went on, "See how beautiful he is? We call him the Decoy. He tells ladies about the working classes, and we get cakes with pink frosting, huh, Dick?"

"Go to hell," said Dick pleasantly.

Mac, guiding Jim by his arm, turned him toward the man on the other cot. It was impossible to tell how old he was. His face was wizened and battered, his nose crushed flat against his face; his heavy jaw sagged sideways. "This is Joy," said Mac. "Joy is a veteran, aren't you, Joy?"

"Damn right," said Joy. His eyes flared up, then almost instantly the light went out of them again. His head twitched several times. He opened his mouth to speak, but he only repeated, "Damn right," very solemnly, as though it finished off an argument. He caressed one hand with the other. Jim saw that they were crushed and scarred.

Mac explained, "Joy won't shake hands with anybody. Bones are all broken. It hurts Joy to shake hands."

The light flared in Joy's eyes again. "Why is it?" he cried shrilly. " 'Cause I've been beat, that's why! I been handcuffed to a bar and beat over the head. I been stepped on by horses." He shouted, "I been beat to hell, ain't I, Mac?"

"That's right, Joy."

"And did I ever crawl, Mac? Didn't I keep on calling 'em sons-of-bitches till they knocked me cold?"

"That's right, Joy. And if you'd kept your trap shut, they wouldn't have knocked you cold."

Joy's voice rose to a frenzy. "But they was sons-of-bitches. I told 'em, too. Let 'em beat me over the head with my hands in 'cuffs. Let 'em ride over me! See that hand? That was rode over with a horse. But I told 'em, didn't I, Mac?"

Mac leaned over and patted him. "You sure did, Joy. Nobody's going to make you keep quiet."

"Damn right," said Joy, and the light went out of his eyes again.

Mac said, "Come on over here, Jim." He led him to the other end of the room, where the typewriter stood on a little table. "Know how to type?"

"A little," said Jim.

"Thank God! You can get right to work." Mac lowered his voice. "Don't mind Joy. He's slug-nutty. He's been smacked over the head too much. We take care of him and try to keep him out of trouble."

"My old man was like that," said Jim. "One time I found him in the street. He was walking in big circles off to the left. I had to steer him straight. A scab had smashed him under the ear with a pair of brass knuckles. Seemed to affect his sense of direction."

"Now look here," said Mac. "Here's a general letter. I've got four carbons in the typewriter. We've got to have twenty copies. You want to get to it while I fix some supper?"

"Sure," said Jim.

"Well, hit the keys hard. Those carbon sheets aren't much good." Mac went into the kitchen calling, "Dick, come out and peel some onions if you can stand the horrible smell."

Dick got up from the couch; after rolling the sleeves of his white shirt neatly above his elbows, he followed Mac into the kitchen.

Jim had just started his heavy, deliberate typing when Joy eased himself off the couch and walked over. "Who produces the goods?" Joy demanded.

"Why—the workers," said Jim.

A foxy look came on Joy's face, a very wise and secret look. "And who takes the profits?"

"The people with invested capital."

Joy shouted, "But they don't produce nothing. What right they got to the profits?"

Mac looked in through the kitchen door. He walked quickly over, a stirring spoon in his hand. "Now listen to me, Joy," he said. "Stop trying to convert our own people. Jesus Christ, it seems to me our guys spend most of their time converting each other. Now you go back and rest, Joy. You're tired. Jim here's got work to do. After he finishes, I'll maybe let you address some of the letters, Joy."

"Will you, Mac? Well, I sure told 'em, didn't I, Mac? Even when they was smackin' me, I told 'em."

Mac took him gently by the elbow and led him back to his cot. "Here's a copy of *New Masses*. You just look at the pictures till I get dinner ready."

Jim pounded away at the letter. He wrote it four times and laid the twenty copies beside the typewriter. He called into the kitchen, "Here they are, all ready, Mac."

Mac came in and looked at some of the copies. "Why, you type fine, Jim. You don't cross out hardly anything. Now here's some envelopes. Put these letters in. We'll address 'em after we eat."

Mac filled the plates with corned beef and carrots and potatoes and raw sliced onions. Each man retired to his cot to eat. The daylight was dim in the room until Mac turned on a powerful unshaded light that hung from the center of the ceiling.

When they had finished, Mac went into the kitchen again and returned with a platter of cup cakes. "Here's some more of Dick's work," he said. "That Dick uses the bedroom for political purposes. Gentlemen, I give you the Du-Barry of the Party!"

"You go to hell," said Dick.

Mac picked up the sealed envelopes from Jim's bed. "Here's twenty letters. That's five for each one of us to address." He pushed the plates aside on the table, and from a drawer brought out a pen and a bottle of ink. Then, drawing a list from his pocket, he carefully addressed five of the envelopes. "Your turn, Jim. You do these five."

"What's it for?" Jim asked.

"Well, I guess it don't make much difference, but it might make it a little harder. We're getting our mail opened pretty regular. I just thought it might make it a little harder for the dicks if all these addresses were in different writing. We'll put one of each in a mailbox, you see. No good looking for trouble."

While the other two men were writing their addresses, Jim picked up the dishes, carried them into the kitchen and stacked them on the sinkboard.

Mac was stamping the letters and putting them into his pocket when Jim came back. Mac said, "Dick, you and Joy wash the dishes tonight. I did 'em alone last night. I'm going out to mail these letters. Want to walk with me, Jim?"

"Sure," said Jim. "I've got a dollar. I'll get some coffee, and we'll have some when we get back."

Mac held out his hand. "We've got some coffee. We'll get a dollar's worth of stamps."

Jim handed him the dollar. "That cleans me," he said. "It's the last cent I have." He followed Mac out into the evening. They walked along the street looking for mailboxes. "Is Joy really nuts?" Jim asked.

"Pretty nuts, all right. You see the last thing that happened to him was the worst. Joy was speaking at a barber shop. The barber put in a call and the cops raided the meeting. Well, Joy's a pretty tough fighter. They had to break his jaw with a night stick to stop him; then they threw him in the can. Well, I don't know how Joy did much talking with a busted jaw, but he must have worked on the doctor in the jail some, 'cause the doctor said he wouldn't treat a God-damn red, and Joy lay there three full days with a broken jaw. He's been screwy ever since. I expect he'll be put away pretty soon. He's just taken it on the conk too often."

"Poor devil," said Jim.

Mac drew his bundle of envelopes from his pocket and collected five in different handwritings. "Well, Joy just never learned to keep his mouth shut. Look at Dick. Not a mark on him. And that pretty Dick's just as tough as Joy is when there's some good in it. But just as soon as Dick gets picked up he starts calling the cops 'sir,' and they got him sitting in their laps before he gets through with them. Joy's got no more sense than a bulldog."

They found the last of four mailboxes on the edge of Lincoln Square, and after Mac had deposited his letters the two of them strolled slowly up the brick walk. The maples were beginning to drop leaves on the path. Only a few of the benches along the walks were occupied. The high-hung park lights were on now, casting black patterns of the trees on the ground. Not far from the center of the square stood a statue of a bearded man in a frock coat. Jim pointed to it. "I was standing up on that pedestal," he said. "I was trying to see what was going on. A cop must've reached up and swatted me the way a man swats a fly. I knew a little how Joy feels. It was four or five days before I could think straight. Little pictures went flying through my head, and I couldn't quite catch them. Right in the back of the neck I got it."

Mac turned to a bench and sat down. "I know," he said. "I read Harry's report. Is that the only reason you wanted to join the Party?"

"No," said Jim. "When I got in jail, there were five other men in the same cell, picked up at the same time—a Mexican and a Negro and a Jew and a couple of plain mongrel Americans like me. 'Course they talked to me, but it wasn't that. I'd read more than they knew." He picked up a maple leaf from the ground and began carefully stripping the covering from the hand-like skeleton. "Look," he said. "All the time at home we were fighting, fighting something— hunger mostly. My old man was fighting the bosses. I was fighting the school. But always we lost. And after a long time I guess it got to be part of our mind-stuff that we always would lose. My old man was fighting just like a cat in a corner with a pack of dogs around. Sooner or later a dog was sure to kill him; but he fought anyway. Can you see the hopelessness in that? I grew up in that hopelessness."

"Sure, I can see," Mac said. "There's millions of people with just that."

Jim waved the stripped leaf in front of him, and spun it between his thumb and forefinger. "There was more than that to it," he said. "The house where we lived was always filled with anger. Anger hung in the house like smoke; that beaten, vicious anger against the boss, against the superintendent, against the groceryman when he cut off credit. It was an anger that made you sick to your stomach, but you couldn't help it."

"Go on," said Mac. "I don't see where you're getting, but maybe you do."

Jim jumped up and stood in front of the bench and whipped the leaf skeleton across his palm. "I'm getting to this: In that cell were five men all raised in about the same condition. Some of them worse, even. And while there was anger in them, it wasn't the same kind of anger. They didn't hate a boss or a butcher. They hated the whole system of bosses, but that was a different thing. It wasn't the same kind of anger. And there was something else, Mac. The hopelessness wasn't in them. They were quiet, and they were working; but in the back of every mind there was conviction that sooner or later they would win their way out of the system they hated. I tell you, there was a kind of peacefulness about those men."

"Are you trying to convert me?" Mac asked sarcastically.

"No, I'm trying to tell you. I'd never known any hope or peacefulness, and I was hungry for it. I probably knew more about so-called radical movements than any of those men. I'd read more, but they had the thing I wanted, and they'd got it by working."

Mac said sharply, "Well, you typed a few letters tonight. Do you feel any better?"

Jim sat down again. "I liked doing it, Mac," he said softly. "I don't know why. It seemed a good thing to be doing. It seemed to have some meaning. Nothing I ever did before had any meaning. It was all just a mess. I don't think I resented the fact that someone profited from the mess, but I did hate being in the rat-cage."

Mac thrust his legs out straight before him and put his hands in his pockets. "Well," he said, "if work will keep you happy, you've got a pretty jolly time ahead of you. If you'll learn to cut stencils and run a mimeograph I can almost guarantee you twenty hours a day. And if you hate the profit system, I can promise you, Jim, you won't get a damn cent for it." His voice was genial.

Jim said, "Mac, you're the boss in the joint back there, aren't you?"

"Me? No, I tell 'em what to do, but they don't have to do it. I can't issue any orders. The only orders that really stick are the ones that come down after a vote."

"Well, anyway, you've got some say, Mac. What I'd really like to do is get into the field. I'd like to get into the action."

Mac laughed softly. "You want punishment, don't you? Well, I don't know but what the committee'll think a hell of a lot more of a good typist. You'll have to put romance off for a while—the noble Party assaulted by the beast of Capitalism." Suddenly his tone changed and he turned on Jim. "It's all work," he said. "In the field it's hard work and dangerous work. But don't think it's so soft at the joint, either. You don't know what night a bunch of American Legioners all full of whisky and drum-corps music may come down and beat hell out of you. I've been through it, I tell you. There's no veteran like the man who got drafted into the army and served six months in a training camp punching a bayonet into a sack of sawdust. The men who were in the trenches are mostly different; but for pure incendiarism and brass knuckle patriotism, give me twenty training camp ex-soldiers. Why, twenty of 'em will protect their country from five kids any dark night when they can get a little whisky. Most of 'em got their wound stripes because they were too drunk to go to a prophylaxis station."

Jim chuckled. "You don't like soldiers much, do you, Mac?"

"I don't like the ex-soldiers with the gold hats. I was in France. They were good, honest, stupid cattle. They didn't like it, but they were nice guys." His voice sobered down. Jim saw him grin quickly in embarrassment. "I got hot, didn't I, Jim? I'll tell you why. Ten of the brave bastards licked me one night. And after they'd licked me unconscious they jumped on me and broke my right arm. And then they set fire to my mother's house. My mother pulled me out in the front yard."

"What happened?" Jim asked. "What were you doing?"

The sarcasm came back into Mac's voice. "Me? I was subverting the government. I'd made a speech saying there were some people starving." He stood up. "Let's go back, Jim. They ought to have the dishes washed up by now. I didn't mean to get bitter, but somehow that busted arm still makes me mad."

They walked slowly back down the path. A few men on the benches pulled in their legs to let them by.

Jim said, "If you can ever put in a word, Mac, so I can get out in the field to work, I'll be glad."

"O.K. But you'd better learn to cut stencils and run a mimeograph. You're a good kid; I'm glad to have you with us."

3

Jim sat under the hard white light typewriting letters. Occasionally he stopped and listened, his ears turned toward the door. Except for a kettle simmering huskily in the kitchen, the house was still. The soft roar of streetcars on distant streets, the slap of feet on the pavement in front only made the inside seem more quiet. He looked up at the alarm clock hanging to a nail on the wall. He got up and went into the kitchen and stirred the stew, and turned down the gas until each jet held a tiny blue globe.

As he went back to the typewriter he heard quick steps on the gravelled path. Dick came bursting into the house. "Mac's not here yet?"

"No," said Jim. "He hasn't got here. Neither has Joy. Collect any money today?"

"Twenty dollars," said Dick.

"Boy, you sure do it, I don't know how. We could eat for a month on that; but Mac'll probably spend it all on stamps. Lord, how he goes through stamps."

"Listen," Dick cried. "I think I hear Mac now."

"Or Joy."

"No, it's not Joy."

The door opened and Mac entered. "Hello, Jim. Hello, Dick. Get any money out of the sympathizers today?"

"Twenty dollars."

"Good boy!"

"Say, Mac, Joy did it this afternoon."

"Did what?"

"Well, he started a crazy speech on a street corner and a cop picked him up, and Joy stuck the cop in the shoulder with a pocket knife. They got him locked up, and they got felonious assault on the book. He's sitting in a cell right now, yelling 'son-of-a-bitch' at the top of his lungs."

"I thought he was screwier than usual this morning. Now listen, Dick. I've got to get out of here tomorrow morning, and I've got things to do now. You run to a public phone and call George Camp, Ottman 4211. Tell him the works, and tell him Joy's nuts. Tell him to get down there if he can and say he's Joy's attorney. Joy's got a sweet record if they put it on him—about six incites to riot, twenty or thirty vagrancies, and about a dozen resists and simple assaults. They'll give him the works if George doesn't get busy. Tell George to try to spring him for a drunk." He paused. "Jesus! If a sanity board ever gets hold of that poor devil, he's in for life. Tell George to try to get Joy to keep his mouth shut. And when you do that, Dick, you make the rounds and try to pick up some bail money—in case."

"Can't I eat first?" Dick asked.

"Hell, no. Get George down there. Here, give me ten of the twenty. Jim and I are going down to the Torgas Valley tomorrow. After you call George, come back and eat. And then start rounding up the sympathizers for bail. I hope to God George can get out a writ and get bail set sometime tonight."

Dick said, "O.K.," and hurried out.

Mac turned to Jim. "I guess they'll have to lock poor Joy up pretty soon, for good. He's a long way gone. This is the first time he ever used a knife."

Jim pointed to a pile of finished letters on the desk. "There they are, Mac. Three more to do, that's all. Where'd you say we're going?"

"Down the Torgas Valley. There're thousands of acres of apples ready to pick down there. Be damn near two thousand fruit camps. Well, the Growers' Association just announced a pay cut to the pickers. They'll be sore as hell. If we can get a good ruckus going down there we might be able to spread it over to the cotton fields in Tandale. And then we *would* have something. That'd be a fuss!" He sniffed the air. "Say, that stew smells swell. Is it ready?"

"I'll dish it up," said Jim. He brought in two bowls half full of soup, out of which arose a mound of meat squares, potatoes and carrots, pale turnips and steaming whole onions.

Mac put his bowl on the table and tasted it. "Christ! Let it cool. It's like this, Jim, I always said we shouldn't send green men into trouble areas. They make too many mistakes. You can read all the tactics you want and it won't help much. Well, I remembered what you said in the park that night when you first came, so when I got this assignment, and it's a nice assignment, I asked if I could take you along as a kind of understudy. I've been out, see? I'll train you, and then you can train new men. Kind of like teaching hunting dogs by running them with the old boys, see? You can learn more by getting into it than by reading all you like. Ever been in the Torgas Valley, Jim?"

Jim blew on a hot potato. "I don't even know where it is," he said. "I've only been out of town four or five times

in my life. Thanks for taking me, Mac." His small grey eyes were ashine with excitement.

"You'll probably cuss hell out of me before we're through if we get in a mess down there. It's going to be no picnic. I hear the Growers' Association is pretty well organized."

Jim gave up trying to eat the hot stew. "How we going to go about it, Mac? What do we do first?"

Mac looked over at him and saw his excitement, and laughed. "I don't know, Jim. That's the trouble with reading, you see. We just have to use any material we can pick up. That's why all the tactics in the world won't do it. No two are exactly alike." For a while he ate in silence, finished off his stew, and when he exhaled, steam came out of his mouth. "Enough for another helping, Jim? I'm hungry."

Jim went to the kitchen and filled his bowl again.

Mac said, "Here's the layout. Torgas is a little valley, and it's mostly apple orchards. Most of it's owned by a few men. Of course there's some little places, but there's not very many of them. Now when the apples are ripe the crop tramps come in and pick them. And from there they go on over the ridge and south, and pick the cotton. If we can start the fun in the apples, maybe it will just naturally spread over into the cotton. Now these few guys that own most of the Torgas Valley waited until most of the crop tramps were already there. They spent most of their money getting there, of course. They always do. And then the owners announced their price cut. Suppose the tramps are mad? What can they do? They've got to work picking apples to get out even."

Jim's dinner was neglected. With his spoon he stirred the meat and potatoes around and around. He leaned forward.

"So then we try to get the men to strike? Is that it?"

"Sure. Maybe it's all ready to bust and we just give it a little tiny push. We organize the men, and then we picket the orchards."

Jim said, "Suppose the owners raise the wages to get their apples picked?"

Mac pushed away his finished second bowl. "Well, we'd find another job to do somewhere else soon enough. Hell, we don't want only temporary pay raises, even though we're glad to see a few poor bastards better off. We got to take the long view. A strike that's settled too quickly won't teach the men how to organize, how to work together. A tough strike is good. We want the men to find out how strong they are when they work together."

"Well, suppose," Jim insisted, "suppose the owners do meet the demands?"

"I don't think they will. There's the bulk of power in the hands of a few men. That always makes 'em cocky. Now we start our strike, and Torgas County gets itself an ordinance that makes congregation unlawful. Now what happens? We congregate the men. A bunch of sheriff's men try to push them around, and that starts a fight. There's nothing like a fight to cement the men together. Well, then the owners start a vigilantes committee, bunch of fool shoe clerks, or my friends the American Legion boys trying to pretend they aren't middle-aged, cinching in their belts to hide their pot-bellies—there I go again. Well, the vigilantes start shooting. If they knock over some of the tramps we have a public funeral; and after that, we get some real action. Maybe they have to call out the troops." He was breathing hard in excitement. "Jesus, man! The troops win, all right! But every time a guardsman jabs a fruit tramp with a bayonet a thousand men all over the country come on our side. Christ Almighty! If we can only get the troops called out." He settled back on his cot. "Aw, I'm looking ahead too much. Our job's just to push along our little baby strike, if we can. But God damn it, Jim, if we could get the National Guard called out, now with the crops coming ready, we'd have the whole district organized by spring."

Jim had been crouching on his bed, his eyes shining and his jaws set. Now and then his fingers went nervously to his throat. Mac continued, "The damn fools think they can settle strikes with soldiers." He laughed. "Here I go again—talking like a soap-boxer. I get all worked up, and that's not so good. We got to think good. Oh say, Jim, have you got some blue jeans?"

"No. This suit's all the clothes I own."

"Well, we'll have to go out and buy you some in a second-hand store, then. You're going to pick apples, boy. And you're going to sleep in jungles. And you're going to do Party work after you've done ten hours in the orchard. Here's the work you wanted."

Jim said, "Thanks, Mac. My old man always had to fight alone. He got licked every time."

Mac came and stood over him. "Get those three letters finished, Jim, and then we'll go out and buy you some jeans."

4

The sun was just clearing the buildings of the city when Jim and Mac came to the railroad yards, where the shining metals converged and separated and spread out into the great gridiron of storage tracks where line after line of cars stood.

Mac said, "There's a freight train supposed to go out at seven-thirty, empties. Let's go down the track a way." He hurried through the yard toward the end, where the many tracks drew together into the main line.

"Do we have to get it on the move?" Jim asked.

"Oh, it won't be going fast. I forgot, you never caught a freight, did you?"

Jim spread his stride in an attempt to walk on every other tie, and found he couldn't quite make it. "Seems to me I never did much of anything," he admitted. "Everything's new to me."

"Well, it's easy now. The company lets guys ride. In the old days it was tough. Train crews used to throw the stiffs off a moving train when they could catch them."

A great black water tower stood beside the track, its goose-neck spout raised up against its side. The multitude of tracks was behind them, and only one line of worn and mirror-polished rails extended ahead. "Might as well sit down and wait," said Mac. "She'll be along pretty soon now."

The long, lonely howl of a train whistle and the slow crash of escaping steam sounded at the end of his words. And at the signal, men began to stand up out of the ditch beside the track and to stretch their arms lazily in the cool morning sun.

"We're going to have company," Mac observed.

The long freight of empties came slowly down the yard, red box-cars and yellow refrigerator cars, black iron gondolas and round tank cars. The engine went by at little more pace than a man could walk, and the engineer waved a black, shiny glove at the men in the ditch. He yelled, "Going to the picnic?" and playfully released a spurt of white steam from between the wheels.

Mac said, "We want a box-car. There, that one. The door's open a little." Trotting beside the car he pushed at the door. "Give a hand," he called. Jim put his hand to the iron handle and threw his weight against it. The big sliding door screeched rustily open a few feet. Mac put his hands on the sill, vaulted, turned in the air and landed in a sitting position in the doorway. Quickly he stood up out of the way while Jim imitated him. The floor of the car was littered with lining paper, torn down from the walls. Mac kicked a pile of the paper together and forced it against the wall. "Get yourself some," he shouted. "It makes a nice cushion."

Before Jim had piled up his paper, a new head appeared in the doorway. A man flung himself in and two more followed him. The first man looked quickly about the car floor and then stood over Mac. "Got just about all of it, didn't you?"

"Got what?" Mac asked innocently.

"The paper. You done a good clean job."

Mac smiled disarmingly. "We didn't know there was guests coming." He stood up. "Here, take some of it."

The man gaped at Mac for a moment, and then he leaned over and picked up the whole cushion of papers.

Mac touched him gently on the shoulder. "All right, punk," he said in a monotone. "Put it all down. If you're going to be a hog you don't get none."

The man dropped the paper. "You going to make me?" he asked.

Mac dropped daintily back, balancing on the balls of his feet. His hands hung open and loose at his sides. "Do you ever go to the Rosanna Fight Stadium?" he asked.

"Yeah, and what of it?"

"You're a God-damn liar," Mac said. "If you went there, you'd know who I am, and you'd take better care of yourself."

A look of doubt came over the man's face. He glanced uneasily at the two men who had come with him. One stood by the doorway, looking out at the moving country. The other one elaborately cleaned his nostrils with a bandana and inspected his findings. The first man looked at Mac again. "I don't want no trouble," he said. "I just want a little bit of paper to sit on."

Mac dropped on his heels. "O.K.," he said. "Take some. But leave some, too." The man approached the pile and picked up a small handful. "Oh, you can have more than that."

"We ain't goin' far," said the man. He settled down beside the door and clasped his legs with his arms, and rested his chin on his knees.

The blocks were passed now, and the train gathered speed. The wooden car roared like a sounding-box. Jim stood up and pushed the door wide open to let in the morning sunlight. He sat down in the doorway and hung his legs over. For a while he looked down, until the flashing ground made him dizzy. And then he raised his eyes to the yellow stubble fields beside the track. The air was keen and pleasantly flavored with smoke from the engine.

In a moment Mac joined him. "Look you don't fall out," he shouted. "I knew a guy once that got dizzy looking at the ground and fell right out on his face."

Jim pointed to a white farmhouse and a red barn, half hidden beind a row of young eucalyptus trees. "Is the country we're going to as pretty as this?"

"Prettier," said Mac. "It's all apple trees, miles of 'em. They'll be covered with apples this season, just covered with 'em. The limbs just sagging down with apples you pay a nickel apiece for in town."

"Mac, I don't know why I didn't come into the country oftener. It's funny how you want to do a thing and never do it. Once when I was a kid one of those lodges took about five hundred of us on a picnic, took us in trucks. We walked around and around. There were big trees. I remember I climbed up in the top of a tree and sat there most of the afternoon. I thought I'd go back there every time I could. But I never did."

Mac said, "Stand up, Jim. Let's close this door. We're coming to Wilson. No good irritating the railroad cops."

Together they pulled the door shut, and suddenly the car was dark and warm, and it throbbed like the body of a bass viol. The beat of wheels on the rail-ends grew less rapid as the freight slowed to go through the town. The three men stood up. "We get out here," the leader said. He pushed open the door a foot. His two followers swung out. He turned to Mac. "I hope you don't hold no grudge, pardner."

"No, 'course not."

"Well, so long." He swung out. "You dirty son-of-a-bitch," he yelled as he hit the ground.

Mac laughed and pulled the door nearly shut. For a few moments the train rolled slowly. And the rail-end tempo increased. Mac threw the door wide again and sat down in the sun. "There was a beauty," he said.

Jim asked, "Are you really a prize-fighter, Mac?"

"Hell no. He was the easiest kind of a sucker. He figured I was scared of him when I offered him some of my paper. You can't make a general rule of it, because sometimes it flops, but mostly a guy that tries to scare you is a guy that can be scared." He turned his heavy, good-natured face to Jim. "I don't know why it is, but every time I talk to you I either end up soap-boxing or giving a lecture."

"Well, hell, Mac, I like to listen."

"I guess that's it. We've got to get off at Weaver and catch an east-bound freight. That's about a hundred miles down. If we're lucky, we ought to get to Torgas in the middle of the night." He pulled out a sack of tobacco and rolled a cigarette, holding the paper in out of the rushing air. "Smoke, Jim?"

"No, thanks."

"You got no vices, have you? And you're not a Christer either. Don't you even go out with girls?"

"No," said Jim. "Used to be, when I got riled up I'd go to a cat-house. You wouldn't believe it, Mac, but ever since I started to grow up I been scared of girls. I guess I was scared I'd get caught."

"Too attractive, huh?"

"No, you see all the guys I used to run around with went through the mill. They used to try to make girls behind billboards and down in the lumber yard. Well, sooner or later some girl'd get knocked higher than a kite, and then— well, hell, Mac, I was scared I'd get caught like my mother and my old man—two-room flat and a wood stove. Christ knows I don't want luxury, but I don't want to get batted around the way all the kids I knew got it. Lunch pail in the morning with a piece of soggy pie and a thermos bottle of stale coffee."

Mac said, "You've picked a hell of a fine life if you don't want to get batted around. Wait till we finish this job, you'll get batted plenty."

"That's different," Jim protested. "I don't mind getting smacked on the chin. I just don't want to get nibbled to death. There's a difference."

Mac yawned. "It's not a difference that's going to keep me awake. Cathouses aren't much fun." He got up and went back to the pile of papers, and he spread them out and lay down and went to sleep.

For a long time Jim sat in the doorway, watching the farms go by. There were big market vegetable gardens with rows of round lettuces and rows of fernlike carrots, and red beet leaves, with glistening water running between the rows. The train went by fields of alfalfa, and by great white dairy barns from which the wind brought the rich, healthy smell of manure and ammonia. And then the freight entered a pass in the hills, and the sun was cut off. Ferns and green live oaks grew on the steep sides of the right-of-way. The roaring rhythm of the train beat on Jim's senses and made him drowsy. He fought off sleep so that he might see more of the country, shook his head violently to jar himself awake; but at last he stood up, ran the door nearly closed, and retired to his own pile of papers. His sleep was a shouting, echoing black cave, and it extended into eternity.

Mac shook him several times before he could wake up. "It's nearly time to get off," Mac shouted.

Jim sat up. "Good God, have we gone a hundred miles?"

"Pretty near. Noise kind of drugs you, don't it? I can't ever stay awake in a boxcar. Pull yourself together. We're going to slow down in a couple of minutes."

Jim held his dull head between his hands for a moment. "I do feel slugged," he said.

Mac threw open the door. He called, "Jump the way we're going, and land running." He leaped out, and Jim followed him.

Jim looked at the sun, almost straight overhead. In front of him he could see the clustered houses and the shade trees of a little town. The freight pulled on and left them standing.

Mac explained, "The railroad branches here. The line we want cuts over that way toward the Torgas Valley. We won't go through town at all. Let's jump across the fields and catch the line over there."

Jim followed him over a barbed-wire fence and across a stubble field, and into a dirt road. They skirted the edge of the little town, and in half a mile came upon another railroad right-of-way.

Mac sat down on the embankment and

called Jim to sit beside him. "Here's a good place. There's lots of cars moving. I don't know how long we'll have to wait." He rolled a brown cigarette. "Jim," he said. "You ought to take up smoking. It's a nice social habit. You'll have to talk to a lot of strangers in your time. I don't know any quicker way to soften a stranger down than to offer him a smoke, or even to ask him for one. And lots of guys feel insulted if they offer you a cigarette and you don't take it. You better start."

"I guess I will," said Jim. "I used to smoke with the kids. I wonder if it'd make me sick now."

"Try it. Here, I'll roll one for you."

Jim took the cigarette and lighted it. "It tastes pretty good," he said. "I'd almost forgotten what it tasted like."

"Well, even if you don't like it, it's a good thing to do in our work. It's the one little social thing guys in our condition have. Listen, there's a train coming." He stood up. "It looks like a freight, too."

The train came slowly down the track. "Well, for Christ's sake!" Mac cried. "Eighty-seven! It's our own train. They told me in town that train went on south. It must of dropped off a few cars and then come right out."

"Let's get our old car back," said Jim. "I liked that car."

As it came abreast, they hopped aboard the box-car again. Mac settled into his pile of papers. "We might just as well have stayed asleep."

Jim sat in the doorway again, while the train crept into the round brown hills, and through two short tunnels. He could still taste the tobacco in his mouth, and it tasted good. Suddenly he dug in the pocket of his blue denim coat. "Mac," he cried.

"Yeah? What?"

"Here's a couple of chocolate bars I got last night."

Mac took one of the bars and lazily unwrapped it. "I can see you're going to be an asset in any man's revolution," he said.

In about an hour the drowsiness came upon Jim again. Reluctantly he closed the door of the car and curled up in his papers. Almost instantly he was in the black, roaring cave again, and the sound made dreams of water pouring over him. Vaguely he could see debris and broken bits of wood in the water. And the water bore him down and down into the dark place below dreaming.

He awakened when Mac shook him. "I bet you'd sleep a week if I'd let you. You've put in over twelve hours today."

Jim rubbed his eyes hard. "I feel slugged again."

"Well, get yourself together. We're coming into Torgas."

"Good God, what time is it?"

"Somewhere about midnight, I guess. Here we come; you ready to hop?"

"Sure."

"O.K. Come on."

The train pulled slowly on away from them. The station of Torgas was only a little way ahead, with its red light on and glancing along the blade of the semaphore. The brakeman was swinging a lantern back and forth. Over to the right the lonely, cold street lights of the town burned and put a pale glow in the sky. The air was cold now. A sharp, soundless wind blew.

"I'm hungry," Jim said. "Got any ideas about eating, Mac?"

"Wait till we get to a light. I think I've got a good prospect on my list." He hurried away into the darkness, and Jim trotted after him. They came immediately into the edge of the town, and on a corner, under one of the lights, Mac stopped and pulled out a sheet of paper. "We got a nice town here, Jim," he said. "Nearly fifty active sympathizers. Guys you can rely on to give you a lift. Here's the guy I want. Alfred Anderson, Townsend, between Fourth and Fifth, Al's Lunch Wagon. What do you think of that?"

"What's that paper?" Jim asked.

"Why, it's a list of all the people in town we know to be sympathizers. With this list we can get anything from knitted wristlets to a box of shotgun shells. But Al's Lunch Wagon—lunch wagons generally stay open all night, Jim. Townsend, that'll be one of the main streets. Come on, but let me work this."

They turned soon into the main street, and walked down its length until, near the end, where stores were vacant and lots occurred between buildings, they found Al's Lunch Wagon, a cozy looking little car with red stained glass in the windows, and a sliding door. Through the window they could see that two customers sat on the stools, and that a fat young man with heavy, white, bare arms hovered behind the counter.

"Pie and coffee guys," Mac said. "Let's wait till they finish."

While they loitered, a policeman approached, and eyed them. Mac said loudly, "I don't want to go home till I get a piece of pie."

Jim reacted quickly. "Come on home," he said. "I'm too sleepy to eat."

The policeman passed them. He seemed almost to sniff at them as he went by. Mac said quietly, "He thinks we're trying to get up our nerve to stick up the wagon." The policeman turned and walked back toward them. Mac said, "Well, go home then, if you want. I'm going to get a piece of pie." He climbed the three steps and slid open the door of the lunch wagon.

The proprietor smiled at them. " 'Evening, gents," he said. "Turning on cold, ain't it?"

"Sure is," said Mac. He walked to the end of the counter farthest from the other two customers and sat down. A shadow of annoyance crossed Al's face.

"Now listen, you guys," he said. "If you got no money you can have a cup of coffee and a couple of sinkers. But don't eat up a dinner on me and then tell me to call a cop. Jesus, I'm being busted by panhandlers."

Mac laughed shortly. "Coffee and sinkers will be just elegant, Alfred," he said.

The proprietor glanced suspiciously at him and took off his high white cook's hat, and scratched his head.

The customers drained their cups together. One of them asked, "Do you always feed bums, Al?"

"Well, Jesus, what can you do? If a guy wants a cup of coffee on a cold night, you can't let him down because he hasn't got a lousy nickel."

The customer chuckled. "Well, twenty cups of coffee is a dollar, Al. You'll fold up if you go about it that way. Coming, Will?" The two got up and paid their checks and walked out.

Al came around the corner and followed them to the door and slid it more tightly closed. Then he walked back down the counter and leaned over toward Mac. "Who are you guys?" he demanded. He had fat, comfortable white arms, bare to the elbows. He carried a damp cloth with which he wiped and wiped at the counter, with little circular movements. His manner of leaning close when he spoke made every speech seem secret.

Mac winked solemnly, like a conspirator. "We're sent down from the city on business," he said.

A red flush of excitement bloomed on Al's fat cheeks. "Oho-o. That's just what I thought when you come in. How'd you know to come to me?"

Mac explained. "You been good to our people, and we don't forget things like that."

Al beamed importantly, as though he were receiving a gift instead of being bummed for a meal. "Here, wait," he said. "You guys probably ain't ate today. I'll sling on a couple of hamburg steaks."

"That'll be swell," Mac agreed enthusiastically. "We're just about starved."

Al went to his ice-box and dug out two handfuls of ground meat. He patted them thin between his hands, painted the gas plate with a little brush and tossed down the steaks. He put chopped onions on top and around the meat. A delicious odor filled the room instantly.

"Lord," said Mac. "I'd like to crawl right over this counter and nest in that hamburger."

The meat hissed loudly and the onions began to turn brown. Al leaned over the counter again. "What you guys got on down here?"

"Well, you got a lot of nice apples," said Mac.

Al pushed himself upright and leaned against the fat buttresses of his arms. His little eyes grew very wise and secret. "Oho," he said. "O-ho-o, I get you."

"Better turn over that meat, then," said Mac.

Al flipped the steaks and pressed them down with his spatula. And he gathered in the vagrant onions and heaped them on top of the meat, and pressed them in. Very deliberate he was in his motions, as inwardly-thoughtful-looking as a ruminating cow. At last he came back and planted himself in front of Mac. "My old man's got a little orchard and a piece of land," he said. "You guys wouldn't hurt him none, would you? I been good to you."

"Sure you been good," said Mac. "The little farmers don't suffer from us. You tell your father we won't hurt him; and if he gives us a break, we'll see his fruit gets picked."

"Thanks," said Al. "I'll tell him." He took up the steaks, spooned mashed potatoes on the plates from the steam table, made a hollow in each potato mountain and filled the white craters with light brown gravy.

Mac and Jim ate voraciously and drank the mugs of coffee Al set for them. And they wiped their plates with bread and ate the bread while Al filled up their coffee cups again. "That was swell, Al," Jim said. "I was starved."

Mac added, "It sure was. You're a good guy, Al."

"I'd be along with you," Al explained, "if I didn't have a business, and if my old man didn't own land. I guess I'd get this joint wrecked if anybody ever found out."

"They'll never find out from us, Al."

"Sure, I know that."

"Listen, Al, are there many working stiffs in yet for the harvest?"

"Yeah, big bunch of them. Good many eat here. I set up a pretty nice dinner for a quarter—soup, meat, two vegetables, bread and butter, pie and two cups of coffee for a quarter. I take a little profit and sell more."

"Good work," said Mac. "Listen, Al, did you hear any of the stiffs talking about a leader?"

"Leader?"

"Sure, I mean some guy that kind of tells 'em where to put their feet."

"I see what you mean," said Al. "No, I don't rightly recall nothing about it."

"Well, where are the guys hanging out?"

Al rubbed his soft chin. "Well, there's two bunches I know of. One's out on Palo Road, alongside the county highway, and then there's a bunch jungled up by the river. There's a regular old jungle down there in the willows."

"That's the stuff. How do we get there?"

Al pointed a thick finger. "You take that cross street and stay on it till you get to the edge of town, and there's the river and the bridge. Then you'll find a path through the willows, off to the left. Follow that about a quarter mile, and there you are. I don't know how many guys is there."

Mac stood up and put on his hat. "You're a good guy, Al. We'll get along now. Thanks for the feed."

Al said, "My old man's got a shed with a cot in it, if you'd like to stay out there."

"Can't do it, Al. If we're going to work, we got to get out among them."

"Well, if you want a bite now and then, come on in," said Al. "Only pick it like tonight when there's nobody here, won't you?"

"Sure, Al. We get you. Thanks again."

Mac let Jim precede him through the door and then slid it closed behind him. They walked down the steps and took the street Al had pointed out. At the corner the policeman stepped out of a doorway. "What's on your minds?" he asked harshly.

Jim jumped back at the sudden appearance, but Mac stood quietly. "Couple of workin' stiffs, mister," he said. "We figure to pick a few apples."

"What you doing on the street this time of night?"

"Hell, we just got off that freight that went through an hour ago!"

"Where you going now?"

"Thought we'd jungle up with the boys down by the river."

The policeman maintained his position in front of them. "Got any money?"

"You saw us buy a meal, didn't you? We got enough to keep out of jail on a vag charge."

The policeman stood aside then. "Well, get going, and keep off the streets at night."

"O.K., mister."

They walked quickly on. Jim said, "You sure talked to him pretty, Mac."

"Why not? That's the first lesson. Never argue with a cop, particularly at night. It'd be swell if we got thirty days for vagrancy right now, wouldn't it?"

They hugged their denim clothes against their chests and hurried along the street, and the lights grew more infrequent.

"How are you going to go about getting started?" Jim asked.

"I don't know. We've got to use everything. Look, we start out with a general plan, but the details have to be worked out with any materials we can find. We use everything we can get hold of. That's the only thing we can do. We'll just look over the situation."

Jim lengthened his stride with a drive of energy. "Well, let me do things, won't you, Mac? I don't want to be a stooge all my life."

Mac laughed. "You'll get used, all right. You'll get used till you'll wish you was back in town with an eight-hour job."

"No, I don't think I will, Mac. I never felt so good before. I'm all swelled up with a good feeling. Do you feel that way?"

"Sometimes," said Mac. "Mostly I'm too damn busy to know how I feel."

The buildings along the street were more dilapidated as they went. Welding works and used car lots and the great trash piles of auto-wrecking yards. The street lights shone on the blank, dead windows of old and neglected houses, and made shadows under shrubs that had gone to brush. The men walked quickly in the cool night air. "I think I see the bridge lights now," Jim said. "See those three lights on each side?"

"I see 'em. Didn't he say turn left?"

"Yeah, left."

It was a two-span concrete bridge over a narrow river that was reduced at this season to a sluggish little creek in the middle of a sandy bed. Jim and Mac went to the left of the bridge ramp, and near the edge of the river bed they found the opening of a trail into the willows. Mac took the lead. In a moment they were out of range of the bridge lights, and the thick willow scrub was all about them. They could see the branches against the lighter sky, and, to the right, on the edge of the river bed, a dark wall of large cottonwoods.

"I can't see this path," Mac said. "I'll just have to feel it with my feet." He moved carefully, slowly. "Hold up your arms to protect your face, Jim."

"I am. I got switched right across the mouth a minute ago." For a while they felt their way along the hard, used trail. "I smell smoke," Jim said. "It can't be far now."

Suddenly Mac stopped. "There's lights ahead. Listen, Jim, the same thing goes as back there. Let me do the talking."

"O.K."

The trail came abruptly into a large clearing, flickeringly lighted by a little bonfire. Along the farther side were three dirty white tents; and in one of them a light burned and huge black figures moved on the canvas. In the clearing itself there were perhaps fifty men, some sleeping on the ground in sausage rolls of blankets, while a number sat around the little fire in the middle of the flat cleared place. As Jim and Mac stepped clear of the willows they heard a short, sharp cry, quickly checked, which came from the lighted tent. Immediately the great shadows moved nervously on the canvas.

"Somebody's sick," Mac said softly. "We didn't hear it yet. It pays to appear to mind your own business."

They moved toward the fire, where a ring of men sat clasping their knees. "Can a guy join this club?" Mac asked. "Or does he got to be elected?"

The faces of the men were turned up at him, unshaven faces with eyes in which the firelight glowed. One of the men moved sideways to make room. "Ground's free, mister."

Mac chuckled. "Not where I come from."

A lean, lighted face across the fire spoke. "You come to a good place, fella. Everything's free here, food, liquor, automobiles, houses. Just move in and set down to a turkey dinner."

Mac squatted and motioned Jim to sit beside him. He pulled out his sack of tobacco and made a careful, excellent cigarette; then, as an afterthought, "Would any of you capitalists like a smoke?"

Several hands thrust out. The bag went from man to man. "Just get in?" the lean face asked.

"Just. Figure to pick a few apples and retire on my income."

Lean-face burst out angrily. "Know what they're payin', fella? Fifteen cents, *fifteen lousy cents!*"

"Well, what do you want?" Mac demanded. "Jesus Christ, man! You ain't got the nerve to say you want to eat? You can eat an apple while you're workin'. All them nice apples!" His tone grew hard. "S'pose we don't pick them apples?"

Lean-face cried, "We got to pick 'em. Spent every God-damned cent gettin' here."

Mac repeated softly, "All them nice apples. If we don't pick 'em, they'll rot."

"If we don't pick 'em, somebody else will."

"S'pose we don't let nobody else pick?" Mac said.

The men about the fire grew tense. "You mean—strike?" Lean-face asked.

Mac laughed. "I don't mean nothin'."

A short man who rested his chin between his knees said, "When London found out what they was payin' he damned near had a stroke." He turned to the man next to him. "You see him, Joe. Didn't he damn near have a stroke?"

"Turned green," said Joe. "Just stood there and turned green. Picked up a stick and bust it to splinters in his hands."

The bag of tobacco came back to its

starting place, but there was not much left in it. Mac felt it with his fingers and then put it in his pocket. "Who's London?" he asked.

Lean-face answered him. "London's a good guy—a big guy. We travel with him. He's a big guy."

"The boss, huh?"

"Well, no, he ain't a boss, but he's a good guy. We kind of travel with him. You ought to hear him talk to a cop. He——"

The cry came from the tent again, more prolonged this time. The men turned their heads toward it, and then looked apathetically back at the fire.

"Somebody sick?" Mac asked.

"London's daughter'n-law. She's havin' a kid."

Mac said, "This ain't no place t'have a kid. They got a doctor?"

"Hell no! Where'd they get a doctor?"

"Why'n't they take her to the county hospital?"

Lean-face scoffed. "They won't have no crop tramps in the county hospital. Don't you know that? They got no room. Always full-up."

"I know it," said Mac. "I just wondered if you did."

Jim shivered and picked up a little willow stick and thrust the end into the coals until it flared into flame. Mac's hand came stealing out of the darkness and took his arm for a moment, and gripped it.

Mac asked, "They got anybody that knows anything about it?"

"Got an old woman," Lean-face said. His eyes turned suspicious under the questioning. "Say, what's it to you?"

"I had some training," Mac explained casually. "I know something about it. Thought I might help out."

"Well, go see London." Lean-face shucked off responsibility. "It ain't none of our business to answer questions about him."

Mac ignored the suspicion. "Guess I will." He stood up. "Come on, Jim. Is London in that tent with the light?"

"Yeah, that's him."

A circle of lighted faces watched Jim and Mac walk away, and then the heads swung back to the fire again. The two men picked their way across the clearing, avoiding the bundles of cloth that were sleeping men.

Mac whispered, "What a break! If I can pull it off, we're started."

"What do you mean? Mac, I didn't know you had medical training."

"A whole slough of people don't know it," said Mac. They approached the tent, where dark figures moved about on the canvas. Mac stepped close and called, "London."

Almost instantly the tent-flap bellied and a large man stepped out. His shoulders were immense. Stiff dark hair grew in a tonsure, leaving the top of the head perfectly bald. His face was corded with muscular wrinkles and his dark eyes were as fierce and red as those of a gorilla. A power of authority was about the man. It could be felt that he led men as naturally as he breathed. With one big hand he held the tent-flap closed behind him. "What you want?" he demanded.

"We just got in," Mac explained. "Some guys over by the fire says there was a girl havin' a baby."

"Well, what of it?"

"I thought I might help out as long as you got no doctor."

London opened the flap and let a streak of light fall on Mac's face. "What you think you can do?"

"I worked in hospitals," Mac said. "I done this before. It don't pay to take no chances, London."

The big man's voice dropped. "Come on in," he said. "We got an old woman here, but I think she's nuts. Come in and take a look." He held up the tent-flap for them to enter.

Inside it was crowded and very hot. A candle burned in a saucer. In the middle of the tent stood a stove made of a kerosene can, and beside it sat an old and wrinkled woman. A white-faced boy stood in one corner of the tent. Along the rear wall an old mattress was laid on the ground, and on this lay a young girl, her face pale and streaked with brown dirt, her hair matted. The eyes of all three turned to Mac and Jim. The old woman looked up for a moment and then dropped her eyes to the red-hot stove. She scratched the back of one hand with the nails of the other.

London walked over to the mattress and kneeled down beside it. The girl pulled her frightened eyes from Mac and looked at London. He said, "We got a doctor here now. You don't need to be scared no more."

Mac looked down at her and winked. Her face was stiff with fright. The boy came over from his corner and pawed Mac's shoulder. "She gonna be all right, Doc?"

"Sure, she's O.K."

Mac turned to the old woman. "You a midwife?"

She scratched the backs of her wrinkled hands and looked vacantly up at him, but she didn't answer. "I asked if you was a midwife?" he cried.

"No—but I've took one or two babies in my life."

Mac reached down and picked up one of her hands and held the lighted candle close to it. The nails were long and broken and dirty, and the hands were bluish-grey. "You've took some dead ones, then," he said. "What was you goin' to use for cloths?"

The old woman pointed to a pile of newspapers. "Lisa ain't had but two pains," she whined. "We got papers to catch the mess."

London leaned forward, his mouth slightly open with attention, his eyes searching Mac's eyes. The tonsure shone in the candle-light. He corroborated the old woman. "Lisa had two pains, just finished one."

Mac made a little gesture toward the outside with his head. He went out through the tent-flap and London and Jim followed him. "Listen," he said to London, "you seen them hands. The kid might live if he's grabbed with hands like that, but the girl don't stand a hell of a chance. You better kick that old girl out."

"You do the job then?" London demanded.

Mac was silent for a moment. "Sure I'll do it. Jim, here'll help me some; but I got to have more help, a whole hell of a lot more help."

"Well, I'll give you a hand," London said.

"That ain't enough. Will any of the guys out there give a hand?"

London laughed shortly. "You damn right they will if I tell 'em."

"Well, you tell 'em, then," Mac said. "Tell 'em now." He led the way to the little fire, around which the circle of men still sat. They looked up as the three approached.

Lean-face said, "Hello, London."

London spoke loudly. "I want you guys should listen to Doc, here." A few other men strolled up and stood waiting. They were listless and apathetic, but they came to the voice of authority.

Mac cleared his throat. "London's got a daughter'n-law, and she's goin' to have a baby. He tried to get her in the county hospital, but they wouldn't take her. They're full-up, and besides we're a bunch of lousy crop tramps. O.K. They won't help us. We got to do it ourselves."

The men seemed to stiffen a little, to draw together. The apathy began to drop from them. They hunched closer to the fire. Mac went on, "Now I worked in hospitals, so I can help, but I need you guys to help too. Christ, we got to stand by our own people. Nobody else will."

Lean-face boosted himself up. "All right, fella," he said. "What do you want us to do?"

In the firelight Mac's face broke into a smile of pleasure and of triumph. "Swell!" he said. "You guys know how to work together. Now first we got to have water boiling. When it's boiling, we got to get white cloth into it, and boil the cloth. I don't care where you get the cloth, or how you get it." He pointed out three men. "Now you and you and you get a big fire going. And you get a couple of big kettles. There ought to be some five-gallon cans around. The rest of you gather up cloth; get anything, handkerchiefs, old shirts—anything, as long as it's white. When you get the water boiling, put the cloth in and keep it boiling for half an hour. I want a little pot of hot water as quick as I can get it." The men were beginning to get restive. Mac said, "Wait. One more thing. I want a lamp, a good one. Some of you guys get me one. If nobody'll give you one, steal it. I got to have light."

A change was in the air. The apathy was gone from the men. Sleepers were awakened and told, and added themselves to the group. A current of excitement filled the jungle, but a kind of joyful excitement. Fires were built up. Four big cans of water were put on to boil; and then cloth began to appear. Every man seemed to have something to add to the pile. One took off his undershirt and threw it into the water and then put on his shirt again. The men seemed suddenly happy. They laughed together as they broke dead cottonwood branches for the fire.

Jim stood beside Mac, watching the activity. "What do you want me to do?" he asked.

"Come in with me. You can help me in the tent." At that moment a cry came

from the tent. Mac said quickly, "Bring me a can of hot water as quick as you can, Jim. Here," he held out a little bottle. "Put about four of these tablets in each of those big cans. Bring the bottle back to me when you bring the water." He hurried away toward the tent.

Jim counted the tablets into the cans, and then he scooped a large bucketful of water from one of them and followed Mac into the tent. The old woman was crouched in a corner, out of the way. She scratched her hands and peered out suspiciously while Mac dropped two of the tablets into the warm water and dipped his hands into it. "We can anyway get our hands clean," he said.

"What's the bottle?"

"Bichloride of mercury. I always take it with me. Here, you wash your hands, Jim, and then get some fresh water."

A voice outside the tent called, "Here's your lamps, Doc."

Mac went to the flap and brought them back, a roundwick Rochester lamp and a powerful gasoline lantern. "Some poor devil's going to do his milking in the dark," he said to Jim. He pumped up pressure in the gasoline lamp, and when he lighted it the mantles glared, a hard, white light, and the lantern's hiss filled the tent. The crack of breaking wood and the sound of voices came in from outside.

Mac set his lantern down beside the mattress. "Going to be all right, Lisa," he said. Gently he tried to lift the dirty quilt which covered her. London and the white-faced boy looked on. In a panic of modesty Lisa held the quilt down about her. "Come on, Lisa, I've got to get you ready," Mac said persuasively. Still she clutched at the quilt.

London stepped over. "Lisa," he said, "you do it." Her frightened eyes swung to London, and then reluctantly she let go her hold on the quilt. Mac folded it back over her breast and unbuttoned her cotton underwear. "Jim," he called, "go out and fish me a piece of cloth and get me some soap."

When Jim had brought him a steaming cloth and a thin, hard piece of soap, Mac washed the legs and thighs and stomach. He worked so gently that some of the fear left Lisa's face.

The men brought in the boiled cloths.

The pains came quicker and quicker.

It was dawn when the birth started. Once the tent shook violently. Mac looked over his shoulder. "London, your kid's fainted," he said. "Better take him out in the air." With a look of profound embarrassment London slung the frail boy over his shoulder and carried him out.

The baby's head appeared. Mac supported it with his hands, and while Lisa squealed weakly, the birth was completed. Mac cut the cord with a sterilized pocketknife.

The sun shone on the canvas and the lantern hissed on. Jim wrung out the warm cloths and handed them to Mac when he washed the shrunken little baby. And Jim washed and scrubbed the hands of the old woman before Mac let her take the baby. An hour later the placenta came, and Mac carefully washed Lisa again. "Now get all this mess out," he told London. "Burn all these rags."

London asked, "Even the cloths you didn't use?"

"Yep. Burn it all. It's no good." His eyes were tired. He took a last look around the tent. The old woman held the wrapped baby in her arms. Lisa's eyes were closed and she breathed quietly on her mattress. "Come on, Jim. Let's get some sleep."

In the clearing the men were sleeping again. The sun shone on the tops of the willows. Mac and Jim crawled into a little cave in the undergrowth and lay down together.

Jim said, "My eyes feel sandy. I'm tired. I never knew you worked in a hospital, Mac."

Mac crossed his hands behind his head. "I never did."

"Well, where did you learn about births?"

"I never learned till now. I never saw one before. The only thing I knew was that it was a good idea to be clean. God, I was lucky it came through all right. If anything'd happened, we'd've been sunk. That old woman knew lots more than I did. I think she knew it, too."

"You acted sure enough," Jim said.

"Well, Christ Almighty, I had to! We've got to use whatever material comes to us. That was a lucky break. We simply had to take it. 'Course it was nice to help the girl, but hell, even if it killed her—we've got to use anything." He turned on his side and pillowed his head on his arm. "I'm all in, but I feel good. With one night's work we've got the confidence of the men and the confidence of London. And more than that, we made the men work for themselves, in their own defense, as a group. That's what we're out here for anyway, to teach them to fight in a bunch. Raising wages isn't all we're after. You know all that."

"Yes," Jim said. "I knew that, but I didn't know how you were going to go about it."

"Well, there's just one rule—use whatever material you've got. We've got no machine-guns and troops. Tonight was good; the material was ready, and we were ready. London's with us. He's the natural leader. We'll teach him where to lead. Got to go awful easy, though. Leadership has to come from the men. We can teach them method, but they've got to do the job themselves. Pretty soon we'll start teaching method to London, and he can teach it to the men under him. You watch," Mac said, "the story of last night will be all over the district by tonight. We got our oar in already, and it's better than I hoped. We might go to the can later for practicing medicine without a license, but that would only tie the men closer to us."

Jim asked, "How did it happen? You didn't say much, but they started working like a clock, and they liked it. They felt fine."

"Sure they liked it. Men always like to work together. There's a hunger in men to work together. Do you know that ten men can lift nearly twelve times as big a load as one man can? It only takes a little spark to get them going. Most of the time they're suspicious, because every time someone gets 'em working in a group the profit of their work is taken away from them; but wait till they get working for themselves. Tonight the work concerned them, it was their job; and see how well they did it."

Jim said, "You didn't need all that cloth. Why did you tell London to burn it?"

"Look, Jim. Don't you see? Every man who gave part of his clothes felt that the work was his own. They all feel responsible for that baby. It's theirs, because something from them went to it. To give back the cloth would cut them out. There's no better way to make men part of a movement than to have them give something to it. I bet they all feel fine right now."

"Are we going to work today?" Jim asked.

"No, we'll let the story of last night go the rounds. It'll be a hell of a big story by tomorrow. No, we'll go to work later. We need sleep now. But Jesus, what a swell set-up it is for us so far."

The willows stirred over their heads, and a few leaves fell down on the men. Jim said, "I don't know when I ever was so tired, but I do feel fine."

Mac opened his eyes for a moment. "You're doing all right, kid. I think you'll make a good worker. I'm glad you came down with me. You helped a lot last night. Now try to shut your God-damned eyes and mouth and get some sleep."

5

The afternoon sun glanced on the tops of the apple trees and then broke into stripes and layers of slanting light beneath the heavy branches, and threw blots of sunshine on the ground. The wide aisles between the trees stretched away until the rows seemed to meet in a visual infinity. The great orchard crawled with activity. Long ladders leaned among the branches and piles of new yellow boxes stood in the aisles. From far away came the rumble of the sorting machines and the tap of the boxers' hammers. The men, with their big buckets slung to baldrics, ran up the ladders and twisted the big green pippins free and filled the buckets until they could hold no more, and then they ran down the ladders to empty the buckets into the boxes. Between the rows came the trucks to load the picked apples and take them to the sorting and packing plant. A checker stood beside the boxes and marked with a pencil in his little book as the bucket men came up. The orchard was alive. The branches of the trees shook under the ladders. The overripes dropped with dull plops to the ground underneath the trees. Somewhere, hidden in a tree-top, a whistling virtuoso trilled.

Jim hurried down his ladder and carried his bucket to the box pile and emptied the load. The checker, a blond young man in washed white corduroys, made a mark in his book and nodded his head. "Don't dump 'em in so hard, buddy," he warned. "You'll bruise 'em."

"O.K.," said Jim. He walked back to his ladder, drumming on the bucket with his knee as he went. Up the ladder he climbed, and he hooked the wire of the balehook over a limb. And then in the tree he saw another man, who had stepped off the ladder and stood on a big limb. He reached high over his head for a cluster of apples. He felt the tree shudder under Jim's weight and looked down.

"Hello, kid. I didn't know this was your tree."

Jim stared up at him, a lean old man with black eyes and a sparse, chewed beard. The veins stood out heavy and blue on his hands. His legs seemed as thin and straight as sticks, too thin for the big feet with great heavy-soled shoes.

Jim said, "I don't give a damn about the tree. Aren't you too old to be climbing around like a monkey, Dad?"

The old man spat and watched the big white drop hit the ground. His bleak eyes grew fierce. "That's what you think," he said. "Lots of young punks think I'm too old. I can out-work you any day in the week, and don't you forget it, neither." He put an artificial springiness in his knees as he spoke. He reached up and picked the whole cluster of apples, twig and all, skinned the apples into his bucket and contemptuously dropped the twig on the ground.

The voice of the checker called, "Careful of those trees, over there."

The old man grinned maliciously, showing two upper and two lower yellow teeth, long and sloped outward, like a gopher's teeth. "Busy bastard, ain't he," he remarked to Jim.

"College boy," said Jim. "Every place you go you run into 'em."

The old man squatted down on his limb. "And what do they know?" he demanded. "They go to them colleges, and they don't learn a God-damn thing. That

smart guy with the little book couldn't keep his ass dry in a barn." He spat again.

"They get pretty smart, all right," Jim agreed.

"Now you and me," the old man went on, "we know—not much, maybe, but what we know we know good."

Jim was silent for a moment, and then he lanced at the old man's pride as he had heard Mac do to other men. "You don't know enough to keep out of a tree when you're seventy. I don't know enough to wear white cords and make pencil marks in a little book."

The old man snarled, "We got no pull, that's what. You got to have pull to get an easy job. We just get rode over because we got no pull."

"Well, what you going to do about it?"

The question seemed to let air out of the old man. His anger disappeared. His eyes grew puzzled and a little frightened. "Christ only knows," he said. "We just take it, that's all. We move about the country like a bunch of hogs and get beat on the ass by a college boy."

"It's not his fault," said Jim. "He's just got a job. If he's going to keep the job, he's got to do it."

The old man reached for another cluster of apples, picked them with little twisting lifts and put each one carefully into his bucket. "When I was a young man, I used to think somethin' could be done," he said, "but I'm seventy-one." His voice was tired.

A truck went by, carrying off the filled boxes. The old man continued, "I was in the north woods when the Wobblies was raising hell. I'm a top-faller, a damn good one. Maybe you noticed how I take to a tree at my age. Well, I had hopes then. 'Course the Wobblies done some good, used to be there was no crappers but a hole in the ground, and no place to take a bath. The meat used to spoil. Well, them Wobblies made 'em put in toilets and showers; but, hell, it all went to pieces." His hand went up automatically for more apples. "I joined unions," he said. "We'd elect a president and first thing we knowed, he'd be kissing the ass of the superintendent, and then he'd sell us out. We'd pay dues, and the treasurer'd run out on us. I don' know. Maybe you young squirts can figure something out. We done what we could."

"You all ready to give up?" Jim asked, glancing at him again.

The old man squatted down on his limb and held himself there with one big skinny hand. "I got feelings in my skin," he said. "You may think I'm a crazy old coot; them other things was planned; nothing come of 'em; but I got feelings in my skin."

"What kind of feelings?"

"It's hard to say, kid. You know quite a bit before water boils, it gets to heavin' around? That's the kind of feeling I got. I been with workin' stiffs all my life. There ain't a plan in this at all. It's just like that water heavin' before it boils." His eyes were dim, seeing nothing. His head rose up so that two strings of skin tautened between his chin and his throat. "Maybe there's been too much goin' hungry; maybe too many bosses've kicked hell out of the men. I dunno. I just feel it in my skin."

"Well, what is it?" Jim asked.

"It's anger," the old man cried. "That's what it is. You know when you're about to get fightin', crazy mad, you get a hot, sick, weak feelin' in your guts? Well, that's what it is. Only it ain't just in one man. It's like the whole bunch, millions and millions was one man, and he's been beat and starved, and he's gettin' that sick feelin' in his guts. The stiffs don't know what's happenin', but when the big guy gets mad, they'll all be there; and by Christ, I hate to think of it. They'll be bitin' out throats with their teeth, and clawin' off lips. It's anger, that's what it

is." He swayed on his limb, and tightened his arms to steady himself. "I feel it in my skin," he said. "Ever' place I go, it's like water just before it gets to boilin'."

Jim trembled with excitement. "There's got to be a plan," he said. "When the thing busts, there's got to be a plan all ready to direct it, so it'll do some good."

The old man seemed tired after his outburst. "When that big guy busts loose, there won't be no plan that can hold him. That big guy'll run like a mad dog, and bite anything that moves. He's been hungry too long, and he's been hurt too much; and worst thing of all, he's had his feelings hurt too much."

"But if enough men expected it and had a plan——" Jim insisted.

The old man shook his head. "I hope I'm dead before it happens. They'll be bitin' out throats with their teeth. They'll kill each other off an' after they're all wore out or dead, it'll be the same thing over again. I want to die and get shut of it. You young squirts got hopes." He lifted his full bucket down. "I got no hope. Get out of the way, I'm comin' down the ladder. We can't make no money talkin': that's for college boys."

Jim stood aside on a limb and let him down the ladder. The old man emptied his bucket and then went to another tree. Although Jim waited for him, he did not come back. The sorting belt rumbled on its rollers in the packing-house, and the hammers tapped. Along the highway the big transport trucks roared by. Jim picked his bucket full and took it to the box pile. The checker made a mark in his book.

"You're going to owe us money if you don't get off your dime," the checker said.

Jim's face went red and his shoulders dropped. "You keep to your God-damn book," he said.

"Tough guy, huh?"

Then Jim caught himself and grinned in embarrassment. "I'm tired," he apologized. "It's a new kind of work to me."

The blond checker smiled. "I know how it is," he said. "You get pretty touchy when you're tired. Why don't you get up in a tree and have a smoke?"

"I guess I will." Jim went back to his tree. He hooked his bucket over a limb and went to picking again. He said aloud to himself, "Even me, like a mad dog. Can't do that. My old man did that." He did not work quickly, but he reduced his movements to a machine-like perfection. The sun went low, until it left the ground entirely and remained only on the tops of the trees. Far away, in the town, a whistle blew. But Jim worked steadily on. It was growing dusky when the rumble in the packing-house stopped at last and the checkers called out, "Come on in, you men. It's time to quit."

Jim climbed down the ladder, emptied his bucket and stacked it up with the others. The checker marked in the buckets and then totalled the picking. The men stood about for a few moments, rolling cigarettes, talking softly in the evening. They walked slowly away down a row, toward the county road, where the orchard bunk houses were.

Jim saw the old man ahead of him and speeded up to catch him. The thin legs moved with jointed stiffness. "It's you again," he said as Jim caught up with him.

"Thought I'd walk in with you."

"Well, who's stoppin' you?" Obviously he was pleased.

"You got any folks here?" Jim asked.

"Folks? No."

Jim said, "Well, if you're all alone, why don't you get into some charity racket and make the county take care of you?"

The old man's tone was chilled with contempt. "I'm a top-faller. Listen, punk, if you never been in the woods, that don't mean nothing to you. Damn few top-fallers ever get to be my age. I've had punks like you damn near die of heart failure just *watchin'* me work; and here I'm climbin' a lousy apple tree. Me take charity! I done work in my life that took guts. I been ninety foot up a pole and had the butt split and snap my safety-belt. I worked with guys that got swatted to pulp with a limb. Me take charity! They'd say, 'Dan, come get your soup,' and I'd sop my bread in my soup and suck the soup out of it. By Christ, I'd jump out of an apple tree and break my neck before I'd take charity. I'm a top-faller."

They trudged along between the trees. Jim took off his hat and carried it in his hand. "You didn't get anything out of it," he said. "They just kicked you out when you got too old."

Dan's big hand found Jim's arm just above the elbow, and crushed it until it hurt. "I got things out of it while I was at it," he said. "I'd go up a pole, and I'd know that the boss and the owner of the timber and the president of the company didn't have the guts to do what I was doing. It was *me*. I'd look down on ever'thing from up there. And ever'thing looked small, and the men were little, but I was up there. I was my own size. I got things out of it, all right."

"They took all the profits from your work," Jim said. "They got rich, an' when you couldn't go up any more, they kicked you out."

"Yes," said Dan, "they did that, all right. I guess I must be gettin' pretty old, kid. I don't give a damn if they did—I just don't give a damn."

Ahead they could see the low, whitewashed building the owners set aside for the pickers—a low shed nearly fifty yards long, with a door and a little square window every ten feet. Through some of the open doors lamps and candles could be seen burning. Some men sat in the doorways and looked out at the dusk. In front of the long building stood a faucet where a clot of men and women had gathered. As the turn of each came, he cupped his hands under the stream and threw water on his face and hair and rubbed his hands together for a moment. The women carried cans and cooking pots to fill at the faucet. In and out of the dark doorways children swarmed, restless as rats. A tired, soft conversation arose from the group. Men and women were coming back, men from the orchard, women from the sorting and packing house. So built that it formed a short angle at the north end of the building stood the orchard's store, brightly lighted now. Here food and work clothes were sold on credit against the working sheets. A line of women and men stood waiting to get in, and another line came out carrying canned goods and loaves of bread.

Jim and old Dan walked up to the building. "There's the kennel," Jim said. "It wouldn't be so bad if you had a woman to cook for you."

Dan said, "Guess I'll go over to the store and get me a can of beans. These damn fools pay seventeen cents for a pound of canned beans. Why, they could get four pounds of dried beans for that, and cooked up that'd make nearly eight pounds."

Jim asked, "Why don't you do that, Dan?"

"I ain't got the time. I come in tired an' I want to eat."

"Well, what time have the others got? Women work all day, men work all day; and the owner charges three cents extra for a can of beans because the men are too damn tired to go into town for groceries."

Dan turned his bristly beard to Jim. "You sure worry at the thing, don't you, kid? Just like a puppy with a knuckle-bone. You chew and chew at it, but you don't make no marks on it, and maybe pretty soon you break a tooth."

"If enough guys got to chewing they'd split it."

"Maybe—but I lived seventy-one years with dogs and men, and mostly I seen 'em try to steal the bone from each other. I never seen two dogs help each other break a bone; but I seen 'em chew hell out of each other tryin' to steal it."

Jim said, "You make a guy feel there isn't much use."

Old Dan showed his four long, gopher teeth. "I'm seventy-one," he apologized. "You get on with your bone, and don't mind me. Maybe dogs and men ain't the same as they used to be."

As they drew nearer on the cloddy ground a figure detached itself from the crowd around the faucet and strolled out toward them. "That's my pardner," Jim said. "That's Mac. He's a swell guy."

Old Dan replied ungraciously, "Well, I don't want to talk to nobody. I don't think I'll even heat my beans."

Mac reached them. "Hello, Jim. How'd you make out?"

"Pretty good. This is Dan, Mac. He was in the north woods when the Wobblies were working up there."

"Glad to meet you." Mac put a tone of deference in his voice. "I heard about that time. There was some sabotage."

The tone pleased old Dan. "I wasn't no Wobbly," he said. "I'm a top-faller. Them Wobblies was a bunch of double-crossin' sons-of-bitches, but they done the work. Damn it, they'd burn down a sawmill as quick as they'd look at it."

The tone of respect remained in Mac's voice. "Well, if they got the work done, I guess that's all you can expect."

"They was a tough bunch," said Dan. "A man couldn't take no pleasure talkin' to 'em. They hated ever'thing. Guess I'll go over and get my beans." He turned to the right and walked away from them.

It was almost dark. Jim, looking up at

the sky, saw a black V flying across. "Mac, look, what's that?"

"Wild ducks. Flying pretty early this year. Didn't you ever see ducks before?"

"I guess not," said Jim. "I guess I've read about them."

"Say, Jim, you won't mind if we just have some sardines and bread, will you? We've got things to do tonight. I don't want to take time to cook anything."

Jim had been walking loosely, tired from the new kind of work. Now his muscles tightened and his head came up. "What you got on, Mac?"

"Well, look. I worked alongside London today. That guy doesn't miss much. He came about two-thirds of the way. Now he says he thinks he can swing this bunch of stiffs. He knows a guy that kind of throws another crowd. They're on the biggest orchard of the lot, four thousand acres of apples. London's so damn mad at this wage drop, he'll do anything. His friend on the Hunter place is called Dakin. We're going over there and talk to Dakin tonight."

"You got it really moving, then?" Jim demanded.

"Looks that way." Mac went into one of the dark doorways and in a moment he emerged with a can of sardines and a loaf of bread. He laid the bread down on the doorstep and turned the key in the sardine can, rolling back the tin. "Did you sound out the men the way I told you, Jim?"

"Didn't have much chance. I talked some to old Dan, there."

Mac paused in opening the can. "What in Christ's name for? What do you want to talk to him for?"

"Well, we were up in the same tree."

"Well, why didn't you get in another tree? Listen, Jim, lots of our people waste their time. Joy would try to convert a litter of kittens. Don't waste your time on old guys like that. He's no good. You'll get yourself converted to hopelessness if you talk to old men. They've had all the kick blasted right out of 'em." He turned the can lid off and laid the open tin in front of him. "Here, put some fish on a slice of bread. London's eating his dinner right now. He'll be ready pretty soon. We'll go in his Ford."

Jim took out his pocket-knife, arranged three sardines on a slice of bread and crushed them down a little. He poured some olive oil from the can over them, and then covered them with another slice of bread. "How's the girl?" he asked.

"What girl?"

"The girl with the baby."

"Oh, she's all right. But you'd think I was God the way London talks. I told him I wasn't a doctor, but he goes right on calling me 'Doc.' London gives me credit for a lot. You know, she'll be a cute little broad when she gets some clothes and some make-up on. Make yourself another sandwich."

It was quite dark by now. Many of the doors were closed, and the dim lights within the little rooms threw square patches of light on the ground outside. Mac chewed his sandwich. "I never saw such a bunch of bags as this crowd," he said. "Only decent one in the camp is thirteen years old. I'll admit she's got an eighteen-year-old can, but I'm doing no fifty years."

Jim said, "You seem to be having trouble keeping your economics out of the bedroom."

"Who the hell wants to keep it out?" Mac demanded. He chuckled. "Every time the sun shines on my back all afternoon I get hot pants. What's wrong with that?"

The bright, hard stars were out, not many of them, but sharp and penetrating in the cold night sky. From the rooms nearby came the rise and fall of many voices talking, with now and then a single voice breaking clear.

Jim turned toward the sound. "What's going on over there, Mac?"

"Crap game. Got it started quick. I don't know what they're using for money. Shooting next week's pay, maybe. Most of 'em aren't going to have any pay when they settle up with the store. One man tonight in the store got two big jars of mincemeat. Probably eat both jars tonight and be sick tomorrow. They get awful hungry for something nice. Ever notice when you're hungry, Jim, your mind fastens on just one thing? It's always mashed potatoes with me, just slimy with melted butter. I s'pose this guy tonight had been thinking about mincemeat for months."

Along the front of the building a big man moved, and the lights from the windows flashed on him as he passed each one. "Here comes London," Mac said.

He strode up to them, swinging his shoulders. The tonsure showed white against the black rim of hair. "I finished eatin'," London said. "Let's get goin'. My Ford's around back." He turned and walked in the direction from which he had come; Mac and Jim followed him. Behind the building a topless Model T Ford touring car stood nosed in against the building. The oilcloth seats were frayed and split, so that the coil spring stuck through, and wads of horsehair hung from the holes. London got in and turned the key. The rasp of the points sounded.

"Crank 'er, Jim," said Mac.

Jim put his weight on the stiff crank. "Spark down? I don't want my head kicked off."

"She's down. Pull out the choke in front there," said London.

The gas wheezed in. Jim spun the crank. The engine choked and the crank kicked viciously backward. "Nearly got me! Keep that spark down!"

"She always kicks a little," said London. "Don't give her no more choke."

Jim spun the crank again. The engine roared. The little dim lights came on. Jim climbed into the back seat among old tubes and tire-irons and gunny sacks.

"Makes a noise, but she still goes," London shouted. He backed around and drove out the rough dirt road through the orchard, and turned right on the concrete state highway. The car chattered and rattled over the road; the cold air whistled in through the broken windshield so that Jim crouched down behind the protection of the front seat. Town lights glowed in the sky behind them. On both sides the road was lined with big dark apple trees, and sometimes the lights of houses shone from behind them. The Ford overtook and passed great transport trucks, gasoline tank trucks, silver milk tanks, outlined with little blue lights. From a small ranch house a shepherd dog ran out, and London swerved sharply to avoid hitting him.

"He won't last long," Mac shouted.

"I hate to hit a dog," said London. "Don't mind cats. I killed three cats on the way here from Radcliffe."

The car rattled on, going about thirty miles an hour. Sometimes two of the cylinders stopped firing, so that the engine jerked along until the missing two went back to work.

When they had gone about five miles, London slowed down. "Road ought to be somewhere in here," he said. A little row of silver mail boxes showed him where to turn into the dirt road. Over the road was a wooden arch bearing the words, "Hunter Bros. Fruit Co. S Brand Apples." The car stuttered slowly along the road. Suddenly a man stepped into the road and held up his hand. London brought the Ford to a stop.

"You boys working here?" the man asked.

"No, we ain't."

"Well, we don't need any more help. We're all full up."

London said, "We just come to see some friends of ours. We're workin' on the Talbot place."

"Not bringing in liquor to sell?"

"Sure not."

The man flashed a light into the back of the car and looked at the litter of iron and old inner tubes. The light snapped off. "O.K., boys. Don't stay too long."

London pushed down the pedal. "That smart son-of-a-bitch," he growled. "There ain't no nosey cops like private cops. Busy little rat." He swung the car savagely around a turn and brought it to a stop behind a building very like the one from which they had come, a long, low, shed-like structure, partitioned into little rooms. London said, "They're workin' a hell of a big crew here. They got three bunk houses like this one." He walked to the first door and knocked. A grunt came from inside, and heavy steps. The door opened a little. A fat woman with stringy hair looked out. London said gruffly, "Where's Dakin puttin' up?"

The woman reacted instantly to the authority of his voice. "He's the third door down, mister, him and his wife and a couple of kids."

London said, "Thanks," and turned away, leaving the woman with her mouth open to go on talking. She stuck out her head and watched the three men while London knocked on the third door. She didn't go inside until Dakin's door was closed again.

"Who was it?" a man asked from behind her.

"I don't know," she said. "A big guy. He wanted Dakin."

Dakin was a thin-faced man with veiled, watchful eyes and an immobile mouth. His voice was a sharp monotone. "You old son-of-a-bitch," he said. "Come on in. I ain't seen you since we left Radcliffe." He stepped back and let them in.

London said, "This here's Doc and his friend, Dakin. Doc helped Lisa the other night. Maybe you heard about it."

Dakin put out a long, pale hand to Mac. "Sure I heard. Couple of guys working right here was there. You'd think Lisa'd dropped an elephant the way they don't talk about nothing else. This here's the missus, Doc. You might take a look at them two kids, too, they're strong."

His wife stood up, a fine, big-bosomed woman with a full face, with little red spots of rouge on her cheeks, and with a gold upper bridge that flashed in the lamplight. "Glad to meet you boys," she said in a husky voice. "You boys like a spot of coffee or a little shot?"

Dakin's eyes warmed a trifle out of pride in her.

"Well, it was pretty cold coming over," Mac said tentatively.

The gold bridge flashed. "Just what I thought. You'll do with a snort." She set out a bottle of whisky and a jigger. "Pour your own, boys. You can't pour it no higher'n the top."

The bottle and the glass went around. Mrs. Dakin tossed hers off last. She corked the bottle and stood it in a small cupboard.

Three folding canvas chairs were in the room, and two canvas cots for the children. A big patent camp bed stood against the wall. Mac said, "You do yourself pretty nice, Mr. Dakin."

"I got a light truck," said Dakin. "I get some truckin' to do now and then, and besides I can move my stuff. The missus is quick with her hands; in good times she can make money doin' piece work." Mrs. Dakin smiled at the praise.

Suddenly London dropped his social manner. "We want to go somewheres and talk," he said.

"Well, why not here?"

"We want to talk some kind of private stuff."

Dakin turned slowly to his wife. His

voice was monotonous. "You and the kids better pay a call to Mrs. Schmidt, Alla."

Her face showed her disappointment. Her lips pouted and closed over the gold. For a moment she looked questioningly at her husband, and he stared back with his cold eyes. His long white hands twitched at his sides. Suddenly Mrs. Dakin smiled widely. "You boys stay right here an' do your talkin'," she said. "I ought to been to see Mrs. Schmidt before. Henry, take your brother's hand." She put on a short jacket of rabbit's fur and pushed at her golden hair. "You boys have a good time." They heard her walk away and knock at a door down the line.

Dakin pulled up his trousers and sat down on the big bed and waved the others to the folding canvas chairs. His eyes were veiled and directionless, like the eyes of a boxer. "What's on your mind, London?"

London scratched his cheek. "How you feel about that pay cut just when we was here already?"

Dakin's tight mouth twitched. "How do you think I feel? I ain't givin' out no cheers."

London moved forward on his chair. "Got any idears what to do?"

The veiled eyes sharpened a little bit. "No. You got any idears?"

"Ever think we might organize and get some action?" London glanced quickly sideways at Mac.

Dakin saw the glance. He motioned with his head to Mac and Jim. "Radicals?" he asked.

Mac laughed explosively. "Anybody that wants a living wage is a radical."

Dakin stared at him for a moment. "I got nothing against radicals," he said. "But get this straight. I ain't doin' no time for no kind of outfit. If you belong to anythin', I don't want to know about

it. I got a wife and kids and a truck. I ain't doin' no stretch because my name's on somebody's books. Now, what's on your mind, London?"

"Apples got to be picked, Dakin. S'pose we organize the men?"

Dakin's eyes showed nothing except a light grey threat. His toneless voice said, "All right. You organize the stiffs and get 'em all hopped up with a bunch of bull. They vote to call a strike. In twelve hours a train-load of scabs comes rollin' in. Then what?"

London scratched his cheek. "Then I guess we picket."

Dakin took it up. "So then they pass a supervisors' ordinance—no congregation, and they put a hundred deputies out with shotguns."

London looked around questioningly at Mac. His eyes asked Mac to answer for him. Mac seemed to be thinking hard. He said, "We just thought we'd see what you thought about it, Mr. Dakin. Suppose there's three thousand men strikin' from a steel mill and they picket? There's a wire fence around the mill. The boss gives the wire a jolt of high voltage. They put guards at the gate. That's soft. But how many deputy sheriffs you think it'll take to guard a whole damn valley?"

Dakin's eyes lighted for a moment, and veiled. "Shotguns," he said. "S'pose we kick hell out of the scabs, and they start shootin'? This bunch of bindle-stiffs won't stand no fire, and don't think they will. Soon's somebody sounds off with a ten-gauge, they go for the brush like rabbits. How about this picketin'?"

Jim's eyes leaped from speaker to speaker. He broke in, "Most scabs'll come off the job if you just talk to 'em."

"And how about the rest?"

"Well," said Mac, "a bunch of quick-movin' men could fix that. I'm out in the trees pickin', myself. The guys are sore as hell about this cut. And don't forget, apples got to be picked. You can't close down no orchard the way you do a steel mill."

Dakin got up and went to the box-cupboard and poured himself a short drink. He motioned to the others with the bottle, but all three shook their heads. Dakin said, "They say we got a right to strike in this country, and then they make laws against picketin'. All it amounts to is that we got a right to quit. I don't like to get mixed up in nothing like this. I got a light truck."

Jim said, "Where——," found that his throat was dry, and coughed to clear it. "Where you going when we get the apples picked, Mr. Dakin?"

"Cotton," said Dakin.

"Well, the ranches over there are bigger, even. If we take a cut here, the cotton people will cut deeper."

Mac smiled encouragement and praise. "You know damn well they will," he seconded. "They'll do it every time; cut and cut until the men finally fight."

Dakin set the whisky bottle gently down and walked to the big bed and seated himself. He looked at his long white hands, kept soft with gloves. He looked at the floor between his hands. "I don't want no trouble," he said. "The missus, the kids and me got along fine so far; but damn it, you're right, we'll get a cotton cut sure as hell. Why can't they let things alone?"

Mac said, "I don't see we got anything to do but organize."

Dakin shook himself nervously. "I guess we got to. I don't want to much. What you guys want me to do?"

London said, "Dakin, you can swing this bunch, and I can swing my bunch, maybe."

Mac broke in, "You can't swing nobody that doesn't want to be swung. Dakin and London got to start talkin', that's all. Get the men talkin'. They're mad already, but they ain't talked it out.

We got to get talk goin' on all the other places, too. Let 'em talk tomorrow and the next day. Then we'll call a meetin'. It'll spread quick enough, with the guys this mad."

Dakin said, "I just thought of somethin'. S'pose we go out on strike? We can't camp here. They won't let us camp on the county or the state roads. Where we goin' to go?"

"I thought of that," said Mac. "I got an idear, too. If there was a nice piece of private land, it'd be all right."

"Maybe. But you know what they done in Washington. They kicked 'em out because they said it was a danger to public health. An' then they burned down the shacks and tents."

"I know all about that, Mr. Dakin. But s'pose there was a doctor takin' care of all that? They couldn't do much then."

"You a real doctor?" Dakin said suspiciously.

"No, but I got a friend that is, and he'd prob'ly do it. I been thinkin' about it, Mr. Dakin. I've read quite a bit about strikes."

Dakin smiled frostily. "You done a hell of a lot more'n read about 'em," he said. "You know too much. I don't want to hear nothin' about you. I don't know nothin'."

London turned to Mac. "Do you honest think we can lick this bunch, Doc?"

Mac said, "Listen, London, even if we lose we can maybe kick up enough hell so they won't go cuttin' the cotton wages. It'll do that much good even if we lose."

Dakin nodded his head slowly in agreement. "Well, I'll start talkin' the first thing in the morning. You're right about the guys bein' mad; they're sore as hell, but they don't know what to do about it."

"We'll give 'em an idear," said Mac. "Try to contact the other ranches all you can, Mr. Dakin, won't you?" He stood up. "I guess we better move along." He held out his hand. "Glad I met you, Mr. Dakin."

Dakin's stiff lips parted, showing even, white false teeth. He said, "If I owned three thousand acres of apples, d'you know what I'd do? I'd get behind a bush an' when you went by, I'd blow your God-damn head off. It'd save lots of trouble. But I don't own nothing but a light truck and some camp stuff."

"Good night, Mr. Dakin. Be seein' you," said Mac.

Jim and Mac went out. They heard London talking to Dakin. "These guys are O.K. They may be reds, but they're good guys." London came out and closed the door. A door down the building a bit opened and let out a square of light. Mrs. Dakin and the two kids walked toward them. "G'night, boys," she said. "I was watchin' to see when you come out."

The Ford rattled and chuckled homeward, and pushed its nose up against the bunk house. Mac and Jim parted from London and went to their dark little room. Jim lay on the floor wrapped in a piece of carpet and a comforter. Mac leaned against the wall, smoking a cigarette. After a while he crushed out the spark. "Jim, you awake?"

"Sure."

"That was a smart thing, Jim. She was beginning to drag when you brought in that thing about that cotton. That was a smart thing."

"I want to help," Jim cried. "God, Mac, this thing is singing all over me. I don't want to sleep. I want to go right on helping."

"You better go to sleep," Mac said. "We're going to do a lot of night work."

6

The wind swept down the rows, next morning, swaying the branches of the trees, and the windfalls dropped on the ground with soft thuds. Frost was in the wind, and between the gusts the curious stillness of autumn. The pickers scurried at their work, coats buttoned close over their chests. When the trucks went by between the rows, a wall of dust rolled out and went sailing down the wind.

The checker at the loading station wore a sheepskin coat, and when he was not tallying, thrust hands and book and pencil into his breast pocket and moved his feet restlessly.

Jim carried his bucket to the station. "Cold enough for you?"

"Not as cold as it will be if this wind doesn't change. Freeze the balls off a brass monkey," the checker said.

A sullen-looking boy came up and dumped his bucket. His dark brows grew low to his eyes and his dark, stiff hair grew low on his forehead. His eyes were red and hot. He dumped his bucketful of apples into a box.

"Don't bruise those apples," the checker said. "Rot sets in on a bruise."

"Oh, yeah?"

"Yeah, that's what I said." The checker made a slashing mark with his pencil. "That bucket's out. Try again."

The smouldering eyes regarded him with hostility. "You sure got it comin'. An' you're goin' to get it."

The checker reddened with anger. "If you're going to get smart, you'd better pad along out and hit the road."

The boy's mouth spat venomously. "We'll get you; one of the first." He looked knowingly at Jim. "O.K., pal?"

"You'd better get on to work," Jim said quietly. "We can't make wages if we don't work."

The boy pointed down the row. "I'm in that fourth tree, buddy," he said, and moved away.

"What's the gag?" the checker asked. "Everybody's touchy this morning."

"It's the wind, maybe," said Jim. "I

guess it's the wind. Makes people nervous when the wind blows."

The checker glanced quickly at him, for his tone had been satiric. "You too?"

"Me too."

"What's in the air, Nolan? Something up?"

"What you mean, 'something'?"

"You know God-damn well what I mean."

Jim knocked his bucket lightly against his leg. He stepped aside as a truck went by, and a dust wall covered him for a moment. "Maybe the little black book keeps you ignorant," he said. "You might turn in the little book, and then see if you can find out."

"So that's it. Organizing for trouble, are you? Well, the air's full of it."

"Air's full of dust," said Jim.

"I've seen that kind of dust before, Nolan."

"Well, then you know all about it." He started to move away.

"Wait a minute, Nolan." Jim stopped and turned. "You're a good man, Nolan, a good worker. What's going on?"

"I can't hear you," said Jim. "I don't know what you're talking about."

"I'll put the black mark on you."

Jim took two fierce steps toward him. "Put down your black mark and be damned," he cried. "I never said a thing. You've built all this up because a kid got smart with you."

The checker glanced away uneasily. "I was just kidding," he said. "Listen, Nolan, they need a checker up on the north end. I thought you might do for the job. You can go to work tomorrow. It would be better pay."

Jim's eyes darkened in anger for a second, and then he smiled and stepped close to the checker again. "What do you want?" he asked softly.

"I'll tell you straight, Nolan. There's something going on. The 'super' told me to try and find out. You get the dope for me and I'll put in a word for you on that checker's job, fifty cents an hour."

Jim seemed to study. "I don't know anything," he said slowly. "I might try to find out if there was anything in it for me."

"Well, would five bucks say anything?"

"Sure would."

"O.K. You circulate around. I'll check you in on buckets so you won't lose anything today. See what you can dig up for me."

Jim said, "How do I know you won't double-cross me? Maybe I find something out and tell you. If the men ever found I told you, they'd skin me."

"Don't you worry about that, Nolan. If the 'super' can get a good man like you, he won't throw him over. There might be a steady job here for you when the picking's over, running a pump or something."

Jim thought for a moment. "I don't promise anything," he said. "I'll keep my ears open, and if I find anything, I'll let you know."

"Good boy. There's five in it, and a job."

"I'll try that tough kid," Jim said. "He seemed to know something." He walked down the row toward the fourth tree. Just as he reached it the boy came down the ladder with a full bucket.

"Hi," he said, "I'll dump these and be back."

Jim went up the ladder and sat down on a limb. The muttering of a sorting belt at the packing-plant blew clearly on the wind, and the smell of fresh cider came from the presses. From a long way off Jim could hear the hiss and bark of a switch-engine making up a train.

The sullen boy came running up the ladder like a monkey. He said angrily, "When we get down to business I'm gonna get me a nice big rock, and I'm gonna sock that bastard."

Jim used Mac's method. "A nice guy

like that? What you want to hurt him for? What do you mean 'when we get down to business'?"

The boy squatted down beside him. "Ain't you heard?"

"Heard what?"

"You ain't a rat?"

"No, I won't rat."

The boy cried, "We're goin' to strike, that's what!"

"Strike? With nice jobs? What you want to strike for?"

" 'Cause we're gettin' screwed, that's why. The bunk houses is full of pants rabbits, and the company's store is takin' five per cent house-cut, and they drop the pay after we get here, that's why! And if we let 'em get by with it, we'll be worse in the cotton. We'll get screwed there, too; and you know it damn well."

"Sounds reasonable," said Jim. "Who's strikin' besides you?"

The boy squinted at him with his hot eyes. "Gettin' smart, ain't you?"

"No. I'm trying to find out something, and you aren't telling me."

"I can't tell you nothing. We can't let nothing out yet. You'll find out when it's time. We got the men all organized. We got ever'thing about ready, and we're gonna raise hell. There's gonna be a meetin' tonight for a few of us, then we'll let the rest of you guys in on it."

"Who's in back of it?" Jim asked.

"I ain't tellin'. Might spoil ever'thing if I was to tell."

"O.K.," said Jim, "if that's the way you feel about it."

"I'd tell you if I could, but I promised not to. You'll know in time. You'll go out with us, won't you?"

"I don't know," said Jim. "I won't if I don't know any more about it than I do now."

"Well, by Christ, we'll kill anybody that scabs on us; I'm tellin' you that now."

"Well, I don't ever like to get killed."

Jim hung his bucket on a limb and slowly set about filling it. "What's chances of goin' to that meeting?"

"Not a chance. That's going to be only the big guys."

"You a big guy?"

"I'm on the in," said the boy.

"Well, who are these big guys?"

The sullen eyes peered suspiciously at Jim. "You ask too damn many questions. I ain't tellin' you nothin'. You act to me like a pigeon."

Jim's bucket was full. He lifted it down. "Are the guys talking it up in the trees?"

"Are they? Where you been all morning?"

"Working," said Jim. "Making my daily bread. It's a nice job."

The boy blazed at him. "Don't you get pushin' me around unless you'd like to step down on the ground with me."

Jim winked at him the way he'd seen Mac do. "Turn off the heat, kid. I'll be along when the stuff starts."

The boy grinned foolishly. "You catch a guy off balance," he said.

Jim carried his bucket down the row and emptied it gently into a box. "Got the time?"

The checker looked at his watch. "Eleven-thirty. Find out anything?"

"Hell, no. That kid's just shooting off his face. He thinks he's a newspaper. I'll mix around some after dinner and see."

"Well, get the dope as quick as you can. Can you drive a truck?"

"Why not?"

"We might be able to put you on a truck."

"That'd be swell." Jim walked away, down the row. The men in the trees and on the ladders were talking. He went up a heavy-laden tree where two men were.

"Hello, kid. Come on up and join the party."

"Thanks." Jim settled to picking. "Lots of talk this morning," he observed.

"Sure is. We was just doin' some. Ever'body's talkin' strike."

Jim said, "When enough guys talk strike, a strike usually come off."

The second man, high up in the tree, broke in. "I was just tellin' Jerry, I don't like it. Christ knows we ain't makin' much, but if we strike, we don't make nothin'."

"Not right now we don't," said Jerry. "But later we make more. This damn apple pickin' don't last long, but cotton pickin' lasts longer. The way I figure it out, the cotton people is watchin' this thing. If we take dirt like a bunch of lousy sheep then the cotton people will nick us deeper. That's the way I figure it out, anyway."

Jim smiled. "Sounds reasonable."

The other man said, "Well, I don't like it. I don't like no trouble if I can get out of it. Lot of men'll get hurt. I can't see no good in it at all. I never yet seen a strike raise wages for long."

Jerry said, "If the guys go out, you goin' to be a scab?"

"No, Jerry, I wouldn't do that. If the men go out, I'll go too. I won't scab, but I don't like it."

Jim asked, "They got any organization going yet?"

"Not that I heard," said Jerry. "Nobody's called a meeting up yet. We'll just sit tight; but the way I got it figured, if the guys go out, I'm goin' out too."

A wheezy whistle tooted at the packing-plant. "Noon," said Jerry. "I got some sanriches under that pile of boxes there. Want some?"

"No, thanks," said Jim. "I got to meet the guy I travel with."

He left his bucket at the checker's post and walked toward the packing-plant. Through the trees he could see a tall, whitewashed building with a loading platform along one side. The sorting belt was still now. As Jim drew near he saw men and women sitting on the platform, hanging their legs over while they ate their lunches. A group of about thirty men had collected at one end of the building. Someone in the center of the crowd was talking excitedly. Jim could hear the rise and fall of his voice, but not his words.

The wind had fallen now, so that the warmth of the sunshine got through. As Jim approached, Mac detached himself from the group and came toward him carrying two paper-wrapped parcels. "Hi, Jim," he said. "Here's lunch, French bread and some sliced ham."

"Swell. I'm hungry."

Mac observed, "More of our men go out with stomach ulcers than with firing squads. How're things out your way?"

"Buzzing," said Jim. "Buzzing to beat hell. I met a kid who knows all about it. There's going to be a meeting of the big guys tonight."

Mac laughed. "That's good. I wondered whether the men with secret knowledge had got working yet. They can do us a lot of good. Men out your way getting mad?"

"They're talking a lot, anyway. Oh, say, Mac, the checker's going to give me five bucks and a permanent job if I find out what's going on. I told him I'd keep my ears open."

"Nice work," said Mac. "Maybe you can make a little money on the side."

"Well, what do you want me to tell him?"

"Well, let's see—tell him it's just a splash, and it'll blow over. Tell him it's nothing to get excited about." He swung his head. A man had approached quietly, a heavy man dressed in dirty overalls, with a face nearly black with dirt. He came close and glanced about to see that they were alone.

"The committee sent me down," he said softly. "How're things going?"

Mac looked up at him in surprise. "What things you talkin' about, mister?"

"You know what I mean. The committee wants a report."

Mac looked helplessly at Jim. "The man's crazy," he said. "What committee's this?"

"You know what I mean—" the voice sank, "comrade."

Mac stepped stiffly forward, his face black with anger. "Where you get this 'comrade' stuff?" he growled. "If you're one of them lousy radicals, I got no use for you. Now you get on your way before I call some of the boys."

The intruder's manner changed. "Watch your step, baby," he said. "We've got the glass on you." He moved slowly away.

Mac sighed. "Well, these apple boys think quick even if they don't think awful good," he said.

"That guy a dick?" Jim asked.

"Hell, yes. A man couldn't get his face that dirty without giving nature a lift. They lined us up quick, though, didn't they? Sit down and have something to eat."

They sat in the dirt and made thick ham sandwiches. "There goes your chance for a bribe," Mac said. He turned a serious face to Jim and quoted, " 'Watch your step, baby,' and that's straight. We can't afford to drop out now. And just remember that a lot of these guys will sell out for five bucks. Make other people talk, but keep pretty quiet yourself."

"How'd they make us, d'you s'pose?" Jim asked.

"I don't know. Some bull from town put the finger on us, I guess. Maybe I better get some help down here in case you or I go out. This thing's coming off, and it needs direction. It's a pretty good layout, too."

"Will they jail us?" Jim asked.

Mac chewed a thick crust before he answered. "First they'll try to scare us," he said. "Now listen, if any time when I'm not around somebody tells you you're going to be lynched, you just agree to anything. Don't let 'em scare you, but don't go to using Joy's tricks. Jesus, they got moving quick! Oh, well, we'll get moving tomorrow, ourselves. I sent off last night for some posters. They should be here by tomorrow morning if Dick got off his dime. There ought to be some kind of word by mail tonight."

"What do you want me to do?" Jim asked. "All I do is just listen. I want to do something."

Mac looked around at him and grinned. "I'll use you more and more," he said. "I'll use you right down to the bone. This is going to be a nice mess, from the looks of it. That crack of yours about the cotton was swell. I've heard half a dozen guys use it for their own idea this morning."

"Where we going tonight, Mac?"

"Well, you remember Al, the fellow in the lunch wagon? He said his old man had a little orchard. I thought we might go out and see Al's father."

"Is that what you meant about getting a place for the guys when they go out?"

"I'm going to try to work it, anyway," Mac said. "This thing's going to break any time now. It's like blowing up a balloon. You can't tell when it's going to bust. No two of 'em bust just the same."

"You figure the big meeting for tomorrow night?"

"Yeah, that's what I figure; but you can't ever tell. These guys are plenty steamed up. Something might set 'em off before. You can't tell. I want to be ready. If I can get that place for the guys, I'll send for Doc Burton. He's a queer kind of a duck, not a Party man, but he works all the time for the guys. He'll lay out the place and tend to the sanitation, so the Red Cross can't run us off."

Jim lay back in the dirt and put his arms under his head. "What's the big argument over by the packing-house?"

"I don't know. The men just feel like arguing, that's all. By now maybe it's Darwin versus Old Testament. They'd just as soon fight over that. When they get to feeling like this, they'll fight about anything. Be pretty careful for yourself, Jim. Some guy might slug you just because he's feeling nervous."

"I wish it would start," Jim said. "I'm anxious for it to get going. I think I can help more when it once gets going."

"Keep your pants on," said Mac.

They rested in the dirt until the wheezy whistle blew a short toot for one o'clock. As they parted, Mac said, "Come running when we quit. We've got to cover some ground tonight. Maybe Al'll give us a hand-out again."

Jim walked back to the checking station, where his bucket was. The sorting belts began rumbling in the plant. Truck motors roared as they were started. Among the trees the pickers were sullenly going back to work. A number of men were standing around the checking station when Jim got his bucket. The checker did not speak to him then; but when Jim brought in his first full bucket, the question came. "Find out anything, Nolan?"

Jim leaned over the apple box and put his apples in it by hand. "I think it's all going to blow over. Most of the guys don't seem very mad."

"Well, what makes you think that?"

Jim asked, "Did you hear what made 'em mad?"

"No, I didn't. I thought it was the cut."

"Hell, no," said Jim. "A guy over on the Hunter place got a can of fish at the Hunter store that was bad. Made him sick. Well, you know how working stiffs are; they got sore, then the feeling spread over here. But I talked to some of the guys at noon. They're getting over it."

The checker asked, "You pretty sure that's all it is?"

"Sure. How about my five bucks?"

"I'll get it for you tomorrow."

"Well, I want that five, and you said you'd see about a better job."

"I will see about it. Let you know tomorrow."

"I should've got the money first, before I told you," Jim complained.

"Don't worry, you'll get it."

Jim walked off into the orchard. Just as he started to climb a ladder, a voice called from above him, "Look out for that ladder, she's shaky."

Jim saw old Dan standing in the tree. "By God, it's the boy radical," said old Dan.

Jim climbed up carefully. The rungs were loose in the ladder. "How's things, Dan?" he asked as he hung up his bucket.

"Oh, pretty good. I ain't feeling so good. Them cold beans lay like a flatiron in me all night."

"Well, you ought to have a warm supper."

"I was just too tired to build a fire. I'm getting on. I didn't want to get up this morning. It was cold."

"You should try one of the charity rackets," said Jim.

"I don't know. All the men is talkin' strike, and there's goin' t' be trouble. I'm tired. I don't want no trouble to come now. What'll I do if the men strike?"

"Why, strike with them. Lead them." Jim tried to spur him through pride. "The men would respect an old worker like you. You could lead the pickets."

"I s'pose I could," said Dan. He wiped his nose with a big hand and flicked his fingers. "I just don't want to. It's goin' to get cold early this afternoon. I'd like a little hot soup for supper—hot as hell, with little bits of meat in it, and some hot toast to soak in it. I *love* poached eggs. When I used to come to town out of the woods, with money, sometimes I'd get me half a dozen eggs poached in milk, and let 'em soak into toast. And then I'd mash the eggs up into the toast, and I'd eat 'em. Sometimes eight eggs. I made good pay in the woods. I could just as easy of got two dozen poached eggs. I wish I had. Lots of butter, an' all sprinkled with pepper."

"Not so hard-boiled as you were yesterday, huh, Pop? Yesterday you could out-work anybody on the lot."

The light of reminiscence went out of old Dan's eyes. His scraggly chin thrust forward. "I still can out-work a bunch of lousy punks that spends their time talkin'." He reached indignantly for the apples, fumbling over his head. One big, bony hand clung to a branch.

Jim watched him with amusement. "You're just showing off, Pop."

"Think I am? Well, try an' keep up with me, then."

"What's the use of you an' me racing, and then the orchard owner's the only one that makes anything?"

Old Dan piled apples into his bucket. "You punks got something to learn yet. There's more to work than you ever knew. Like a bunch of horses—you want more hay! Whining around for more hay. Want all the hay there is! You make a good man sick, that's what you do, whining around." His bucket was over-full. When he lifted it clear of the hook, five or six fat apples rolled out and bounced on the limbs and struck the ground under the tree. "Get out o' my way, punk," Dan cried. "Go on, get out o' the way o' that ladder."

"O.K., Pop, but take your time. You won't get a thing for rushing." Jim stepped clear of the ladder-top and climbed out on a limb. He hung his bucket and reached for an apple. Behind him he heard a splintering crash and a sullen thump. He looked around. Old Dan lay on his back on the ground under the tree. His open eyes looked stunned. His face was blue pale under the white

stubble. Two rungs were stripped out of the ladder.

Jim cried, "That was a fall! Hurt yourself, Pop?"

The old man lay still. His eyes were full of a perplexed question. His mouth writhed, and he licked his lips.

Jim shinnied down the tree and knelt beside him. "Where are you hurt, Pop?"

Dan gasped, "I don't know. I can't move. I think I've bust my hip. It don't hurt none, yet."

Men were running toward them. Jim could see men dropping from the trees all around and running toward them. The checker trotted over from his pile of boxes. The men crowded close. "Where's he hurt?"

"How'd it happen?"

"Did he bust his leg?"

"He's too old to be up a tree."

The ring of men was thrust inward by more arriving. Jim heard the checker cry, "Let me through here." The faces were dull and sullen and quiet.

Jim shouted, "Stand back, can't you. Don't crowd in." The men shifted their feet. A little growl came from the back row. A voice shouted, "Look at that ladder."

All heads went up with one movement, and all eyes looked to where the old loose rungs had splintered and torn out. Someone said, "That's what they make us work on. Look at it!"

Jim could hear the thudding of feet as more men ran up in groups. He stood up and tried to push the ring apart. "Get back, you bastards. You'll smother him."

Old Dan had closed his eyes. His face was still and white with shock. On the outskirts of the mob the men began to shout, "Look at the ladder! That's what they make us work on!" The growl of the men, and the growl of their anger arose. Their eyes were fierce. In a moment their vague unrest and anger centered and focused.

The checker still cried, "Let me through there."

Suddenly a voice shrill with hysteria shouted, "You get out of here, you son-of-a-bitch." There was a scuffle.

"Look out, Joe. Hold Joe. Don't let him. Grab his feet."

"Now, mister, scram, and go fast."

Jim stood up. "You guys clear away. We got to get this poor fellow out of here." The men seemed to awaken from a sleep. The inner ring pushed violently outward. "Get a couple of sticks. We can make a stretcher out of a pair of coats. There, put the sticks through the arms. Now, button up the fronts." Jim said, "Easy now, with him. I think his hip's busted." He looked down at Dan's quiet, white face. "I guess he's fainted. Now, easy."

They lifted Dan on to the coat stretcher. "You two guys carry him," Jim said. "Some of you clear a way."

At least a hundred men had collected by this time. The men with the stretcher stepped out. Newcomers stood looking at the broken ladder. Over and over the words, "Look what they give us to use."

Jim turned to a man who stood stupidly staring up into the tree. "What happened to the checker?"

"Huh? Oh, Joe Teague slugged him. Tried to kick his brains out. The guys held Joe. Joe went to pieces."

"Damn good thing he didn't kill him," Jim said.

The band of men moved along behind the stretcher, and more were running in from all over the orchard. As they drew near the packing-plant the rumble of the sorting belt stopped. Men and women crowded out of the loading doors. A quiet had settled on the growing mob. The men walked stiffly, as men do at a funeral.

Mac came tearing around the corner of the packing-plant. He saw Jim and ran

to him. "What is it? Come over here away from the mob." The crowd of ominous, quiet people moved on after the stretcher. Newcomers were told in low tones, "The ladder. An old ladder." The body of the mob went ahead of Mac and Jim.

"Now what happened? Tell me quick. We've got to move while they're hot."

"It was old Dan. He got smart about how strong he was. Broke a couple of rungs out of a ladder and fell on his back. He thought he broke his hip."

Mac said, "Well, it's happened. I kind of expected it. It doesn't take much when the guys feel this way. They'll grab on anything. The old buzzard was worth something after all."

"Worth something?" Jim asked.

"Sure. He tipped the thing off. We can use him now." They walked quickly after the mob of men. The dust, raised by many feet, filled the air with a slow-blowing brown cloud. From the direction of the town the switch-engine crashed monotonously making up a train. On the outskirts of the mob women ran about, but the men were silent, trudging on after the stretcher, toward the bunk houses.

"Hurry up, Jim," Mac cried. "We've got to rush."

"Where we going?"

"We've got to find London first, and tell him how to work; then we've got to go in and send a telegram; and I want to go and see Al's old man, right away. Look, there's London over there."

"Hi, London." Mac broke into a run, and Jim ran behind. "It's busted out, London," Mac said breathlessly. "That old guy, Dan, fell out of a tree. It's wide open, now."

"Well, that's what we want, ain't it?" said London. He took off his hat and scratched his tonsure.

"The hell it is," Mac broke in. "These guys'll go nuts if we don't take charge.

Look, there goes your long lean buddy. Call him over."

London cupped his hands. "Sam," he yelled.

Jim saw that it was the same man who had sat by the campfire in the jungle. Mac said, "Listen, London, and you, Sam. I'm going to tell you a lot of stuff quick, 'cause I've got to get along. These guys are just as likely to pop in a few minutes. You go over, Sam, and tell 'em they ought to hold a meeting. And then you nominate London, here, for chairman. They'll put him in all right. They'll do almost anything. That's all you got to do, Sam." Mac picked up a handful of dirt and rubbed it between his palms. His feet stirred and kicked at the ground. "Now listen, London, soon's you're chairman, you tell 'em we got to have order. You give 'em a list of guys, about ten, and tell 'em to vote for those guys as a committee to figure things out. Got that?"

"Sure. I get you."

"Now look—here's the way to do it. If you want 'em to vote for something, you say, 'Do you want to do it?' and if you want to vote down somethin', just say, 'You don't want to do this, do you?' and they'll vote no. Make 'em vote on everythin', *everythin'*, see? They're all ready for it."

They looked toward the crowd at the bunk house. The men were still quiet, shifting about, never standing very long in a place, moving their arms; their faces were as relaxed as those of sleeping men.

London demanded, "Where you guys going now?"

"We're going to see about that place for the crowd to stay when the thing busts open, that little farm. Oh, one other thing, you pick out a bunch of the craziest of these guys and send 'em over to the other ranches to talk. Get the men that are doin' the most talkin'. You all set now?"

"All set," said London.

"Well, let us use your Ford, will you? We got to cover ground."

"Sure, take it, if you can run it; it's got tricks."

Mac turned to Sam. "All right, get over there. Just stand up on somethin' and yell, 'Boys, we ought to hold a meetin',' and then yell, 'I move London for chairman.' Get going, Sam. Come on, Jim."

Sam trotted off toward the bunk houses, and London followed more slowly. Mac and Jim circled the buildings and went to the ancient Ford touring car. "Get in, Jim. You drive the jalopy." A roar of voices came from the other side of the bunk house. Jim turned the key and retarded the spark lever. The coils buzzed like little rattlesnakes. Mac spun the crank and primed, and spun again. A second roar from the mob came over the house. Mac threw his shoulder into the work. The engine caught and its noise drowned the shouting of the men. Mac leaped into the car, yelling, "Well, I guess London's our new chairman. Push 'er along."

Jim backed around and drove out to the highway. The road was deserted. The green, heavy-laden trees threw their shadows' weight sideways under the declining sun. The car rolled along, its pistons battering in the cylinders. "First to a telegraph office, and then to the post office," Mac shouted.

They rolled into the town. Jim drove to the main street and parked in front of a Western Union office. "Post office is just a block up, see?" he said.

"Well, listen, Jim, while I send the wire, you go up and ask for mail for William Dowdy."

In a few moments Jim came back with three letters. Mac was already sitting in the car. He ripped the letters open and read them. "Hot-damn, listen. This one's from Dick. He says Joy broke jail; they

don't know where he is. He was bein'
taken for a hearing and he smacked a
cop and beat it. I just wired for more
help, and for Doc Burton to take over
the sanitation. Wait, I'll crack 'er up.
Let's move along to Al's lunch wagon."

When Jim drew up in front of the
lunch wagon, he could see Al through
the windows, leaning over his deserted
counter, staring out at the sidewalk. Al
recognized them as they got out. He
raised a fat arm at them.

Mac pushed open the sliding door.
"Hi, Al. How's business?"

Al's eyes were bright with interest.
"Been just fine," he said. "Whole flock of
guys from the orchards come in last
night."

"I been tellin' 'em what a swell steak
you put out," said Mac.

"Nice of you. Like a bite yourself?"

"Sure," said Mac. "We could even pay
for it. Imagine us guys payin' for anything."

"Aw, this is just your cut," said Al.
"Kind of a commission for sending the
guys in town." He opened his ice-box
and patted out two hamburger steaks and
slapped them down on the stove-top; and
he arranged a wreath of chopped onions
about each one. "How's things coming
out your way?" he asked.

Mac leaned confidentially over the
counter. "Listen, Al. I know you're a guy
I can trust. We got you on the books.
You been swell to us."

Al blushed with pleasure at the praise.
"Well, I'd be out with you guys if I didn't
have a business to keep up. A man sees
the way conditions is, and injustice, and
things—and if he's got any brains he
comes to it."

"Sure," said Mac hurriedly. "A guy
with brains don't have to be taught. He
sees things for himself."

Al turned away to hide his pleasure.
He flipped the steaks and pressed them
down with his spatula and gathered up

the wilting onions and forced them into
the meat. He scraped the grease into the
little trough on the side of the stove-top.
When he had forced his face back to a
proper gravity, he turned around again.
"Sure you guys can trust me," he said.
"You ought to know it. What you got
on?" He filled two cups with coffee and
slid them along the counter.

Mac tapped delicately on the counter
with a knifeblade. "There may be bulls
askin' about me and Jim."

"Sure. I don't know nothin' about
you," said Al.

"That's right. Now here's the dope, Al.
This valley's about to bust wide open.
Already has over on the place where we
been working. The others'll probably
crack tonight."

Al said softly, "You know, the way the
guys was talkin' in here, I thought it
wasn't far off. What d'you want me to
do?"

"Better take up that meat." Al held
two plates fanwise in one hand, put a
steak on each, mashed potatoes, carrots
and turnips, loaded the plates.

"Gravy, gents?"

"Smear it," said Mac.

Al ladled gravy over the whole pile of
food and set the plates before them.
"Now go on," he said.

Mac filled his mouth. His speech was
muffled and spaced with chewing. "You
said your old man had a little ranch."

"He has. Want to hide out there?"

"No." Mac pointed his fork at Al.
"There won't be an apple picked in this
valley."

"Well, say—mister——"

"Wait. Listen. Any plow land on your
old man's place?"

"Yeah, about five acres. Had it in hay.
Hay's all out now."

"Here it is," said Mac. "We're goin' to
have a thousand or two men with no
place to go. They'll kick 'em off the
ranches and won't let 'em on the road.

Now if they could camp on that five acres, they'd be safe."

Al's face sagged with fear and doubt. "Aw, no, mister. I don't think my old man'd do it."

Mac broke in, "He'd get his apples picked, picked quick, and picked for nothing. Price'll be high with the rest of 'em shut off."

"Well, wouldn't the town guys raise hell with him afterwards?"

"Who?" Mac asked.

"Why, the Legion, and guys like that. They'd sneak out and beat him up."

"No, I don't think they would. He's got a right to have men on his place. I'll have a doctor lay out the camp and see it's kept clean, and your old man'll get his crop picked for nothing."

Al shook his head. "I don't know."

"Well, we can easy find out," said Mac. "Let's go talk to your old man."

"I got to keep this place open. I can't go away."

Jim suddenly saw his neglected food and began to eat. Mac's squinted eyes never left Al's face. He sat and chewed and looked. Al began to get nervous. "You think I'm scared," he began.

"I don't think anything before I see it," said Mac. "I just wondered why a guy can't close up his own joint for an hour, if he wants to."

"Well, the guys that eat early'll be here in an hour."

"You could get back in an hour."

Al fidgeted. "I don't think my old man'll do it. He's got to look out for himself, don't he?"

"Well, he ain't been jumped yet. How do you know what'll happen?" A chill was creeping into Mac's voice, a vague hostility.

Al picked up a rag and mopped around on the counter. His nervous eyes came to Mac's and darted away and came back. At last he stepped close. "I'll do it," he said. "I'll just pin a little card

to the door. I don't think my old man'll do it, but I'll take you out there."

Mac smiled broadly. "Good guy. We won't forget it. Next time I see any stiff with a quarter, I'll send him in to get one of your steaks."

"I give a nice dinner for the money," said Al. He took off his tall cook's hat and rolled down his shirt sleeves, and turned the gas off under the cooking plate.

Mac finished his food. "That was good."

Jim had to bolt his dinner not to be late.

"I got a little car in the lot behind here," said Al. "Maybe you guys could just follow me; then I don't get into no trouble and I'm still some good to you."

Mac drained his cup. "That's right, Al. Don't you get into no bad company."

"You know what I mean."

"Sure, I know. Come on, Jim, let's go."

Al wrote a sign and pinned it inside the door, facing out through the glass. He struggled his chubby arms into his coat and held the door open for Mac and Jim.

Mac cranked the Ford and jumped in, and Jim idled the motor until Al came bumping out of the lot in an old Dodge roadster. Jim followed him down the street to the east, across the concrete bridge over the river and out into the pleasant country. The sun was nearly down by now, red and warm with autumn dust. The massed apple trees along the road were grey with dust.

Mac turned in the seat and looked down the rows as they passed. "I don't see anybody working," he cried to Jim. "I wonder if he took hold already. There's boxes, but nobody working."

The paved road gave way to a dirt road. The Ford leaped and shuddered on the rough road. About a mile further Al's dust-cloud swung off into a yard. Jim followed and came to a stop beside the Dodge. A white tank-house rose into the air, and on its top a windmill thrashed and glittered in the sun, and the pump bonged with a deep, throaty voice. It was a pleasant place. The apple trees grew in close to a small white ranch house. Tame mallards nuzzled the mud in the overflow under the tank. In a wire-bounded kennel against a big barn two rubbery English pointers stood against the screen and yearned out at the men with little yelps. The house itself was surrounded by a low picket fence, behind which geraniums grew big and red, and a Virginia creeper, dropping its red leaves, hung over the porch. Big square Plymouth Rock chickens strolled about, cawing contentedly and cocking their heads at the newcomers.

Al got out of the car. "Look a' them dogs," he said. "Best pointers in the Valley. My old man loves them better'n me."

Mac asked, "Where's the five acres, Al?"

"Down that way, behind the trees, on the other road."

"Good. Let's find your old man. You say he likes his dogs?"

Al laughed shortly. "Just make a pass at one o' them dogs an' see. He'll eat you."

Jim stared at the house, and at the newly whitewashed barn. "This is nice," he said. "Makes a man want to live in a place like this."

Al shook his head. "Takes an awful lot of work to keep it up. My old man works from dawn till after dark, and then he don't keep up with the work."

Mac insisted, "Where is your old man? Let's find him."

"Look," Al said. "That's him coming in from the orchard."

Mac glanced up for a moment, and then he moved back to the kennel. The squirming pointers flung themselves at the wire, moaning with love. Mac stuck his fingers through the mesh and rubbed their muzzles.

Jim said, "Do you like dogs, Mac?"

Mac retorted irritably, "I like anything."

Al's father came walking up. He was totally unlike Al, small and quick as a terrier. The energy seemed to pour out of some inner reservoir into his arms and legs, and into his fingers so that all of him was on the move all of the time. His white hair was coarse, and his eyebrows and mustache bristled. His brown eyes flitted about as restlessly as bees. Because his fingers had nothing else to do while he walked, they snapped at his sides with little rhythmic reports. When he spoke, his words were like the rest of him, quick, nervous, sharp. "What's the matter with your business?" he demanded of Al.

Al went heavily on the defensive. "Well, you see—I thought——"

"You wanted to get off the ranch, wanted to go into town, start a business, town boy, wanted to lounge around. Didn't like to whitewash, never did. What's the matter with your business?" His eyes hovered on each of the men, on their shoes and on their faces.

Mac still looked into the kennel and rubbed the dogs' noses. Al explained, "Well, you see, I brang these guys out, they wanted to see you."

The old man eliminated Al. "Well, they're here. You can get back to your business now."

Al looked at his little father with the hurt eyes of a dog about to be bathed, and then reluctantly he climbed into his car and drove disconsolately away.

Mac said, "I haven't seen such pointers in a long time."

Al's father stepped up beside him. "Man, you never seen such pointers in your life." A warmth was established.

"Do you shoot over 'em much?"

"Every season. And I get birds, too. Lots of fools use setters. Setter's a net dog, nobody nets birds any more. Pointer's a real gun dog."

"I like the looks of that one with the liver saddle."

"Sure, he's good. But he can't hold up to that sweet little bitch. Name's Mary, gentle as Jesus in the pen, but she's jumping hell in the field. Never seen a dog could cover the ground the way she can."

Mac gave the noses a rub. "I see they got holes into the barn. You let 'em run in the barn?"

"No, their beds are tight against the wall. Warmer in there."

"If the bitch ever whelps, I'd like to speak a pup."

The old man snorted. "She'd have to whelp ever'day in the year to supply the people that wants her pups."

Mac turned slowly from the pen and looked into the brown eyes. "My name's McLeod," he said, and held out his hand.

"Anderson's mine. What you want?"

"I want to talk straight to you."

The sun was gone now, and the chickens had disappeared from the yard. The evening chill settled down among the trees. "Selling something, Mr. McLeod? I don't want none."

"Sure, we're selling something, but it's a new product."

His tone seemed to reassure Anderson. "Why'n't you come into the kitchen and have a cup of coffee?"

"I don't mind," said Mac.

The kitchen was like the rest of the place, painted, scrubbed, swept. The nickel trimmings on the stove shone so that it seemed wet.

"You live here alone, Mr. Anderson?"

"My boy Al comes out and sleeps. He's a pretty good boy." From a paper bag the old man took out a handful of carefully cut pine splinters and laid them

in the stove, and on top he placed a few little scraps of pitchwood, and on top of those, three round pieces of seasoned apple wood. It was so well and deftly done that the fire flared up when he applied a match. The stove cricked, and a burst of heat came from it. He put on a coffee-pot and measured ground coffee into it. From a bag he took two egg shells and dropped them into the pot.

Mac and Jim sat at a kitchen table covered with new yellow oilcloth. Anderson finished his work at the stove. He came over, sat primly down, put his two hands on the table; they lay still, even as good dogs do when they want to be off. "Now, what is it, McLeod?"

A look of perplexity lay on Mac's muscular face. "Mr. Anderson," he said hesitatingly, "I haven't got a hell of a lot of cards. I ought to play 'em hard and get the value out of 'em. But I don't seem to want to. I think I'll lay 'em down. If they take the pot, O.K. If they don't, there's no more deal."

"Well, lay 'em then, McLeod."

"It's like this. By tomorrow a couple of thousand men will be on strike, and the apple picking will stop."

Anderson's hands seemed to sniff, to stiffen, and then to lie still again.

Mac went on, "The reason for the strike is this pay-cut. Now the owners'll run in scabs, and there'll be trouble. But there's a bunch of men going out, enough to picket the Valley. D'you get the picture?"

"Part of it; but I don't know what you're driving at."

"Well, here's the rest. Damn soon there'll be a supervisors' ordinance against gathering on a road or on any public property. The owners'll kick the strikers off their land for trespassing."

"Well, I'm an owner. What do you want of me?"

"Al says you've got five acres of plow

land." Anderson's hands were still and tense as dogs at point. "Your five acres are private property. You can have men on it."

Anderson said cautiously, "You're selling something; you don't say what it is."

"If the Torgas Valley apples don't go on the market, the price'll go up, won't it?"

"Sure it will."

"Well, you'll get your crop picked free."

Anderson relaxed slightly in his chair. The coffee-pot began to breathe gently on the stove. "Men like that'd litter the land up," he said.

"No, they won't. There's a committee to keep order. There won't even be any liquor allowed. A doctor's coming down to look out for the sanitation. We'll lay out a nice neat camp, in streets."

Anderson drew a quick breath. "Look here, young fellow, I own this place. I got to get along with my neighbors. They'd raise hell with me if I did a thing like that."

"You say you own this place?" Mac said. "Is it clear? Is there any paper on it?"

"Well, no, it ain't clear."

"And who are your neighbors?" Mac asked quickly. "I'll tell you who they are: Hunter, Gillray, Martin. Who holds your paper? Torgas Finance Company. Who owns Torgas Finance Company? Hunter, Gillray, Martin. Have they been squeezing you? You know God damn well they have. How long you going to last? Maybe one year; and then Torgas Finance takes your place. Is that straight? Now suppose you got a crop out with no labor charges; suppose you sold it on a rising market? Could you clear out your paper?"

Anderson's eyes were bright and beady. Two little spots of anger were on his cheeks. His hands crept under the edge of the table and hid. For a moment

he seemed not to breathe. At last he said softly, "You didn't lay 'em down, fellow, you played 'em. If I could get clear—if I could get a knife in——"

"We'll give you two regiments of men to get your knife in."

"Yeah, but my neighbors'd run me out."

"Oh, no they won't. If they touch you or your place we won't leave a barn standing in the Valley."

Anderson's lean old jaw was set hard. "What you getting out of it?"

Mac grinned. "I could tell you the other stuff straight. I don't know whether you'd believe the answer to that one or not. Me an' Jim here get a sock in the puss now and then. We get sixty days for vagrancy pretty often."

"You're one of those reds?"

"You win; we're reds, as you call them."

"And what do you figure to do with your strike?"

"Don't get us wrong, Mr. Anderson. We didn't start it. Gillray, Martin and Hunter started it. They told you what to pay the men, didn't they?"

"Well, the Growers' Association did. Torgas Finance Company runs that."

"O.K. We didn't start it. But once it's started, we want to help it win. We want to keep the men from running to hell, teach 'em to work together. You come in with us, and you'll never have labor trouble as long as you live."

Anderson complained, "I don't know whether I can trust a red."

"You never tried; but you've tried trusting Torgas Finance."

Anderson smiled coldly. His hands came up on the table, and played together like puppies. "It'll probably break me, and put me on the road. Christ knows I'm headed for it anyway. Might as well have some fun. I'd give a hell of a lot to stick Chris Hunter." The coffee boiled over and fizzed fiercely on the stove, and the smell of burning coffee filled the air. The electric light glistened on Anderson's white eyebrows, and on his stiff hair. He lifted the coffee-pot and wiped the stove carefully with a newspaper. "I'll pour you out some coffee, Mr. Red."

But Mac sprang to his feet. "Thanks, but we've got to get along. We'll see you get a square deal out of this. Right now we got a million things to do. Be seeing you tomorrow." They left the old man standing holding the coffee-pot in his hand. Mac forced a trot across the yard. He muttered, "Jesus, that was ticklish. I was scared I'd slip any minute. What a tough old baby he is. I knew a hunting man'd be tough."

"I like him," said Jim.

"Don't you go liking people, Jim. We can't waste time liking people."

"Where'd you get that dope on him about the Finance Company, Mac?"

"Came in the mail tonight. But thank God for those dogs! Jump in, Jim. I'll turn her over."

They rattled through the clear night. The little flaring headlamps flickered dizzily along the road. Jim looked up at the sky for a moment. "Lord, I'm excited. Look at the stars, Mac. Millions of 'em."

"You look at the road," Mac growled. "Listen, Jim, I just happened to think. That guy this noon means they've got us spotted. From now on you be careful, and don't go away from the crowd very far. If you want to go someplace, see you take about a dozen men with you."

"You mean they'll try to get us?"

"You're damn right! They'll figure they can stop the ruckus with us out of it."

"Well, when're you going to give me something to do, Mac? I'm just following you around like a little dog."

"You're learning plenty, kid. When there's some use for you, I'll get it out,

don't you worry. You can take out a flock of pickets in a day or so. Turn off to the left, Jim. We won't be wanting to go through town much from now on."

Jim bumped the car along rutty sideroads. It was an hour before he came finally to the ranch and turned into the dark road among the apple trees. He throttled down the Ford until it was barely able to fire. The headlights jerked and shivered. Without warning a blinding light cut out through the darkness and fell on the men's faces. At the same moment two men, muffled in overcoats, stepped into the road ahead. Jim ground the Ford to a stop.

A voice behind the light called, "These are the guys." One of the overcoated men lounged around the car and leaned on the door. The motor idled unevenly. Because of the light beam, the man leaning on the door was almost invisible. He said, "We want you two out of the Torgas Valley by daylight tomorrow, get it? Out."

Mac's foot crept over and pressed Jim's leg. His voice became a sweet whine. "Wha's the matter 'th us, mister? We never done nothing."

The man answered angrily, "Lay off, buddy. We know who you are, and what you are. We want you *out*."

Mac whined, "If you're the law, we're citizens. We got a right to stand trial. I pay taxes back home."

"Well, go home and pay 'em. This isn't the law: this is a citizens' committee. If you think you God-damned reds can come in here and raise hell, you're crazy. You get out of here in your tin can or you'll go out in a box. Get it?"

Jim felt Mac's foot creep under his legs and find the gear pedal of the Ford. Jim tapped the foot with his toe to show he understood. The old engine staggered around and around. Sometimes one cylinder missed fire, sometimes two. Mac said, "You got us wrong, mister. We're just workin' stiffs. We don't want no trouble."

"I said *'out.'* "

"Well, leave us get our stuff."

"Listen, you're turning right around and getting out."

Mac cried, "You're yellow, that's what you are. You put twenty men hiding along the road. You're yellow as hell."

"Who's yellow? There's just three of us. But if you're not out of the Valley by morning, there'll be fifty."

"Step on it, Jim!"

The engine roared. The Ford bucked ahead like a horse. The man on the side spun off into the darkness, and the man in front jumped for his life. The rattling car leaped over the road with a noise of falling andirons.

Mac looked over his shoulder. "The flashlight's gone," he shouted.

Jim ran the car behind the long building. They jumped out and sprinted around the end of the bunk house.

The space in front of the doorways was dense with men standing in groups, talking in low tones. On the doorsteps the women sat, hugging their skirts down around their knees. A droning, monotonous hum of talk came from the groups. At least five hundred men were there, men from other ranches. The tough kid Jim had spoken to stalked near. "Didn't believe me, huh? Well, how's this look to you?"

Mac asked him, "Seen London?"

"Sure I seen him. We elected him chairman. He's in his room now with the committee. Thought I was nuts, didn't you?" he said to Jim. "I told you I was on the in."

Mac and Jim edged their way among the crowded men and into the hum of voices. London's door was closed, and his window was closed. A press of men stood on tiptoe and looked through the glass into the lighted room. Mac started up the steps. Two men threw themselves

in his way. "What the hell do you want?"

"We want to see London."

"Yeah? Does London want to see you?"

"Ask him, why don't you?"

"What's your name?"

"Tell London Doc and Jim want to see him."

"You're the guy that helped the girl have a kid?"

"Sure."

"Well, I'll ask." The man opened the door and stepped inside. A second later he emerged and held the door open. "Go right on in, boys, London's waitin' for you."

London's room had been hurriedly made into an office by bringing in boxes for seats. London sat on his bed, his tonsured head forward. A committee of seven men stood, sat on boxes, smoked cigarettes. They turned their heads when Jim and Mac entered. London looked glad. "Hello, Doc. Hello, Jim. Glad to see you. Heard the news?"

Mac flopped down on a box. "Heard nothing," he said. "Me and Jim been covering ground. What happened?"

"Well, it seems to be all right. Dakin's crowd went out. There's a guy named Burke, chairman on the Gillray place. There's a meetin' of everybody called for tomorrow."

"Fine," said Mac. "Workin' out fine. But we can't do much till we get an executive committee and a general chairman."

London asked, "How'd you come out on that thing you went for? I didn't tell the boys, case it didn't come off."

"Got it." Mac turned to the seven men. "Listen," he said. "A guy's loaned us five acres for the guys to camp on. It's private property, so nobody but the health people can kick us off. We got a doctor coming down to take care of that." The committeemen sat up straight, grinning with enthusiasm. Mac continued, "Now I've promised this farmer that the men'd pick his crop for nothing. It won't take 'em long. There's plenty of water. It's a good central location, too."

One of the men stood up excitedly. "Can I go tell the guys outside, London?"

"Sure, go ahead. Where is this place, Doc? We can have our big meetin' there tomorrow."

"It's Anderson's orchard, a little way out of town." Three of the committee-men broke for the door, to tell the news. Outside there was first a silence, and then a roll of voices, not shouting, but talking excitedly; and the roll spread out and grew louder, until the air was full of it.

Jim asked: "What happened to old Dan?"

London raised his head. "They wanted to take him to a hospital. He wouldn't do no good in a hospital. We got a doctor to set his hip. He's down the row a little. Couple of good women takin' care of the poor old bum. He's havin' a fine time. Couldn't get 'im out of here now. He just gives everybody hell, women and all."

Mac asked, "Have you heard from the owners yet?"

"Yeah, 'super' came in. Asked if we was goin' back to work. We says 'no.' He says, 'Get the hell off the place by morn-ing.' Says he'll have a trainload of stiffs in here by mornin'."

"He won't," Mac interrupted. "He can't get 'em in before day after tomor-row. It takes some time to handpick a bunch of scabs. And day after tomorrow we'll be ready for 'em. Say, London, some guys that call 'emselves a commit-tee tried to run me and Jim out of the Valley. Better pass the word to the guys not to go out alone. Tell 'em if they want to go any place take some friends along for company."

London nodded at one of his commit-teemen. "Pass the word, Sam." Sam went out. Again the roll of voices spreading out and rumbling, like a wave over round stones. This time the tone was deep and angry.

Mac slowly rolled a brown cigarette. "I'm tired," he said. "We got so much to do. I guess we can do it tomorrow."

"Go to bed," said London. "You been goin' like a fool."

"Yep, I been goin', all right. Seems kind of hard when you're tired. They got guns. We can't have no guns. They got money. They can buy our boys. Five bucks looks like a hell of a lot of jack to these poor half-starved bastards. Be pretty sure before you tell anythin', Lon-don. After all, you can't blame the guys much if they sell out. We got to be clever and mean and quick." His voice had grown sad. "If we don't win, we got to start all over again. It's too bad. We could win so easy, if the guys would only stick together. We could just kick Billy Hell out of the owners. No guns, no money. We got to do it with our hands and our teeth." His head jerked up. Lon-don was grinning in sympathy, embar-rassed, as men are when one of their number opens his heart.

Mac's heavy face flushed with shame. "I'm tired. You guys carry it while me and Jim get some sleep. Oh, London, in the mail tomorrow there'll be a package for Alex Little. It's handbills. Ought to be in by eight o'clock. Send some of the guys down to get it, will you? And see the handbills get around. They ought to do some good. Come on, Jim. Let's sleep."

They lay in their room in the dark. Outside the men sat and waited, and the murmur of their voices penetrated the walls and seemed to penetrate the world. Away, in town, a switch-engine crashed back and forth making up a train. The night milk trucks rumbled over the high-way beside the orchard. Then oddly, sweetly, someone played a few tunes on a harmonica, and the murmur of voices stopped and the men listened. It was quiet outside, except for the harmonica, so quiet that Jim heard a rooster crowing before he went to sleep.

7

The day was coming in grey and cold when Jim started awake at voices outside the door. He heard a man say, "They're in here, probably asleep yet." The door opened. Mac sat up.

A familiar voice said, "You here, Mac?"

"Dick! How the hell'd you get here this early?"

"Came down with Doc Burton."

"Doc here too?"

"Sure, he's right outside the door."

Mac scratched a match and lighted a candle in a broken saucer. Dick turned to Jim. "Hello, kid. How you makin' it?"

"Fine. What you all dressed up for, Dick? Pants pressed, clean shirt?"

Dick smiled self-consciously. "Somebody in this dump's got to look respectable."

Mac said, "Dick'll be infesting every pink parlor in Torgas. Listen, Dick, I got a list of sympathizers right here. We want money, of course; but we want tents, pieces of canvas, beds. Remember that—tents. Here's your list. There's lots of names on it. Make the contacts, and we'll send cars for the stuff. Lot of the boys 've got cars."

"O.K., Mac. How's she going?"

"Going like a bat out of hell. We got to work quick to keep up." He tied his shoe. "Where's Doc? Why don't you call him in? Come on in, Doc."

A young man with golden hair stepped into the room. His face was almost girlish in its delicacy, and his large eyes had a soft, sad look like those of a blood-hound. He carried his medical bag and a brief case in one hand. "How are you, Mac? Dick got your wire and picked me up."

"I'm sure glad you got here quick, Doc. We need you right away. This is Jim Nolan."

Jim stood up, stamping his heels into his shoes. "Glad to know you, Doc."

Mac said, "Better start, Dick. You can bum breakfast at Al's Lunch Wagon, on Townsend. Don't hit 'im up for anything else but breakfast. We already got a ranch off his old man. Shove along, Dick, and remember: tents, canvas, money—and anything else you can get."

"O.K., Mac. All the names on this list good?"

"I don't know. Try 'em. You want me to drive 'em up to you?"

"Go to hell," said Dick. He went out the door and closed it behind him. The candle and the dawn fought each other so that together they seemed to make less light than either would have made alone. The room was cold.

Dr. Burton said, "There wasn't much information in your wire. What's the job?"

"Wait a minute, Doc. Look out the window and see if you can see any coffee cooking outside."

"Well, there's a little fire outside and a pot on it, or rather a can."

Mac said, "Well, wait a minute." He went outside, and in a moment returned carrying a tin can of steaming, unpleasant-smelling coffee.

"Jesus, that looks hot," said Jim.

"And lousy," Mac added. "All right, Doc. This is the best set-up I've seen for a long time. I want to work out some ideas. I don't want this ruckus to get out of hand." He gulped some of the coffee. "Sit down on that box. We've got five acres of private property. You'll have all the help you need. Can you lay out a camp, a perfect camp, all straight lines? Dig toilets, take care of sanitation, garbage disposal? Try to figure out some way to take baths? And fill the air so God-damn full of carbolic or chloride of lime that it smells healthy? Make the whole district smell clean—can you do that?"

"Yes. I can do it. Give me enough help and I can." The sad eyes grew sadder. "Give me five gallons of crude carbolic and I'll perfume the country for miles."

"Good. Now, we're moving the men today. You look 'em over as quick as you can. See there's no contagion in any of 'em, will you? The health authorities are going to do plenty of snooping. If they can catch us off base, they'll bounce us. They let us live like pigs in the jungle, but just the minute we start a strike, they get awful concerned about the public health."

"All right, all right."

Mac looked confused. "I busted right into a song, didn't I? Well, you know what's needed. Let's go see London now."

Three men sat on the steps of London's room. They got up and moved aside for Mac. Inside, London was lying down, dozing. He rose up on his elbow. "Chroust! Is it morning?"

"It's Christmas," said Mac. "Mr. London, this here's Doc Burton, Director of Public Health. He wants some men. How many you want, Doc?"

"Well, how many men are we going to handle?"

"Oh—between a thousand and fifteen hundred."

"Better give me fifteen or twenty men, then."

London called, "Hi, out there." One of the sentinels opened the door and looked in. "Try to find Sam, will you?"

"Sure."

London said, "We called a meetin' for ten o'clock this mornin'. Great big meetin', I mean. I sent word to the other camps about this Anderson place. They'll start movin' in pretty soon."

The door opened and Sam entered, his lean face sharp with curiosity.

"Sam, this here's Doc Burton. He wants you for his right-hand. Go outside and tell the guys you want volunteers to help the Doc. Get twenty good men."

"O.K., London. When you want 'em?"

Burton said, "Right now. We'll go right over and lay out the camp. I can pile eight or nine in my old car. Get somebody with a car to take the rest."

Sam glanced from London to Burton, and back to London to verify the authority. London nodded his big head. "That's straight, Sam. Anything Doc says."

Burton stood up to go with him. "I'd like to help pick the men."

"Wait," Mac said. "You're all clear in town, aren't you, Doc?"

"What do you mean 'clear'?"

"I mean, is there anything they could hang a malpractice charge on you for?"

"Not that I know of. 'Course they can do anything if they want to bad enough."

"Sure," said Mac. "I know; but it might take 'em some time. 'Bye, Doc. See you later."

When Burton and Sam were gone, Mac turned to London. "He's a good guy. Looks like a pansy with his pretty face, but he's hard-boiled enough. And he's thorough as croton oil. Got anything to eat, London?"

"Loaf of bread and some cheese."

"Well, what are we waitin' for? Jim and me forgot to eat last night."

Jim said, "I woke up in the night and remembered."

London brought a bag from the corner and laid out a loaf of bread and a slab of cheese. There was a stirring outside. The hum of voices that had been still for several hours broke out again. Doors opened and slammed. Men hacked their throats clear of mucus and spat and blew their noses. The clear day had come, and the sun was red through the windows.

Mac, talking around a mouthful of cheese, said, "London, what do you think of Dakin for general chairman of the strike committee and boss-in-chief?"

London looked a little disappointed. "Dakin's a good guy," he said. "I've knowed Dakin for a long time."

Mac went into London's disappointment and dug it out. "I'll be straight with you, London. You'd be a hell of a good chairman, except you'd get mad. Now Dakin don't look like a guy that would ever get mad. If the boss of this mess ever gets mad, we're sunk."

The attempt was successful. London agreed, "I get sore as hell. I get so damn mad it makes me sick. You're straight about Dakin, too; he's a gamblin' kind of a man. Never opens up his eyes wide; never lets his voice get loose. The worse things gets, the quieter Dakin gets."

Mac said, "Then when the meetin' comes off, you throw your weight to Dakin, will you?"

"Sure."

"I don't know about this guy Burke, but I think with our guys and Dakin's guys we could soft-pedal him if he gets rank. We better start the guys movin' pretty soon; it's quite a ways over there."

London asked, "When you think the scabs'll start comin'?"

"Not before tomorrow. I don't think the bosses around here think we mean it yet. They can't get in any scabs before tomorrow."

"What we goin' to do when they land?"

"Well," said Mac. "We'll meet the train an' give 'em the keys of the city. I ought to have a wire before they start from town. Some of the boys'll kind of be checkin' up on the employment agencies." He lifted his head and looked toward the door. The hum of voices outside had been casual and monotonous, and now it stopped altogether. Suddenly, through the silence, there came a catcall, and then other voices broke into shouts. There was an argument outside.

London stepped over to the door and opened it. The three sentinels stood side by side before the door, and in front of them stood the orchard superintendent in moleskin trousers and field boots. On either side of him stood a man wearing a deputy sheriff's badge, and in each of his hands were shot-guns.

The superintendent looked over the heads of the guardians. "I want to talk to you, London."

"You sure come with an olive-branch," said London.

"Well, let me come in. Maybe we can work something out." London looked at Mac, and Mac nodded. The great crowd of men was silent, listening. The 'super' stepped forward, with his deputies beside him. The guards maintained their position. One of them said, "Let him leave his bulls outside, chief."

"That's a good idear," said London. "You don't need no buckshot to talk with."

The 'super' glanced nervously about at the silent, threatening men. "What proof have I that you'll play straight?" he demanded.

"Just about as much as I have that you will."

The 'super' made his decision. "Stay outside and keep order," he said.

Now the guardians stepped aside, letting the one man enter, and then resumed their position. The deputies were nervous. They stood fingering their guns and looking fiercely about them.

London closed the door. "I don't know why you couldn't say it outside, where the guys could hear."

The 'super' saw Mac and Jim. He looked angrily at London. "Put those men out."

"Uh-uh," said London.

"Now look here, London, you don't know what you're doing. I'm offering you the chance to go back to work if you kick those men out."

"What for?" London asked. "They're good guys."

"They're reds. They're getting a lot of good men into trouble. They don't give a *damn* about you men if they can start trouble. Get rid of 'em and you can go back to work."

London said, "S'pose we kick 'em out? Do we get the money we're strikin' for? Do we get what we would of got before the cut?"

"No; but you can go back to work with no more trouble. The owners will overlook everything that's happened."

"Well, what good was the strike, then?"

The 'super' lowered his voice. "I'll tell you what I'm prepared to offer. You get the men back to work and you'll get a steady job here as assistant superintendent at five dollars a day."

"And how about these guys, these friends of mine?"

"Fifty dollars apiece if they get out of the Valley."

Jim looked at the heavy, brooding face of London. Mac was grinning meanly. London went on, "I like to see both sides. S'pose me an' my friends here don't take it, what then?"

"Then we kick you off this place in half an hour. Then we blacklist the whole damn bunch of you. You can't go any place; you can't get a job any place. We'll have five hundred deputy sheriffs if we need 'em. That's the other side. We'll see you can't get a job this side of hell. What's more, we'll jug your pals here, and see they get the limit."

London said, "You can't bag 'em if they've got money."

The 'super' stepped closer, pressing his advantage. "Don't be a fool, London. You know as well as I do what the vagrancy laws are. You know vagrancy's anything the judge doesn't want you to do. And if you *don't* know it, the judge here's named Hunter. Come on, now, London. Bring the men back to work. It's a steady job for you, five dollars a day."

London's eyes fell away. He looked at Mac, asking mutely for instructions. Mac let the silence hang.

"Well, come on, London. How about it? Your red pals here can't help you, and you know it damn well."

Jim, on the outskirts, was shivering. His eyes were wide and quiet. Mac watched London and saw what the 'super' did not see, the shoulders gradually settling and widening, the big, muscled neck dropping down between the shoulders, the arms hooking slowly up, the eyes taking on a dangerous gleam, a flush stealing up the neck and out on the cheeks.

Suddenly Mac cried sharply, "London!" London jerked, and then relaxed a little. Mac said quietly, "I know a way out, London. While this gent is here, let's hold a meetin' of all the men. Let's tell the guys what we've been offered to sell 'em out. We'll take a vote on whether you get that five dollar job and—then—we'll try to keep the guys from lynchin' this gent here."

The 'super' turned red with anger. "This is the last offer," he cried. "Take this, or get out."

"We was just about to get out," Mac said.

"You'll get out of the Torgas Valley. We'll run you out."

"Oh, no, you won't. We got a piece of private property we can stay on. The owner invited us."

"That's a lie!"

"Listen, mister," Mac said, "we're goin' to have a little trouble gettin' you and your bodyguard out of here as it is. Don't make it no worse."

"Well, where do you think you're going to stay?"

Mac sat down on a box. His voice grew cold. "Listen, mister, we're goin' to camp on the Anderson place. Now the first thing you babies are goin' to think of is gettin' us off. That's O.K. We'll take our chance. The second thing you weasels are goin' to do is try to get back at Anderson. Now I'm tellin' you this, if any of your boys touch that property or hurt Anderson, if you hurt one single fruit tree, a thousand guys'll start out an' every one of 'em'll have a box of matches. *Get it, mister?* Take it as a threat if you want to: you touch Anderson's ranch and by Christ we'll burn every fucking house and barn on every ranch in the Valley!" Tears of fury were in Mac's eyes. His chest shuddered as though he were about to cry.

The 'super' snapped his head around to London. "You see the kind of men you're mixed up with, London? You know how many years you can get for arson?"

London choked. "You better scram on, Mister. I'm goin' to kill you if you don't. You better go now. Make him go now, Mac," he cried. "For Christ's sake, make him *go!*"

The 'super' backed away from the heavy, weaving body of London and reached behind him to find the doorknob. "Threat of murder," he said thickly. The door was open behind him.

"You got no witness to a threat," Mac said.

Outside the deputies tried to see in between the stiff bodies of the guardians. "You're fools, all of you," the 'super' said. "If I need 'em, I'll have a dozen

witnesses to anything I want. You've had my last word."

The guardians stepped aside for the 'super.' The deputies ranged up beside him. Not a sound came from the bunched men. A lane opened up for the three and they strode out through it. The silent men followed them with their eyes, and the eyes were puzzled and angry. The three marched stiffly to a big roadster that stood at one end of the building. They climbed in and drove away. And then the crowd looked slowly back at the open door of London's room. London stood leaning against the doorjamb, looking weak and sick.

Mac stepped into the doorway and put his arm around London's shoulders. They were two feet above the heads of the quiet men. Mac cried, "Listen, you guys. We didn't want to tell you before they got away; we was afraid you'd stomp 'em to death. That mug come here to try to get London to sell you out. London was goin' to get a steady job, an' you guys was goin' to get screwed."

A growl started, a snarling growl. Mac held up his hand. "No need to get mad, wait a minute, now. Jus' remember it later; they tried to buy London—an' they couldn't. Now shut up for a minute. We got to get out o' here. We got a ranch to stay on. There's goin' to be order, too. That's the only way we can win this. We all got to take orders. Now the guys that got cars take all the women an' kids an' the truck that can't be carried. The rest'll have to walk. Now be nice. Don't break nothing—yet. An' stay together. While you're gettin' your stuff picked up, London wants to see his committee."

The moment he stopped talking a turbulence broke out. Shouting and laughing, the men eddied. They seemed filled with a terrible joy, a bloody, lustful joy. Their laughter was heavy. Into the rooms they swarmed, and carried out their things and piled them on the ground —pots and kettles, blankets, bundles of clothing. The women rolled out push-carts for the children. Six of the commit-teemen forced and shouldered their way through the press, and entered London's room.

The sun was clear of the trees now, and the air was warmed by it. Behind the buildings battered old cars began to start with bursts of noise. There were sounds of hammering as possessions were boxed. The place swam with activity, with the commotion of endless trips back and forth, of opinions shouted, of judgments made and overruled.

London let his committee in and shut the door to keep out the noise. The men were silent, dignified, grave and impor-tant. They sat on boxes and clasped their knees and bent portentous looks at the walls.

Mac said, "London, d'you mind if I talk to them?"

"Sure, go ahead."

"I don't mean to hog the show, gents," Mac continued. "I had some experience. I been through this before. Maybe I can show you where the thing breaks down, and maybe we can steer clear of some of the things that conk us."

One of the men said, "Go ahead, fella. We'll listen."

"O.K. We got plenty of fire now. That's the trouble with workin' stiffs, though. One minute they're steamed up like a keg of beer, and the next, they're cold as a whore's heart. We got to cut down the steam and warm up the cold. Now I want to make a suggestion. You guys can think it over, an' then you can maybe get the whole bunch to vote on it. Most strikes break down because they got no discipline. Suppose we divide the men in squads, let each squad elect a leader, and then he's responsible for his squad. We can work 'em in groups, then."

One of the men said, "Lot of these guys was in the army. They di'n't like it none."

"Sure they didn't. They was fightin' some other guy's war. They had officers shoved down their throats. If they elect their officers and fight their own war, it'd be different."

"Most o' these guys don't like *no* officers."

"Well, they got to have 'em. We'll get the pants kicked off us if we got no disci-pline. If the squad don't like the leader, let 'em vote 'im into the ranks an' elect another leader. That ought to satisfy 'em. Then we ought to have officers over hun-dreds, an' one chief high-tail boss. Just give it a thought, gents. There's goin' to be a big meetin' in about two hours. We got to have a plan ready."

London scratched his tonsure. "Sounds O.K. to me. I'll talk it over with Dakin soon's I see him."

"All right," said Mac. "Let's get movin'. Jim, you stay close to me."

"Give *me* some work," Jim said.

"No, you stay close. I may need you."

8

The five acres of plow land on the Anderson place were surrounded on three sides by big, dark apple trees; and on the fourth it was bounded by the narrow, dusty county road. The men had arrived in droves, laughing and shouting to one another, and they had found preparations made for them. Stakes were driven into the soft ground defining the streets for the camp. There were five streets running parallel to the county road, and opposite the end of each street a deep hole was dug in the ground as a toilet.

Before the work of building the camp

started, they held their general meeting with some order; elected Dakin chairman and assented to his committee. They agreed with enthusiasm to the suggestion of the squads.

Hardly had they begun to assemble when five motorcycle police rode up and parked their motors in the county road. They leaned against the machines and watched the work. Tents were pitched, and shelters laid out. The sad-eyed Dr. Burton was everywhere, ordering the building of the camp. At least a hundred old automobiles lined the road, drawn up like caissons in an artillery park, all facing out toward the road. There were ancient Fords, ravaged in their upholstery; Chevrolets and Dodges with rusty noses, paintless, with loose fenders or no fenders at all. There were worn-out Hudsons that made a noise like machine-guns when they were starting. They stood like aged soldiers at a reunion. At one end of the line of cars stood Dakin's Chevrolet truck, clean and new and shiny. Alone of all the cars it was in good condition; and Dakin, as he walked about the camp, surrounded by members of his committee, rarely got out of sight of his truck. As he talked or listened his cold, secret eyes went again and again to his shining green truck.

When the grey old tents were pitched Burton insisted that the canvas be scrubbed with soap and water. Dakin's truck brought barrels of water from Anderson's tank. The women washed the tents with old brooms.

Anderson walked out and watched with worried eyes while his five acres were transformed into a camp. By noon it was ready; and nine hundred men went to work in the orchard, picking apples into their cooking kettles, into their hats, into gunny sacks. There were not nearly ladders enough. The men climbed up the trunks into the trees. By dark the crop was picked, the lines of boxes filled, the boxes trucked to Anderson's barn and stored.

Dick had worked quickly. He sent a boy to ask for men and a truck to meet him in town, and the truck came back loaded with tents of all kinds—umbrella tents of pale brown canvas, pup-tents, low and peaked, big troop tents with room in them for ten men. And the truck brought two sacks of rolled oats and sacks of flour, cases of canned goods, sacks of potatoes and onions and a slaughtered cow.

The new tents went up along the streets. Dr. Burton superintended the cooking arrangements. Trucks went out to the city dump and brought back three rusty, discarded stoves. Pieces of tin covered the gaping tops. Cooks were assigned, washtubs filled with water, the cow cut up and potatoes and onions set to cooking in tremendous stews. Buckets of beans were boiled. In the dusk, when the picking was over, the men came in and found tubs of stew waiting for them. They sat on the ground and ate from basins and cups and tin cans.

As darkness fell, the motorcycle police were relieved by five deputy sheriffs armed with rifles. For a time they marched up and down the road in military manner, but finally they sat in the ditch and watched the men. There were few lights in the camp. Here and there a tent was lighted with a lantern. The flares of little fires threw shadows. At one end of the first street, so pitched that it was directly behind his shining green truck, stood Dakin's tent—a large, patented affair with a canvas wall in the middle, making two rooms. His folding table and chairs were set up. A ground cloth lay on the floor, and from the center pole a hissing gasoline lantern hung. Dakin lived in style and traveled in luxury. He had no vices; every cent he or his wife made went to his living, to his truck, to providing new equipment for his camp.

When it was dark, London and Mac and Jim strolled to the tent and went in. With Dakin in the tent sat Burke, a lowering, sullen Irishman, and two short Italian men who looked very much alike. Mrs. Dakin had retired to the other side of the partition. Under the white light of the gasoline lamp Dakin's pink scalp showed through his blond hair. His secret eyes moved restlessly about. "Hello, boys, find some place to sit."

London chose a chair, the only one left. Mac and Jim squatted on the ground; Mac brought out his Durham bag and made a cigarette. "Things seem to be goin' O.K.," he observed.

Dakin's eyes flicked to him, and then away. "Yeah, they seem to be all right."

"They got those cops here quick," said Burke. "I'd like to take a poke at a few of 'em."

Dakin reproved him calmly. "Let cops alone till you can't no more. They ain't hurtin' a thing."

Mac asked, "How the squads shapin'?"

"All right. They all elected their chiefs. Some of 'em kicked out the chief and elected new ones already. Say, that Doc Burton is a swell guy."

"Yeah," Mac said. "He's O.K. Wonder where he's at? You better have one of the squads watch out for him. When we get started, they'll try to get him out of here. If they can get him out, they can clear us out. 'Danger to public health,' they call it."

Dakin turned to Burke. "Fix that up now, will you, Burke? Tell a good bunch to keep care o' Doc. The guys like him." Burke got up and went out of the tent.

London said, "Tell 'im what you told me, Mac."

"Well, the guys think this is a kind of a picnic, Dakin. Tomorrow morning the picnic's over. The fun begins."

"Scabs?"

"Yep, a train-load. I got a kid in town. He goes to the telegraph office for me. Got a wire tonight. A freight train-load of scabs is startin' out from the city today. Ought to be in some time in the mornin'."

"Well," said Dakin. "Guess we better meet that train an' have a talk with the new guys. Might do some good, before they all get scattered."

"That's what I thought," said Mac. "I've saw the time when a whole slough of scabs come over if you just told 'em how things was."

"We'll tell 'em, all right."

"Listen," said Mac. "The cops'll try to head us off. Couldn't we let the guys kind of sneak off through the trees just before daylight, and leave them cops holding the bag here?"

For a second Dakin's cold eyes twinkled. "Think that'd work, you guys?" They laughed delightedly. Dakin went on, "Well, go out an' tell the men about it."

Mac said, "Wait a minute, Dakin. If you tell the guys tonight, it won't be no secret."

"What do you mean?"

"Well, you don't think we ain't got stools in the camp, do you? I bet there's at least five under cover, besides the guys that'd spill anything and hope to get a buck out of it. Hell, it's always that way. Don't tell 'em nothing till you're ready to start."

"Don't trust the guys, huh?"

"Well, if you want to take the chance, go ahead. I bet you find the cops comin' right along with us."

Dakin asked, "What do you guys think?"

"I guess he's right," said one of the little Italian men.

"O.K. Now we got to leave a bunch to take care of the camp."

"At least a hundred," Mac agreed. "If we leave the camp, they'll burn 'er, sure as hell."

"The boys sure got Anderson's crop down quick."

"Yeah," said Dakin. "There's two or three hundred of 'em out in the orchard next door right now. Anderson's goin' to have a bigger crop than he thought."

"I hope they don't cause trouble yet," Mac said. "There'll be plenty later on."

"How many scabs comin'? Did you find out?"

"Somewheres between four and five hundred tomorrow. Be more later, I guess. Be sure an' tell the guys to take plenty of rocks in their pockets."

"I'll tell 'em."

Burke came back in. He said, "The Doc's goin' to sleep in one of them big army tents. There'll be ten guys sleepin' in the same tent with him."

"Where's Doc at now?" Mac asked.

"He's dug up a couple of ringworms on a guy. He's fixin' 'im over by the stoves."

At that moment a chorus of yells broke out in the camp, and then a high, angry voice shouting. The six men ran out of the tent. The noise came from a group of men standing in front of the camp street that faced the road. Dakin pushed his way in among the men. "What th' hell's the matter here?"

The angry voice answered, "I'll tell you. Your men started throwin' rocks. I'm tellin' you now if there's any more rocks we're goin' to start shootin', an' we don't care who we hit."

Mac turned to Jim, standing beside him. He said softly, "I wish they would start shooting. This bunch of mugs is going to pieces, maybe, if something dirty doesn't happen pretty soon. They're feeling too good. They'll start fighting themselves."

London walked fiercely into the crowd of men. "You guys get back," he cried.

"You got enough to do without no kid tricks. Go on, now, get back where you belong." The authority of the man drove them sullenly back, but they dispersed reluctantly.

The deputy shouted, "You keep those guys in order or we'll do it with Winchesters."

Dakin said coldly, "You can pull in your neck and go back to sleep."

Mac muttered to Jim, "Those cops are scared as hell. That makes 'em dangerous. Just like rattlesnakes when they're scared: they'll shoot at anything."

The crowd had moved away now and the men were scattering to their tents. Mac said, "Let's go have a look at Doc, Jim. Come on over by the stoves." They found Dr. Burton sitting on a box, bandaging a man's arm. A kerosene lantern shed a thin yellow light on his work and illumined a small circle on the ground. He stuck down the bandage with adhesive.

"There you are," he said. "Next time don't let it get so sore. You'll lose an arm some day, if you do."

The man said, "Thanks, Doc," and went away, rolling down his sleeve.

"Hello, Mac. Hello, Jim. I guess I'm finished."

"Was that the ringworm?"

"No, just a little cut, and a nice infection started. They won't learn to take care of cuts."

Mac said, "If Doc could only find a case of small-pox now and set up a quarantine ward, he'd be perfectly happy. What're you going to do now, Doc?"

The sad brown eyes looked tiredly up at Mac. "Well, I think I'm all through. I ought to go and see whether the squad disinfected the toilets the way I told them."

"They smell disinfected," Mac said. "Why don't you get some sleep, Doc? You didn't have any last night."

"Well, I'm tired, but I don't feel

sleepy. For the last hour I've thought when I was through I might walk out into the orchard and sit down against a tree and rest."

"Mind company?"

"No. I'd like to have you." Burton stood up. "Wait till I wash my hands." He scrubbed his hands in a pan of warm water and covered them with green soap and rinsed them. "Let's stroll, then," he said.

The three walked slowly away from the tent streets and toward the dark orchard. Their feet crunched softly on the crisp little clods of the plowed ground.

"Mac," Burton said wearily. "You're a mystery to me. You imitate any speech you're taking part in. When you're with London and Dakin you talk the way they do. You're an actor."

"No," said Mac. "I'm not an actor at all. Speech has a kind of a feel about it. I get the feel, and it comes out, perfectly naturally. I don't try to do it. I don't think I could help doing it. You know, Doc, men are suspicious of a man who doesn't talk their way. You can insult a man pretty badly by using a word he doesn't understand. Maybe he won't say anything, but he'll hate you for it. It's not the same thing in your case, Doc. You're supposed to be different. They wouldn't trust you if you weren't."

They entered the arches under the trees, and the leaf clusters and the limbs were dark against the sky. The little murmuring noise of the camp was lost. A barn-owl, screeching overhead with a ripping sound, startled the men.

"That's an owl, Jim," Mac explained. "He's hunting mice." And then to Burton, "Jim's never been in the country much. The things we know are new to him. Let's sit down here."

Mac and the doctor sat on the ground and leaned against the big trunk of an old apple tree. Jim sat in front of them,

folding his legs before him. The night was still. Above, the black leaves hung motionless in the quiet air.

Mac spoke softly, for the night seemed to be listening. "You're a mystery to me, too, Doc."

"Me? A mystery?"

"Yes, you. You're not a Party man, but you work with us all the time; you never get anything for it. I don't know whether you believe in what we're doing or not, you never say, you just work. I've been out with you before, and I'm not sure you believe in the cause at all."

Dr. Burton laughed softly. "It would be hard to say. I could tell you some of the things I think; you might not like them. I'm pretty sure you wouldn't like them."

"Well, let's hear them, anyway."

"Well, you say I don't believe in the cause. That's like not believing in the moon. There've been communes before, and there will be again. But you people have an idea that if you can *establish* the thing, the job'll be done. Nothing stops, Mac. If you were able to put an idea into effect tomorrow, it would start changing right away. Establish a commune, and the same gradual flux will continue."

"Then you don't think the cause is good?"

Burton sighed. "You see? We're going to pile up on that old rock again. That's why I don't like to talk very often. Listen to me, Mac. My senses aren't above reproach, but they're all I have. I want to see the whole picture—as nearly as I can. I don't want to put on the blinders of 'good' and 'bad,' and limit my vision. If I used the term 'good' on a thing I'd lose my license to inspect it, because there might be bad in it. Don't you see? I want to be able to look at the whole thing."

Mac broke in heatedly, "How about social injustice? The profit system? You have to say they're bad."

Dr. Burton threw back his head and

looked at the sky. "Mac," he said. "Look at the physiological injustice, the injustice of tetanus, the injustice of syphilis, the gangster methods of amoebic dysentery—that's my field."

"Revolution and communism will cure social injustice."

"Yes, and disinfection and prophylaxis will prevent the others."

"It's different, though; men are doing one, and germs are doing the other."

"I can't see much difference, Mac."

"Well, damn it, Doc, there's lockjaw every place. You can find syphilis in Park Avenue. Why do you hang around with us if you aren't for us?"

"I want to *see*," Burton said. "When you cut your finger, and streptococci get in the wound, there's a swelling and a soreness. That swelling is the fight your body puts up, the pain is the battle. You can't tell which one is going to win, but the wound is the first battleground. If the cells lose the first fight the streptococci invade, and the fight goes on up the arm. Mac, these little strikes are like the infection. Something has got into the men; a little fever had started and the lymphatic glands are shooting in reinforcements. I want to see, so I go to the seat of the wound."

"You figure the strike is a wound?"

"Yes. Group-men are always getting some kind of infection. This seems to be a bad one. I want to *see*, Mac. I want to watch these group-men, for they seem to me to be a new individual, not at all like single men. A man in a group isn't himself at all, he's a cell in an organism that isn't like him any more than the cells in your body are like you. I want to watch the group, and see what it's like. People have said, 'mobs are crazy, you can't tell what they'll do.' Why don't people look at mobs not as men, but as mobs? A mob nearly always seems to act reasonably, for a mob."

"Well, what's this got to do with the cause?"

"It might be like this, Mac: When group-man wants to move, he makes a standard. 'God wills that we recapture the Holy Land'; or he says, 'We fight to make the world safe for democracy'; or he says, 'We will wipe out social injustice with communism.' But the group doesn't care about the Holy Land, or Democracy, or Communism. Maybe the group simply wants to move, to fight, and uses these words simply to reassure the brains of individual men. I say it *might* be like that, Mac."

"Not with the cause, it isn't," Mac cried.

"Maybe not, it's just the way I think of things."

Mac said, "The trouble with you, Doc, is you're too God-damn far left to be a communist. You go too far with collectivization. How do you account for people like me, directing things, moving things? That puts your group-man out."

"You might be an effect as well as a cause, Mac. You might be an expression of group-man, a cell endowed with a special function, like an eye cell, drawing your force from group-man, and at the same time directing him, like an eye. Your eye both takes orders from and gives orders to your brain."

"This isn't practical," Mac said disgustedly. "What's all this kind of talk got to do with hungry men, with layoffs and unemployment?"

"It might have a great deal to do with them. It isn't a very long time since tetanus and lockjaw were not connected. There are still primitives in the world who don't know children are the result of intercourse. Yes, it might be worth while to know more about group-man, to know his nature, his ends, his desires. They're not the same as ours. The pleasure we get in scratching an itch causes death to a great number of cells. Maybe group-man gets pleasure when individual men are wiped out in a war. I simply want to see as much as I can, Mac, with the means I have."

Mac stood up and brushed the seat of his pants. "If you see too darn much, you don't get anything done."

Burton stood up too, chuckling softly. "Maybe some day—oh, let it go. I shouldn't have talked so much. But it does clarify a thought to get it spoken, even if no one listens."

They started back over the crisp clods toward the sleeping camp. "We can't look up at anything, Doc," Mac said. "We've got to whip a bunch of scabs in the morning."

"Deus vult," said Burton. "Did you see those pointers of Anderson's? Beautiful dogs; they give me a sensual pleasure, almost sexual."

A light still burned in Dakin's tent. The camp slept. Only a few coals of fire still burned in the streets. The silent line of old cars stood against the road, and in the road itself a clump of sparks waxed and waned, cigarettes of the watchful deputies.

"D'you hear that, Jim? That'll show you what Burton is. Here's a couple of fine dogs, good hunting dogs, but they're not dogs to Doc, they're feelings. They're dogs, to me. And these guys sleeping here are men, with stomachs; but they're not men to Doc, they're a kind of a collective Colossus. If he wasn't a doctor, we couldn't have 'im around. We need his skill, but his brain just gets us into a mess."

Burton laughed apologetically. "I don't know why I go on talking, then. You practical men always lead practical men with stomachs. And something always gets out of hand. Your men get out of hand, they don't follow the rules of common sense, and you practical men either deny that it is so, or refuse to think about

it. And when someone wonders what it is that makes a man with a stomach something more than your rule allows, why you howl, 'Dreamer, mystic, metaphysician.' I don't know why I talk about it to a practical man. In all history there are no men who have come to such wild-eyed confusion and bewilderment as practical men leading men with stomachs."

"We've a job to do," Mac insisted. "We've got no time to mess around with high-falutin ideas."

"Yes, and so you start your work not knowing your medium. And your ignorance trips you up every time."

They were close to the tents now. "If you talked to other people that way," Mac said, "we'd have to kick you out."

A dark figure arose suddenly from the ground. "Who is it?" a voice demanded; and then, "Oh, hello. I didn't know who it was coming in."

"Dakin set out guards?" Mac asked.

"Yeah."

"He's a good man. I knew he was a good man, coolheaded man."

They stopped by a big, peaked troop tent. "Guess I'll turn in," Doc said. "Here's where my bodyguard sleeps."

"Good idea," Mac agreed. "You'll probably have some bandaging to do tomorrow."

When Doc had disappeared inside the tent, Mac turned to Jim. "No reason why you shouldn't get some sleep too."

"What are you going to do, Mac?"

"Me? Oh, I thought I'd take a look around, see if everything's all right."

"I want to go with you. I just follow you around."

"Sh-h, don't talk so loud." Mac walked slowly toward the line of cars. "You do help me, Jim. It may be sloppy as an old woman, but you keep me from being scared."

"I don't do anything but pad around after you," said Jim.

"I know. I guess I'm getting soft. I'm scared something might happen to you. I shouldn't have brought you down, Jim. I'm getting to depend on you."

"Well, what're we going to do now, Mac?"

"I wish you'd go to bed. I'm going to try to have a talk with those cops in the road."

"What for?"

"Listen, Jim, you didn't get bothered by what Doc said, did you?"

"No. I didn't listen."

"Well, it's a bunch of bunk; but here's something that isn't bunk. You win a strike two ways, because the men put up a steady fight, and because public sentiment comes over to your side. Now most of this valley belongs to a few guys. That means the rest of the people don't own much of anything. The few owners either have to pay 'em or lie to 'em. Those cops out in the road are special deputies, just working stiffs with a star and a gun and a two-weeks' job. I thought I'd try and sound 'em out; try and find out how they feel about the strike. I guess how they feel is how the bosses told 'em to feel. But I might get a line on 'em, anyway."

"Well, how about it if they arrest you? Remember what that man said in the road last night."

"They're just deputies, Jim. They won't recognize me the way a regular cop would."

"Well, I want to go with you."

"O.K., but if anything looks funny, you cut for the camp and yell like hell."

In a tent behind them a man started shouting in his sleep. A soft chorus of voices awakened him and stopped his dreaming. Mac and Jim wedged their way silently between two cars and approached a little group of glowing cigarettes. The sparks died down and shifted as they approached.

Mac called, "Hey, you guys, can we come out there?"

From the group a voice, "How many of you?"

"Two."

"Come on, then." As they drew near, a flashlight glanced out and touched their faces for a second, and then went off. The deputies stood up. "What do you want?" their spokesman demanded.

Mac replied, "We just couldn't sleep; thought we'd come out and talk."

The man laughed. "We been having lots of company tonight."

In the dark Mac pulled out his Bull Durham bag. "Any of you guys want to smoke?"

"We got smokes. What is it you want?"

"Well, I'll tell you. A lot of the guys want to know how you fellows feel about the strike. They sent us out to ask. They know you're just working men, the same as them. They want to know if you maybe won't help your own kind of guys."

Silence met his words. Mac looked uneasily around.

A voice said softly, "All right, you chickens. Get 'em up. Let out a squawk and we plug you."

"Say, what the hell is this? What's the idea?"

"Get behind 'em, Jack, and you, Ed, get your guns in their backs. If they move, let 'em have it. Now, march!"

The rifles pushed into their backs and punched them along through the darkness. The leader's voice said, "Thought you was God-damn smart, didn't you? You didn't know those day-cops pointed you two guys out." They marched across the road, and in among the trees on the other side. "Thought you was darn smart, getting the men out of here before daylight; thought you'd leave us holding the sack. Hell, we knew that gag ten minutes after you decided it."

"Who told you, mister?"

"Don't you wish you knew?" Their

feet pounded along. The rifles jabbed into their backs.

"You takin' us to jail, mister?"

"Jail, hell, we're takin' you God-damn reds to the Vigilance Committee. If you're lucky they'll beat the crap out of you and dump you over the county line; if you ain't lucky, they'll string you up to a tree. We got no use for radicals in this valley."

"But you guys are cops, you got to take us to jail."

"That's what *you* think. There's a nice little house a little ways from here. That's where we're taking you."

Under the orchard trees even the little light from the stars was shut off. "Now be quiet, you guys."

Jim cried, "Go, Mac!" and at the same instant he dropped. His guard toppled over him. Jim rolled around the trunk of a tree, stood up and bolted. At the second row he climbed up into an apple tree, far up, among the leaves. He heard a scuffle and a grunt of pain. The flashlight darted about and then fell to the ground and aimlessly lighted a rotten apple. There came a rip of cloth, and then steady pounding of footsteps. A hand reached down and picked up the flashlight and switched it off. Muffled, arguing voices came from the place of the scuffle.

Jim eased himself gently out of the tree, panting with apprehension every time the leaves quivered. He moved quietly along, came to the road and crossed it. At the line of cars a guard stopped him. "This is the second time tonight, kid. Whyn't you go to bed?"

Jim said, "Listen, did Mac come through?"

"Yeah, goin' like a bat out of hell. He's in Dakin's tent."

Jim hurried on, lifted the brown tent-flap and went in. Dakin and Mac and Burke were there. Mac was talking excitedly. He stopped on a word and stared as Jim came in. "Jesus, I'm glad," he said. "We was just goin' to send out a party to try and get you. What a damn fool I was! What a damn fool! You know, Dakin, they was marchin' us along, had guns right in our backs. I didn't think they'd shoot, but they might of. Jim, what in hell did you do?"

"I just dropped, and the guy fell over me, and his gun dug in the dirt. We used to do that trick in the school yard."

Mac laughed uneasily. "Soon's the guns wasn't touching us, I guess they was afraid they'd kill each other. I jumped sideways and kicked my guy in the stomach."

Burke was standing behind Mac. Jim saw Mac wink at Dakin. The cold eyes almost disappeared behind pale-lashed lids. Dakin said, "Burke, you'd better make the rounds, and see if the guards are all awake."

Burke hesitated. "I think they're O.K."

"Well, you better see, anyway. We don't want no more raids. What they got in their hands, Burke?"

"They got nice clubs."

"Well, go take a look around."

Burke went out of the tent. Mac stepped close to Dakin. "Tent walls is thin," he said quietly. "I'd like to talk to you alone. Want to take a little walk?"

Dakin nodded his head with two jerks. The three of them strolled out into the darkness, going in the direction Dr. Burton had taken earlier. A guard looked them over as they passed.

Mac said, "Somebody's double-crossin' us already. Them deputies knew we was goin' to shove off before daylight."

Dakin asked coldly, "D'you think it's Burke? He wasn't there, even."

"I don't know who it was. Anybody hanging around could of heard through the tent."

"Well, what are we goin' to do about it? You seem to know all about this stuff." The cold voice went on, "I got an idea you reds ain't goin' to do us no good. A guy come in tonight and says if we kick you out, maybe the bosses'll talk business."

"And you think they will? They cut the wages before we showed up, don't forget that. Hell, you'd think we started this strike, and you know damn well we didn't. We're just helpin' it to go straight instead of shootin' its wad."

Dakin's monotone cut him off. "What you gettin' out of this?"

Mac retorted hotly, "We ain't gettin' nothin'."

"How do I know that?"

"You don't know it unless you believe it. They ain't no way to prove it."

Dakin's voice became a little warmer. "I don't know that I'd trust you guys if that was so. If a man's gettin' somethin' you know he's only goin' to do one or two things, he's goin' to take orders, or he's goin' to double-cross. But if a guy ain't gettin' nothin', you can't tell what he'll do."

"All right," Mac said irritably. "Let's lay off that junk. When the guys want to kick us out, let 'em take a vote on us. And let us argue our case. But there ain't no good of us fighting each other."

"Well, what we goin' to do, then? No good sneakin' the guys out tomorrow mornin' if the cops know we're goin' to do it."

"Sure not. Let's just march along the road and take our chances. When we see the scabs, and see how they act, we'll know whether we got to fight or talk."

Dakin stopped and moved his foot sideways against the dirt. "What do you want me out here for?"

"I just wanted to tell you we're bein' double-crossed. If you get somethin' you don't want the cops to know, don't tell nobody."

"All right, I got that. Long as everybody's goin' to know, we might as well

let 'em know. I'm goin' to bed. You guys see if you can keep out of a mess till morning."

Mac and Jim shared a little pup-tent with no floor cloth. They crawled into the little cave and curled up in their old comforters. Mac whispered, "I think Dakin's straight, but he isn't taking orders."

"You don't think he'll try to get us out of here, do you, Mac?"

"He might. I don't think he will. By tomorrow night enough guys will be bruised up and mad so they'll be meat for us. Jesus, Jim, we can't let this thing peter out. It's too good."

"Mac?"

"Yeah?"

"Why don't the cops just come and take us out of here, you and me?"

"Scared to. They're scared the men might go haywire. It might be like when old Dan fell off the ladder. Cops know pretty well when they've got to leave the stiffs alone. We better go to sleep."

"I just want to ask, Mac, how'd you get loose over in the orchard? You had a battle, didn't you?"

"Sure, but it was so dark they couldn't see who they were socking. I knew I could sock anybody."

Jim lay quiet for a while. "Were you scared, Mac, when they had the guns in our backs?"

"Damn right. I've been up against vigilantes before; so's poor old Joy. Ten or fifteen of 'em gang up on you and beat you to a pulp. Oh, they're brave guys, all right. Mostly they wear masks. Damn right I was scared, weren't you?"

"Sure, I guess so. At first I was. And then they started marching us, and I got cold all over. I could see just what would happen if I dropped. I really saw that guy fall over me, saw it before it happened. I was mostly scared they'd plug you."

Mac said, "It's a funny thing, Jim,

how the worse danger you get in, the less it scares you. Once the fuss started, I wasn't scared. I still don't like the way that gun felt."

Jim looked out through the tent opening. The night seemed grey in contrast with the blackness inside the tent. Footsteps went by, crushing the little clods. "D'you think we'll win this strike, Mac?"

"We ought to go to sleep; but you know, Jim, I wouldn't have told you this before tonight: No, I don't think we have a chance to win it. This valley's *organized*. They'll start shooting, and they'll get away with it. We haven't a chance. I figure these guys here'll probably start deserting as soon as much trouble starts. But you don't want to worry about that, Jim. The thing will carry on and on. It'll spread, and some day—it'll work. Some day we'll win. We've got to believe that." He raised up on one elbow. "If we didn't believe that, we wouldn't be here. Doc was right about infection, but that infection is invested capital. We've *got* to believe we can throw it off, before it gets into our hearts and kills us. You never change, Jim. You're always here. You give me strength."

Jim said, "Harry told me right at first what to expect. Everybody hates us, Mac."

"That's the hardest part," Mac agreed. "Everybody hates us; our own side and the enemy. And if we won, Jim, if we put it over, our own side would kill us. I wonder why we do it. Oh, go to sleep!"

9

Before the night had broken at all the voice of awakening men sounded through the camp. There were axe-strokes on wood, and the rattling of the rusty stoves. In a few moments the sweet smell of burning pine and apple wood filled the camp. The cooks' detail was busy. Near the roaring stoves the buckets of coffee were set. The wash boilers of beans began to warm. Out of the tents the people crept, and went to stand near the stoves where they crowded so closely that the cooks had no room to work.

Dakin's truck drove off to Anderson's house and came back with three barrels of water. The word passed, "Dakin wants to see the squad leaders. He wants to talk to 'em right away." The leaders walked importantly toward Dakin's tent.

Now the line of orchard top grew sharp against the eastern sky and the parked cars were greyly visible. The buckets of coffee began to boil, and a rank, nourishing smell came from the bean kettles. The cooks ladled out beans into anything the people brought, pans, jars, cans and tin plates. Many sat on the ground, and with their pocket-knives carved little wooden paddles with which to eat their beans. The coffee was black and bitter, but men and women who had been silent and uncomfortable were warmed by it so that they began to talk, to laugh, to call greetings to one another. The daylight came over the trees and the ground turned greyish-blue. Three great bands of geese flew over, high in the light.

Meanwhile Dakin, flanked by Burke and London, stood in front of his tent. Before Dakin the squad leaders stood and waited, and Mac and Jim stood among them, for Mac had explained to Jim, "We've got to go pretty slow for a while. We don't want the guys to throw us out now."

Dakin had put on a short denim jacket and a tweed cap. His pale eyes darted about over the faces of the men. He said, "I'm goin' to tell you guys what's on, and then you can pull out of it if you want to. I don't want nobody to come that don't want to come. There's a train-load of scabs comin' in. We figure to go in town an' try to stop 'em. We'll talk to 'em some, and then we might have to fight 'em. How's that sound to you?"

A murmur of assent arose.

"All right, then. We'll march in. Keep your guys in hand. Keep 'em quiet, and on the side of the road." He grinned coldly. "If any of 'em want to pick up a few rocks an' shove 'em in their pockets, I can't see no harm in that."

The men laughed appreciatively.

"O.K. If you got that, go talk to your men. I want to get all the kicks in before we start. I'm goin' to leave about a hundred guys to look after the camp. Go get some breakfast."

The men broke and hurried back to the stoves. Mac and Jim moved up to where the leaders stood. London was saying, "I wouldn't trust 'em to put up much of a scrap. They don't look none too mean to me."

"Too early in the morning," Mac assured him. "They ain't had their coffee yet. Guys are different before they've ate."

Dakin demanded, "You guys goin' along?"

"Damn right," said Mac. "But look, Dakin, we got men out gettin' food and supplies together. Fix it so some cars can go in for the stuff when they send the word."

"O.K. We'll need it by tonight, too. Them beans'll be all gone. It takes a hell of a lot to feed a bunch like this."

Burke said, "I'm for startin' a mix soon's the scabs get off the train. Scare hell out of 'em."

"Better talk first," Mac said. "I seen half a train-load of scabs go over to the strike if they was talked to first. You jump on 'em and you'll scare some, and make some mad."

Dakin watched him suspiciously while he talked. "Well, let's be movin'," he

said. "I got to pick the guys to stay. Doc and his men can clean up the camp. I'm goin' in my truck; London an' Burke can ride with me. We better leave these damn old cans here."

The sun was just coming up when the long, ragged column started out. The squad leaders kept their men to one side of the road. Jim heard a man say, "Don't bother with clods. Wait till we get to the railroad right-of-way. There's nice granite rocks in the roadbed."

Singing broke out, the tuneless, uneven singing of untrained men. Dakin's green Chevrolet truck led off, idling in low gear. The column of men followed it, and the crowd left in camp with the women howled good-byes after them.

They had hardly started when ten motorcycle policemen rode up and spaced themselves along the line of march. When they had gone half a mile along the road a big open car, jammed with men, dashed to the head of the column and parked across the road. All of the men carried rifles in their hands, and all wore deputies' badges. The driver stood up on the seat. "You men are going to keep order, and don't forget it," he shouted. "You can march as long as you don't block traffic, but you're not going to interfere with anybody. Get that?" He sat down, moved his car in front of Dakin's truck and led the whole march.

Jim and Mac marched fifty feet behind Dakin's truck. Mac said, "They got a reception committee for us. Ain't that kind of 'em?" The men about him tittered. Mac continued, "They say 'you got a right to strike, but you can't picket,' an' they know a strike won't work without picketin'." There was no laughter this time. The men growled, but there was little anger in the tone. Mac glanced nervously at Jim. "I don't like it," he said softly. "This bunch of bums isn't keyed up. I hope to Christ something happens to make 'em mad before long. This's going to fizzle out if something don't happen."

The straggling parade moved into town and took to the sidewalks. The men were quiet now, and most of them looked shamefaced. As they came into the town, householders watched through the windows, and children stood on the lawns and looked at them until the parents dragged them into the houses and shut the doors. Very few citizens moved about in the streets. The motorcycles of the police idled along so slowly that the riders had to put out their feet and touch the ground occasionally to keep upright. Led by the sheriff's car, the procession moved along back streets until it came at last to the railroad yard. The men stopped along the edge of the right-of-way, for the line was guarded by twenty men armed with shot-guns and tear gas bombs.

Dakin parked his truck at the curb. The men silently spread out and faced the line of special policemen. Dakin and London walked up and down the dense front, giving instructions. The men must not start any trouble with the cops if they could help it. There was to be talk first, and that was all.

On the right-of-way two long lines of refrigerator cars stood idle. Jim said, aside, to Mac, "Maybe they'll stop the freight way up the track and unload the guys. Then we wouldn't get a chance at them."

Mac shook his head. "Later they might, but now I think they want a show-down. They figure they can scare us off. Jesus, I wish the train'd come in. Waiting raises hell with guys like ours. They get scared when they have to wait around."

A number of the men were sitting down on the curb by now. A buzz of quiet talk came from the close-pressed line. They were hemmed in, railroad guards on one side, motorcycle police and deputy sheriffs on the other. The men looked nervous and self-conscious. The sheriff's deputies carried their rifles in two hands, held across their stomachs.

"The cops are scared, too," Mac said.

London reassured a group of men. "They ain't a goin' to do no shootin'," he said. "They can't afford to do no shootin'."

Someone shouted, "She's in the block!" Far along the track the block arm of the semaphore was up. A line of smoke showed above the trees, and the tracks rumbled under approaching wheels. Now the men stood up from the curb and craned their necks up the track.

London bellowed, "Hold the guys in, now."

They could see the black engine and the freight cars moving slowly in; and in the doorways of the cars they could see the legs of men. The engine crashed slowly in, puffing out bursts of steam from under its wheels. It drew into a siding and its brakes set. The cars jarred together, the engine stood wheezing and panting.

Across the street from the right-of-way stood a line of dilapidated stores and restaurants with furnished rooms in their upper storeys. Mac glanced over his shoulder. The windows of the rooms were full of men's heads looking out. Mac said, "I don't like the looks of those guys."

"Why not?" Jim asked.

"I don't know. There ought to be some women there. There aren't any women at all."

In the doorways of the box-cars strike-breakers sat, and standing behind them were others. They stared uneasily. They made no move to get out on to the ground.

Then London stepped out in front, stepped so close to a guard that the shot-gun muzzle turned and pointed at his stomach, and the guard moved back a pace. The engine panted rhythmically, like a great, tired animal. London cupped his hands around his mouth. His deep voice roared, "Come on over, you guys. Don't fight against us. Don't help the cops." His voice was cut off by a shriek of steam. A jet of white leaped from the side of the engine, drowning London's voice, blotting out every sound but its own swishing scream. The line of strikers moved restively, bellied out in the middle, toward the guards. The shot-gun muzzles turned and swept the ranks. The guards' faces tightened, but their threat had stopped the line. The steam shrieked on, and its white plume rose up and broke into little pieces.

In the doorway of one of the box-cars a commotion started, a kind of a boiling of the men. A man squirmed through the seated scabs and dropped to the ground.

Mac shouted in Jim's ear, "My God! It's Joy!"

The misshapen, gnome-like figure faced the doorway, and the men. The arms waved jerkily. Still the steam screeched. The men in the doorway dropped to the ground and stood in front of the frantic, jerking Joy. He turned and waved his arm toward the strikers. His beaten face was contorted. Five or six of the men fell in behind him, and the whole group moved toward the line of strikers. The guards turned sideways, nervously trying to watch both sides at once.

And then—above the steam—three sharp, cracking sounds. Mac looked back at the stores. Heads and rifles were withdrawn quickly from the room windows and the windows dropped.

Joy had stopped, his eyes wide. His mouth flew open and a jet of blood rolled down his chin, and down his shirt. His eyes ranged wildly over the crowd of men. He fell on his face and clawed outward with his fingers. The guards stared unbelievingly at the squirming fig-

ure on the ground. Suddenly the steam stopped; and the quietness fell on the men like a wave of sound. The line of strikers stood still, with strange, dreaming faces. Joy lifted himself up with his arms, like a lizard, and then dropped again. A little thick river of blood ran down on the crushed rock of the roadbed.

A strange, heavy movement started among the men. London moved forward woodenly, and the men moved forward. They were stiff. The guards aimed with their guns, but the line moved on, unheeding, unseeing. The guards stepped swiftly sideways to get out of the way, for the box-car doors were belching silent men who moved slowly in. The ends of the long line curled and circled slowly around the center of the dead man, like sheep about a nucleus.

Jim clung shivering to Mac's arm. Mac turned and muttered. "He's done the first real, useful thing in his life. Poor Joy. He's done it. He'd be so glad. Look at the cops, Jim. Let go my arm. Don't lose your nerve. Look at the cops!"

The guards were frightened; riots they could stop, fighting they could stop; but this slow, silent movement of men with the wide eyes of sleepwalkers terrified them. They held to their places, but the sheriff started his car. The motorcycle police moved imperceptibly toward their parked machines.

The strike-breakers were out of the cars by now. Some of them crept between the box-cars or under the wheels and hurried away on the other side, but most of them moved up and packed tightly about the place where Joy lay.

Mac saw Dakin standing on the outskirts of the mob, his little pale eyes for once looking straight ahead and not moving. Mac walked over to him. "We better get him in your truck and take him out to the camp."

Dakin turned slowly. "We can't touch

him," he said. "The cops'll have to take him."

Mac said sharply, "Why didn't the cops catch those guys in the windows? Look at the cops, they're scared to death. We've got to take him, I tell you. We've got to use him to step our guys up, to keep 'em together. This'll stick 'em together, this'll make 'em fight."

Dakin grimaced. "You're a cold-blooded bastard. Don't you think of nothing but 'strike'?"

Jim broke in, "Dakin, that little guy got shot trying to help us. D'you want to stop him now from doing it?"

Dakin's eyes moved slowly from Mac to Jim, and then to Mac again. He said, "What do you know about what he was doin'? Couldn't hear nothing but that damn steam."

"We know him," Mac said. "He was a pal of ours."

Dakin's eyes were filled with dislike. "Pal of yours, and you won't let him rest now. You want to use him. You're a pair of cold-blooded bastards."

Mac cried, "What do you know about it? Joy didn't want no rest. Joy wanted to work, and he didn't know how." His voice rose hysterically. "And now he's got a chance to work, and you don't want to let 'im."

A number of the men had turned toward the voices, turned with a dull curiosity. Dakin peered at Mac for a moment longer. "Come on," he said. They pushed and jabbed their way into the tight mass of men, who gave way reluctantly.

Mac shouted, "Come on, you guys, let us in. We got to get this poor fellow out o' there." The men opened a narrow pathway, pushing violently backward to make it.

London joined them, and helped to force a way in. Joy was quite dead. When they had cleared a little space around him, London turned him over and started to wipe the bloody dirt from Joy's mouth. There was a foxy look in the open eyes; the mouth smiled terribly.

Mac said, "Don't do that, London. Leave it that way, just the way it is."

London lifted the little man in his arms. Joy looked very small against London's big chest. A path opened for them easily this time. London marched along, and the men arranged themselves into a crude column, and followed.

Beside Dakin's bright green truck the sheriff stood, surrounded by his deputies. London stopped, and the following men stopped. "I want that body," the sheriff said.

"No. You can't have it."

"You men shot a strike-breaker. We'll bring the charge. I want that body for the coroner."

London's eyes glowed redly. He said simply, "Mister, you know the guys that killed this little man; you know who did it. You got laws and you don't keep 'em." The mob was silent, listening.

"I tell you, I want that body."

London said plaintively, "Can't you see, mister? If you guys don't get the hell out of here, can't you see you're goin' get *killed?* Can't you see *that,* mister? Don't you *know* when you can't go no further?"

From the mob there came a rustle of released breath. The sheriff said, "I'm not through with you," but he backed away, and his deputies backed away. The mob growled, so softly that it sounded like a moan. London set Joy over the tailboard of the truck, and he climbed in and lifted the body forward, until it leaned against the back of the cab.

Dakin started his motor and backed around and rolled along the street, and the dull, menacing mob fell in behind. They made no noise. They walked with heavy, padding footsteps.

No motorcycle police lined the road. The streets and the roads were deserted on their line of march. Mac and Jim walked a little to one side of the truck. "Was it vigilantes, Mac?"

"Yep. But they overdid it this time. Everything went wrong for them. That steam—if our guys could've heard the shooting better, they'd probably have run away. But the steam was too loud. It was over too soon; our guys didn't have a chance to get scared. No, they made a mistake."

They trudged slowly along, beside the column of marching men. "Mac, who in hell are these vigilantes, anyway? What kind of guys are they?"

"Why, they're the dirtiest guys in any town. They're the same ones that burned the houses of old German people during the war. They're the same ones that lynch Negroes. They like to be cruel. They like to hurt people, and they always give it a nice name, patriotism or protecting the constitution. But they're just the old nigger torturers working. The owners use 'em, tell 'em we have to protect the people against reds. Y'see that lets 'em burn houses and torture the beat people with no danger. And that's all they want to do, anyway. They've got no guts; they'll only shoot from cover, or gang a man when they're ten to one. I guess they're about the worst scum in the world." His eyes sought the body of Joy, in the truck. He said, "During the war there was a little fat German tailor in my town, and a bunch of these patriotic bastards, about fifty of 'em, started his house on fire, and beat him to a pulp. They're great guys, these vigilantes. Not long ago they shot tracer bullets through a kerosene tank and started a fire in a bunk house. They didn't have the guts to do it with a match."

The column marched on through the country, raising a great dust. The men were coming slowly out of their dream. They talked together in low voices. Their feet scuffed heavily against the ground. "Poor Joy," Jim said. "He was a good little fellow. He'd been beaten so much.

He reminded me of my old man, always mad."

Mac reproved him. "Don't feel sorry for Joy. If he could know what he did, he'd be cocky. Joy always wanted to lead people, and now he's going to do it, even if he's in a box."

"How about the scabs, Mac? We got a bunch of them with us."

"Sure, a bunch came over, but a lot of 'em beat it. Some of our guys beat it, too. We got just about the same number we started with. Didn't you see 'em crawling under the cars and running away?" Mac said, "Look at these guys. They're waking up. It's just as though they got a shot of gas for a while. That's the most dangerous kind of men."

"The cops knew it, too," said Jim.

"Damn right they did. When a mob don't make a noise, when it comes on with dead pans, that's the time for a cop to get out of the way."

They were nearing the Anderson place. Jim asked, "What do we do now, Mac?"

"Well, we hold the funeral, and we start picketing. It'll settle down now. They'll run in scabs with trucks."

"You still think we'll get beat, Mac?"

"I don't know. They got this valley organized. God, how they've got it organized. It's not so hard to do when a few men control everything, land, courts, banks. They can cut off loans, and they can railroad a man to jail, and they can always bribe plenty."

Dakin's truck pulled to the end of the line of cars and backed into place. The camp guards came streaming out, and the column of returning men deployed among them. Groups collected to hear the story, over and over. Dr. Burton trotted over to Dakin's truck. London stood up heavily. His wide blue shirt-front was streaked with Joy's blood. Burton took one look at Joy. "Killed him, eh?"

"Got him," said London.

Burton said, "Bring him to my tent. I'll look him over." From behind the tents a hoarse, bubbling scream broke out. All of the men turned, frozen at the sound. Burton said, "Oh, they're killing a pig. One of the cars brought back a live pig. Bring this body to my tent."

London bent over wearily and lifted Joy in his arms again. A crowd of men followed him, and stood clustered about the big troop tent. Mac and Jim followed Dr. Burton inside the tent. They watched silently while he unbuttoned the stiff, bloody shirt and disclosed a wound in the chest. "Well, that's it. That'd do it."

"Recognize him, Doc?"

Burton looked closely at the distorted face. "I've seen him before."

"Sure you have. It's Joy. You've set damn near every bone in his body."

"Well, he's through this time. Tough little man. You'll have to send his body to town. The coroner'll have to have it."

London said, "If we do that, they'll bury him, hide him."

Mac said, "We can send some guys in to see that he gets back here. Let 'em picket the morgue till they get the body back. Those damn vigilantes made a mistake; an' they know it by now."

Dakin lifted the flap and stepped into the big tent. "They're fryin' pork," he said. "They sure cut up that pig quick."

Mac said, "Dakin, can you have the guys build a kind of a platform? We'll want some place for the coffin to set. Y'ought to have a place to talk from, too."

"Want to make a show of it, do you?"

"You're damn right! You got me kinda wrong, Dakin. What we got to fight with? Rocks, sticks. Even Indians had bows an' arrows. But let us get one little gun to protect ourselves, an' they call out the troops to stop the revolution. We got damn few things to fight with. We got to use what we can. This little guy was my friend. Y'can take it from me he'd want

to get used any way we can use him. We got to use him." He paused. "Dakin, can't you see? We'll get a hell of a lot of people on our side if we put on a public funeral. We got to get public opinion."

London was nodding his head slowly up and down. "The guy's right, Dakin."

"O.K., if you want it too, London. I s'pose somebody's got to make a speech, but I ain't goin' to do it."

"Well, I will if I have to," London cried. "I seen the little guy start over to us. I seen him get it. I'll make the speech if you won't."

"Sounds like Cock Robin," Burton said.

"Huh?"

"Nothing. I was just talking. Better get the body taken in now, and turn it over to the coroner."

London said, "I'm going to send a flock of my own guys to stay with him."

Jim's voice came from outside the tent. "Oh, Mac, come on out. Anderson wants to see you."

Mac walked quickly outside. Anderson was standing with Jim. He looked tired and old. "You just played hell," he began fiercely.

"What's the matter, Mr. Anderson?"

"Said you'd protect us, didn't you?"

"Sure I did. The guys here'll take care of you. What's the matter?"

"I'll tell you what's the matter. Bunch of men burned up Al's lunch wagon last night. They jumped on Al an' broke his arm an' six ribs. They burned his lunch wagon right down."

"Jesus!" Mac said. "I didn't think they'd do that."

"You didn't think, but they did it just the same."

"Where's Al now, Mr. Anderson?"

"He's over to the house. I had to bring him out from the hospital."

"I'll get the doctor. We'll go over and see him."

"Eighteen hundred dollars!" the old

man cried. "He got some of it together, and I loaned him some, and then along you come. Now he hasn't got a thing."

"I'm awful sorry," Mac said.

"Sure, you're sorry. That don't unburn Al's wagon. That don't mend his arm and his ribs. And what you doing to protect me? They'll burn my house next."

"We'll put a guard around your house."

"Guards, hell. What good's a bunch of bums? I wish I never let you on the place. You'll ruin me." His voice had risen to a high squeak. His old eyes were watering. "You just played hell, that's what you did. That's what we get for mixing up with a bunch of damn radicals."

Mac tried to soothe him. "Let's go over and see Al," he suggested. "Al's a swell guy. I want to see him."

"Well, he's all busted up. They kicked 'im in the head, too."

Mac edged him slowly away, for the men were beginning to move in, toward the shrill voice. "What you blaming us for?" he said. "We didn't do it. It was those nice neighbors of yours."

"Yes, but it wouldn't have happened if we didn't get mixed up with you."

Mac turned angrily on him. "Listen, mister, we know you got a sock in the teeth; little guys like you and me get it all the time. We're tryin' to make it so guys like you won't get it."

"That wagon cost eighteen hundred dollars. Why, man, I can't go in town without the kids throw rocks at me. You ruined us, that's what you did."

Mac asked, "How's Al feel about it?"

"I think Al's red as hell himself. Only people he's sore at are the men that did it."

"Al's got a good head," Mac said. "Al sees the whole thing. You would of been out on your can anyway. Now, if you get bounced, you got a big bunch of men in back of you. These men aren't going to

forget what you're doing for 'em. And we'll put a guard around your house tonight. I'll have the doctor come over pretty soon and look at Al."

The old man turned tiredly, and walked away.

Smoke from the rusty stoves hung low over the camp. The men had begun to move in toward the smell of frying pork. Mac looked after the retreating figure of Anderson. "How's it feel to be a Party man now, Jim? It's swell when you read about it—romantic. Ladies like to get up and squawk about the 'boss class' and the 'downtrodden working man.' It's a heavy weight, Jim. That poor guy. The lunch wagon looks bigger than the world to him. I feel responsible for that. Hell," Mac continued. "I thought I brought you out here to teach you, to give you confidence; and here I spend my time bellyaching. I thought I was going to bolster you up, and instead—oh, what the hell! It's awful hard to keep your eyes on the big issue. Why the devil don't you say something?"

"You don't give me a chance."

"I guess I don't. Say something now! All I can think of is that poor little Joy shot up. He didn't have much sense, but he wasn't afraid of anything."

"He was a nice little guy," Jim said.

"'Member what he said? Nobody was going to make him stop calling sons-of-bitches 'sons-of-bitches.' I wish I didn't get this lost feeling sometimes, Jim."

"A little fried pork might help."

"By God, that's right. I didn't have much this morning. Let's go over."

A long delivery wagon drove up the road and stopped in front of the line of cars. From the seat a fussy little man stepped down and walked into the camp. "Who's in charge here?" he demanded of Mac.

"Dakin. He's over in that big tent."

"Well, I'm the coroner. I want that corpse."

"Where's your bodyguard?" Mac asked.

The little man puffed at him. "What do I want with a bodyguard? I'm the coroner. Where's that corpse?"

"In the big tent over there. It's all ready for you."

"Well, why didn't you say so?" He went puffing away like a small engine.

Mac sighed. "Thank God we don't have many like him to fight," he said. "That little guy's got guts. Came out all alone. He's kind of like Joy, himself." They walked on toward the stoves. Two men passed, carrying the body of Joy between them, and the coroner walked fussily along behind.

Men were walking away from the stoves with pieces of greasy fried pork in their hands. They wiped their lips with their sleeves. The tops of the stoves were covered with little slabs of hissing meat. "God, that smells good," said Mac. "Let's get some. I'm hungry as hell." The cooks handed out ill-cut, half-cooked pieces of pork to them, and they strolled away, gnawing at the soft meat. "Only eat the outside," Mac said. "Doc shouldn't let the men eat raw pork. They'll all be sick."

"They got too hungry to wait," said Jim.

10

An apathy had fallen on the men. They sat staring in front of them. They seemed not to have the energy to talk, and among them the bedraggled, discontented women sat. They were listless and stale. They gnawed thoughtfully at their meat, and when it was finished, wiped their hands on their clothes. The air was full of their apathy, and full of their discontent.

Mac, walking through the camp with Jim, grew discontented, too. "They ought to be doing something," Mac complained. "I don't care what it is. We can't let 'em sit around like this. Our strike'll go right out from under us. Christ, what's the matter with 'em? They had a man killed this morning; that ought to keep 'em going. Now it's just after noon, and they're slumped already. We got to get them working at something. Look at their eyes, Jim."

"They're not looking at anything—they're just staring."

"Yeah, they're thinking of themselves. Every man there is thinkin' how hurt he is, or how much money he made during the war. Just like Anderson. They're falling apart."

"Well, let's do something. Let's make them move. What is there to do?"

"I don't know. If we could make 'em dig a hole, it'd be as good as anything else. If we can just get 'em all pushing on something, or lifting something, or all walking in one direction—doesn't matter a hell of a lot. They'll start fighting each other if we don't move 'em. They'll begin to get mean, pretty soon."

London, hurrying past, caught the last words. "Who's goin' to get mean?"

Mac turned around. "Hello, London. We been talkin' about these here guys. They're all fallin' to pieces."

"I know it. I been around with these stiffs long enough to tell."

"Well, I just said they'd start fightin', if we didn't put 'em to work."

"They already did. That bunch we left in camp this morning had a fuss. One of the guys tried to make another guy's woman. An' the first guy come in an' stuck him with a pair of scissors. Doc fixed him up. He like to bled to death, I guess."

"You see, Jim? I told you. Listen, London, Dakin's sore at me. He don't want to listen to nothing I tell him, but he'll listen to you. We got to move these guys before they get into trouble. Make 'em march in a circle—make 'em dig a hole and then fill it up. It don't make no difference."

"I know it. Well, how about picketin'?"

"Swell, but I don't think there's much work goin' on yet."

"What do we care, if it moves the guys off their ass."

"You got a head, London. See if you can get Dakin to send 'em out, about fifty in a bunch, out in different directions. Let 'em keep to the roads, and if they see any apple pickin', let 'em break it up."

"Sure I will," London said, and he turned and walked toward Dakin's brown tent.

Jim began, "Mac, you said I could go out with the pickets."

"Well, I'd rather have you with me."

"I want to get into it, Mac."

"O.K., go with one of the bunches, then. But stick close to them, Jim. They got your number here. You know that. Don't let 'em pick you off."

They saw Dakin and London come out of the tent. London talked rapidly. Mac said, "You know, I think we made a mistake about putting Dakin in. He's too tied up with his truck, and his tent, and his kids. He's too careful. London'ud have been the best man. London hasn't got anything to lose. I wonder if we could get the guys to kick Dakin out and put London in. I think the guys like London better. Dakin's got too much property. Did you see that folding stove of his? He don't even eat with the guys. Maybe we better start working and see if we can't get London in. I thought Dakin was cool, but he's too damn cool. We need somebody that can work the guys up a little."

Jim said, "Come on, Dakin's making up the pickets now."

Jim joined a picket group of about fifty men. They moved off along the road in a direction away from town. Almost as soon as they started the apathy dropped away. The straggling band walked quickly along.

The lean-faced Sam was in charge of it, and he instructed the men as he walked along. "Pick up rocks," he said. "Get a lot of good rocks in your pocket. And keep lookin' down the rows."

For a distance the orchards were deserted. The men began to sing tunelessly,

"It was Christmas on the Island,
All the convicts they were there——"

They scuffed their feet in time. Across the intersecting road they marched, and a cloud of grey dust followed them. "Like France," a man said. "If it was all mud, it's just like France."

"Hell, you wasn't in France."

"I was so. I was five months in France."

"You don't walk like no soldier."

"I don't want to walk like no soldier. I walked like a soldier enough. I got schrap' in me, that's what I got."

"Where's them scabs?"

"Looks like we got 'em tied up. I don't see nobody workin'. We got this strike tied up already."

Sam said, "Sure, you got it won, fella. Just set on your can and won it, didn't you? Don't be a damn fool."

"Well, we sure scared hell out of the cops this mornin'. You don't see no cops around, do you?"

Sam said, "You'll see plenty before you get out of this, fella. You're just like all the stiffs in the world. You're king of hell, now. In a minute you'll start belly-achin', an' the *next* thing, you'll sneak out." An angry chorus broke on him.

"You think so, smart guy? Well, just show us somethin' to do."

"You got no call to be talkin' like that. What the hell'd you ever do?"

Sam spat in the road. "I'll tell you what I done. I was in 'Frisco on Bloody

Thursday. I smacked a cop right off a horse. I was one of the guys that went in and got them night sticks from a carpenter's shop that the cops was gettin' made. Got one of 'em right now, for a souvenir."

"Tha's a damn lie. You ain't no longshoreman; you're a lousy fruit tramp."

"Sure I'm a fruit tramp. Know why? 'Cause I'm blacklisted with every shippin' company in the whole damn country, that's why." He spoke with pride. A silence met his assertion. He went on, "I seen more trouble than you can-heat bindle-stiffs ever seen." His contempt subjugated them. "Now keep your eyes down them rows, and cut out all this talk." They marched along a while.

"Look. There's boxes."

"Where?"

"Way to hell an' gone down that row."

Jim looked in the pointed direction. "There's guys down there," he cried.

A man said, "Come on, longshoreman, let's see you go."

Sam stood still in the road. "You guys takin' orders?" he demanded.

"Sure, we'll take 'em if they're any damn good."

"All right, then. Keep in hand. I don't want no rush at first, and then you guys runnin' like hell when anythin' busts. Come on, stick together."

They turned off the road and crossed a deep irrigation ditch, and they marched down the row between the big trees. As they approached the pile of boxes men began to drop out of the trees and to gather in a nervous group.

A checker stood by the box pile. As the pickets approached he took a double-barreled shot-gun from a box and advanced toward them a few steps. "Do you men want to go to work?" he shouted.

A chorus of derisive yells answered him. One man put his forefingers in his mouth and whistled piercingly.

"You get off this land," the checker said. "You've got no right on this land at all."

The strikers marched slowly on. The checker backed up to the box pile, where his pickers shifted nervously, and watched with frightened faces.

Sam said, over his shoulder, "All right. You guys stop here." He stepped forward alone a few paces. "Listen, you workers," he said. "Come over to our side. Don't go knifin' us guys in the back. Come on and join up with us."

The checker answered, "You take those men off this land or I'll have the whole bunch of you run in."

The derisive yell began again, and the shrill whistling.

Sam turned angrily. "Shut up, you crazy bastards. Lay off the music."

The pickers looked about for a retreat. The checker reassured them. "Don't let him scare you, men. You've got a right to work if you want to."

Sam called again, "Listen, guys, we're givin' you this chance to come along with us."

"Don't let him bully you," the checker cried. His voice was rising. "They can't tell a man what he's got to do."

The pickers stood still. "You comin'?" Sam demanded. They didn't answer. Sam began to move slowly toward them.

The checker stepped forward. "There's buckshot in this gun. I'll shoot you if you don't get off."

Sam spoke softly as he moved. "You ain't shootin' nobody, fella. You might get one of us, and the rest'd slaughter you." His voice was low and passionless. His men moved along, ten feet behind him. He stopped, directly in front of the checker. The quivering gun pointed at his chest. "We just want to talk," he said, and with one movement he stooped and dived, like a football tackle, and clipped the feet from under the checker. The gun exploded, and dug a pit in the ground.

Sam spun over and drove his knees between the legs of the checker. Then he jumped up, leaving the man, writhing and crying hoarsely, on the ground. For a second both the pickers and the strikers had stood still. Too late the pickers turned to run. Men swarmed on them, cursing in their throats. The pickers fought for a moment, and then went down.

Jim stood a little apart; he saw a picker wriggle free and start to run. He picked up a heavy clod and hurled it at the man, struck him in the small of the back, and brought him down. The group surrounded the fallen man, feet working, kicking and stamping; and the picker screamed from the ground. Jim looked coldly at the checker. His face was white with agony and wet with the perspiration of pain.

Sam broke free and leaped at the kicking, stamping men. "Lay off, God-damn you, lay off," he yelled at them; and still they kicked, growling in their throats. Their lips were wet with saliva. Sam picked up an apple box from the pile and smashed it over a head. "Don't kill 'em," he shouted. "Don't kill 'em."

The fury departed as quickly as it had come. They stood away from the victims. They panted heavily. Jim looked without emotion at the ten moaning men on the ground, their faces kicked shapeless. Here a lip was torn away, exposing bloody teeth and gums; one man cried like a child because his arm was bent sharply backward, broken at the elbow. Now that the fury was past, the strikers were sick, poisoned by the flow from their own anger glands. They were weak; one man held his head between his hands as though it ached terribly.

Suddenly a man went spinning around and around, croaking. A rifle-crack sounded from down the row. Five men came running along, stopping to fire now and then. The strikers broke and ran, dodging among the trees to be out of the line of fire.

Jim ran with them. He was crying to himself, "Can't stand fire. We can't stand fire." The tears blinded him. He felt a heavy blow on the shoulder and stumbled a little. The group reached the road and plunged on, looking back over their shoulders.

Sam was behind them, running beside Jim. "O.K.," he shouted. "They stopped." Still some of the men ran on in a blind panic, ran on and disappeared at the road intersection. Sam caught the rest. "Settle down," he shouted. "Settle down. Nobody's chasin' you." They came to a stop. They stood weakly at the side of the road. "How many'd they get?" Sam demanded.

The men looked at one another. Jim said, "I only saw one guy hit."

"O.K. He'll be all right, maybe. Got him in the chest." He looked more closely at Jim. "What's the matter with you, kid? You're bleedin'."

"Where?"

"All down your back."

"I ran into a limb, I guess."

"Limb, hell." Sam pulled the blue denim coat down from Jim's shoulder. "You got bored with a high-power. Can you move your arm?"

"Sure. It just feels numb."

"I guess it didn't get a bone. Shoulder muscle. Must of been a steel-jacket. You ain't even bleedin' much. Come on, guys, let's get back. There's goin' to be cops thick as maggots around here."

They hurried along the road. Sam said, "If you get feelin' weak, I'll help you, kid."

"I'm all right. We couldn't take it, Sam."

Sam said bitterly, "We done noble when we was five to one; we made messes of them scabs."

Jim asked, "Did we kill any of 'em?"

"I don't think so. Some of 'em ain't ever goin' be the same again."

Jim said, "Jesus, it was pretty awful, wasn't it. Did you see that guy with his lip torn?"

"Hell, they'll sew his lip back on. We got to do it, kid. We just got to. If they won't come over, we just got to scare 'em."

"Oh, I know it," said Jim. "I'm not worrying about 'em."

Far ahead they heard a siren. Sam cried, "Jump for the ditch, you guys. Lie down in the ditch. Here comes the cops." He saw that they were all flat in a deep irrigation ditch along the road. The motorcycles roared by, and crossed the intersection, and an ambulance clanged after them. The men did not raise their heads until the motors had disappeared across the intersection. Sam jumped up. "Come on, now. We got to beat it fast."

They dog-trotted along the road. The sun was going down by now, and the road was in a blue evening shadow. A heavy cloud sailed like a ship toward the sun, and its dark edge reddened as it drew near. The men jumped for the ditch again when the ambulance came back. The motorcycles went by more slowly this time, the policemen looking down the rows as they went, but they did not search the ditch.

As the evening fell the pickets came back to the camp. Jim's legs were wobbling under him. His shoulder stung deeply, for the nerves were awakening after being stunned by the high-powered bullet. The men dispersed into camp.

Mac walked over toward Jim, and when he saw how white Jim was, he broke into a trot. "What's the matter with you, Jim? Did you get hurt?"

"No, not much. Sam says I'm shot in the shoulder. I can't see it. It doesn't hurt much."

Mac's face turned red. "By God, I knew I shouldn't let you go."

"Why not? I'm no pansy."

"Maybe you aren't one, but you'll be pushing 'em up pretty soon, if I don't watch you. Come on, let Doc look at you. He was right here a minute ago. There he goes. Hi, Doc!" They took Jim into a white tent. "This one just came in. Doc's going to use it for a hospital," said Mac.

The autumn darkness was falling quickly, and the evening was hastened by the big black cloud, which spread out over the western sky. Mac held a lantern while Burton pulled Jim's shirt free of his shoulder. He washed the wound carefully, with hot, sterile water. "Lucky boy," he said. "A lead slug would have smashed your shoulder to pieces. You've got a little auger-hole through the muscle. It'll be stiff for a while. Bullet went right on through." His deft hands cleansed the wound with a probe, applied a dressing and taped it on. "You'll be all right," he said. "Take it easy for a couple of days. Mac, I'm going over to see Al Anderson later. Want to come?"

"Sure, I'll be with you. I want to get Jim a cup of coffee." He shoved a tin can of black, ugly coffee in Jim's hand. "Come on, sit down," he said. He shoved a box out and sat Jim down on it, and reclined on the ground beside him. "What happened, Jim?"

"We went in after some scabs. Mac, our guys just kicked hell out of 'em. Kicked 'em in the heads."

Mac said softly, "I know, Jim. It's terrible, but it's the only thing to do if they won't come over. We've got to do it. It's not nice to see a sheep killed, either, but we've got to have mutton. What happened then?"

"Well, five men came running and shooting. Our guys ran like rabbits. They couldn't take it."

"Well, why should they, Jim, with nothing to fight with but their bare hands?"

"I hardly knew it when I got hit. One of our guys went down. I don't know whether he was killed or not."

"Nice party," Mac said. "The other crowds brought in about thirty scabs. They didn't have any trouble; just called 'em out, and they came along." He reached up and touched Jim's leg for a moment. "How's the shoulder feel now?"

"Hurts a little, not much."

"Oh say, Jim. Looks like we're goin' to have a new boss."

"Kicked Dakin out, you mean?"

"No, but he's out, all right. Dick sent word he had a load of blankets. Well, Dakin took six men and went in with his shiny truck. One of the six guys got away and came back and told how it was. They got their load and started back. A little way this side of town they ran over a bunch of nails, stopped to change a tire. Well, then a dozen men with guns jumped out and held them up. Well, six of them stand the guys up while they wreck Dakin's truck, smash the crankcase and set it on fire. Dakin stands there with a gun on him. He turns white, and then he turns blue. Then he lets out a howl like a coyote and starts for 'em. They shoot him in the leg, but that don't stop him. When he can't run any more, he crawls for 'em, slavering around the mouth like a mad dog—just nuts, he just went *nuts!* I guess he loved that truck better'n anything in the world. The guy that came back said it was just awful, the way he crawled for 'em. Tried to bite 'em. He was snarling—like a mad dog. Well, then, some traffic cops come along, and the vigilante boys fade. The cops pick Dakin up and take him in. The guy that came in and told about it was up a gum tree watching. He says Dakin bit a cop on the hand, and they had to stick a screw-driver back in his teeth to pry 'im

loose. And that's the guy I said wouldn't lose his temper. He's in the can now. I guess the guys'll elect London in his place."

Jim said, "Well, he sure looked cool enough to me. I'm glad I didn't lay a finger on his truck."

Mac heaped a little pile of dirt on the floor with his hand, and moulded it round, and patted a little flat top on it. "I'm kind of worried, Jim. Dick hasn't sent any food today. We haven't heard anything from him except those blankets. They're cooking up all the rest of the beans with pork bones, but that's all there is, except some mush. That's all there is for tomorrow."

"Do you suppose they knocked Dick off?"

Mac patted his mound flatter. "Dick's clever as a weasel. I don't think they could catch him. I don't know what's the matter. We've got to get food in. The minute the guys get hungry, they're through, I'm afraid."

"Maybe he didn't collect anything. He sent that pig this morning."

"Sure, and the pig's in the beans now. Dick knows how much it takes to feed these guys. Dick must have organized the sympathizers by now."

Jim asked, "How do the guys feel now?"

"Oh, they're better. They got a shot of life, this afternoon. I know it's quick, but we got to have that funeral tomorrow. That ought to steam 'em up for a while." He looked out the tent entrance. "God, look at that cloud!" He stepped outside and looked overhead. The sky was nearly dark with the thick black cloud. A skirmishing wind sprang up, blowing the dust along, blowing the smoke from the fires, flapping the canvases, whisking the apple trees that surrounded the camp. "That looks like a rain cloud," Mac said. "Lord, I hope it doesn't rain. It'll drown this bunch like rats."

Jim said, "You worry too much about what might happen, Mac. All the time you're worrying. These guys are used to the open. A little rain won't hurt 'em. You fidget all the time."

Mac sat down on the floor again, "Maybe that's right, Jim. I get so scared the strike'll crack, maybe I imagine things. I've been in so many strikes that got busted, Jim."

"Yeah, but what do you care if it's busted? It solidifies the unrest, you said so yourself."

"Sure, I know. I s'pose it wouldn't matter if the strike broke right now. The guys won't ever forget how Joy got killed; and they won't ever forget about Dakin's truck."

"You're getting just like an old woman, Mac."

"Well, it's my strike—I mean, I feel like it's mine. I don't want to see it go under now."

"Well, it won't, Mac."

"Huh? What do you know about it?"

"Well, I was thinkin' this morning. Ever read much history, Mac?"

"A little, in school. Why?"

"Well, you remember how the Greeks won the battle of Salamis?"

"Maybe I knew. I don't remember."

"Well, here's the Greeks with some ships, all boxed in a harbor. They want to run away to beat hell. And here's a whole slough of Persian ships out in front. Well, the Greek admiral knows his guys are going to run away, so he sends word to the enemy to box 'em in tight. Next morning the Greeks see they can't run away; they've got to fight to get away, and they win. They beat hell out of the Persian fleet." Jim fell silent.

Men began moving past, toward the stoves. Mac patted the ground hard with his open hand. "I see what you mean, Jim," he said. "We don't need it now, but if we do, by God, it's an idea. Jim," he said plaintively. "I bring you out here to teach you things, and right away you start teaching me things."

"Nuts," said Jim.

"O.K., then, nuts. I wonder how men know when food's ready. Kind of mind reading, I guess. Or maybe they've got that same kind of a sense that vultures have. Look, there they go. Come on, Jim. Let's eat."

11

They had beans, swimming in pork fat, to eat. Mac and Jim brought their cans from the tent and stood in line until some of the mess was dumped into each of their cans. They walked away. Jim took a little wooden paddle from his pocket and tasted the beans. "Mac," he said, "I can't eat it."

"Used to better things, huh? You've got to eat it." He tasted his own, and immediately dumped the can on the ground. "Don't eat it, Jim. It'll make you sick, beans and grease! The guys'll raise hell about this."

They looked at the men sitting in front of the tents, trying to eat their food. The storm cloud spread over the sky and swallowed the new stars. Mac said, "Somebody'll try to kill the cooks, I guess. Let's go over to London's tent."

"I don't see Dakin's tent, Mac."

"No, Mrs. Dakin took it down. She went into town and took it along with her. Funny guy, Dakin; he'll have money before he's through. Let's find London."

They walked down the line to the grey tent of London. A light shone through the canvas. Mac raised the flap. Inside, London sat on a box, holding an open can of sardines in his hand. The dark girl, Lisa, crouched on the floor mattress nursing the baby. She drew a piece of blanket about the baby and the exposed breast as the men entered. She smiled quickly at them, and then looked down at the baby again.

"Just in time for dinner!" Mac said.

London looked embarrassed. "I had a little stuff left over."

"You tasted that mess out there?"

"Yeah."

"Well, I hope the other guys got some stuff left over. We got to do better than that, or them guys'll run out on us."

"Food kind of stopped comin' in," said London. "I got another can of sardines. You guys like to have it?"

"Damn right." Mac took the proffered can greedily, and twisted the key to open it. "Get out your knife, Jim. We'll split this."

"How's your arm?" London asked.

"Getting stiff," said Jim.

Outside the tent a voice said, "That's the place, that one with the light." The flap raised and Dick entered. His hair was combed neatly. He held a grey cap in his hand. His grey suit was clean, but unpressed. Only his dusty, unpolished shoes showed that he had been walking through the country. He stood in the tent entrance, looking about. "Hi, Mac. Hello, Jim," and to the girl, "Hi ya, baby?" Her eyes brightened. A spot of red came into her cheeks. She drew the piece of blanket coquettishly down around her shoulders.

Mac waved his hand. "This here's London—this here's Dick." Dick made a half salute. "H'ya?" he said. "Look, Mac, these babies in town have been taking lessons."

"What do you mean? What you doin' out here anyways?"

Dick took a newspaper from his outside pocket and handed it over. Mac opened it and London and Jim looked over his shoulder. "Come out before noon," said Dick.

Mac exclaimed, "Son-of-a-bitch!" The paper carried a headline, "Supervisors vote to feed strikers. At a public meeting last night the Board of Supervisors voted unanimously to feed the men now striking against the apple growers."

"They sure took lessons," Mac said. "Did it start workin' yet, Dick?"

"Hell, yes."

London broke in, "I don't see no reason to kick. If they want to send out ham and eggs, it's O.K. by me."

"Sure," Mac said sarcastically, "*if* they want to. This paper don't tell about the other meeting right afterwards when they repealed the vote."

"What's the gag?" London demanded. "What the hell's it all about?"

"Listen, London," Mac said. "This here's an old one, but it works. Here's Dick got the sympathizers lined up. We got food and blankets and money comin'. Well, then *this* comes out. Dick goes the round. The sympathizers say, 'What the hell? The county's feeding 'em.' 'Th' hell it is,' says Dick. And the guy says, 'I seen it in the paper. It says they're sendin' food to you. What you gettin' out of this?' That's how it works, London. Did you see any county food come in today?"

"No——"

"Well, Dick couldn't get a rise either. Now you know. They figure to starve us out. And by God they can do it, too, if we don't get help." He turned to Dick. "You was goin' good."

"Sure," Dick agreed. "It was a push-over. Take me some time to work it all up again. I want a paper from this guy here saying you aren't getting any food. I want it signed by the strike chairman."

"O.K.," said London.

"Lots of sympathizers in Torgas," Dick went on. "'Course the joint's organized by the Growers' Association, so the whole bunch is underground like a flock o' gophers. But the stuff is there, if I can get to it."

"You were doin' swell till this busted," Mac said.

"Sure I was. I had some trouble with one old dame. She wanted to help the cause somethin' terrible."

Mac laughed. "I never knew no maiden modesty to keep you out of the feed bag. S'pose she *did* want to give her all to the cause?"

Dick shuddered. "Her all was sixteen axe-handles acrost," he said.

"Well, we'll get your paper for you, and then I want you to get the hell out of here. They ain't got you spotted yet, have they?"

"I don't know," said Dick. "I kind of think they have. I wrote in for Bob Schwartz to come down. I got a feeling I'm going to get vagged pretty soon. Bob can take over then."

London rooted in a box and brought out a tablet of paper and a pencil. Mac took them from him and wrote out the statement. "You write nice," London said admiringly.

"Huh? Oh, sure. Can I sign it for you, London?"

"Sure. Go ahead."

"Hell," said Dick. "I could of done that myself." He took the paper and folded it carefully. "Oh, say, Mac. I heard about one of the guys gettin' bumped."

"Didn't you know, Dick? It was Joy."

"Th' hell!"

"Sure, he come down with a bunch of scabs. He was tryin' to bring 'em over when he got it."

"Poor bastard."

"Got him quick. He didn't suffer more'n a minute."

Dick sighed. "Well, it was in the books for Joy. He was sure to get it sooner or later. Going to have a funeral?"

"Tomorrow."

"All the guys goin' to march in it?"

Mac looked at London. "Sure they

are," he said. "Maybe we can drag public sympathy our way."

"Well, Joy would like that," Dick said. "Nothing he'd like better. Too bad he can't see it. Well, so long, I got to go." He turned to leave the tent. Lisa raised her eyes. " 'Bye, baby. See you sometime," said Dick. The spots of color came into her cheeks again. Her lips parted a little and, when the tent flaps dropped behind Dick, her eyes remained there for some time.

Mac said, "Jesus, they got an organization here. Dick's a good man. If he can't get stuff to eat, it ain't to be got."

Jim asked, "How about that platform for the speech?"

Mac turned to London, "Yeah, did you get at it, London?"

"The guys'll put it up tomorrow mornin'. Couldn't get nothing but some old fence posts to make it. Have to be just a little one."

"Don't matter," Mac said, "just as long as it's high enough so every guy here can see Joy, that's enough."

A worried look came on London's face. "What t'hell am I goin' to say to the guys? You said I ought to make a speech."

"You'll get steamed up enough," said Mac. "Tell 'em this little guy died for 'em. And if he could do that they can at least fight for themselves."

"I never made no speeches much," London complained.

"Well, don't make a speech. Just talk to the guys. You done that often enough. Just tell 'em. That's better'n a speech, anyway."

"Oh. Like that. O.K."

Mac turned to the girl. "How's the kid?"

She blushed and pulled the blanket closer over her shoulders. Her lashes shadowed her cheeks. "Pretty good," she whispered. "He don't cry none."

The tent-flap jerked open and the doctor entered, his quick, brusque movements at variance with the sad, doglike eyes. "I'm going over to see young Anderson, Mac," he said. "Want to come?"

"Sure I do, Doc." And to London, "Did you send the guys over to guard Anderson's place?"

"Yeah. They didn't want to go none, but I sent 'em."

"All right. Let's go, Doc. Come on, Jim, if you can make it."

"I feel all right," said Jim.

Burton looked steadily at him. "You should be in bed."

Mac chuckled. "I'm scared to leave him. He raises hell when I leave him alone for a minute. See you later, London."

Outside the darkness was thick. The big cloud had spread until it covered the sky, and all the stars were gone. A muffled quietness lay on the camp. Those men who sat around a few little fires spoke softly. The air was still and warm and damp. Doc and Mac and Jim picked their way carefully out of the camp and into the blackness that surrounded it. "I'm afraid it's going to rain," Mac said. "We'll have one hell of a time with the guys when they get wet. It's worse than gun-fire for taking the hearts out of men. Most of those tents leak, I guess."

"Of course they do," said Burton.

They reached the line of the orchard and walked down between the rows of trees. And it was so dark that they put their hands out in front of them.

"How do you like your strike now?" Doc asked.

"Not so good. They've got this valley organized like Italy. Food supply's cut off now. We're sunk if we can't get some food. And if it rains good and hard tonight the men'll be sneaking out on us. They just won't take it, I tell you. It's a

funny thing, Doc. You don't believe in the cause, and you'll probably be the last man to stick. I don't get you at all."

"I don't get myself," Doc said softly. "I don't believe in the cause, but I believe in men."

"What do you mean?"

"I don't know. I guess I just believe they're men, and not animals. Maybe if I went into a kennel and the dogs were hungry and sick and dirty, and maybe if I could help those dogs, I would. Wouldn't be their fault they were that way. You couldn't say, 'Those dogs are that way because they haven't any ambition. They don't save their bones. Dogs always are that way.' No, you'd try to clean them up and feed them. I guess that's the way it is with me. I have some skill in helping men, and when I see some who need help, I just do it. I don't think about it much. If a painter saw a piece of canvas, and he had colors, well, he'd want to paint on it. He wouldn't figure why he wanted to."

"Sure, I get you. In one way it seems cold-blooded, standing aside and looking down on men like that, and never getting yourself mixed up with them; but another way, Doc, it seems fine as the devil, and clean."

"Oh, Mac, I'm about out of disinfectant. You'll get no more fine smell if I don't get some more carbolic."

"I'll see what I can do," said Mac.

A hundred yards away a yellow light was shining. "Isn't that Anderson's house?" Jim asked.

"I guess it is. We ought to pick up a guard pretty soon." They walked on toward the light, and they were not challenged. They came to the gate of the houseyard without being challenged. Mac said, "God-damn it, where *are* the guys London sent over? Go on in, Doc, I'm going to see if I can find 'em." Burton walked up the path and into the lighted kitchen. Mac and Jim went toward the barn, and inside the barn they found the men, lying down in the low bed of hay smoking cigarettes. A kerosene lamp hung on a hook on the wall and threw a yellow light on the line of empty stalls and on the great pile of boxed apples—Anderson's crop, waiting to be moved.

Mac spluttered with anger, but he quickly controlled himself, and when he spoke his voice was soft and friendly. "Listen, you guys," he argued. "This isn't any joke. We got the word the damn vigilantes is going to try something on Anderson to get back at him for lettin' us stay on his place. S'pose he never let us stay? They'd be kickin' us all over hell by now. Anderson's a nice guy. We hadn't ought to let nobody hurt him."

"There ain't nobody around," one of the men protested. "Jesus, mister, we can't hang around all night. We was out picketin' all afternoon."

"Go on, then," Mac cried angrily. "Let 'em raid this place. Then Anderson'll kick us off. Then where in hell would we be?"

"We could jungle up, down by the river, mister."

"You *think* you could. They'd run you over the county line so quick your ass'd smoke, and you know it!"

One of the men got slowly to his feet. "The guy's right," he said. "We better drag it out of here. My old woman's in the camp. I don't want to have her get in no trouble."

"Well, put out a line," Mac suggested. "Don't let nobody through. You know what they done to Anderson's boy—burned his lunch wagon, kicked hell out of Al."

"Al put out a nice stew," said one of the men. They stood up tiredly. When they were all out of the barn Mac blew out the lantern. "Vigilantes like to shoot at a light," he explained. "They take big

chances like that. We better have Anderson pull down his curtains, too."

The guards filed off into the darkness. Jim asked, "You think they'll keep watch now, Mac?" he asked.

"I wish I thought so. I think they'll be back in that barn in about ten minutes. In the army they can shoot a guy if he goes to sleep. We can't do a thing but talk. God, I get sick of this helplessness! If we could only use guns! If we could only use punishment to keep discipline!" The sound of the guards' footsteps died away in the darkness. Mac said, "I'll rouse 'em out once more before we go back." They walked up on the kitchen porch and knocked on the door. Barking and growling dogs answered them. They could hear the dogs leaping around inside the house, and Anderson quieting them. The door opened a crack. "It's us, Mr. Anderson."

"Come on in," he said sullenly.

The pointers weaved about, whipping their thin, hard tails and whining with pleasure. Mac leaned over and patted each one and pulled the leathers. "You ought to leave the dogs outside, Mr. Anderson, to watch the place," he said. "It's so dark the guards can't see anything. But the dogs could smell anybody coming through."

Al lay on a cot by the stove. He looked pale and weak. He seemed to have grown thin, for the flesh on his jowls was loose. He lay flat on his back, and one arm was strapped down in front of him. Doc sat in a chair beside the cot.

"Hello, Al," Mac said quietly. "How's she go, boy?"

The eyes brightened. "O.K.," said Al. "It hurts quite a lot. Doc says it'll keep me down some time." Mac leaned over the cot and picked up Al's good hand. "Not too hard," Al said quickly. "There's busted ribs on that side."

Anderson stood by; his eyes were

burning. "Now you see," he said. "You see what comes of it. Lunch wagon burned, Al hurt, now you see."

"Oh, for Christ's sake, Dad," Al said weakly. "Don't start that again. They call you Mac, don't they?"

"Right."

"Well, look, Mac. D'you think I could get into the Party?"

"You mean you want to go in active work?"

"Yeah. Think I could get in?"

"I think so—" Mac said slowly. "I'll give you an application card. What you want to come in for, Al?"

The heavy face twisted in a grimace. Al swung his head back and forth. "I been thinkin'," he said. "Ever since they beat me up I been thinkin'. I can't get those guys outa my head—my little wagon all burned up, an' them jumpin' on me with their feet; and two cops down on the corner watchin', and not doin' a thing! I can't get that outa my head."

"And so you want to join up with us, huh, Al?"

"I want to be against 'em," Al cried. "I want to be fightin' 'em all my life. I want to be on the other side."

"They'll just beat you up worse, Al. I'm tellin' you straight. They'll knock hell out of you."

"Well, I won't care then, because I'll be fightin' 'em, see? But there I was, just runnin' a little lunch wagon, an' givin' bums a handout now an' then—" His voice choked and tears squeezed out of his eyes.

Dr. Burton touched him gently on the cheek. "Don't talk any more, Al."

"I'll see you get an application card," Mac said. And he continued, "By God, it's funny. Guy after guy gets knocked into our side by a cop's night stick. Every time they maul hell out of a bunch of men, we get a flock of applications. Why, there's a Red Squad cop in Los Angeles that sends us more members than a dozen of our organizers. An' the damn fools haven't got sense enough to realize it. O.K., Al. You'll get your application. I don't know whether it'll go through, but it will if I can push it through." He patted Al's good arm. "I hope it goes through. You're a good guy, Al. Don't blame me for your wagon."

"I don't, Mac. I know who to blame."

Burton said, "Take it easy, Al. Just rest; you need it."

Anderson had been fidgeting about the room. The dogs circled him endlessly, putting up their liver-colored noses and sniffing, waving their stiff tails like little whips. "Well, I hope you're satisfied," he said helplessly. "You break up everything I've got. You even take Al away. I hope you take good joy of it."

Jim broke in, "Don't worry, Mr. Anderson. There's guards around your house. You're the only man in the Valley that has his apples picked."

Mac asked, "When are you going to move your apples?"

"Day after tomorrow."

"Well, do you want some guards for the trucks?"

"I don't know," Anderson said uneasily.

"I guess we better put guards on the trucks," said Mac, "just in case anybody tried to dump your crop. We'll get going now. Good night, Mr. Anderson. 'Night, Al. In one way I'm glad it happened."

Al smiled. " 'Night, you guys. Don't forget that card, Mac."

"I won't. Better pull your curtains down, Mr. Anderson. I don't think they'll shoot through your windows, but they might; they've done it before, other places."

The door closed instantly behind them. The lighted spot on the ground, from the window, shrank to darkness as the curtain was pulled down. Mac felt his way to the gate, and when they were out, shut it after them. "Wait here a minute," he said "I'm going to look at those guards again." He stepped away into the darkness.

Jim stood beside the doctor. "Better take good care of that shoulder," Burton advised. "It might cause you some trouble later."

"I don't care about it, Doc. It seems good to have it."

"Yes, I thought it might be like that."

"Like what?"

"I mean you've got something in your eyes, Jim, something religious. I've seen it in you boys before."

Jim flared, "Well, it isn't religious. I've got no use for religion."

"No, I guess you haven't. Don't let me bother you, Jim. Don't let me confuse you with terms. You're living the good life, whatever you want to call it."

"I'm happy," said Jim. "And happy for the first time. I'm full-up."

"I know. Don't let it die. It's the vision of Heaven."

"I don't believe in Heaven," Jim said. "I don't believe in religion."

"All right, I won't argue any more. I don't envy you as much as I might, Jim, because sometimes I love men as much as you do, maybe not in just the same way."

"Do you get that, Doc? Like that— like troops and troops marching into you? And you closing around them?"

"Yes, something like that. Particularly when they've done something stupid, when a man's made a mistake, and died for it. Yes, I get it, Jim—pretty often."

They heard Mac's voice, "Where are you guys? It's so damn dark."

"Over here." They joined him and all three moved along into the orchard, under the black trees.

"The guards weren't in the barn," said Mac. "They were out on watch. Maybe they're going to stick it."

Far down the road they heard the mutter of a truck coming toward them.

"I feel sorry for Anderson," Burton said quietly. "Everything he respects, everything he's afraid of is turning against him. I wonder what he'll do. They'll drive him out of here, of course."

Mac said harshly, "We can't help it, Doc. He happens to be the one that's sacrificed for the men. Somebody has to break if the whole bunch is going to get out of the slaughter-house. We can't think about the hurts of one man. It's necessary, Doc."

"I wasn't questioning your motives, nor your ends. I was just sorry for the poor old man. His self-respect is down. That's a bitter thing to him, don't you think so, Mac?"

"I can't take time to think about the feelings of one man." Mac said sharply. "I'm too busy with big bunches of men."

"It was different with the little fellow who was shot," Doc went on musingly. "He liked what he did. He wouldn't have had it any other way."

"Doc, you're breakin' my heart," Mac said irritably. "Don't you get lost in a lot of sentimental foolishness. There's an end to be gained; it's a real end, hasn't anything to do with people losing respect. It's people getting bread into their guts. It's *real,* not any of your highfalutin ideas. How's the old guy with the broken hip?"

"All right, then, change the subject. The old man's getting mean as a scorpion. Right at first he got a lot of attention, he got pretty proud for a while; and now he's mad because the men don't come and listen to him talk."

"I'll go in and see him in the morning," said Jim. "He was a kind of a nice old fellow."

Mac cried, "Listen! Didn't that truck stop?"

"I think it did. Sounded as though it stopped at the camp."

"I wonder what the hell. Come on, let's hurry. Look out for trees." They had gone only a little distance when the truck roared, its gears clashed, and it moved away again. Its sound softened into the distance until it merged with the quiet. "I hope nothing's wrong," said Mac.

They trotted out of the orchard and crossed the cleared space. The light still burned in London's tent, and a group of men moved about near it. Mac dashed up, threw up the tent-flap and went inside. On the ground lay a long, rough pine box. London sat on a box and stared morosely up at the newcomers. The girl seemed to cower down on her mattress, while London's dark-haired, pale son sat beside her and stroked her hair. London motioned to the box with his thumb. "What the hell 'm I goin' to do with it?" he asked. "It's scared this here girl half to death. I can't keep it in here."

"Joy?" Mac asked.

"Yeah. They just brang him."

Mac pulled his lip and studied the coffin. "We could put it outside, I guess. Or we can let your kids sleep in the hospital tent tonight and leave it here, that is, unless it scares you, London."

"It don't mean nothing to me," London protested. "It's just another stiff. I seen plenty in my time."

"Well, let's leave it here, then. Jim an' me'll stay here with it. The guy was a friend of ours." Behind him the doctor chuckled softly. Mac reddened and swung around. "S'pose you do win, Doc? What of it? I knew the little guy."

"I didn't say anything," Burton said.

London spoke softly to the girl, and to the dark boy, and in a moment they went out of the tent, she holding the shoulder blanket tight about herself and the baby.

Mac sat down on one end of the oblong box and rubbed the wood with his forefinger. The coarse pine grains wriggled like little rivers over the wood. Jim stood behind Mac and stared over his shoulder. London moved nervously

about the tent, and his eyes avoided the coffin. Mac said, "Nice piece o' goods the county puts out."

"What you want for nothing?" London demanded.

"Well," Mac replied, "I don't want nothing for myself but a bonfire, just a fire to get rid of me, so I won't lie around." He stood up and felt in his jeans pocket and brought out a big knife. One of the blades had a screwdriver end. He fitted it to a screw in the coffin-lid and twisted.

London cried, "What do you want to open it for? That won't do no good. Leave him be."

"I want to see him," said Mac.

"What for? He's dead—he's a lump of dirt."

The doctor said softly, "Sometimes I think you realists are the most sentimental people in the world."

Mac snorted and laid the screw carefully on the ground. "If you think this is sentiment, you're nuts, Doc. I want to see if it'd be a good idea for the guys to look at him tomorrow. We got to shoot some juice into 'em some way. They're dyin' on their feet."

Burton said, "Fun with dead bodies, huh?"

Jim insisted earnestly, "We've got to use every means, Doc. We've got to use every weapon."

Mac looked up at him appreciatively. "That's the idea. That's the way it is. If Joy can do some work after he's dead, then he's got to do it. There's no such things as personal feelings in this crowd. Can't be. And there's no such things as good taste, don't you forget it."

London stood still, listening and nodding his big head slowly up and down. "You guys got it right," he agreed. "Look at Dakin. He let his damn truck make him mad. I heard he comes up for trial tomorrow—for assault."

Mac quickly turned out the screws and laid them in a line on the ground. The lid was stuck. He kicked it loose with his heel.

Joy looked flat and small and painfully clean. He had on a clean blue shirt, and his oil-soiled blue jeans. The arms were folded stiffly across the stomach. "All he got was a shot of formaldehyde," Mac said. A stubble was growing on Joy's cheeks, looking very dark against the grey, waxy skin. His face was composed and rested. The gnawing bitterness was gone from it.

"He looks quiet," Jim remarked.

"Yes," said Mac. "That's the trouble. It won't do no good to show him. He looks so comfortable all the guys'll want to get right in with him." The doctor moved close and looked down at the coffin for a moment, and then he walked to a box and sat down. His big, plaintive eyes fastened on Mac's face. Mac still stared at Joy. "He was such a good little guy," he said. "He didn't want nothing for himself. Y'see, he wasn't very bright. But some way he got it into his head something was wrong. He didn't see why food had to be dumped and left to rot when people were starving. Poor little fool, he could never understand that. And he got the notion he might help to stop it. I wonder how much he helped? It's awful hard to say. Maybe not at all—maybe a lot. You can't tell." Mac's voice had become unsteady. The doctor's eyes stayed on his face, and the doctor's mouth was smiling a curious, half-sardonic, half-kindly smile.

Jim interposed, "Joy wasn't afraid of anything."

Mac picked up the coffin-lid and set it in place again. "I don't know why we say 'poor little guy.' He wasn't poor. He was greater than himself. He didn't know it—didn't care. But there was a kind of ecstasy in him all the time, even when they beat him. And Jim says it—he wasn't afraid." Mac picked up a screw, and stuck it through the hole and turned it down with his knife.

London said, "That sounds like a speech. Maybe you better give the speech. I don't know nothin' about talkin'. That was a pretty speech. It sounded nice."

Mac looked up guiltily and searched London for sarcasm, and found none. "That wasn't a speech," he said quietly. "I guess it could be, but it wasn't. It's like tellin' the guy he hasn't been wasted."

"Why don't you make the speech tomorrow? You can talk."

"Hell, no. You're the boss. The guys'd be sore if I sounded off. They expect you to do it."

"Well, what do I got to say?"

Mac drove the screws in, one after another. "Tell 'em the usual stuff. Tell 'em Joy died for 'em. Tell 'em he was tryin' to help 'em, and the best they can do for him is to help 'emselves by stickin' together, see?"

"Yeah, I get it."

Mac stood up and regarded the grained wood of the lid. "I hope somebody tries to stop us," he said. "I hope some of them damn vigilantes gets in our way. God, I hope they try to stop us paradin' through town."

"Yeah, I see," said London.

Jim's eyes glowed. He repeated, "I hope so."

"The guys'll want to fight," Mac continued. "They'll be all sore inside. They'll want to bust something. Them vigilantes ain't got much sense; I hope they're crazy enough to start something tomorrow."

Burton stood up wearily from his box and walked up to Mac. He touched him lightly on the shoulder. "Mac," he said, "you're the craziest mess of cruelty and hausfrau sentimentality, of clear vision and rose-colored glasses I ever saw. I don't know how you manage to be all of them at once."

"Nuts," said Mac.

The doctor yawned. "All right. We'll leave it at nuts. I'm going to bed. You know where to find me if you want me, only I hope you won't want me."

Mac looked quickly at the tent ceiling. Fat, lazy drops were falling on the canvas. One—two—three, and then a dozen, patting the tent with a soft drumming. Mac sighed. "I hoped it wouldn't. Now by morning the guys'll be drowned rats. They won't have no more spirit than a guinea pig."

"I'm still going to bed," the doctor said. He went out and dropped the flaps behind him.

Mac sat down heavily on the coffin. The drumming grew quicker. Outside, the men began calling to one another, and their voices were blurred by the rain. "I don't suppose there's a tent in the camp that don't leak," said Mac. "Jesus, why can't we get a break without getting it cancelled out? Why do we always have to take it in the neck—always?"

Jim sat gingerly down on the long box beside him. "Don't worry about it, Mac. Sometimes, when a guy gets miserable enough, he'll fight all the harder. That's the way it was with me, Mac, when my mother was dying, and she wouldn't even speak to me. I just got so miserable I'd've taken any chance. Don't you worry about it."

Mac turned on him. "Catching me up again, are you? I'll get mad if you show me up too often. Go lie down on the girl's mattress there. You've got a bad arm. It must hurt by now."

"It burns some, all right."

"Well, lie down there. See if you can't get some sleep." Jim started to protest, and then he went to the mattress on the ground and stretched out on it. The wound throbbed down his arm and across his chest. He heard the rain in-

crease until it swept on the canvas, like a broom. He heard the big drops falling inside the tent, and then, when a place leaked in the center of the tent, he heard the heavy drops splash on the coffin box.

Mac still sat beside it, holding his head in his arms. And London's eyes, like the sleepless eyes of a lynx, stared and stared at the lamp. The camp was quiet again, and the rain fell steadily, out of a windless sky. It was not very long before Jim fell into a burning sleep. The rain poured down hour after hour. On the tentpole the lamplight yellowed and dropped to the wick. A blue flame sputtered for a while, and then went out.

12

To Jim it seemed that he awakened out of a box. One whole side of him was encased in painful stiffness. He opened his eyes and looked about the tent. A grey and listless dawn had come. The coffin still lay in its place, but Mac and London were gone. He heard the pounding that must have awakened him, hammers on wood. For a time he lay quietly looking about the tent, but at last he tried to sit up. The box of pain held him. He rolled over and climbed up to his knees, and then stood up, drooping his hurt shoulder to protect it from tension.

The flap swung up and Mac entered. His blue denim jacket glistened with moisture. "Hi, Jim. You got some sleep, didn't you. How's the arm?"

"Stiff," he said. "Is it still raining?"

"Dirty drizzle. Doc's coming to look at your shoulder in a minute. Lord, it's wet outside! Soon's the guys walk around a little bit, it'll be all slop."

"What's the pounding?"

"Well, we've been building the stand for Joy. Even dug up an old flag to go over him." He held up a small dingy package of cloth, and unrolled it, a threadbare and stained American flag. He spread it carefully on the coffin top. "No," he said. "I think that's wrong. I think the field should be over the left breast, like this?"

"It's a lousy dirty flag," Jim said.

"I know, but it'll get over big. Doc ought to be along any minute now."

"I'm hungry as hell," said Jim.

"Who isn't? We're going to have rolled oats, straight, for breakfast, no sugar or no milk—just oats."

"Even that sounds good to me. You don't sound so low this morning, Mac."

"Me? Well, the guys aren't knocked out as much as I thought they would be. The women 're raising hell, but the guys are in pretty good shape, considering."

Burton hustled in. "How's it feel, Jim?"

"Pretty sore."

"Well, sit down over here. I'll put on a clean bandage." Jim sat on a box and braced himself against expected pain, but the doctor worked deftly, removed the old wrapping and applied a new one without hurting him. "Old Dan's upset," he said. "He's afraid he isn't going to get to go to the funeral. He says he started this strike, now everybody's forgetting him."

Mac asked, "Do you think we could put him on a truck and take him along, Doc? It'd be swell publicity if we could."

"You could, Mac, but it'd hurt him like the devil; and it might cause shock complications. He's an old man. Hold still, Jim. I'm nearly through. No, I'll tell you what we'd better do. We'll tell him we're going to take him, and then when we start to lift him, I think he'll beg off. His pride's just hurt. He thinks Joy stole the show from him." He patted the finished bandage. "There you are, Jim. How do you feel now?"

Jim moved his shoulder cautiously. "Better. Sure, that's lots better."

Mac said. "Why don't you go and see the old guy, Jim, after you eat. He's a friend of yours."

"I guess I will."

Burton explained, "He's a little bit off, Jim. Don't worry him. All this excitement has gone to his head a little bit."

Jim said, "Sure, I'll lead him along." He stood up. "Say, that feels lots better."

"Let's get some mush," said Mac. "We want to start this funeral in time so it'll tie up the noon traffic in town, if we can."

Doc snorted. "Always a friend to man. God, you're a scorpion, Mac! If I were bossing the other side I'd take you out and shoot you."

"Well, they'll do that some day, I guess," Mac replied. "They've done everything else to me."

They filed out of the tent. Outside the air was filled with tiny drops of falling water, a grey, misty drizzle. The orchard trees were dim behind a curtain of grey gauze. Jim looked down the line of sodden tents. The streets between the lines were already whipped to slushy mud by the feet of moving people, and the people moved constantly for there was no dry place to sit down. Lines of men waited their turns at the toilets at the ends of the streets.

Burton and Mac and Jim walked toward the stoves. Thick blue smoke from wet wood poured from the chimneys. On the stove-tops the wash-boilers of mush bubbled, and the cooks stirred with long sticks. Jim felt the mist penetrating down his neck. He pulled his jacket closer and buttoned the top button. "I need a bath," he said.

"Well, take a sponge bath. That's the only kind we have. Here, I brought your food can."

They stepped to the end of the line of men waiting by the stove. The cooks filled the containers with mush as the line filed by. Jim gathered some of it on his eating stick and blew it cool. "It tastes good," he said, "I'm half-starved, I guess."

"Well, you ought to be, if you aren't. London's over supervising the platform. Come on, let's go over." They slushed through the mud, stepping clear of the tracks when any untrampled ground showed. In back of the stoves the new platform stood, a little deck, constructed of old fence-posts and culvert planks. It was raised about four feet above the ground level. London was just nailing on a hand-rail. "Hello," he said. "How was breakfast?"

"Roast dirt would taste swell this morning," said Mac. "This is the last, ain't it?"

"Yep. They ain't no more when that's gone."

"Maybe Dick'll have better luck to-day," Jim suggested. "Why don't you let me go out and rustle food, Mac? I'm not doing anything."

Mac said, "You're stayin' here. Look, London, this guy's marked; they try to get him twice already, and here he wants to go out and walk the streets alone."

"Don't be a damn fool," said London. "We're goin' to put you on the truck with the coffin. You can't walk none with that hurt. You ride on the truck."

"What th' hell?" Jim began.

London scowled at him. "Don't get smart with me," he said. "I'm the boss here. When you get to be boss, you tell me. I'm tellin' you, now."

Jim's eyes flared rebelliously. He looked quickly at Mac and saw that he was grinning and waiting. "O.K.," said Jim. "I'll do what you say."

Mac said, "Here's something you can do, Jim. See if you think it's all right, London. S'pose Jim just circulates and talks to the guys? Just finds out how they feel? We ought to know how far we can go. I think the guys'd talk to Jim."

"What do you want to know?" London asked.

"Well, we ought to know how they feel about the strike now."

"Sounds all right to me," said London.

Mac turned to Jim. "Go and see old Dan," he said. "And then just get to talkin' to a lot of the guys, a few at a time. Don't try and sell 'em nothing. Just 'yes' 'em until you find out how they feel. Can you do that, Jim?"

"Sure. Where do they keep old Dan?"

"Look. See down that second row, that tent that's whiter'n the rest? That's Doc's hospital tent. I guess old Dan'll be in there."

"I'll look in on him," said Jim. He scraped up the last of his mush on his paddle and ate it. At one of the water barrels he dipped water to wash the eating can, and, on passing his pup-tent, threw the can inside. There was a little movement in the tent. Jim dropped on his knees and crawled inside. Lisa was there. She had been nursing the baby. She covered her breast hastily.

"Hello," said Jim.

She blushed and said faintly, "Hello."

"I thought you were going to sleep in the hospital tent."

"There was guys there," she said.

"I hope you didn't get wet here last night."

She pulled the shoulder blanket neatly down. "No, there wasn't no leak."

"What you scared of?" Jim asked. "I won't hurt you. I helped you once, Mac and I did."

"I know. That's why."

"What are you talking about?"

Her head almost disappeared under the blanket. "You seen me—without no clothes on," she said faintly.

Jim started to laugh, and then caught himself. "That doesn't mean anything," he said. "You shouldn't feel bad about that. We had to help you."

"I know." Her eyes rose up for a moment. "Makes me feel funny."

"Forget it," said Jim. "How's the baby?"

"All right."

"Nursing it all right?"

"Yeah." Then her face turned very red. She blurted, "I like to nurse."

" 'Course you do."

"I like to—because it—feels good." She hid her face. "I hadn't ought to told you."

"Why not?"

"I don't know, but I hadn't ought to of. It ain't—decent, do you think? You won't tell nobody?"

" 'Course not." Jim looked away from her and out the low doorway. The mist drifted casually down. Big drops slid down the tent slope like beads on a string. He continued to stare out of the tent, knowing instinctively that the girl wanted to look at him, and that she couldn't until he looked away.

Her glance went over his face, a dark profile against the light. She saw the lumpy, bandaged shoulder. "What's the matter 'th your arm?" she demanded.

He turned back and this time her eyes held. "I got shot yesterday."

"Oh. Does it hurt?"

"Little bit."

"Just shot? Just up an' shot by a guy?"

"Fight with some scabs. One of the owners potted me with a rifle."

"You was fightin'? You?"

"Sure."

Her eyes stayed wide. She looked fascinatedly at his face. "You don't have no gun, do you?"

"No."

She sighed. "Who was that fella come in the tent last night?"

"Young fellow? That was Dick. He's a friend of mine."

"He looks like a nice fella," she said.

Jim smiled. "Sure, he's O.K."

"Kinda fresh, though," she said. "Joey, that's my hubby, he didn't like it none. I thought he was a nice fella."

Jim got to his knees and prepared to crawl out of the tent. "Had any breakfast?"

"Joey's out gettin' me some." Her eyes were bolder now. "You goin' to the funeral?"

"Sure."

"I can't go. Joey says I can't."

"It's too wet and nasty." Jim crawled out. " 'Bye, kid. Take care o' yourself."

" 'B-bye." She paused. "Don't tell nobody, will you?"

He looked back into the tent. "Don't tell 'em what? Oh, about the baby. No, I won't."

"Y'see," she explained, "you seen me that way, so I told you. I don't know why."

"I don't either. 'Bye, kid." He straightened up and walked away. Few men were moving about in the mist. Most of the strikers had taken their mush and gone back to the tents. The smoke from the stoves swirled low to the ground. A little wind blew the drizzle in a slow, drifting angle. As Jim went by London's tent, he looked in and saw a dozen men standing about the coffin, all looking down at it. Jim started to go in, but he caught himself and walked to the white hospital tent down the row. There was a curious, efficient neatness inside the tent, a few medical supplies, bandage, bottles of iodine, a large jar of salts, a doctor's bag, all arranged with precision on a big box.

Old Dan lay propped in a cot, and on the ground stood a wide-necked bottle for a urinal, and an old-fashioned chamber for a bed-pan. Old Dan's beard had grown longer and fiercer, and his cheeks were more sunken. His eyes glinted fiercely at Jim. "So," he said. "You finally come. You damn squirts get what you want, and then run out on a man."

"How you feeling, Dan?" Jim asked placatingly.

"Who cares? That doctor's a nice man; he's the only nice one in this bunch of lice."

Jim pulled up an apple box and sat down. "Don't be mad, Dan. Look, I got it myself; got shot in the shoulder."

"Served you damn well right," Dan said darkly. "You punks can't take care o' yourselves. Damn wonder you ain't all dead fallin' over your feet." Jim was silent. "Leave me lyin' here," Dan cried. "Think I don't remember nothing. Up that apple tree all you could talk was strike, strike. And who starts the strike? You? Hell, no. I start it! Think I don't know. I start it when I bust my hip. An' then you leave me here alone."

"We know it, Dan. All of us know it."

"Then why don't I get no say? Treat me like a God-damn baby." He gesticulated furiously, and then winced. "Goin' to leave me here an' the whole bunch go on a funeral! Nobody cares about me!"

Jim interposed, "That's not so, Dan. We're going to put you on a truck and take you right along, right at the head of the procession."

Dan's mouth dropped open, exposing his four long squirrel-teeth. His hands settled slowly to the bed. "Honest?" he said. "On a truck?"

"That's what the chief said. He said you were the real leader, and you had to go."

Dan looked very stern. His mouth became dignified and military. "He damn well ought to. He knows." He stared down at his hands. His eyes grew soft and childlike. "I'll lead 'em," he said gently. "All the hundreds o' years that's what the workin' stiffs needed, a leader. I'll lead 'em through to the light. All they got to do is just what I say. I'll say, 'You guys do this,' an' they'll do it. An' I'll

say, 'You lazy bastards get over there!' an' by Christ, they'll git, 'cause I won't have no lazy bastards. When I speak, they got to jump, right now." And then he smiled with affection. "The poor damn rats," he said. "They never had nobody to tell 'em what to do. They never had no real leader."

"That's right," Jim agreed.

"Well, you'll see some changes now," Dan exclaimed. "You tell 'em I said so. Tell 'em I'm workin' out a plan. I'll be up and around in a couple of days. Tell 'em just to have patience till I get out an' lead 'em."

"Sure I'll tell 'em," said Jim.

Dr. Burton came into the tent. " 'Morning, Dan. Hello, Jim. Dan, where's the man I told to take care of you?"

"He went out," Dan said plaintively. "Went out to get me some breakfast. He never come back."

"Want the pot, Dan?"

"No."

"Did he give you the enema?"

"No."

"Have to get you another nurse, Dan."

"Say, Doc, this young punk here says I'm goin' to the funeral on a truck."

"That's right, Dan. You can go if you want."

Dan settled back, smiling. "It's about time somebody paid some attention," he said with satisfaction.

Jim stood up from his box. "See you later, Dan." Burton went out with him. Jim asked, "Is he going nuts, Doc?"

"No. He's an old man. He's had a shock. His bones don't knit very easily."

"He talks crazy, though."

"Well, the man I told to take care of him didn't do it. He needs an enema. Constipation makes a man lightheaded sometimes; but he's just an old man, Jim. You made him pretty happy. Better go in and see him often."

"Do you think he'll go to the funeral?"

"No. It'd hurt him, banging around in

a truck. We'll have to get around it some way. How is your arm feeling?"

"I forgot all about it."

"Fine. Try not to get cold in it. It could be nasty, if you don't take care of it. See you later. The men won't shovel dirt in the toilets. We're out of disinfectant. Simply have to get some disinfectant—anything." He hurried away, muttering softly to himself as he went.

Jim looked about for someone to talk to. Those men who were in sight walked quickly through the drizzle from one tent to another. The slush in the streets was deep and black by now. One of the big brown squad tents stood nearby. Hearing voices inside, Jim went in. In the dim brown light he saw a dozen men squatting on their blankets. The talk died as he entered. The men looked up at him and waited. He reached in his pocket and brought out the bag of tobacco Mac had given him. "Hi," he said. The men still waited. Jim went on, "I've got a sore arm. Will one of you guys roll me a cigarette?"

A man sitting in front of him held out a hand, took the bag and quickly made the cigarette. Jim took it and waved it to indicate the other men. "Pass it around. God knows they ain't much in this camp." The bag went from hand to hand. A stout little man with a short mustache said, "Sit down, kid, here, on my bed. Ain't you the guy that got shot yesterday?"

Jim laughed. "I'm one of 'em. I'm not the dead one. I'm the one that got away."

They laughed appreciatively. A man with a lantern-jaw and shiny cheek-bones broke up the laughter. "What they goin' to bury the little guy today for?"

"Why not?" Jim asked.

"Yeah, but ever'body waits three days."

The stout little man blew a jet of smoke. "When you're dead, you're dead."

Lantern-jaw said somberly, "S'pose he ain't dead. S'pose he's just in a kind of a state? S'pose we bury him alive. I think we ought to wait three days, like ever'body else."

A smooth, sarcastic voice answered. Jim looked at a tall man with a white, unlined forehead. "No, he isn't sleeping," the man said. "You can be very sure of that. If you knew what an undertaker does, you'd be sure he isn't in any 'state'."

Lantern-jaw said, "He might just be. I don't see no reason to take a chance."

White-forehead scoffed. "Well, if he can sleep with his veins full of embalming fluid, he's a God-damn sound sleeper."

"Is that what they do?"

"Yes it is. I knew a man who worked for an undertaker. He told me things you wouldn't believe."

"I rather not hear 'em," said Lantern-jaw. "Don't do no good to talk like that."

The stout man asked, "Who was the little guy? I seen him try to get the scabs over, an' then I seen 'im start over, an' then, whang! Down he goes."

Jim held his unlighted cigarette to his lips for a moment. "I knew him. He was a nice little guy. He was a kind of a labor leader."

White-forehead said, "There seems to be a bounty on labor leaders. They don't last long. Look at that rattlesnake, Sam. Says he's a longshoreman. I bet he's dead inside of six months."

A dark boy asked, "How about London? Think they'll get him like they got Dakin?"

Lantern-jaw: "No, by God. London can take care of himself. London's got a head on him."

White-forehead: "If London has a head on him, why in hell are we sitting around here? This strike's screwy. Somebody's making money out of it. When it gets tough somebody'll sell out and leave the rest of us to take it on the chin."

A broad, muscular man got to his

knees and crouched there like an animal. His lips snarled away from his teeth and his eyes blazed with a red light. "That's enough from you, wise guy," he said. "I've knew London for a long time. If you're gettin' around to sayin' London's fixin' to sell out, me an' you's goin' round and round, right now! I don't know nothin' about this here strike. I'm doin' it 'cause London says it's O.K. But you lay off the smart cracks."

White-forehead looked coldly at him. "You're pretty hard, aren't you?"

"Hard enough to beat the ass off you anyway, mister."

"Lay off," Jim broke in. "What do we want to get fighting for? If you guys want to fight, there's going to be plenty of it for everybody."

The square man grunted and sat back on his blankets. "Nobody's sayin' nothin' behind London's back when I'm there," he said.

The little stout man looked at Jim. "How'd you get shot, kid?"

"Running," said Jim. "I got winged running."

"I heard a guy say you all beat hell out of some scabs."

"That's right."

White-forehead said, "They say there are scabs coming in in trucks. And they say every scab has tear gas bombs in his pocket."

"That's a lie," Jim said quickly. "They always start lies like that to scare the guys off."

White-forehead went on, "I heard that the bosses sent word to London that they won't deal as long as there's reds in camp."

The broad, muscular man came to life again. "Well, who's the reds? You talk more like a red than anybody I seen."

White-forehead continued, "Well, I think that doctor's a red. What's a doctor want out here? He doesn't get any pay.

Well, who's paying him? He's getting his; don't worry about that." He looked wise. "Maybe he's getting it from Moscow."

Jim spat on the ground. His face was pale. He said quietly, "You're the God-damned meanest son-of-a-bitch I ever saw! You make everybody out the kind of a rat you are."

The square man got to his knees again. "The kid's right," he said. "He can't kick hell out of you, but I can. And by Christ I will if you don't keep that toilet seat of yours shut."

White-forehead got up slowly and went to the entrance. He turned back. "All right, you fellows, but you watch. Pretty soon London'll tell you to settle the strike. An' then he'll get a new car, or a steady job. You just watch."

The square man leaped to his knees again, but White-forehead dodged out of the tent.

Jim asked, "Who is that guy? Does he sleep in here?"

"Hell, no. He just come in a little while ago."

"Well, did any of you guys ever see him before?"

They shook their heads. "Not me."

"I never."

Jim cried, "By Christ! Then they sent him in."

The fat man asked, "Who sent him?"

"The owners did. He's sent in here to talk like that an' get you guys suspecting London. Don't you see? It splits the camp up. Couple you guys better see he gets run out of camp."

The square man climbed to his feet. "I'll do it myself," he said. "They's nothin' I'd admire better." He went out of the tent.

Jim said, "You got to watch out. Guys like that'll give you the idea the strike's just about through. Don't listen to lies."

The fat man gazed out of the tent. "It ain't a lie that the food's all gone," he said. "It ain't a lie that boiled cow food ain't much of a breakfast. It don't take no spies to spread that."

"We got to stick," Jim cried. "We simply got to stick. If we lose this, we're sunk; and not only us, either. Every other working stiff in the country gets a little of it."

The fat man nodded. "It all fits together," he agreed. "There ain't nothing separate. Guys think they want to get something soft for themselves, but they can't without everybody gets it."

A middle-aged man who had been lying down toward the rear of the tent sat up. "You know the trouble with workin' men?" he asked. "Well, I'll tell you. They do too God-damn much talkin'. If they did more sluggin' an' less arguin', they'd get some place." He stopped. The men in the tent listened. From outside there came the sound of a little bustling, the mutter of footsteps, the murmur of voices, the sound of people, penetrating as an odor, and soft. The men in the tent sat still and listened. The sound of people grew a little louder. Footsteps were slushing in the mud. A group walked past the tent.

Jim stood up and walked to the entrance just as a head was thrust in. "They're goin' to bring out the coffin. Come on, you guys." Jim stepped out between the tent-flaps. The mist still fell, blowing sideways, drifting like tiny, light snowflakes. Here and there the loose canvas of a tent moved soddenly in the wind. Jim looked down the street. The news had traveled. Out of the tents men and women came. They moved slowly in together and converged on the platform. And as their group became more and more compact, the sound of their many voices blended into one voice, and the sound of their footsteps became a great restlessness. Jim looked at the faces. There was a blindness in the eyes. The

heads were tipped back as though they sniffed for something. They drew in about the platform and crowded close.

Out of London's tent six men came, bearing the box. There were no handles on the coffin. Each pair of men locked hands underneath, and bore the burden on their forearms. They hesitated jerkily, trying to get in step, and having established the swinging rhythm, moved slowly through the slush toward the platform. Their heads were bare, and the drops of moisture stood out on their hair like grey dust. The little wind raised a corner of the soiled flag, and dropped it, and raised it again. In front of the casket a lane opened through the people, and the bearers moved on, their faces stiff with ceremonial solemnity, necks straight, chins down. The people on the edge of the lane stared at the box. They grew quiet during the movement of its passage, and when it was by whispered nervously to one another. A few men surreptitiously crossed themselves. The bearers reached the platform. The leading pair laid the end on the planks, and the others pushed the box forward until it rested safely.

Jim hurried to London's tent. London and Mac were there. "Jesus, I wish you'd do the talkin', I can't talk."

"No. You'll do fine. 'Member what I told you. Try to get 'em answering you. Once you get responses started, you've got 'em. Regular old camp-meeting stuff; but it sure works on a crowd."

London looked frightened. "You do it, Mac. Honest to God I can't. I didn't even know the guy."

Mac looked disgusted. "Well, you get up there and make a try. If you fall down, I'll be there to pick it up."

London buttoned the collar of his blue shirt and turned up the flaps against his throat. He buttoned his old black serge coat over his stomach and patted it down. His hand went up to the tonsured hair and brushed it down, back and sides; and then he seemed to shake himself down to a tight, heavy solemnity. The lean-faced Sam came in and stood beside him. London stepped out of the tent, great with authority. Mac and Jim and Sam fell in behind him, but London walked alone, down the muddy street, and his little procession followed him. The heads of the people turned as he approached. The tissue of soft speech stopped. A new aisle opened to allow the leader to pass, and the heads turned with him as he passed.

London climbed up on the platform. He was alone, over the heads of the people. The faces pointed up at him, the eyes expressionless as glass. For a moment London looked down at the pine coffin, and then his shoulders squared. He seemed reluctant to break the breathing silence. His voice was remote and dignified. "I come up here to make some kind of speech," he said. "And I don't know no speeches." He paused and looked out over the upturned faces. "This little guy got killed yesterday. You all seen it. He was comin' over to our side, an' somebody plugged him. He wasn't doin' no harm to nobody." Again he stopped, and his face grew puzzled. "Well, what can a guy say? We're goin' to bury him. He's one of our own guys, an' he got shot. What can I say? We're goin' to march out and bury him—all of us. Because he was one of us. He was kind of like all of us. What happened to him is like to happen to any guy here." He stopped, and his mouth stayed open. "I—I don't know no speeches," he said uneasily. "There's a guy here that knowed this little fellow. I'm goin' to let him talk." His head turned slowly to where Mac stood. "Come on up, Mac. Tell 'em about the little guy."

Mac broke out of his stiffness and almost threw himself on the platform.

His shoulders weaved like a boxer's. "Sure I'll tell 'em," he cried passionately. "The guy's name was Joy. He was a radical. Get it? A radical. He wanted guys like you to have enough to eat and a place to sleep where you wouldn't get wet. He didn't want nothing for himself. He was a radical!" Mac cried. "D'ye see what he was? A dirty bastard, a danger to the government. I don't know if you saw his face, all beat to rags. The cops done that because he was a radical. His hands were broke, an' his jaw was broke. One time he got that jaw broke in a picket line. They put him in the can. Then a doctor come an' looked at him. 'I won't treat a God-damned red,' the doctor says. So Joy lies there with a busted jaw. He was dangerous—he wanted guys like you to get enough to eat." His voice was growing softer and softer, and his eyes watched expertly, saw faces becoming tense, trying to catch the words of his softening tone, saw the people leaning forward. "I knew him." Suddenly he shouted, "What are you going to do about it? Dump him in a mud-hole, cover him with slush. Forget him."

A woman in the crowd began to sob hysterically. "He was fightin' for you," Mac shouted. "You goin' to forget it?"

A man in the crowd yelled, "No, by Christ!"

Mac hammered on, "Goin' to let him get killed, while you lie down and take it?"

A chorus this time, "No-o-o!"

Mac's voice dropped into a sing-song. "Goin' to dump him in the mud?"

"No-oo." The bodies swayed a little bit.

"He fought for you. Are you going to forget him?"

"No-o-o."

"We're going to march through town. You going to let any damn cops stop us?"

The heavy roar, "No-oo." The crowd

swayed in the rhythm. They poised for the next response.

Mac broke the rhythm, and the break jarred them. He said quietly, "This little guy is the spirit of all of us. We won't pray for him. He don't need prayers. And we don't need prayers. We need clubs!"

Hungrily the crowd tried to restore the rhythm. "Clubs," they said. "Clubs." And then they waited in silence.

"O.K.," Mac said shortly. "We're going to throw the dirty radical in the mud, but he's going to stay with us, too. God help anybody that tries to stop us." Suddenly he got down from the platform, leaving the crowd hungry and irritated. Eyes looked wondering into other eyes.

London climbed down from the platform. He said to the bearers, "Put him in Albert Johnson's truck. We'll get goin' in a few minutes now." He followed Mac, who was working his way out of the crowd.

Dr. Burton fell in beside Mac when he was clear of the bunched people. "You surely know how to work them, Mac," he said quietly. "No preacher ever brought people to the mourners' bench quicker. Why didn't you keep it up awhile? You'd've had them talking in tongues and holy-rolling in a minute."

Mac said irritably, "Quit sniping at me, Doc. I've got a job to do, and I've got to use every means to do it."

"But where did you learn it, Mac?"

"Learn what?"

"All those tricks."

Mac said tiredly, "Don't try to see so much, Doc. I wanted them mad. Well, they're mad. What do you care how it's done?"

"I know how it's done," said Burton. "I just wondered how you learned. By the way, old Dan's satisfied not to go. He decided when we lifted him."

London and Jim caught up with them. Mac said, "You better leave a big guard here, London."

"O.K. I'll tell Sam to stay and keep about a hundred. That sure was a nice speech, Mac."

"I didn't have no time to figure it out ahead. We better get movin' before these guys cool off. Once they get goin' they'll be O.K. But we don't want 'em just to stand around and cool off."

They turned and looked back. Through the crowd the bearers came swinging, carrying the box on their forearms. The clot of people broke up and straggled behind. The light mist fell. To the west a rent in the cloud showed a patch of pale blue sky, and a high, soundless wind tore the clouds apart as they watched.

"It might be a nice day yet," Mac said. He turned to Jim. "I nearly forgot about you. How do you feel?"

"All right."

"Well, I don't think you better walk all that distance. You ride on the truck."

"No. I'll walk. The guys wouldn't like it if I rode."

"I thought of that," said Mac. "We'll have the pallbearers ride too. That'll make it all right. We all set, London?"

"All set."

13

The coffin rested on the flat bed of an old Dodge truck. On each side of it the bearers sat, hanging their legs over. And Jim rode hanging his feet over the rear. The motor throbbed and coughed, Albert Johnson drove out of the park and stopped in the road until the line formed, about eight men to a file. Then he dropped into low gear and moved slowly along the road, and the long line of men shuffled after him. The hundred guards stood in the camp and watched the parade move away.

At first the men tried to keep step, saying, "Hep, hep," but they tired of it soon. Their feet scuffed and dragged on the gravel road. A little hum of talk came from them, but each man was constrained to speak softly, in honor to the coffin. At the concrete state highway the speed cops were waiting, a dozen of them on motorcycles. Their captain, in a roadster, shouted, "We're not interfering with you men. We always conduct parades."

The feet sounded sharply on the concrete. The ranks straggled along in disorder. Only when they reached the outskirts of the town did the men straighten up. In the yards and on the sidewalks the people stood and watched the procession go by. Many took off their hats to the casket. But Mac's wish was denied. At each corner of the line of march the police stood, re-routing the traffic, turning it aside, and opening the way for the funeral. As they entered the business district of Torgas the sun broke through and glittered on the wet streets. The damp clothes of the marching men steamed under the sudden warmth. Now the sidewalks were dense with curious people, staring at the coffin; and the marchers straightened up. The squads drew close together. The men fell into step, while their faces took on expressions of importance. No one interfered, and the road was kept clear of vehicles.

Behind the truck, they marched through the town, through the thinning town again, and out into the country, toward the county cemetery. About a mile out they came to it, weed-grown and small. Over the new graves were little galvanized posts, stamped with names and dates. At the back of the lot a pile of new, wet dirt was heaped. The truck stopped at the gate. The bearers climbed down and took the casket on their forearms again. In the road the traffic cops rested their machines and stood waiting. Albert Johnson took two lengths of tow-rope from under his seat and fol-

lowed the bearers. The crowd broke ranks and followed. Jim jumped down from the truck and started to join the crowd, but Mac caught him. "Let them do it now; the main thing was the march. We'll wait here."

A young man with red hair strolled through the cemetery gate and approached. "Know a guy they call Mac?" he asked.

"They call me Mac."

"Well, do you know a guy they call Dick?"

"Sure."

"Yeah? What's his other name?"

"Halsing. What's the matter with him?"

"Nothing, but he sent you this note."

Mac opened the folded paper and read it. "Hot damn," he said. "Look, Jim!"

Jim took the note. It said:

"The lady wins. She has got a ranch, R.F.D. Box 221, Gallinas Road. Send out a truck there right away. They have got two cows, old, and one bull calf and ten sks. lima beans. Send some guys to kill the cows.

Dick.

P.S. I nearly got picked up last night.
P.P.S. Only twelve axe-handles."

Mac was laughing. "Oh, Jesus! Oh, Christ! Two cows and a calf and beans. That gives us time. Jim, run over and find London. Tell him to come here as quick as he can."

Jim plunged off, and walked through the crowd. In a moment he came back, with London hurrying beside him.

Mac cried, "Did he tell you, London? Did he?"

"He says you got food."

"Hell yes. Two cows and a calf. Ten

sacks of beans! Why, the guys can go right out in this truck now."

From the crowded side of the cemetery came the beating of mud thrown down on the pine casket. "Y'see," Mac said. "The guys'll feel fine when they get their stomachs full of meat and beans."

London said, "I could do with a piece of meat myself."

"Look, London, I'll go on the truck. Give me about ten men to guard it. Jim, you can come with me." He hesitated. "Where we going to get wood? We're about out of wood. Look, London, let every guy pick up a piece or two of wood, fence picket, piece of culvert, anything. Tell 'em what it's for. When you get back, dig a hole and start a fire in it. You'll find enough junk in those damned old cars to piece out a screen. Get your fire going." He turned back to the red-haired young man. "Where is this Gallinas Road?"

" 'Bout a mile from here. You can drop me off on the way."

London said, "I'll get Albert Johnson and some men." He hurried over and disappeared in the crowd.

Mac still laughed softly to himself. "What a break!" he said. "New lease on life. Oh, Dick's a great guy. He's a great guy."

Jim, looking at the crowd, saw it stir to life, it swirled. An excited commotion overcame it. The mob eddied, broke and started back to the truck. London, in the lead, was pointing out men with his finger. The crowd surrounded the truck, laughing, shouting. Albert Johnson put his muddy ropes under the seat and climbed in. Mac got in beside him, and helped Jim in. "Keep the guys together, London," he shouted. "Don't let 'em straggle." The ten chosen men leaped on the bed of the truck.

And then the crowd played. They held the tailboard until the wheels churned.

They made mud-balls and threw them at the men sitting on the truck. Outside, in the road, the police stood quietly and waited.

Albert Johnson jerked his clutch in and tore loose from the grip of the crowd. The motor panted heavily as he struck the road. Two of the cops kicked over their motors and fell in beside the truck. Mac turned and looked out through the rear window of the cab at the crowd. They came boiling out of the cemetery in a wave. They broke on the road, hurrying along, filling the road, while the cops vainly tried to keep a passage clear for automobiles. The jubilant men mocked them and pushed them and surged around them, laughing like children. The truck, with its escorts, turned a corner and moved quickly away.

Albert watched his speedometer warily. "I guess these babies'd like to pick me up for speeding."

"Damn right," said Mac. He turned to Jim. "Keep your head down if we pass anybody, Jim." And then to Albert, "If anybody tries to stop us, drive right over 'em. Remember what happened to Dakin's truck."

Albert nodded and dropped his speed to forty. "Nobody ain't goin' to stop me," he said. "I've drove a truck all my life when I could get it."

They did not go through the town, but cut around one end of it, crossed a wooden bridge over the river and turned into Gallinas Road. Albert slowed up to let the red-haired youth drop off. He waved his hand airily as they drove away. The road lay between the interminable apple trees. They drove three miles to the foothills before the orchards began to fall off, giving place to stubble fields. Jim watched the galvanized postboxes at the side of the road. "There's two-eighteen," he said. "Not very far now."

One of the cops turned back and went toward the town, but the other hung on.

"There it is," Jim said. "That big white gate there."

Albert headed in, and stopped while one of the men jumped down and opened the gate. The cop cut off his motor and leaned it against its stand.

"Private property," Mac called to him.

"I'll stick around, buddy," he said. "I'll just stick around."

A hundred yards ahead a little white house stood under a huge, spreading pepper tree, and behind it a big white barn reared. A stocky ranchman with a straw-colored mustache slouched out of the house and stood waiting for them. Albert pulled up. Mac said, "Hello, mister. The lady told us to come for some stuff."

"Yah," said the man. "She told me. Two old milk cow, little bully calf."

"Well, can we slaughter 'em here, mister?"

"Yah. You do it yourself. Clean up after. Don't make mess."

"Where are they, mister?"

"I got them in barn. You don't kill them there. Makes mess in the barn."

"Sure, mister. Pull around by the barn, Albert."

When the truck was stopped, Mac walked around it. "Any of you guys ever slaughter a cow?"

Jim broke in, "My old man was a slaughterhouse man. I can show 'em. My arm's too sore to hit 'em myself."

"O.K.," said Mac.

The farmer had walked around the house toward them. Jim asked, "You got a sledge-hammer?"

He pointed a thumb at a little shed that sloped off the barn.

"And a knife?"

"Yah. I got goot knife. You give him back." He walked away toward the house.

Jim turned toward the men. "Couple of you guys go into the barn and bring out the calf first. He's probably the liveliest."

The farmer hurried back carrying a short-handled, heavy-headed hammer in one hand and a knife in the other. Jim took the knife from him and looked at it. The blade was ground away until it was slender and bright, and the point was needle-like. He felt the edge with his thumb. "Sharp," the farmer said. "He's always sharp." He took the knife back, wiped it on his sleeves and reflected the light from it. "Cherman steel. Goot steel."

Four men came running out of the barn with a red yearling bull calf between them. They clung to a rope around its neck and steered it by butting it with their shoulders. They dug their heels into the ground to stop it, and held it, plunging, between them.

"Over here," the farmer said. "Here the blood could go into the ground."

Mac said, "We ought to save the blood. It's good strong food. If only we had something to carry it in."

"My old man used to drink it," said Jim. "I can't drink it: makes me sick. Here, Mac, you take the hammer. Now, you hit him right here on the head, good and hard." He handed the knife to Albert Johnson. "Look. See where my hand is? Now that's the place to stick him, just as soon as Mac hits him. There's a big artery there. Get it open."

"How's a guy to know?"

"You'll know, all right. It'll shoot blood like a half-inch pipe. Stand back out of the way, you guys."

Two men on the sides held the plunging calf. Mac slugged it to its knees. Albert drove in the knife and cut the artery open and jumped back from the spurting blood. The calf leaped, and then settled slowly down. Its chin rested flat on the ground, and its legs folded up. The thick, carmine blood pool spread out on the wet ground.

"It's a damn shame we can't save it," Mac said. "If we only had a little keg we could."

Jim cried, "O.K. Bring out another. Bring her over here." The men had been curious at the first slaughter, but when the two old cows were killed, they did not press in so close to see. When all the animals were down and the blood oozed slowly from their throats, Albert wiped the sticky knife on a piece of sack and handed it back to the farmer. He backed his truck to the animals and the men lifted the limp, heavy creatures up on the bed, and let the heads hang loosely over so that they might bleed on the ground. Last, they piled the ten sacks of lima beans on the front of the truck bed and took their places on the sacks.

Mac turned to the farmer. "Thanks, mister."

"Not my place," he said. "Not my cow. I farm shares."

"Well, thanks for the loan of your knife." Mac helped Jim a little as he got into the truck and moved over against Albert Johnson. The shirt sleeve on Albert's right arm was red to the shoulder with blood. Albert started his slow, chugging motor and moved carefully over the rough road. At the gate the traffic cop waited for them, and when they got out on the country road he followed a little way behind.

The men on the sacks started to sing.

"Soup, soup, give us some soup—
  We don't want nothing but just some soup."

The cop grinned at them. One of the men chanted at him,

"Whoops my dear, whoops my dear,
  Even the chief of police is queer."

In the cab, Mac leaned forward and spoke across Jim. "Albert, we want to dodge the town. We got to get this stuff to the camp. See if you can sort of edge around it, will you, even if it's longer?"

Albert nodded morosely.

The sun shone now, but it was high, and there was no warmth in it. Jim said, "This ought to make the guys feel fine."

Albert nodded again. "Let 'em get their guts full of meat, and they'll go to sleep."

Mac laughed. "I'm surprised at you, Albert. Haven't you got no idears about the nobility of labor?"

"I got nothing," Albert said. "No idears, no money, no nothing."

"Nothing to lose but your chains," Jim put in softly.

"Bull," said Albert, "nothing to lose but my hair."

"You got this truck," Mac said. "How'd we get this stuff back without a truck?"

"This truck's got me," Albert complained. "The God-damned truck's just about two-bitted me to death." He looked sadly ahead. His lips scarcely moved when he talked. "When I'm workin' and I get three dollars to the good and I get set to look me up a floozy, somethin' on this buggy busts and costs three dollars. Never fails. God damn truck's worse'n a wife."

Jim said earnestly, "In any good system, you'd have a good truck."

"Yeah? In any good system I'd have a floozy. I ain't Dakin. If Dakin's truck could of cooked, he wouldn't of wanted nothing else."

Mac said to Jim, "You're talkin' to a man that knows what he wants, and it ain't an automobile."

"That's the idear," said Albert. "I guess it was stickin' them cows done it. I felt all right before."

They were back in the endless orchards now, and the leaves were dark and the earth was dark with the rain. In the ditches beside the road a little muddy storm water ran. The traffic cop rode behind them as Albert turned from road to road, making an angular circuit of the town. They could see among the trees the houses where the owners or the resident share-croppers lived.

Mac said, "If it didn't make our guys so miserable, I wish the rain'd go on. It isn't doin' those apples no good."

"It isn't doin' my blankets no good, neither," Albert said sullenly.

The men on the back were singing in chorus,

"Oh, we sing, we sing, we sing
Of Lydia Pinkham
And her gift to the human race——"

Albert turned a corner and came into the road to Anderson's place. "Nice work," said Mac. "You didn't go near the town. It would of been hell if we'd got held up and lost our load."

Jim said, "Look at the smoke, Mac. They've got a fire going, all right." The blue smoke rolled among the trees, hardly rising above their tops.

"Better drive along the camp, near the trees," Mac advised. "They're going to have to cut up these animals, and there's nothing to hang them on but the apple trees."

Men were standing in the road, watching for them. As the truck moved along the men on the bean sacks stood up and took off their hats and bowed. Albert dropped into low gear and crawled through the crowd of men to the end of the camp, near the apple trees.

London, with Sam behind him, came pushing through the shouting mill of hysterical men and women.

Mac cried, "String 'em up. And listen, London, tell the cooks to cut the meat thin, so it'll cook quick. These guys are hungry."

London's eyes were as bright as those of the men around him. "Jesus, could I eat," he said. "We'd about give you up."

The cooks came through the crowd. The animals were hung to the lower branches of the trees, entrails scooped out, skins ripped off. Mac cried, "London, don't let 'em waste anything. Save all the bones and heads and feet for soup." A pan of hacked pieces of meat went to the pit, and the crowd followed, leaving the butchers more room to work. Mac stood on the running-board, overlooking the scene, but Jim still sat in the cab, straddling the gear-shift lever. Mac turned anxiously to him. "What's the matter, Jim? You feel all right?"

"Sure, I'm O.K. My shoulder's awful stiff, though. I darn near can't move it."

"I guess you're cold. We'll see if Doc can't loosen you up a little." He helped Jim down from the truck and supported him by the elbow as they walked across toward the meat pit. A smell of cooking meat hung over the whole camp, and the meat dripped fat on the coals so that fierce little flames leaped up and devoured each drop. The men crowded so densely about the pit that the cooks, who went about turning the meat with long pointed sticks, had to push their way through the throng. Mac guided Jim toward London's tent. "I'm going to ask Doc to come over. You sit down in there. I'll bring you some meat when it's done."

It was dusky inside the tent. What little light got through the grey canvas was grey. When Jim's eyes grew accustomed to the light, he saw Lisa sitting on her mattress holding the baby under her shoulder blanket. She looked at him with dark, questionless eyes. Jim said, "Hello. How you getting along?"

"All right."

"Well, can I sit down on your mattress? I feel a little weak."

She gathered her legs under her and

moved aside. Jim sat down beside her. "What's that good smell?" she asked.

"Meat. We're going to have lots of meat."

"I like meat," she said. "I could just about live on meat." London's dark, slender son came through the tent-flaps. He stopped and stared at the two of them. "He's hurt," Lisa said quickly. "He ain't doin' nothing. He's hurt in the shoulder."

The boy said, "Oh," softly. "I wasn't thinkin' he was." He said to Jim, "She always thinks I'm lookin' at her that way, and I ain't." He said sententiously, "I always think, if you can't trust a girl, it don't do no good to try to watch her. A tramp is a tramp. Lisa ain't no tramp. I got no call to treat her like a tramp." He stopped. "They got meat out there, lots of meat. They got limey beans, too. Not for now, though."

Lisa said, "I like them, too."

The boy went on, "The guys don't want to wait till the meat's done. They want to eat it all pink inside. It'll make 'em sick if they ain't careful."

The tent-flaps whipped open, admitting Dr. Burton. In his hands he carried a pot of steaming water. "This looks like the holy family," he said. "Mac told me you were stiffening up."

"I'm pretty sore," said Jim.

Doc looked down at the girl. "Do you think you could put that baby down long enough to hold some hot cloths on his shoulder?"

"Me?"

"Yes. I'm busy. Get his coat off and keep hot water on the stiff place. Don't get it in the wound if you can help."

"D'you think I could?"

"Well, why not? He did things for you. Come on, get his coat off and strip down his shirt. I'm busy. I'll put on a new bandage when you finish." He went out.

The girl said, "D'you want me to?"

"Sure. Why not? You can."

She handed the baby to Joey, helped Jim off with his blue denim jacket and slipped his shirt down. "Don't you wear no un'erclo's?"

"No."

She fell silent then, and put the hot cloths on the shoulder muscle until the sore stiffness relaxed. Her fingers pressed the cloth down and moved about, pressing and pressing, gently, while her young husband looked on. In a little while Dr. Burton returned, and Mac came with him, carrying a big piece of black meat on a stick.

"Feel better now?"

"Better. Much better. She did it fine."

The girl backed away, her eyes dropped with self-consciousness. Burton quickly put on a new bandage and Mac handed over the big piece of meat. "I salted it out there," he said. "Doc thinks you better not run around any more today."

Burton nodded. "You might catch cold and go into a fever," he said. "Then you couldn't do anything."

Jim filled his mouth with tough meat and chewed. "Guys like the meat?" he asked.

"Cocky'r'n hell. They think they run the world now. They're going out and clean up on somebody. I knew it would happen."

"Are they going out to picket today?"

Mac thought a moment. "You're not, anyhow. You're going to sit here and keep warm."

Joey handed the baby to his wife. "Is they plenty meat, mister?"

"Sure."

"Well, I'm goin' to get some for Lisa and I."

"Well, go ahead. Listen, Jim. Don't go moaning around. There's not going to be much going on. It's along in the afternoon now. London's going to send out some guys in cars to see how many scabs are working. They'll see how many and where, an' then, tomorrow morning, we'll start doing something about it. We can feed the guys for a coupla days now. Clouds are going. We'll have clear, cold weather for a change."

Jim asked, "Did you hear anything about scabs?"

"No, not much. Some of the guys say that scabs are coming in in trucks with guards on them, but you can't believe anything in a camp like this. Damnedest place in the world for rumors."

"The guys are awful quiet now."

"Sure. Why not? They've got their mouths full. Tomorrow we've got to start raising hell. I guess we can't strike long, so we've got to strike hard."

The sound of a motor came up the road and stopped. Outside the tent there was a sudden swell of voices, and then quiet again. Sam stuck his head into the tent. "London here?" he demanded.

"No. What's the matter?"

"There's a dressed-up son-of-a-bitch in a shiny car wants to see the boss."

"What about?"

"I don't know. Says he wants to see the chief of the strikers."

Mac said, "London's over by the pit. Tell him to come over. The guy probably wants to talk things over."

"O.K. I'll tell him."

In a moment London came into the tent, and the stranger followed him, a chunky, comfortable-looking man dressed in a grey business suit. His cheeks were pink and shaven, his hair nearly white. Wrinkles of good nature radiated from the corners of his eyes. On his mouth an open, friendly smile appeared every time he spoke. To London he said, "Are you the chairman of the camp?"

"Yeah," said London suspiciously. "I'm the elected boss."

Sam came in and took his place just behind London, his face dark and sullen. Mac squatted down on his haunches and balanced himself with his fingers. The newcomer smiled. His teeth were white and even. "My name's Bolter," he said simply. "I own a big orchard. I'm the new president of the Fruit Growers' Association of this valley."

"So what?" said London. "Got a good job for me if I'll sell out?"

The smile did not leave Bolter's face, but his clean, pink hands closed gently at his sides. "Let's try to get a better start than that," he begged. "I told you I was the *new* president. That means there's a change in policy. I don't believe in doing things the way they were being done." While he spoke Mac looked not at Bolter, but at London.

Some of the anger left London's face. "What you got to say?" he asked. "Spill it out."

Bolter looked around for something to sit on, and saw nothing. He said, "I never could see how two men could get anything done by growling at each other. I've always had an idea that no matter how mad men were, if they could only get together with a table between them, something good would come out of it."

London snickered. "We ain't got a table."

"You know what I mean," Bolter continued. "Everybody in the Association said you men wouldn't listen to reason, but I told them I know American working men. Give American working men something reasonable to listen to, and they'll listen."

Sam spat out, "Well, we're listenin', ain't we? Go on an' give us somethin' reasonable."

Bolter's white teeth flashed. He looked around appreciatively. "There, you see? That's what I told them. I said, 'Let me lay our cards down on the table, and then let them lay theirs down, and see if we can't make a hand.' American working men aren't animals."

Mac muttered, "You ought to run for Congress."

"I beg your pardon?"

"I was talkin' to this here guy," said Mac. London's face had grown hard again.

Bolter went on, "That's what I'm here for, to lay our cards on the table. I told you I own an orchard, but don't think because of that I haven't your interests at heart. All of us know we can't make money unless the working man is happy." He paused, waiting for some kind of answer. None came. "Well, here's the way I figure it; you're losing money and we're losing money because we're sitting growling at each other. We want you to come back to work. Then you'll get your wages, and we'll get our apples picked. That way we'll both be happy. Will you come back to work? No questions, no grudges, just two people who figured things out over the table?"

London said, "Sure we'll go back to work, mister. Ain't we American working men? Just give us the raise we want and kick out the scabs and we'll be up in those old trees tomorrow morning."

Bolter smiled around at them, one at a time, until his smile had rested on each face. "Well, I think you ought to have a raise," he said. "And I told everybody I thought so. Well, I'm not a very good business man. The rest of the Association explained it all to me. With the price of apples what it is, we're paying the top price we can. If we pay any more, we lose money."

Mac grinned. "I guess we ain't American workin' men after all," he said. "None of this sounds reasonable to me. So far it's sounded like a sock full of crap."

Jim said, "The reason they can't pay the raise is because that'd mean we win the strike; and if we did that, a lot of other poor devils'd go on strike. Isn't that it, mister?"

Bolter's smile remained. "I thought from the first you deserved a raise, but I didn't have any power. I still believe it, and I'm the president of the Association. Now I've told the Association what I'm going to do. Some of 'em don't like it, but I insisted you men have to have a raise. I'm going to offer you twenty cents, and no questions and no grudges. And we'll expect you back at work tomorrow morning."

London looked around at Sam. He laughed at Sam's scowling face, and slapped the lean man on the shoulder. "Mr. Bolter," he said, "like Mac says, I guess we ain't American workin' men. You wanted cards laid down, and then you laid yours down backs up. Here's ours, and by Christ, she's a full house. Your God-damn apples got to be picked and we ain't pickin' 'em without our raise. Nor neither is nobody else pickin' 'em. What do you think of that, Mister Bolter?"

At last the smile had faded from Bolter's face. He said gravely, "The American nation has become great because everybody pitched in and helped. American labor is the best labor in the world, and the highest paid."

London broke in angrily, "S'pose a Chink does get half a cent a day, if he can eat on it? What the hell do we care how much we get, if we got to go hungry?"

Bolter put on his smile again. "I have a home and children," he said. "I've worked hard. You think I'm different from you. I want you to look on me as a working man, too. I've worked for everything I've got. Now we've heard that radicals are working among you. I don't believe it. I don't believe American men, with American ideals, will listen to radicals. All of us are in the same boat. Times are hard. We're all trying to get along, and we've got to help each other."

Suddenly Sam yelled, "Oh, for Christ's sake, lay off. If you got somethin' to say, say it; only cut out this God-damn speech."

Bolter looked very sad. "Will you accept half?"

"No," said London. "You wouldn't offer no half unless you was pressed."

"How do you know the men wouldn't accept, if you put it to a vote?"

"Listen, mister," London said, "them guys is so full of piss and vinegar they'll skin you if you show that slick suit outside. We're strikin' for our raise. We're picketin' your God-damn orchards, and we're kickin' hell out of any scabs you run in. Now come on through with your 'or else.' Turn your damn cards over. What you think you're goin' to do if we don't go back?"

"Turn the vigilantes loose," said Mac.

Bolter said hurriedly, "We don't know anything about any vigilantes. But if the outraged citizens band together to keep the peace, that's their affair. The Association knows nothing about that." He smiled again. "Can't you men see that if you attack our homes and our children we have to protect them? Wouldn't you protect your own children?"

"What the hell do you think we're doin'?" London cried. "We're trying to protect 'em from starving. We're usin' the only way a workin' stiff's got. Don't you go talkin' about no children, or we'll show you something."

"We only want to settle this thing peacefully," said Bolter. "American citizens demand order, and I assure you men we're going to have order if we have to petition the governor for troops."

Sam's mouth was wet. He shouted, "And you get order by shootin' our men

from windows, you yellow bastard. And in 'Frisco you got order by ridin' down women. An' the newspapers says, 'This mornin' a striker was killed when he threw himself on a bayonet.' *Threw himself!*"

London wrapped his arm about the furious man and forced him slowly away from Bolter. "Lay off, Sam. Stop it, now. Just quiet yourself."

"Th' hell with you," Sam cried. "Stand there and take the lousy crap that big baloney hands you!"

London stiffened suddenly. His big fist lashed out and cracked into Sam's face, and Sam went down. London stood looking at him. Mac laughed hysterically. "A striker just threw himself into a fist," he said.

Sam sat up on the ground. "O.K., London. You win. I won't make no more fuss, but you wasn't in 'Frisco on Bloody Thursday."

Bolter stood where he was. "I hoped you would listen to reason," he said. "We have information that you're being influenced by radicals, sent here by red organizations. They are misleading you, telling you lies. They only want to stir up trouble. They're professional trouble-makers, paid to cause strikes."

Mac stood up from his haunches. "Well, the dirty rats," he said. "Mis-leadin' American workin' men, are they? Prob'ly gettin' paid by Russia, don't you think, Mr. Bolter?"

The man looked back at him for a long time, and the healthy red was gone from his cheeks. "You're going to make us fight, I guess," he said. "I'm sorry. I wanted peace. We know who the radicals are, and we'll have to take action against them." He turned imploringly to London. "Don't let them mislead you. Come back to work. We only want peace."

London was scowling. "I had enough o' this," he said. "You want peace. Well, what we done? Marched in two parades. An' what you done? Shot three of our men, burned a truck and a lunch wagon and shut off our food supply. I'm sick o' your God-damned lies, mister. I'll see you get out without Sam gets his hands on you, but don't send nobody else again till you're ready to talk straight."

Bolter shook his head sadly. "We don't want to fight you men," he said. "We want you to come back to work. But if we do have to fight, we have weapons. The health authorities are pretty upset about this camp. And the government doesn't like uninspected meat moving in this county. The citizens are pretty tired of all this riot. And of course we may have to call troops, if we need them."

Mac got up and went to the tent-flaps and looked out. Already the evening was coming. The camp was quiet, for the men stood watching London's tent. All the faces, white in the gathering evening, were turned in toward the tent. Mac yelled, "All right, boys. We ain't goin' to sell you out." He turned back into the tent. "Light the lamp, London. I want to tell this friend of man a few things."

London set a match to the tin lantern and hung it on the tent-pole, where it cast a pale, steady light. Mac took up a position in front of Bolter, and his muscled face broke into a derisive grin. "All right, Sonny Boy," he said. "You been talkin' big, but I know you been wettin' your pants the whole time. I admit you can do all the things you say you can, but look what happens after. Your health service burned the tents in Washington. And that was one of the reasons that Hoover lost the labor vote. You called out guardsmen in 'Frisco, and damn near the whole city went over to the strikers. Y' had to have the cops stop food from comin' in to turn public opinion against the strike. I'm not talkin' right an' wrong now, mister. I'm tellin' you what happens." Mac stepped back a

pace. "Where do you think we're gettin' food and blankets an' medicine an' money? You know damn well where we're gettin' 'em. Your valley's lousy with sympathizers. Your 'outraged citizens' are a little bit outraged at you babies, and you know it. And you know, if you get too tough, the unions'll go out. Truck drivers and restaurant men and field hands, everybody. And just because you do know it, you try to throw a bluff. Well, it don't work. This camp's cleaner'n the lousy bunk houses you keep for us on your ranches. You come here to try to scare us, an' it don't work."

Bolter was very pale. He turned away from Mac and faced London. "I've tried to make peace," he said. "Do you know that this man was sent out by red headquarters to start this strike? Watch out that when he goes to jail you don't go too. We have a right to protect our property, and we'll do it. I've tried to deal man to man with you, and you won't deal. From now on the roads are closed. An ordinance will go through tonight forbidding any parading on the county roads, or any gathering. The sheriff will deputize a thousand men, if he needs them."

London glanced quickly at Mac, and Mac winked at him. London said, "Jesus, mister, I hope we can get you out of here safe. When the guys out there hear what you just said, why they'll want to take you to pieces."

Bolter's jaw tightened and his eyelids drooped. He straightened his shoulders. "Don't get the idea you can scare me," he said. "I'll protect my home and my children with my life if I have to. And if you lay a hand on me we'll wipe out your strike before morning."

London's arms doubled, and he stepped forward, but Mac jumped in his way. "The guy's right, London. He don't scare. Plenty do, but he don't." He turned around. "Mister Bolter, we'll see you get out of the camp. We understand each other now. We know what to expect from you. And we know how careful you have to be when you use force. Don't forget the thousands of people that are sending us food and money. They'll do other things, if they have to. We been good, Mr. Bolter, but if you start any funny business, we'll show you a riot you'll remember."

Bolter said coldly, "That seems to be all. I'm sorry, but I'll have to report that you won't meet us halfway."

"Halfway?" Mac cried. "There ain't any halfway to nowhere." His voice dropped to softness. "London, you get on one side of him, and Sam on the other, and see that he gets away all right. Then I guess you'd better tell the guys what he said. But don't let 'em get out of hand. Tell 'em to tighten up the squads for trouble."

They surrounded Bolter and took him through the press of silent men, saw him into his coupe and watched him drive away down the road. When he was gone London raised his voice. "If you guys want to come over to the stand, I'll get up on it and tell you what the son-of-a-bitch said, and what we answered him back." He flailed his way through, and the men followed, excitedly. The cooks left the stoves where they were boiling beans and chunks of beef. The women crawled like rodents from the tents and followed. When London climbed up on the stand it was ringed closely with men, standing in the dusk looking up at him.

During the talk with Bolter Doc Burton had effaced himself, had been so quiet that he seemed to have disappeared, but when the group went out, leaving only Jim and Lisa sitting on the mattress, he came out of his corner and sat down on the edge of the mattress beside them. His face was worried. "It's going to be a mean one," he said.

"That's what we want, Doc," Jim told

him. "The worse it is, the more effect it'll have."

Burton looked at him with sad eyes. "You see a way through," he said. "I wish I did. It all seems meaningless to me, brutal and meaningless."

"It has to go on," Jim insisted. "It can only stop when the men rule themselves and get the profits of their labor."

"Seems simple enough," Burton sighed. "I wish I thought it was so simple." He turned smiling to the girl. "What's your solution, Lisa?"

She started. "Huh?"

"I mean, what would you like to have to make you happy."

She looked self-consciously down at the baby. "I like to have a cow," she said. "I like to have butter an' cheese like you can make."

"Want to exploit a cow?"

"Huh?"

"I'm being silly. Did you ever have a cow, Lisa?"

"When I was a little kid we had one," she said. "Went out an' drunk it warm. Old man used to milk it into a cup-like, to drink. Tasted warm. That's what I like. Bet it would be good for the baby." Burton turned slowly away from her. She insisted, "Cow used to eat grass, an' sometimes hay. Not ever'body can milk 'em, neither. They kick."

Burton asked, "Did you ever have a cow, Jim?"

"No."

Burton said, "I never thought of cows as counter-revolutionary animals."

Jim asked, "What are you talking about, Doc, anyway?"

"Nothing. I'm kind of unhappy, I guess. I was in the army in the war. Just out of school. They'd bring in one of our men with his chest shot away, and they'd bring in a big-eyed German with his legs splintered off. I worked on 'em just as though they were wood. But sometimes, after it was all over, when I wasn't working, it made me unhappy, like this. It made me lonely."

Jim said, "Y'ought to think only of the end, Doc. Out of all this struggle a good thing is going to grow. That makes it worthwhile."

"Jim, I wish I knew it. But in my little experience the end is never very different in its nature from the means. Damn it, Jim, you can only build a violent thing with violence."

"I don't believe that," Jim said. "All great things have violent beginnings."

"There aren't any beginnings," Burton said. "Nor any ends. It seems to me that man has engaged in a blind and fearful struggle out of a past he can't remember, into a future he can't foresee nor understand. And man has met and defeated every obstacle, every enemy except one. He cannot win over himself. How mankind hates itself."

Jim said, "We don't hate ourselves, we hate the invested capital that keeps us down."

"The other side is made of men, Jim, men like you. Man hates himself. Psychologists say a man's self-love is balanced neatly with self-hate. Mankind must be the same. We fight ourselves and we can only win by killing every man. I'm lonely, Jim. I have nothing to hate. What are you going to get out of it, Jim?"

Jim looked startled. "You mean me?" He pointed a finger at his breast.

"Yes, you. What will you get out of all the mess?"

"I don't know; I don't care."

"Well, suppose blood-poisoning sets in in that shoulder, or you die of lockjaw and the strike gets broken? What then?"

"It doesn't matter," Jim insisted. "I used to think like you, Doc, but it doesn't matter at all."

"How do you get that way?" Burton asked. "What's the process?"

"I don't know. I used to be lonely, and I'm not any more. If I go out now it won't matter. The thing won't stop. I'm just a little part of it. It will grow and grow. This pain in the shoulder is kind of pleasant to me; and I bet before he died Joy was glad for a moment. Just in that moment I bet he was glad."

They heard a rough, monotonous voice outside, and then a few shouts, and then the angry crowd-roar, a bellow like an animal in fury. "London's telling them," said Jim. "They're mad. Jesus, how a mad crowd can fill the air with madness. You don't understand it, Doc. My old man used to fight alone. When he got licked, he was licked. I remember how lonely it was. But I'm not lonely any more, and I can't be licked, because I'm more than myself."

"Pure religious ecstasy. I can understand that. Partakers of the blood of the Lamb."

"Religion, hell!" Jim cried. "This is men, not God. This is something you know."

"Well, can't a group of men be God, Jim?"

Jim wrenched himself around. "You make too damn many words, Doc. You build a trap of words and then you fall into it. You can't catch me. Your words don't mean anything to me. I know what I'm doing. Argument doesn't have any effect on me."

"Steady down," Burton said soothingly. "Don't get so excited. I wasn't arguing, I was asking for information. All of you people get angry when you're asked a question."

As the dusk turned into night the lantern seemed to grow brighter, to find deeper corners of the tent with its yellow light. Mac came in quietly, as though he crept away from the noise and shouting outside. "They're wild," he said. "They're hungry again. Boiled meat and beans tonight. I knew they'd get cocky on that meat. They'd like to go out and burn houses right now."

"How does the sky look?" Burton asked. "Any more rain in it?"

"Clear and stars. It'll be good weather."

"Well, I want to talk to you, Mac. I'm low in supplies. I need disinfectant. Yes, and I could use some salvarsan. If any kind of epidemic should break out, we'd be out of luck."

"I know," Mac said. "I sent word to town how it was. Some of the boys are out trying to get money. They're trying to get money to bail Dakin out now. I'd just as soon he stayed in jail."

Burton stood up from his seat on the mattress. "You can tell London what to do, can't you. Dakin wouldn't take everything."

Mac studied him. "What's the matter, Doc? Don't you feel well?"

"What do you mean?"

"I mean your temper's going. You're tired. What is it, Doc?"

Burton put his hands in his pockets. "I don't know; I'm lonely, I guess. I'm awfully lonely. I'm working all alone, towards nothing. There's some compensation for you people. I only hear heartbeats through a stethoscope. You hear them in the air." Suddenly he leaned over and put his hand under Lisa's chin and raised her head up and looked into her shrinking eyes. Her hand came slowly up and pulled gently at his wrist. He let go and put his hand back in his pocket.

Mac said, "I wish I knew some woman you could go to, Doc, but I don't. I'm new around here. Dick could steer you, in town. He prob'ly has twenty lined up by now. But you might get caught and jailed, Doc; and if you weren't taking care of us, they'd bounce us off this land in a minute."

Burton said, "Sometimes you understand too much, Mac. Sometimes—nothing. I guess I'll go along and see Al Anderson. I haven't been there all day."

"O.K., Doc, if it'll make you feel any better. I'll keep Jim under cover tonight."

Doc looked down at Lisa once more, and then he went out.

The shouting had settled to talk by now, low talk. It made the night alive outside the tent.

"Doc doesn't eat," Mac complained. "Nobody's seen him sleep. I suppose he'll break, sooner or later, but he never has before. He needs a woman bad; someone that would like him for a night; you know, really like him. He needs to feel someone—with his skin. So do I. Lisa, you're a lucky little twirp, you just had a kid. You'd have me in your hair."

"Huh?"

"I say: How's the baby?"

"All right."

Mac nodded gravely at Jim. "I like a girl who doesn't talk too much."

Jim asked, "What went on out there? I'm sick of staying in already."

"Why, London told what Sonny Boy said, and asked for a vote of confidence. He sure as hell got it, too. He's out there now, talking to the squad leaders about tomorrow."

"What about tomorrow?"

"Well, Sonny Boy was telling the truth about that ordinance. By tomorrow it'll be against the law for the boys to march along the county road. I don't think they'll remember about trucks. So, instead of standing around orchards, we're going to send out flying squads in the cars. We can raid one bunch of scabs and get out, and raid another. It ought to work."

"Where we going to get gasoline?"

"Well, we'll take it out of all the cars and put it in the ones we use. That should last tomorrow. The next day we may have to try something else. Maybe we can hit hard enough tomorrow so we can rest up the next day, until they get in a new load of scabs."

Jim asked, "I can go tomorrow, can't I?"

Mac cried, "What good would you be? The guys that go have to be fighters. You just take up room with that bum arm. Use your head."

London pushed open the flaps and came in. His face was flushed with pleasure. "Them guys is sure steamed up," he said. "Jesus, they're belly-for-back to kick Torgas for a growler."

"Don't give 'em no headway," Mac advised. "They got their guts full of chow. If they go loose, we ain't never goin' to catch up with them."

London pulled up a box and sat down on it. "The chow's about ready, the guy says. I want to ast you, Mac, ever'body says you're a red. Them two guys that come to talk both said it. Seemed to know all about you."

"Yeah?"

"Tell me straight, Mac. Is you an' Jim reds?"

"What do you think?"

London's eyes flashed angrily, but he controlled himself. "Don't get mean, Mac. I don't take it nice if the guys on the other side know more about you'n I do. What the hell do I know? You come into my camp and done us a good turn. I never ast you no questions—never did. I wouldn't ast you any now, on'y I got to know what to expect."

Mac looked puzzled. He glanced at Jim. "O.K.?"

"O.K. by me."

"Listen, London," Mac began. "A guy can get to like you awful well. Sam'll kick the ass off any guy that looks crooked at you."

"I got good friends," said London.

"Well, that's why. I feel the same way. S'pose I was a red, what then?"

London said, "You're a friend of mine."

"O.K., then, I'm a red. There ain't a hell of a secret about it. They say I started this strike. Now get me straight. I would of started it if I could, but I didn't have to. It started itself."

London eyed him cautiously, as though his mind slowly circled Mac's mind. "What do you get out of it?" he asked.

"Money, you mean? Not a damn thing."

"Then what do you do it for?"

"Well, it's hard to say—you know how you feel about Sam an' all the guys that travel with you? Well, I feel that way about all the workin' stiffs in the country."

"Guys you don't even know?"

"Yes, guys I don't even know. Jim here's just the same, just the same."

"Sounds crazy as hell," said London. "Sounds like a gag. An' you don't get no money?"

"You don't see no Rolls-Royces around, do you?"

"But how about after?"

"After what?"

"Maybe after this is over you'll collect."

"There ain't no after," Mac said. "When this one's done, we'll be in another one."

London squinted at him, as though he tried to read his thoughts. "I believe it," he said slowly. "You ain't give me no bum steers yet."

Mac reached over and struck him sharply on the shoulders. "I'd of told you before, if you asked me."

London said, "I got nothing against reds. Y'always hear how they're sons-of-bitches. Sam's kind of rattlesnake and whip-tempered, but he ain't no son-of-a-bitch. Let's go over an' get some food."

Mac stood up. "I'll bring you and Lisa some, Jim."

London said, from the doorway, "Moon's comin' up nice. I didn't know it was full moon."

"It isn't. Where do you see it?"

"Look, see over there? Looks like moonrise."

Mac said, "That ain't east—Oh, Jesus! It's Anderson's. *London,*" he shouted. "They've set fire to Anderson's! Get the guys. Come on, God damn it! Where are those guards? Get the guys quick!" He ran away toward the red, gathering light behind the trees.

Jim jumped up from the mattress. He didn't feel his wounded arm as he ran along, fifty yards behind Mac. He heard London's voice roaring, and then the drumming of many feet on the wet ground. He reached the trees and speeded up. The red light mushroomed out behind the trees. It was more than a glow now. A lance of flame cleared the tree-tops. Above the sound of steps there was a vicious crackling. From ahead came shrill cries and a muffled howling. The trees threw shadows away from the light. The end of the orchard row was blocked with fire, and in front of it black figures moved about. Jim could see Mac pounding ahead of him, and he could hear the increasing, breathy roar of the flames. He sprinted, caught up with Mac, and ran beside him. "It's the barn," he gasped. "Were the apples out yet?"

"Jim! Damn it, you shouldn't come. No, the apples are in the barn. Where the hell were the guards? Can't trust anybody." They neared the end of the row, and the hot air struck their faces. All the barn walls were sheathed in fire, and the strong flames leaped from the roof. The guards stood by Anderson's little house,

quiet, watching the light, while Anderson danced jerkily in front of them.

Mac stopped running. "No go. We can't do a thing. They must of used gasoline."

London plunged past them, and his face was murderous. He drew up in front of the guards and shouted, "You God-damn rats! Where in hell were you?"

One of the men raised his voice above the fire. "You sent a guy to tell us you wanted us. We was halfway to the camp when we seen it start."

London's fury drained out of him. His big fists undoubled. He turned helplessly to where Mac and Jim stood, their eyes glaring in the light. Anderson capered close to them in his jerky, wild dance. He came close to Mac and stood in front of him and pushed his chin up into Mac's face. "You dirty son-of-a-bitch!" His voice broke, and he turned, crying, back toward the tower of flame. Mac put his arm around Anderson's waist, but the old man flung it off. Out of the fire came the sharp, sweet odor of burning apples.

Mac looked weak and sad. To London he said, "God, I wish it hadn't happened. Poor old man, it's all his crop." A thought stopped him. "Christ Almighty! Did you leave anybody to look after the camp?"

"No. I never thought."

Mac whirled. "Come on, a flock of you. Maybe they're drawin' us. Some of you stay here so the house won't get burnt too." He sprinted back, the way he had come. His long black shadow leaped ahead of him. Jim tried to keep up with him, but a sick weakness set in. Mac drew away from him, and the men passed him, until he was alone, behind them, stumbling along giddily over the uneven earth. No flames broke from the camp ahead. Jim settled down to walk along the vague aisle between the rows. He heard the crash of the falling barn, and did not even turn to look. When he was halfway back, his legs buckled with weakness, and he sat down heavily on the ground. The sky was bright with fire over his head, and behind the low, rosy light the icy stars hung.

Mac, retracing his steps, found him there. "What's the matter, Jim?"

"Nothing. My legs got weak. I'm just resting. Is the camp all right?"

"Sure. They didn't get to it. There's a man hurt. Fell down, I think he busted his ankle. We've got to find Doc. What a damn fool easy trick that was! One of their guys tells the guards to get out while the rest splash gasoline around and throw in a match. Jesus, it was quick! Now we'll get *hell* from Anderson. Get kicked off the place tomorrow, I guess."

"Where'll we go then, Mac?"

"Say! You're all in. Here, give me your arm. I'll help you back. Did you see Doc at the fire?"

"No."

"Well, he said he was going over to see Al. I didn't see him come back. Come on, climb to your feet. I've got to get you bedded down."

Already the light was dying. At the end of the row lay a pile of fire, but the flames no longer leaped up in long streamers. "Hold on to me, now. Anderson was nearly crazy, wasn't he? Thank God they didn't get his house."

London, with Sam behind him, caught up. "How's the camp?"

"O.K. They didn't get it."

"Well, what's the matter with the kid?"

"Just weak from his wound. Give 'im a lift on that side." Together they half-carried Jim down the row and across the open space to London's tent. They set him down on the mattress. Mac asked, "Did you see the Doc over there? A guy's bust his ankle."

"No. I never seen him."

"Well, I wonder where he is?"

Sam entered the tent silently. His lean face was ridged with tight muscles. He walked stiffly over and stood in front of Mac. "That afternoon, when that guy says what he'd do——"

"What guy?"

"That first guy that come, an' you told him."

"I told him what?"

"Told 'im what we'd do."

Mac started and looked at London. "I don't know, Sam. It might switch public sympathy. We should be getting it now. We don't want to lose it."

Sam's voice was thick with hatred. "You can't let 'em get away with it. You can't let the yellow bastards burn us out."

London said, "Come out of it, Sam. What do you want?"

"I want to take a couple guys—an' play with matches." Mac and London watched him carefully. "I'm goin'," Sam said. "I don' give a damn. I'm goin'. There's a guy name Hunter. He's got a big white house. I'm takin' a can of gasoline."

Mac grinned. "Take a look at this guy, London. Ever see him before? Know who he is?"

London caught it. "No, can't say I do. Who is he?"

"Search me. Was he ever in camp?"

"No, by God! Maybe he's just a guy with a grudge. We get all kind of things pinned on us."

Mac swung back on Sam. "If you get caught, you got to take it."

"I'll take it," Sam said sullenly. "I ain't sharin' no time. I ain't takin' nobody with me, neither. I changed my mind."

"We don't know you. You just got a grudge."

"I hate the guy 'cause he robbed me," said Sam.

Mac stepped close to him and gripped his arm. "Burn the bastard into the ground," he said viciously. "Burn every stick in the house. I'd like to go with you. Jesus, I would!"

"Stick here," said Sam. "This ain't your fight. This guy robbed me—an' I'm a firebug. I always like to play with matches."

London said, "So long, Sam. Drop in some time."

Sam slipped quietly out of the tent and disappeared. London and Mac looked for a moment at the gently swaying tent-flap. London said, "I got a feelin' he ain't comin' back. Funny how you can get to like a mean man like that. Always got his chin stuck out, lookin' for trouble."

Jim had sat quietly on the mattress. His face was troubled. Through the tent walls the glow of the fire was still faintly visible, and now the shriek of sirens sounded, coming nearer and nearer, lonely and fierce in the night.

Mac said bitterly, "They gave it a good long time to get started before the trucks came out. Hell, we never did get anything to eat. Come on, London. I'll get some for you, Jim."

Jim sat waiting for them to come back. Lisa, beside him, was secretly nursing the baby under the blanket again. "Don't you ever move around?" Jim asked.

"Huh?"

"You just sit still. All these things go on around you, and you pay no attention. You don't even hear."

"I wisht it was over," she replied. "I wisht we lived in a house with a floor, an' a toilet close by. I don't like this fightin'."

"It's got to be done," Jim said. "It will be over sometime, but maybe not in our lives."

Mac came in carrying two steaming food cans. "Well, the fire trucks got there before it was all out, anyway. Here, Jim, I put the beef in with the beans. You take this one, Lisa."

Jim said, "Mac, you shouldn't've let Sam go."

"Why the hell shouldn't I?"

"Because you didn't feel right about it, Mac. You let your own personal hatred get in."

"Well, Jesus! Think of poor old Anderson, losing his barn and all his crop."

"Sure, I know. Maybe it's a good idea to burn Hunter's house. You got hot about it, though."

"Yeah? An' I guess you're goin' to be reportin' me, maybe. I bring you out to let you get some experience, an' you turn into a God-damn school teacher. Who th' hell do you think you are, anyway? I was doin' this job when you were slobberin' your bib."

"Now wait a minute, Mac. I can't do anything to help but use my head. Everything's going on, and I sit here with a sore shoulder. I just don't want you to get mad, Mac. You can't think if you get mad."

Mac glared sullenly at him. "You're lucky I don't knock your can off, not because you're wrong, but because you're right. You get sick of a guy that's always right." Suddenly he grinned. "It's done, Jim. Let's forget it. You're turning into a proper son-of-a-bitch. Everybody's going to hate you, but you'll be a good Party man. I know I get mad; I can't help it. I'm worried as hell, Jim. Everything's going wrong. Where you s'pose Doc is?"

"No sign of him yet? Remember what he said when he went out?"

"Said he was going to see Al."

"Yes, but before that, how lonely he was. He sounded screwy, like a guy that's worked too hard. Maybe he went off his nut. He never did believe in the cause, maybe he's scrammed."

Mac shook his head. "I've been around with Doc plenty. That's one thing he didn't do. Doc never ran out on anybody. I'm worried, Jim. Doc was headed for Anderson's. S'pose he took those raiders for our guards, an' they caught him?

They'd sure as hell catch him if they could."

"Maybe he'll be back later."

"Well, I'll tell you. If the health office gets out an order against us tomorrow, we can be damn sure that Doc was snatched. Poor devil! I don't know what to do about the man with the busted ankle. One of the guys set it, but he probably set it wrong. Oh, well, maybe Doc's just wanderin' around in the orchard. It's my fault for letting him start over there alone, all my fault. London's doing everything he can. I forget things. I'm getting a weight on me, Jim. Anderson's barn's right on top of me."

"You're forgetting the whole picture," Jim said.

Mac sighed. "I thought I was a tough baby, but you're a hell of a lot tougher. I hope I don't get to hate you. You better sleep in the hospital tent, Jim. There's an extra cot, and I don't want you sleeping on the ground until you feel better. Why don't you eat?"

Jim looked down at the can. "Forgot it, and I'm hungry, too." He picked up a piece of boiled beef out of the beans and gnawed it. "You better get some yourself," he said.

"Yeah, I'm going now."

After he had gone, Jim quickly ate the beans, the big oval, golden beans. He speared three of them at a time on a sharpened stick, and when they were gone tilted the can and drank the juice. "Tastes good, doesn't it," he said to Lisa.

"Yeah. I always like limey beans. Don't need nothing but salt. Salt pork's better."

"The men are quiet, awfully quiet."

"They got their mouths full," said the girl. "Always talkin', except their mouths' full. Always talkin'. If they got to fight, why don' they fight an' get it over, 'stead o' talkin'?"

"This is a strike," Jim said defensively.

"Even you talk all the time," she said. "Talk don't turn no wheel."

"Sometimes it gets steam up to turn 'em, Lisa."

London came in, and stood picking his teeth with a sharpened match. The bald spot in his tonsure shone dully in the lamplight. "I been watchin' all over the country," he said. "Ain't seen no fire yet. Mebbe they caught Sam."

"He was a clever guy," said Jim. "The other day he knocked over a checker, and the checker had a gun, too."

"Oh, he's smart all right. Smart like a snake. Sam's a rattlesnake, only he don't never rattle. He went out alone, didn't take nobody with him."

"All the better. If he gets caught, he's just a nut. If three guys got caught, it'd be a plot, see?"

"I hope he don't get caught, Jim. He's a nice guy, I like him."

"Yeah, I know."

Mac came back in with his can of food. "Jesus, I'm hungry. I didn't know it till I got the first bite. Have enough to eat, Jim?"

"Sure. Why don't the men build fires to sit by? They did last night."

"They got no wood," said London. "I made 'em put all the wood over by the stoves."

"Well, what makes 'em so quiet? You can hardly hear a thing," Jim said. "It's all quiet."

Mac mused, "It's damn funny about a bunch of men, how they act. You can't tell. I always thought if a guy watched close enough he might get to know what they're goin' to do. They get steamed up, an' then, all of a sudden, they're scared as hell. I think this whole damn camp is scared. Word's got out that Doc's been snatched. An' they're scared to be without 'im. They go an' take a look at the guy with the busted ankle, an' then they walk away. An' then, pretty soon, they go an' take a look at 'im again. He's all covered with sweat, he hurts so bad." Mac gnawed at a beef bone, tearing the white gristle with his teeth.

Jim asked, "D'you suppose anybody knows?"

"Knows what?"

"How a bunch o' guys'll act."

"Maybe London knows. He's been bossin' men all his life. How about it, London?"

London shook his head. "No," he said. "I've saw a bunch of guys run like rabbits when a truck backfired. Other times, seems like nothin' can scare 'em. Y'can kind of feel what's goin' to happen before it starts, though."

"I know," said Mac. "The air gets full of it. I saw a nigger lynched one time. They took him about a quarter of a mile to a railroad overpass. On th' way out that crowd killed a little dog, stoned it to death. Ever'body just picked up rocks. The air was just full of killin'. Then they wasn't satisfied to hang the nigger. They had to burn 'im an' shoot 'im, too."

"Well, I ain't lettin' nothin' like that get started in this camp," London said.

Mac advised, "Well, if it does start, you better stand out of the way. Listen, there's a sound."

There was a tramp of feet outside the tent, almost a military rhythm. "London in there?"

"Yeah. What do you want?"

"We got a guy out here."

"What kind of a guy?" A man came in, carrying a Winchester carbine. London said, "Ain't you one of the guys I left to guard that house?"

"Yes. Only three of us came over. We saw this fellow moving around, and we kind of got around him and caught him."

"Well, who is it?"

"I don't know. He had this gun. The guys wanted to beat hell out of him, but

I says we better bring him here, so we done it. We got him outside, tied up."

London looked at Mac, and Mac nodded toward Lisa. London said, "You better get out, Lisa."

She got slowly to her feet. "Where I'm goin' to go?"

"I don't know. Where's Joey?"

"Talkin' to a guy," said Lisa. "This guy wrote to a school that's goin' to get him to be a postman. Joey, he wants to be a postman too, so he's talkin' to this guy about it."

"Well, you go an' find some woman an' set with her."

Lisa shrugged up the baby on her hip and went out of the tent. London took the rifle from the man and threw down the lever. A loaded shell flipped out. "Thirty-thirty," said London. "Bring the guy in."

"O.K. Bring him in." Two guards pushed the prisoner through the flaps. He stumbled and recovered his balance. His elbows were bound together behind him with a belt, and his wrists were wrapped together with baling wire. He was very young. His body was thin and his shoulders narrow. He was dressed in corduroy trousers, a blue shirt and a short leather jacket. His light blue eyes were fixed with terror.

"Hell," said London. "It's a kid."

"Kid with a thirty-thirty," Mac added. "Can I talk to him, London?"

"Sure. Go ahead."

Mac stepped in front of the captive. "What are you doin' out there?"

The boy swallowed painfully. "I wasn't doing a thing." His voice was a whisper.

"Who sent you?"

"Nobody."

Mac struck him in the face with his open hand. The head jerked sideways, and an angry red spot formed on the white, beardless cheek. "Who sent you?"

"Nobody." The open hand struck again, harder. The boy lurched, tried to recover and fell on his shoulder.

Mac reached down and pulled him to his feet again. "Who sent you?"

The boy was crying. Tears rolled down his nose, into his bleeding mouth. "The fellows at school said we ought to."

"High school?"

"Yes. An' the men in the street said somebody ought to."

"How many of you came out?"

"Six of us."

"Where did the rest go?"

"I don't know, mister. Honest, I lost 'em."

Mac's voice was monotonous. "Who burned the barn?"

"I don't know." This time Mac struck with a closed fist. The blow flung the slight body against the tentpole. Mac jerked him up again. The boy's eye was closed and cut.

"Be careful about that 'don't know' business. Who burned the barn?"

The boy could not speak; his sobs choked him. "Don't hit me, mister. Some fellows at the pool room said it would be a good thing. They said Anderson was a radical."

"All right, now. Did you kids see anything of our doctor?"

The boy looked at him helplessly. "Don't hit me, mister. I don't know. We didn't see anybody."

"What were you going to do with the gun?"

"Sh—sh-shoot through the tents an' try to scare you."

Mac smiled coldly. He turned to London. "Got any ideas what to do with him?"

"Oh, hell," said London. "He's just a kid."

"Yes, a kid with a thirty-thirty. Can I still have him, London?"

"What do you want to do with him?"

"I want to send him back to high school so no more kids with rifles will come out."

Jim sat on the mattress and watched. Mac said, "Jim, you gave me hell about losing my head a little while ago. I'm not losing it now."

"It's O.K. if you're cold," said Jim.

"I'm a sharpshooter," Mac said. "You feeling sorry for the kid, Jim?"

"No, he's not a kid, he's an example."

"That's what I thought. Now listen, kid. We can throw you out to the guys there, but they'll probably kill you. Or we can work you over in here."

The one open eye glared with fear.

"O.K. with you, London?"

"Don't hurt him too much."

"I want a billboard," said Mac, "not a corpse. All right, kid. I guess you're for it." The boy tried to retreat. He bent down, trying to cower. Mac took him firmly by the shoulder. His right fist worked in quick, short hammerblows, one after another. The nose cracked flat, the other eye closed, and the dark bruises formed on the cheeks. The boy jerked about wildly to escape the short, precise strokes. Suddenly the torture stopped. "Untie him," Mac said. He wiped his bloody fist on the boy's leather jacket. "It didn't hurt much," he said. "You'll show up pretty in high school. Now shut up your bawling. Tell the kids in town what's waitin' for 'em."

"Shall I wash his face?" London asked.

"Hell, no! I do a surgeon's job, and you want to spoil it. You think I liked it?"

"I don't know," said London.

The prisoner's hands were free now. He sobbed softly. Mac said, "Listen to me, kid. You aren't hurt bad. Your nose is busted, but that's all. If anybody here but me did it, you'd of been hurt bad. Now you tell your little playmates that the next one gets his leg broke, and the next one after that gets both his legs broke. Get me——? I said, did you get me?"

"Yes."

"O.K. Take him down the road and turn him loose." The guards took the boy under the arms and helped him out of the tent. Mac said, "London, maybe you better put out patrols to see if there's any more kiddies with cannons."

"I'll do it," said London. He had kept his eyes on Mac the whole time, watching him with horror. "Jesus, you're a cruel bastard, Mac. I can unda'stand a guy gettin' mad an' doin' it, but you wasn't mad."

"I know," Mac said wearily. "That's the hardest part." He stood still, smiling his cold smile, until London went out of the tent; and then he walked to the mattress and sat down and clutched his knees. All over his body the muscles shuddered. His face was pale and grey. Jim put his good hand over and took him by the wrist. Mac said wearily, "I couldn't of done it if you weren't here, Jim. Oh, Jesus, you're hard-boiled. You just looked. You didn't give a damn."

Jim tightened his grip on Mac's wrist. "Don't worry about it," he said quietly. "It wasn't a scared kid, it was a danger to the cause. It had to be done, and you did it right. No hate, no feeling, just a job. Don't worry."

"If I could only of let his hands go, so he could take a pop at me once in a while, or cover up a little."

"Don't think of it," Jim said. "It's just a little part of the whole thing. Sympathy is as bad as fear. That was like a doctor's work. It was an operation, that's all. I'd done it for you if I wasn't bunged up. S'pose the guys outside had him?"

"I know," Mac agreed. "They'd butchered him. I hope they don't catch anybody else; I couldn't do it again."

"You'd have to do it again," said Jim.

Mac looked at him with something of

fear in his eyes. "You're getting beyond me, Jim. I'm getting scared of you. I've seen men like you before. I'm scared of 'em. Jesus, Jim, I can see you changing every day. I know you're right. Cold thought to fight madness, I know all that. God Almighty, Jim, it's not human. I'm scared of you."

Jim said softly, "I wanted you to use me. You wouldn't because you got to like me too well." He stood up and walked to a box and sat down on it. "That was wrong. Then I got hurt. And sitting here waiting, I got to know my power. I'm stronger than you, Mac. I'm stronger than anything in the world, because I'm going in a straight line. You and all the rest have to think of women and tobacco and liquor and keeping warm and fed." His eyes were as cold as wet river stones. "I wanted to be used. Now I'll use you, Mac. I'll use myself and you. I tell you, I feel there's strength in me."

"You're nuts," said Mac. "How's your arm feel? Any swelling? Maybe the poison got into your system."

"Don't think it, Mac," Jim said quietly. "I'm not crazy. This is real. It has been growing and growing. Now it's all here. Go out and tell London I want to see him. Tell him to come in here. I'll try not to make him mad, but he's got to take orders."

Mac said, "Jim, maybe you're not crazy. I don't know. But you've got to remember London is the chairman of this strike, elected. He's bossed men all his life. You start telling him what to do, and he'll throw you to the lions." He looked uneasily at Jim.

"Better go and tell him," said Jim.

"Now listen——"

"Mac, you want to obey. You better do it."

They heard a low wail, and then the rising scream of a siren, and then another and another, rising and falling, far away. "It's Sam," Mac cried. "He's set his fire."

Jim scrambled up. Mac said, "You better stay there. You're too weak, Jim."

Jim laughed mirthlessly. "You're going to find out how weak I am." He walked to the entrance and went out, and Mac followed him.

To the north the starred sky was black over the trees. In the direction of Torgas the city lights threw a pale glow into the sky. To the left of the town, over the high rampart of trees, the new fire put a dome of red light over itself. Now the sirens screamed together, and now one was up while another sunk its voice to a growl. "They don't waste any time now," Mac said.

The men came tumbling out of the tents and stood looking at the rising fire. The flames broke over the trees, and the dome of light spread and climbed. "A good start," Mac said. "If they put it out now, the house'll be ruined anyway. They can't use anything but chemicals out that far."

London hurried over to them. "He done it!" London cried. "Christ, he's a mean guy. I knew he'd do it. He wasn't scared of nothing."

Jim said calmly, "We can use him, if he comes back."

"Use him?" London asked.

"Yes, a man who could give a fire that good a start could do other things. It's burning fine. London, come into the tent. We've got to figure some things out."

Mac broke in, "What he means, London——"

"I'll tell him what I mean. Come into the tent, London." Jim led the way inside and seated himself on a box.

"What's the idear?" London demanded. "What's this you're talkin' about?"

Jim said, "This thing is being lost because there's no authority. Anderson's barn was burned because we couldn't trust the guards to obey orders. Doc got

snatched because his bodyguard wouldn't stick with him."

"Sure. An' what we goin' to do about it?"

"We're going to create authority," said Jim. "We're going to give orders that stick. The men elected you, didn't they? Now they've got to take it whether they like it or not."

Mac cried, "For Christ's sake, Jim! It won't work. They'll just fade out. They'll be in the next county in no time."

"We'll police 'em, Mac. Where's that rifle?"

"Over there. What do you want with it?"

"That's authority," said Jim. "I'm damn sick of this circle-running. I'm going to straighten it out."

London stepped up to him. "Say, what the hell is this 'I'm goin' to straighten things out'? You're goin' to jump in the lake."

Jim sat still. His young face was carven, his eyes motionless; his mouth smiled a little at the corners. He looked steadily and confidently at London. "Sit down, London, and put on your shirt," he said gently.

London looked uneasily at Mac. "Is this guy gone screwy?"

Mac missed his eyes. "I don't know."

"Might as well sit down," said Jim. "You will sooner or later."

"Sure, I'll sit down."

"O.K. Now you can kick me out of the camp if you want to. They'll make room for me in jail. Or you can let me stay. But if I stay, I'm going to put this over, and I can do it."

London sighed. "I'm sick of it. Nothin' but trouble. I'd give you the job in a minute, even if you ain't nothing but a kid. I'm the boss."

"That's why," Jim broke in. "I'll put out the orders through you. Don't get me wrong, London; it isn't authority I want, it's action. All I want is to put over the strike."

London asked helplessly, "What d'you think, Mac? What's this kid puttin' over?"

"I don't know. I thought it might be poison from that shot, but he seems to talk sense," Mac laughed, and his laugh dropped heavily into silence.

"The whole thing sounds kind of Bolshevik," London said.

"What do you care what it sounds like, if it works?" Jim replied. "You're ready to listen?"

"I don't know. Oh, sure, shoot."

"All right, tomorrow morning we're going to smack those scabs. I want you to pick the best fighters. Give the men clubs. I want two cars to go together, always in pairs. The cops'll probably patrol the roads, and put up barricades. Now we can't let 'em stop us. If they put up barricades, let the first car knock 'em off the road, and the second pick up the nen from the wreck and go on through. Understand? Anything we start goes through. If we don't succeed, we're farther back than when we started."

"I'm goin' to have a hell of a time with the guys if you give orders," London said.

"I don't want to give orders. I don't want to show off. The guys won't know. I'll tell you, and you tell them. Now the first thing is to send out some men to see how that fire's getting on. We're going to get a dose of trouble tomorrow. I wish Sam hadn't set it; but it's done now. We've got to have this camp plenty guarded tonight, too. There's going to be reprisals, and don't forget it. Put out two lines of guards and have them keep in touch. Then I want a police committee of five to beat hell out of any guy that goes to sleep or sneaks away. Get me five tough ones."

London shook his head. "I don't know if I ought to smack you down or let you go ahead. The whole thing's so damn much trouble."

"Well, put out guards while you think it over. I'm afraid we're going to have plenty of trouble before morning."

"O.K., kid. I'll give it a try."

After he had gone out, Mac still stood beside the box where Jim sat. "How's your arm feel, Jim?" he asked.

"I can't feel it at all. Must be about well."

"I don't know what's happened to you," Mac went on. "I could feel it happen."

Jim said, "It's something that grows out of a fight like this. Suddenly you feel the great forces at work that create little troubles like this strike of ours. And the sight of those forces does something to you, picks you up and makes you act. I guess that's where authority comes from." He raised his eyes.

Mac cried, "What makes your eyes jump like that?"

"A little dizzy," Jim said, and he fainted and fell off the box.

Mac dragged him to the mattress and brought a box for his feet. In the camp there was a low murmur of voices, constant and varying and changing tone like the voice of a little stream. Men passed back and forth in front of the tent. The sirens raised their voices again, but this time there was no excitement in them, for the trucks were going home. Mac unbuttoned Jim's shirt. He brought a bucket of water that stood in a corner of the tent, and splashed water on Jim's head and throat.

Jim opened his eyes and looked up into Mac's face. "I'm dizzy," he said plaintively. "I wish Doc would come back and give me something. Do you think he'll come back, Mac?"

"I don't know. How do you feel now?"

"Just dizzy. I guess I've shot my wad until I rest."

"Sure. You ought to go to sleep. I'm

going out and try to rustle some of the soup that meat was cooked in. That'll be good for you. You just lie still until I bring it."

When he was gone, Jim looked, frowning, at the top of the tent. He said aloud, "I wonder if it passed off. I don't think it did, but maybe." And then his eyes closed, and he went to sleep.

When Mac came in with the soup, he set it on the ground. He took the box from under Jim's legs and then sat down on the edge of the mattress and watched the drawn, sleeping face.

The face was never still. The lips crept back until the teeth were exposed, until the teeth were dry; and then the lips drew down and covered them. The cheeks around the eyes twitched nervously. Once, as though striving against weight, Jim's lips opened to speak and worked on a word, but only a growling mumble was said. Mac pulled the old coverlets over Jim's body.

Suddenly the lamp flame was sucked down, the wick and darkness crept in toward the center of the tent. Mac jumped up and found a spout-can of kerosene. He unscrewed the lantern cap and filled the reservoir. Slowly the flame grew up again, and its edges spread out like a butterfly's wings.

Outside, the slow footsteps of patrolling men went by. In the distance there could be heard the grumble of the great night cargo trucks on the highway. Mac took down the lantern from the tent-pole and carried it to the mattress and set it on the ground. From his hip pocket he brought out a packet of folded papers and a mussy stamped envelope and a broken piece of pencil. With the paper on his knee he wrote slowly, in large, round letters:

Dear Harry:
    Christ sake get some help down

here. Doc Burton was snatched last night. I think he was. Doc was not a man to run out on us, but he is gone. This valley is organized like Italy. The vigilantes are raising hell. We need food and medicine and money. Dick is doing fine, only if we don't get some outside help I am afraid we are sunk. I never ran into a place that was so God damn organized. About three men control the situation. For all I know Dick may be in the can now.

Jim is sure coming through. He makes me look like a pin. Tomorrow I expect that we will get kicked out of this place. The V's. burned the owner's barn, and he is awfully sore. With Doc Burton gone, the county health officers will bounce us. So try to think of something. They are after Jim's and my scalp all the time. There ought to be somebody down here in case they get us.

I am howling for help, Harry. The sympathizers are scared, but that's not the worst.

He picked up a new piece of paper.

The men are touchy. You know how they get. Tomorrow morning they might go down and burn the city hall, or they might bolt for the mountains and hide for six months. So for Christ's sake, Harry, tell everybody we have to have help. If they run us out of here, we'll have trouble finding a spot. We are going to picket in trucks. We can't find out much that's going on.

Well, so long. Jack will hand this to you. And for the love of God try to get some help here.

                                              Mac

He read the letter over, crossed a neglected t, folded the paper and put it in the dirty envelope. This he addressed to John H. Weaver, *esq*.

Outside he heard a challenge. "Who is it?"

"London."

"O.K."

London came into the tent. He looked at Mac, and at the sleeping Jim. "Well, I got the guards out like he said."

"That's good. He's all in. I wish Doc was here. I'm scared of that shoulder. He says it don't hurt, but he's a fool for punishment." Mac turned the lantern back to the tentpole and hung it on its nail.

London sat down on a box. "What got into him?" he asked softly. "One minute he's a blabber-mouth kid, and the next minute, by Christ, he just boots me out and takes over."

Mac's eyes were proud. "I don't know. I've saw guys get out of theirself before, but not like that. Jesus, you *had* to do what he said. At first I thought he was off his nut. I still don't know if he was. Where's the girl, London?"

"I bedded her and my kid down in an empty tent."

Mac looked up sharply. "Where did you get an empty tent?"

"Some of the guys scrammed, I guess, in the dark."

"Maybe it's only the guards."

"No," London said. "I figured on them. I guess some of the guys run off."

Mac rubbed his eyes hard with his knuckles. "I thought it was about time. Some of 'em just can't take it. Listen, London, I got to sneak in an' try to get a letter in the mailbox. I want to take a look around, too."

"Whyn't you let me send one of the guys?"

"Well, this letter's got to get there. I better go myself. I been watched before. They won't catch me."

London regarded his thick hands. "Is—is it a *red* letter?" he asked.

"Well, I guess so. I'm trying to get some help, so this strike won't flop."

London spoke constrainedly. "Mac—like I said, you always hear about reds is a bunch of son-of-bitches. I guess that ain't true, is it, Mac?"

Mac chuckled softly. "Depends on how you look at it. If you was to own thirty thousand acres of land and a million dollars, they'd be a bunch of sons-of-bitches. But if you're just London, a workin' stiff, why they're a bunch of guys that want to help you live like a man, and not like a pig, see? 'Course you get your news from the papers, an' the papers is owned by the guys with land and money, so we're sons-of-bitches, see? Then you come acrost us, an' we ain't. You got to make up your own mind which it is."

"Well, could a guy like I work in with you guys? I been doin' kind o' like that, lookin' out for the guys that travel with me."

"Damn right," said Mac eagerly. "You're damn right. You got leadership, London. You're a workin' stiff, but you're a leader, too."

London said simply, "Guys always done what I told 'em. All my life they done it."

Mac lowered his voice. He moved close and put his hand on London's knee. "Listen," he said. "I guess we're goin' to lose this strike. But we raised enough hell so maybe there won't be a strike in the cotton. Now the papers say we're just causing trouble. But we're getting the stiffs used to working together; getting bigger and bigger bunches working together all the time, see? It doesn't make any difference if we lose. Here's nearly a thousand men who've learned how to strike. When we get a whole slough of men working together, maybe—maybe Torgas Valley, most of it, won't be owned by three men. Maybe a guy can get an apple for himself without going to jail for it, see? Maybe they won't dump apples in the river to keep up the price. When guys like you and me need a apple to keep our God-damn bowels open, see? You've got to look at the whole thing, London, not just this little strike."

London was staring painfully at Mac's mouth, as though he tried to see the words as they came out. "That's kind of reva—revolution, ain't it?"

"Sure it is. It's a revolution against hunger and cold. The three guys that own this valley are going to raise hell to keep that land, and to keep dumping the apples to raise the price. A guy that thinks food ought to be eaten is a God-damned red. D'you see that?"

London's eyes were wide and dreaming. "I heard a lot of radical guys talkin'," he said. "Never paid much attention. They always got mad. I ain't got no faith in a mad guy. I never seen it the way you say it before, never."

"Well, keep on seeing it, London. It'll make you feel different. They say we play dirty, work underground. Did you ever think, London? We've got no guns. If anything happens to us, it don't get in the newspapers. But if anything happens to the other side, Jesus, they smear it in ink. We've got no money, and no weapons, so we've got to use our heads, London. See that? It's like a man with a club fighting a squad with machine-guns. The only way he can do it is to sneak up and smack the gunners from behind. Maybe that isn't fair, but hell, London, this isn't any athletic contest. There aren't any rules a hungry man has to follow."

"I never seen it," London said slowly. "Nobody never took time out to tell me. I like to see some of the guys that talk nice an' quiet. Always, when I hear them, they're mad. 'God damn the cops,' they say. 'T'hell with the government.' They're goin' to burn down the govern-ment buildings. I don't like that, all them nice buildings. Nobody never told me about that other."

"They didn't use their heads, then," said Mac.

"Mac, you said you guessed we'd lose this strike. What makes you think like that?"

Mac considered. "No—" he said, as though to himself. "You wouldn't pull out now. I'll tell you why, London. Power in this valley is in very few hands. The guy that came out yesterday was trying to get us to quit. But now they know we won't quit. The only thing left is to drive us out or to kill us off. We could stand 'em off a while if we had food and a doctor, and if Anderson would back us up. But Anderson's sore. They'll kick us out if they have to use cannons. Once they get a court order, they'll kick us right out. Then where are we going to go? Can't jungle up, because there'll be ordinances. They'll split us up, an' beat us that way. Our guys aren't any too strong as it is. I'm afraid we can't get any more stuff to eat."

London said, "Whyn't we just tell the guys to beat it, an' the whole bunch of us get out?"

"Don't talk so loud. You'll wake up the kid. Here's why. They can scare our guys, but we can throw a scare into them, too. We'll take one last shot at them. We'll hang on as long as we can. If they kill some of us the news'll get around even if the papers don't print it. Other guys'll get sore. And we've got an enemy, see? Guys work together nice when they've got an enemy. That barn was burned down by our own kind of men, but they've been reading the papers, see? We've got to get 'em over on our side as quick as we can." He took out a slim, limp bag of tobacco. "I've been saving this. I want a smoke. You smoke, London?"

"No. I chew when I can get it."

Mac rolled himself a slender cigarette in the brown paper. He raised the lantern chimney to light the cigarette. "You ought to get in a nap, London. Christ knows what's going to happen tonight. I've *got* to go in town and find a mailbox."

"You might get caught."

"No, I won't. I'll go in through the orchards. I won't even get seen." He stared past London, at the back of the tent. London swung around. The tent wall bellied up from the bottom, and Sam wriggled in, and stood up. He was muddy, and his clothes were torn. A long cut extended down his lean cheek. His lips were drawn back with fatigue, and his eyes were sunken.

"I on'y got a minute," he said softly. "Jesus, what a job! You got a lot of guards out. I didn't want nobody to see me. Somebody'd double-cross us sure."

"You done it nice," Mac said. "We seen the fire."

"Sure. Damn near the whole house gone. But that ain't it." He looked nervously at Jim, sleeping on the mattress. "I—got caught."

"Th' hell!"

"Yeah, they grabbed me and got a look at me."

"You oughtn't to be here," London said severely.

"I know. I wanted to tell you, though. You ain't never seen me or heard of me. I had to—I kicked his brains out. I got to go now. If they get me again, I don't want nothing, see? I'm nuts, see? I'm screwy. I talk about God told me to do it, see? I wanted to tell you. Don't take no risk for me. I don't want it."

London went over to him and took his hand. "You're a good guy, Sam. They don't make 'em no better. I'll see you sometime."

Mac had his eye on the tent-flap. He said very quietly, over his shoulder, "If you get to town, forty-two Center Ave-

nue. Say Mabel sent you. It's only a meal. Don't go more than once."

"O.K., Mac. G'bye." He was on his knees, with his head out, looking into the dark. In a second he squirmed out, and canvas dropped back into place.

London sighed. "I hope he makes it, Mac. He's a good guy. They don't make 'em no better."

Mac said, "Don't give it a thought. Somebody'll kill him sometime, like that little guy, Joy. He was sure to get popped off. Me an' Jim'll go that way, sooner or later. It's almost sure, but it doesn't make any difference."

London's mouth was open. "Jesus, what a hell of a way to look at it. Don't you guys get no pleasure?"

"Damn right," said Mac. "More than most people do. It's an important job. You get a hell of a drive out of something that has some meaning to it, and don't you forget it. The thing that takes the heart out of a man is work that doesn't lead any place. Ours is slow, but it's all going in one direction. Christ, I stand here shooting off my face. I've got to go."

"Don't let 'em get you, Mac."

"I won't, but listen, London, there's nothing those guys would like better than to rub me and Jim out. I can take care of myself. Will you stay right here and not let anything happen to Jim? Will you?"

"Sure I will. I'll set right here."

"No, lie down on part of the mattress and get some sleep. But don't let 'em get the kid. We need him, he's valuable."

"O.K."

"So long," said Mac. "I'll get back as soon as I can. I'd like to find out what's going on. Maybe I can get a paper."

"So long."

Mac went silently out of the doorway. London heard him speak to a guard, and then, farther off, to another. Even after he was gone, London listened to the sounds of the night. It was quiet outside, but there was no feeling of sleep. The footsteps of the prowling guards came and went, and their voices sounded in short greetings when they met. The roosters crowed, one near, and far away the deep voice of an old, wise cock— train bell and spurt of steam and pounding of a starting engine. London sat down on the mattress, beside Jim, one folded leg flat, and the other standing up and clasped between his hands. He bowed his head over his knee and rested his chin, and his eyes questioned Jim and probed him.

Jim moved restlessly. One arm flung out and dropped again. He said, "Oh— and—water." He breathed heavily. "Tar over everything." His eyes opened and blinked quickly, sightlessly. London unclasped his hands as though to touch Jim, but he didn't touch him. The eyes closed and were quiet. A great transport truck rumbled into hearing. London heard a muffled cry outside the tent, some distance away. "Hey," he cried softly.

One of the patrol came up. "What's the matter, boss?"

"Well, who's doin' the yellin'?"

"That? Didn't you hear that before? That's the old guy with the busted hip. He's crazy. They're holdin' him down. Fightin' like a cat, an' bitin'. They got a rag in his mouth."

"Ain't you Jake Pedroni? Sure you are. Look, Jake, I heard Doc say if the old guy didn't get soap and water up him to keep him cleared out, he'd get like that. I got to stay here. You go over and get it done, will you, Jake?"

"Sure, boss."

"O.K. Get along. It ain't doin' his hip no good to fight. How's the guy with the busted ankle?"

"Oh, him. Somebody give 'im a slug of whiskey. He's O.K."

"Call me if anything happens, Jake."

"All right, I will."

London went back to the mattress and lay down beside Jim. Far away, the engine pounded, faster and faster in the night. The old tough rooster crowed first, and the young one answered. London felt heavy sleep creeping into his brain, but he rose up on his elbow and looked at Jim once more before he let the sleep wash over him.

14

The dark was just beginning to thin when Mac looked into the tent. On the central post the lantern still burned. London and Jim were sleeping, side by side. Mac stepped in, and as he did London jerked upright and peered about. "Who is it?"

"Me," said Mac. "Just got in. How's the kid?"

"I been asleep," said London. He yawned and scratched the round bald spot on his head.

Mac stepped over and looked down at Jim. The tired lines were gone out of the boy's face, and the nervous muscles were relaxed. "He looks fine. He got a good rest."

London stood up. "What time is it?"

"I don't know. It's just starting to get light."

"The guys building the fires yet?"

"I saw somebody moving around over there. I smelled wood smoke. It might be Anderson's barn smouldering."

"I didn't leave the kid a minute," said London.

"Good for you."

"When you goin' to get some sleep?"

"Oh, Christ knows. I don't feel it much yet. I got some last night, or rather the night before, it was. Seems a week ago. We just buried Joy yesterday, just yesterday."

London yawned again. "I guess it's

beef and beans this morning. God, I'd like a cup of coffee!"

"Well, let's go in and get coffee and ham and eggs in town."

"Oh, go to hell. I'm goin' to get them cooks movin'." He stumbled sleepily outside.

Mac pulled a box under the light and took a rolled newspaper out of his pocket. As he opened it, Jim said, "I've been awake, Mac. Where have you been?"

"Had to go mail a letter. I picked a paper off a lawn. We'll see what's going on."

"Mac, did I make a horse's ass of myself last night?"

"Hell, no, Jim. You made it stick. You had us eating out of your hand."

"It just came over me. I never felt that way before."

"How do you feel this morning?"

"Fine. But not like that. I could of lifted a cow last night."

"Well, you sure lifted us around. That's a good gag about the two trucks, too. The owner of the car that has to bust the barricade may not like it much. Now let's see what's going on in town. Oh—oh, headlines for the scrapbook! Listen, Jim:

STRIKERS BURN HOUSES—
KILL MEN!

Last night at ten o'clock fire destroyed the suburban home of William Hunter. Police say the men now on strike from the apple orchards are responsible. A suspect, captured, assaulted his captor and escaped. The injured man, Olaf Bingham, special deputy, is not expected to live.

Now let's see, farther down:—

Earlier in the evening strikers, either through carelessness or malice, burned the barn on the Anderson farm. Mr. Anderson had previously given the men permission to camp on his land.

It's a long story, Jim. You can read it if you want to." He turned the page. "Oh boy, oh boy. Listen to this editorial:

We believe the time has come to take action. When transient laborers tie up the Valley's most important industry, when fruit tramps, led and inspired by paid foreign agitators (That's us, Jim), carry on a campaign of violence and burning, bringing Red Russia into peaceful America, when our highways are no longer safe for American citizens, nor their homes safe from firebrands, we believe the time for action has come!

This county takes care of its own people, but these strikers do not belong here. They flout the laws, and destroy life and property. They are living on the fat of the land, supplied by secret sympathizers. This paper does not, and has never believed in violence; but it does believe that when law is not sufficient to cope with these malcontents and murderers, an aroused citizenry must take a hand. The incendiary deserves no mercy. We must drive out these paid trouble-makers. This paper recommends that citizens inquire into the sources of luxuries these men have been given. It is reported that three prime steers were slaughtered in their camp yesterday."

Mac smashed the paper down on the ground. "And that last means that tonight a flock of pool-room Americans will start slinging rocks through the windows of poor devils who said they wished times might get better."

Jim was sitting up. "Jesus Christ, Mac! Do we have to take all the blame?"

"Every damn bit."

"How about that guy they say was murdered."

"Well, Sam did it. They caught him. He had to get away. The guy had a gun; all Sam had was his feet."

Jim lay back again. "Yeah," he said. "I saw him use his feet the other day. But God, it sounds bad. Sounds awful!"

"Sure. That editor used some dollar-an'-a-half words, all right. 'Paid foreign agitators.' Me, born in Minneapolis! An' granpaw fought in the Battle of Bull Run. He always said he thought it was a bull-fight instead of a battle he was goin' to till they started shootin' at him. An' you're about as foreign as the Hoover administration. Oh, hell, Jim. That's the way it always is. But—" he brought out the last of his tobacco—"it's closing in, Jim. Sam shouldn't of set that fire."

"You told him to go ahead."

"I know, I was mad about the barn."

"Well, what do we do now?"

"Just go ahead, just go ahead. We start those cars out at the scabs. We keep it up as long as we can fight, and then we get away, if we can. Are you scared, Jim?"

"N-no-o."

"It's closing in on us, Jim. I can feel it, closing in." He got up from his box and walked to the mattress and sat down. "Maybe it's because I need sleep. On the way out from town just now it seemed to me there was a bunch of guys waiting for me in the shadow under every tree. I got so scared, I'd of run if a mouse moved."

"You're all tired," Jim said gently. "Maybe I could of been some use around here, if I hadn't got myself hurt. I just lie around, and get in the way."

Mac said, "The hell you do. Every time I get low you steam me up, and, baby, I need steam this morning. My guts are just water! I'd take a drink if I could get it."

"You'll be all right when you get something to eat."

Mac said, "I wrote to Harry Nilson; told him we had to have help and supplies. But I'm afraid it's too late." He stared strangely at Jim. "Listen, Jim, I found Dick last night. Now you listen close. Remember the night we came in?"

"Sure."

"Well, you remember when we turned left at that bridge and went to the jungle?"

"Yeah."

"Well, listen close. If hell should pop and we get separated, you get to that bridge and go underneath, clear up under the arch, on the side away from town. You'll find a pile of dead willows there. Lift 'em aside. There's a deep cave underneath. Get inside, and pull the willows over the hole. You can go in about fifteen feet, see? Now Dick's putting blankets in there, an' canned goods. If they dynamite us, you go there an' wait for me a couple o' days. If I don't come, you'll know something's happened to me. You get back to town. Travel at night till you're clear of this county. They've got nothing on us that'll get us more than six months unless they pad up a murder charge about that guy last night. I don't think they will, because it'd be too much publicity. I.L.D.'d come through and break that upstairs shooting of Joy. Now will you remember, Jim? Go there and wait for a couple of days. I don't think they'll root you out of there."

Jim asked, "What do you know, Mac? You're keeping something back."

"I don't know a thing," Mac said. "I've just got a feeling this joint's closing in on us—just a feeling. A lot of the guys took it on the lam last night, mostly the guys with women and kids. London's O.K. He'll be a Party member pretty soon. But right now I wouldn't trust the rest of these guys with a road-apple at a banquet. They're so God-damn jumpy they might knife us themselves."

"You're jumpy yourself, Mac. Calm

down." Jim got to his knees and stood carefully up, his head cocked as though he listened for pain. Mac watched him in alarm. "It's swell," said Jim. "Shoulder's a little bit heavy, but I feel swell. Not even light-headed. I ought to get around some today."

"That bandage ought to be changed," said Mac.

"Oh, yeah, say, did Doc come back?"

"No, I guess they got him. What a nice guy he was."

"Was?"

"No. I hope not. Maybe they'd only beat hell out of him. But so many of our guys just disappear and never show up again."

"You're a fine, happy influence," said Jim.

"I know. If I wasn't sure you could take it, I'd shut up. Makes me feel better to get it off my chest. I want a cup of coffee so bad I could bust into tears. Just think of all the coffee we used to have in town. Three cups if we wanted. All we wanted."

Jim said sternly, "Maybe a little bit of that might be good for you. You better pull up now. You'll get feeling sorry for yourself."

Mac tightened his loose face. "O.K., kid. I'm all right now. You want to go outside? Can you walk all right?"

"Sure I can."

"Well, blow out that lantern. We'll go see about some beef and beans."

The shade screeched when Jim raised it. The dawn grey leapt into the tent, grey like a wash of ink. Jim lifted the tent-flaps and tied them back. "Let's air this place out," he said. "It's getting strong. The whole damn bunch of us could do with a bath."

Mac agreed. "I'll try to get a bucket of warm water, and we'll sponge off after we eat."

The dawn had come into the sky. The trees were still black against the light east, and a colony of crows, flapping eastward, were etched heavily against it. Under the trees a dusk still held, and the earth was dark, as though the light had to be sucked in slowly. Now that they could see, the guards had given up their pacing. They stood in tired groups, hands in pockets, coats turned up and buttoned over their throats. And they talked in the soft monotone of men who only talk to stay awake.

Mac and Jim approached a group of them on their way to the stove. "Anything happen last night?" Mac asked.

Talk stopped. The men looked at him with weary, blood-shot eyes. "Not a thing, buddy. Frank was just sayin'—sayin' he had a feelin' there was people movin' around all night. I had that feelin' too, just creepin' around; but we didn't hear nothing. We went around two together."

Mac laughed, and his voice seemed to penetrate deep into the air. "I was in the army," he said, "trained in Texas. By Christ, when I'd go on guard duty I could hear Germans all around me, could hear 'em whispering in German." The men chuckled softly, without amusement.

One said, "London told us we could sleep today. Soon's I get somethin' in my stomach, I'm goin' to roll in."

"Me too. Roll right in. I got gravel in my skin, like a hop-head. Ever seen a hop-head when he's got bugs in his skin? Make you laugh to watch him."

Mac asked, "Whyn't you come over to the stoves an' warm up?"

"Well, we was just talkin' about doin' that."

Jim said, "I'm going down to the can, Mac. See you over at the stove." He walked down the line of tents, and each tent was a little cave of darkness. Snores came from some, and in the entrances of others men lay on their stomachs and looked out at the morning, and their eyes were full of the inwardness of sleep. As he walked along, some men came into the air and hunched their shoulders and drew down their necks against the cold. He heard an irritable, sleepy voice of a woman detailing how she felt. "I want to get out o' this dump. What good we doin' here? An' I got a lump in my stomach big's your fist. It's a cancer, that's what it is. Card-reader tol' me two years ago I'd get a cancer if I din' watch out. Said I was the cancer type. Sleepin' on the ground, eatin' garbage." An inaudible grumble answered.

As Jim passed another tent, a tousled head stuck out. "Come on in quick, kid. He's gone."

"Can't," said Jim.

Two tents down a man kneeling on his blanket said, "Got the time, buddy?"

"No. Must be after six, I guess, though."

"I heard her give you the come-on. God damn lucky you didn't go. She's caused more trouble in this camp'n the scabs. They ought to run her out. Gets ever'body fightin'. They got a fire goin' over there?"

"Yes," said Jim. He passed out from between the row of tents. Fifteen yards away, in the open, stood the square canvas screen. Inside there was a two-by-four supported at each end, over a hole. There was room on the board for three men. Jim picked up a box of chloride of lime and shook it, but it was empty. One man sat hunched up on the board. "Sompin' ought to be done about it," he said. "Where in hell is 'at doctor? He ain't done nothing about it since yesterday."

"Maybe we could shovel in a little dirt," said Jim. "That'd help."

"It ain't my business. That doctor ought to do sompin' about it. The guys are liable t'get sick."

Jim's voice was angry. "Guys like you that won't do anything damn well de-

serve to get sick." He kicked dirt into the hole with the side of his foot.

"You're a smart punk, ain't you?" the man said. "Wait till you been around a little and got dry behind the ears, 'n'en maybe you'll know sompin'."

"I know enough right now to know you're a lazy bastard."

"You wait till I get my pants up; I'll show you who's a lazy bastard." But he made no move.

Jim looked down at the ground. "I can't take you on. I'm shot in the shoulder."

"Sure, an' when you know you're safe from a sportin' man, you miscall a man. You lousy punks got sompin' comin' to you."

Jim controlled his voice. "I didn't mean to miscall you, mister. I wouldn't fight you. We got all the fighting to do we can take care of, without fighting each other."

"Well, now, that's better," said the man. "I'll he'p you kick some dirt in when I get through. What's goin' on today? You know?"

Jim began, "We're——" and then he remembered. "Damn' if I know. I guess London'll tell us when he gets ready."

"London ain't done nothing yet," said the man. "Hey, don't sit so near the middle. You're liable to break that two-by-four. Get over near the edge. London ain't done nothing. Just walks around lookin' big. Know what a guy told me? London's got cases an' cases of can' goods in his tent—ever'thing. Corn-beef, an' sardines, an' can' peaches. He won't eat what us poor stiffs got to eat, not him. He's too God-damned good."

"And that's a God-damn lie," said Jim.

"Got smart again, have you? There's plenty guys seen them can' goods. How do you know it's a lie?"

"Because I've been in that tent. He let me sleep in there last night because I was hurt. There's an old mattress and two empty boxes in that tent, and not another damn thing."

"Well, a whole slough o' guys says there's can' peaches an' sardines in there. Some of the boys was goin' to bust in an' get some last night."

Jim laughed hopelessly. "Oh, Jesus, what a bunch of swine! You get a good man, and you start picking him to pieces."

"There you go, miscalling guys again. Wait'll you get well an' somebody's goin' to slap that smart puss right off you."

Jim got up from the plank and buttoned his jeans and went outside. The short stove-pipes of the cook stoves puffed grey smoke into the air, still, straight columns that went up fifty feet before they mushroomed at the top and spread out evenly. The eastern sky was yellow now, and the sky overhead had turned eggshell-blue. From the tents men came rapidly. The awakening silence of the camp was replaced with the rustling footsteps, the voices, the movement of people.

A dark-haired woman stood in front of a tent, her head thrown back; and her throat was white. She combed her hair with long, beautiful sweeps of her arm. When Jim walked by she smiled wisely and said, "Good morning," and the combing didn't pause. Jim stopped. "No," she said. "Only good morning."

"You make me feel good," he said. For a moment he looked at the long white throat and the sharply defined jaws. "Good morning again," he said, and he saw her lips form to a line of deep and delicious understanding. And when he passed along, and the tousled head darted out and the husky voice whispered, "Come on in, quick, he's gone now," Jim only glanced, and went quickly on without responding.

Men were gathering about the old stoves, stretching their hands to the warmth, waiting patiently until the beef and beans in the big wash-boilers should be hot. Jim stepped to a water-barrel and dipped some water into a tin basin. He threw the cold water into his face, and into his hair, and he rubbed his hands together without soap. He let the water cling in drops to his face.

Mac saw him and walked over, holding out a food can. "I rinsed it out," he said. "What's the matter, Jim? You look tickled to death."

"I saw a woman——"

"You couldn't. Didn't have time."

"I just *saw* her," said Jim. "She was combing her hair. It's a funny thing—sometimes a person gets into an ordinary position, and it seems wonderful, it just stays in your mind all your life."

"If I saw a decent-looking woman, I'd go nuts," said Mac.

Jim looked down into the empty can. "She had her head back. She was combing her hair—she had a funny kind of a smile on her face. You know, Mac, my mother was a Catholic. She didn't go to church Sunday because my old man hated churches as bad as we do. But in the middle of the week, sometimes, she'd go into the church when my old man was working. When I was a little kid she took me in sometimes, too. The smile on that woman—that's why I'm telling you this—— Well, there was a Mary in there, and she had the same kind of smile, wise and cool and sure. One time I asked my mother why she smiled like that. My mother said, 'She can smile because she's in Heaven.' I think she was jealous, a little." His voice tumbled on, "And one time I was there, looking at that Mary, and I saw a ring of little stars in the air, over her head, going around and around, like little birds. Really saw them, I mean. It's not funny, Mac. This isn't religion—it's kind of what the books I've read call wish-fulfillment, I guess. I saw them, all right. They made me feel happy, too. My old man would have been sore if he knew. He never took any position that lasted. Everything was wasted in him."

Mac said, "You're going to be a great talker some time, Jim. You got a kind of a persuasive tone. Jesus, just now you made me think it'd be nice to sit in church. Nice! That's good talking. If you can talk guys over to our side, you'll be good." He took a little clean tin can that hung on a nail on the side of the water-barrel, and he filled the can and drank from it. "Let's go over and see if the slum is hot."

The men were forming in a line, and as they passed the stoves, the cooks ladled lima beans and lumps of boiled beef into the cans. Mac and Jim got on the end of the line and eventually passed the boilers. "Is that all the food?" Mac asked a cook.

"There's beans and beef enough for one more meal. We're out of salt, though. We need more salt."

They drifted along, eating as they went. A lance of sunlight shot over the trees and fell on the ground of the clear-ing, fell on the tents and made them seem less dingy. At the line of old cars London was talking to a group of men. "Let's see what's doing," Mac suggested. They walked toward the road, where the old cars stood. A light rust was settling on radiators, and some of the worn tires were down, and all of the cars had the appearance of having stood there a long while.

London saluted with a wave of his hand. "Hello, Mac. H'ya, Jim?"

"Fine," said Jim.

"Me and these guys is lookin' over the heaps. Tryin' to see which ones to send out. There ain't none of 'em worth a hoot in hell."

"How many'd you figure to send out?"

" 'Bout five couples. Two together, so if anything went wrong with one the other'd pick our guys up and go on." He pointed down the line. "That old Hud-

son's all right. There's five four-cylinder Dodges, and them old babies will go to hell on their bellies after you knock the wheels off. My model T's all right—runs, anyway. Let's see, we don't want no closed cars; y'can't heave a rock out of a closed car. Here's a shovel-nose. Think she'll run?"

A man stepped up. "Damn right she'll run. I brung her straight through Louisi-ana in winter. She never even warmed up, even comin' over the mountains."

They walked down the row, picking out prospects in the line of wrecks. "These guys is squad leaders," London explained. "I'm goin' give one of 'em charge of each bus, an' let 'em pick their own guys, five or six apiece. Guys they can trust, good fighters, see?"

"Sounds swell," said Mac. "I don't see how anybody's goin' to stop 'em."

One of the men turned on him. "And they *ain't* nobody goin' to stop us, neither," he said.

"Feelin' pretty tough, huh?"

"Just give us a show, an' see."

Mac said, "We'll walk around a little bit, London."

"Oh, wait a minute, the guys come back from Anderson's a little while ago. They say Anderson cussed 'em all night. An' this mornin' he started in town, still cussin'."

"Well, I thought he would. How about Al?"

"Al?"

"Yeah, Anderson's boy, the one that got smacked."

"Well, the guys went in an' seen him. He wanted to come over here, but they didn't want to move him. Couple guys stayed with him."

London stepped close and lowered his voice so the other men could not hear. "Where do you think Anderson's goin', Mac?"

"I guess he's goin' in town to put in a complaint and get us kicked off. He'll probably claim we burned his barn now. He's so scared he'll do anything to get in good with the other side."

"Uh-huh. Think we ought to fight here?"

"I'll tell you how I think it'll be," said Mac. "I think first they might send out a few guys to try to scare us off. We'll stand up to 'em. After that, they'll come out with a mob. We'll see how our guys feel. If they're sore and mean, we'll fight. But if they look yellow, we'll clear out, if we can." He tapped London on the shoulder. "If that happens, you and me and Jim have to go quick and far. That mob's going to want a chicken to kill, and they won't care much who it is."

London called to the men, "Drain the gas out of all the tanks, and put it in them cars we picked out. Start up the motors 'n' see if they're all right, but don't waste no gas." He turned back. "I'll walk along. I want to talk this out. What you think about our guys? Them babies over by the heaps'll fight. How about the others?"

Mac said, "If I could tell in advance what a bunch of guys'd do, I'd be president. Some things I do know, though. A smell of blood seems to steam 'em up. Let 'em kill somethin', even a cat, an' they'll want to go right on killin'. If there's a fight, an' our guys get first blood, they'll put up a hell of a battle. But if we lose a man first, I wouldn't be surprised to see them hit for the trees."

"I know," London agreed. "Take one guy that you know ever'thing about him, an' take ten more the same, an' you can't tell what in hell they'll do. What you think of doin'? Just waitin' to see?"

"That's it," said Mac. "When you're used to mobs, you can tell, just a little bit ahead of time. You can feel it in the air. But remember, if our guys crack, get under somethin', an' stay there. Listen, under the Torgas River bridge there's a

dug-out covered with dead willows. It's got food and blankets in it. That's the place to hit for. A mob don't stay crazy long. When you get in town, go to forty-two Center Avenue and say I sent you."

"I wish they was some way to get the kid and Lisa out. I don't want 'em to get hurt."

Jim broke in on them. "You guys talk like it was sure to happen. Nothing's happened yet, maybe nothing will. Maybe Anderson only went in to stay with somebody."

"I know it sounds like I'm calamity-howling," Mac said apologetically. "Maybe it won't happen. But London's a valuable guy. We need him. I don't like to get these stiffs killed off; they're good guys. But we need London. This whole strike's worth it if London comes over."

London looked pleased. "You been in plenty strikes, Mac. Always do they go this way?"

"Hell, no. This place is organized, I tell you. None of the other workers came out on strike with us. The owners cut us off out here with nothing to eat. If this bunch of raiders gets stopped today, we'll catch it good. You weren't planning to go out, were you, London?"

"Sure. I ain't been in a fight yet."

"I don't think you'd better go," Mac advised. "We're goin' to need you here. They'll try to root us out today. If you aren't here the guys might get scared and beat it. You're still the boss, London. The boss's got to stick in the center of the biggest group till the last minute. Let's get those cars on the move, shall we? There's plenty of scabs out, and they'll be working by now."

London turned and hurried back to the cars. "Come on, you guys. Step on it. Let's get rollin'."

The squad leaders trotted to the tents and picked their men, men armed with rocks and pieces of wood, and here and

there a knife. The whole crowd moved out of the edge of the road, talking loudly and giving advice.

"Give 'em hell, Joe."

"Knock their can off."

The motors started and struggled against their age. The chosen men climbed in and took their places. London held up both hands to stop the noise. He shouted, "Three pairs go that way, and two this way." The gears dropped in. The cars crawled across the ditch and lined up in the road. Raiders stood up and waved their hats furiously, and shook their fists and made murderous cuts in the air with their clubs. The cars moved away slowly, in two directions, and the mob left in the camp shrieked after them.

When they had gone, the shouting stopped suddenly. The men stood, wondering and uneasy. They looked down the road and saw the cars jog out of sight. Mac and Jim and London walked back into the camp side by side.

"I hope to Christ they do some damage," Mac said. "If everything happens to us and nothing to anybody else, we aren't goin' to last much longer. Come on, Jim. Let's take a look at the old guy Dan. An' then maybe we can get some guys together and go over and see Al. I promised Al something. He'll need some encouragement."

London said, "I'm goin' to see about gettin' some water. The barrel's low."

Jim led the way to the hospital tent. The flaps were tied back to let in the morning sunshine. In a pool of sun old Dan lay. His face was transparent white and waxen, and heavy black veins puffed out on his cheeks. "How you feeling, Dan?" Jim asked.

The old man mumbled weakly.

"What's that you say?" Mac bent over to hear.

Dan's lips worked carefully this time. "I ain't had nothing to eat."

Jim cried, "You poor devil. I'll get you something." He stepped out of the door. "Mac," he shouted, "they're coming back."

From the direction of the town four cars drew up and stopped in the road. London came running and flung himself through the crowd. "What th' hell's the matter?"

The driver of the first car smiled foolishly. The crowd fell completely silent. "We couldn't get through," the driver said, and he smiled again. "There's a barricade across the road."

"I thought I told you to crash it if it was there."

"You don't unda'stan'," the driver said dully. "They was two cars ahead of us. We come to the barricade. There's about twenty guys with guns behind it." He swallowed nervously. "A guy with a star on to him gets up on top an' he says, 'It's unlawful to picket in this county. Get back.' So that old Hudson tries to go around, an' it tips over in a ditch, an' the guys spill out. So, like you said, the guys run an' get in the shovel-nose." The men in the other seats nodded solemnly at his words.

"Go on." London's voice was subdued.

"So then the shovel-nose starts to try to knock over the barricade. So then those guys start the tear gas an' shoot the tires off the shovel-nose. Then our guys start coughin', and there's so much gas you can't see. So then those guys got on gas masks, an' they come in an' they got 'bout a thousan' handcuffs." He smiled again. "So we come back. We couldn't do nothing. We didn' even have a decent rock to throw. They grabbed all the guys in the shovel-nose. Hell, I never seen so much gas." He looked up. "There's the other bunch comin'," he said hopelessly. "I guess they got the road blocked at both ends."

A curious, long sigh escaped from the

crowd. Some of the men turned and walked slowly back toward the tents, walked glidingly, with their heads down, as though they were in deep thought.

London turned to Mac, and his face was perplexed. Mac said, "Do you suppose we could get the cars across the orchard, and out that way? They can't have all the roads blocked."

London shook his head. "Too wet. A car'd squat down in the mud before we could get it ten feet."

Mac leaped on the running-board of one of the cars. "Listen, you guys," he cried. "There's one way we can get through. Let's the whole bunch of us go down there and knock those barricades off the road. They can't block us in, God damn it!" He paused for a response, a quickening. But the men looked away from him, each waiting for another to speak.

At last a man said, "We got nothing to fight with, mister. We can't fight guns an' gas with our han's. Give us guns, an' we'll fight."

Mac's speech turned into fury. "You let 'em shoot our guys, an' burn the buildings of our friends, an' you won't fight. Now they got you trapped, an' still you won't fight. Why even a God-damn rat'll fight when he's in a trap."

The hopelessness hung in the air like a gas itself. The same man repeated, "Mister, we can't fight guns and gas with our han's."

Mac's voice broke with rage. "Will any six of you yellow bastards fight *me* with your hands? *Will you?*" His mouth worked helplessly. "Try to help you—try to get something for you——" he shrieked.

London reached up and pulled him firmly off the running-board. Mac's eyes were mad. He tried to jerk free. "I'll kill the yellow bastards myself," he cried.

Jim stepped over and took his other arm. "Mac," he said. "Mac, for Christ's sake, you don't know what you're saying." Between them, Jim and London turned him and led him through the crowd, and the men looked shamefacedly at the ground. They told each other softly, "But we can't fight guns and gas with our hands."

The raiders climbed stiffly down from their cars and joined the crowd, and left the automobiles standing in the road.

Mac was limp now. He allowed himself to be led into London's tent, and settled down on the mattress. Jim soaked a rag in the water bucket and tried to wash his face, but Mac took the cloth from him and did it for himself. "I'm all right now," he said quietly. "I'm no good. The Party ought to get rid of me. I lose my head."

"You're dead for sleep," said Jim.

"Oh, I know. But it isn't that. They won't help themselves. Sometimes I've seen men just like these go through a machine-gun nest with their hands. And here today they won't fight a few green deputy-sheriffs. Just scared to death." He said, "Jim, I'm as bad as they are. I'm supposed to use my head. When I got up on that running-board, I was going to try to steam them up. An' then the God-damn sheep made me mad. I didn't have any right to get mad. They ought to kick me out of the Party."

London said in sympathy, "I got pretty damn mad myself."

Mac looked at each of his fingers carefully. "Makes me want to run away," he said ruefully. "I'd like to crawl down in a haystack and go to sleep, and to hell with the whole damn bunch of them."

Jim said, "Just as soon as you get rested up, you'll feel strong again. Lie down and get some sleep, Mac. We'll call you if we need you, won't we, London?"

"Sure," said London. "You just stretch out. There ain't nothing you can do now.

I'm goin' to go out an' talk to them squad leaders. Maybe we could take a few good guys an' sneak up on the barricades."

"I'm scared they've got us now," Mac said. "They took the heart out of the guys before they could get going." He lay down on the mattress. "What they need is blood," he muttered. "A mob's got to kill something. Oh, Christ, I guess I've bungled everything right from the start." He closed his eyes, then suddenly opened them again. "Listen, they'll pay us a visit pretty soon, the sheriff or somebody. Be sure and wake me up. Don't let 'em get away with anything. Be sure and call me." He stretched like a cat and clasped his hands over his head. His breathing became regular.

The sun threw shadows of the tent-ropes on the canvas, and in the open entrance a piece of sunlight lay on the foot-beaten earth. Jim and London walked quietly outside. "Poor guy," London said. "He needs it. I never seen a guy so far gone for sleep. I heard how the cops keep a guy awake till he goes crazy."

"He'll be different when he wakes up," said Jim. "Lord, I said I'd take something to old Dan. An' then those cars came up. I better do it now."

"I'll go see how Lisa's getting along. Maybe she better go an' take care of the old duck."

Jim walked to the stove and ladled some beans into a can and carried them to the hospital tent. The idle men, standing about, had collected into little groups. Jim looked into the hospital tent. The triangular sunny place had shortened and fallen off the cot. Old Dan's eyes were closed, and his breathing was slow and light. A curious musty, rancid odor filled the tent, the breath from a congested and slowly dying body. Jim leaned over the cot. "Dan, I brought you something to eat."

Dan opened his eyes slowly. "I don't want none. I ain't got the strength to chew."

"You have to eat, Dan. Have to eat to get strong. Look, I'll put a pillow under your head, and I'll feed you."

"Don't want to get strong." His voice was languorous. "Just want to lay here. I been a top-faller." His eyes closed again. "You'd go up the stick, way up, way up, an' you could see all the little trees, second, third growth timber down below. Then you fix your safety belt." He sighed deeply, and his mouth went on whispering. A shadow fell in the spot of sunlight. Jim looked up.

Lisa stood in the door of the tent, and her baby was under the shoulder blanket. "I got enough to do, takin' care of the baby. He says I got to come an' take care of a old man, too."

Jim said, "Sh-h." He stood from the cot so she could see Dan's sunken face.

She crept in and sat down on the extra cot. "Oh, I di'n' know. What you want me to do?"

"Nothing. Just stay with him."

She said, "I don't like 'em like that. I can smell 'em. I know that smell." She shifted nervously, covered the baby's round face to protect it from the smell.

"Shh-h," Jim said. "Maybe he's going to be all right."

"Not with that smell. I know that smell. Part of 'im's dead already."

"Poor devil!" Jim said.

Something in the words caught at her. Her eyes grew wet with tears. "I'll stay. I seen it before. It don't hurt nobody."

Jim sat down beside her. "I like to be near you," he said softly.

"Don't you come none of that."

"No, I won't. I just wondered why it was warm beside you."

"I ain't cold."

He turned his face away. "I'm going to talk to you, Lisa. You won't understand,

and it won't matter, not a bit. Everything's crumbling down and washing away. But this is just a little bit of the whole thing. This isn't anything, Lisa. You and I aren't much in the whole thing. See, Lisa? I'm telling it to myself, but I understand it better with you listening. You don't know what I'm talking about, do you, Lisa?"

He saw a blush creep up the side of her neck. "I jus' had a baby," she said. "Besides, I ain't that kind." She lifted her shamed eyes. "Don't talk that way. Don't get that tone on you," she begged. "You know I ain't that kind." He reached out his hand to pat her, but she shrank away from him. "No."

He stood up. "Be nice to the old guy. See? There's water and a spoon on the table. Give him a little, now and then." He raised his head tensely to listen to a stir of voices in the camp, a gradually increasing stir. And then, over the bass of voices, a haranguing voice sounded, a voice that rose and fell angrily. "I've got to go," Jim said. "Take care of him." He hurried out of the tent.

By the stoves he saw men collecting around some central object, all faces inward. The angry voice came from the center. As Jim watched, the crowd moved sideways toward the naked little stand that had been built for Joy's body. The mob touched the stand and flowed around it, but out of the group one man shot up and took his position in the stand. Jim ran over. He could see, now. It was the sullen, scowling Burke. His arms gesticulated. His voice bellowed over the heads of the crowd. Jim saw London hurrying in from the road.

Burke grasped the hand-rail. "There he is now," he shouted. "Look at 'im. That's the guy that's spoiled ever'thing. What the hell's he done? Set in his tent an' et canned peaches while we got wet and lived on garbage a pig wouldn't touch."

London's mouth was open with astonishment. "What's goin' on here?" he cried.

Burke leaned forward over the rail. "I'll tell you what's goin' on. Us guys decided we wanted a real leader. We decided we want a guy that won't sell out for a load o' canned goods."

London's face paled, and his shoulders drooped. With a roar he charged the unresisting crowd, flung men aside, burrowed through the mass of men. He came to the stand and grasped the handrail. As he pulled himself up, Burke kicked at his head, missed, struck the shoulder and tore one hand loose from the rail. London roared again. He was under the rail and on his feet. Burke struck at his face, and missed. And then, with the terrible smooth speed of a heavy man, London lanced with his left hand and, as Burke ducked, the great right fist caught him on the side of the jaw, lifted him clear, and dropped him. His head hung over the edge of the platform, broken jaw torn sideways, shattered teeth hanging loosely between his lips. A thin stream of blood flowed from his mouth, beside his nose and eye, and disappeared into his hair.

London stood, panting, over him, looking down. He raised his head slowly. "Does any more sons-of-bitches think I double-crossed 'em?"

The men nearest Burke's hanging head stared, fascinated. From the other sides of the stand the people began to mill, to press in, standing on tiptoes for a look. Their eyes were bright and angry. A man said, "Bust his jaw clean off. That's blood out o' his brain." Another shouted hysterically, "Killed 'um. Busted his head off."

Women swam through the crowd and looked woodenly at the hanging head. A heavy, sobbing gasp went up from the mob. The eyes flared. All the shoulders were dropped, and the arms bowed dangerously. London still stood panting, but his face was perplexed. He looked down at his fist, at the split and bleeding knuckles. Then he looked out over the crowd for help, and he saw Jim standing on the outskirts. Jim shook his clasped hands together over his head. And then he pointed to the road, where the cars stood, and down the road, and to the cars again, and down the road again. London looked back at the snarling mob. The perplexity left his face and he scowled.

"All right, you guys," he yelled. "Why ain't I done nothing? Because you ain't helped me. But by Christ, now you're ready! Nothin' can stop you now." A long, throaty animal howl went up. London held up his hands. "Who'll follow now, and knock hell out o' that barricade?" The crowd was changing rapidly. The eyes of the men and women were entranced. The bodies weaved slowly, in unison. No more lone cries came from lone men. They moved together, looked alike. The roar was one voice, coming from many throats.

"Some of you bring cars," London shouted. "Come on, the rest of you. Come on, we'll see. Come, come on." He vaulted down from the stand and fought his way through to the head of the mob. Quickly the cars were started. The crowd poured into the road, and it was no longer loose and listless. It had become a quick, silent and deadly efficient machine. It swung down the road at a dog-trot, controlled and directed. And behind it the cars moved slowly along.

Jim had watched the start. He commanded himself aloud, "Don't get caught. Don't get caught. Don't let it catch you. Use your head."

Most of the women were running with the departing men, but a few who remained behind looked strangely at Jim, for his eyes, too, were entranced as he stared down the road after the terrible mechanism. When it had disappeared he sighed shudderingly and turned away. His hand went up to the hurt shoulder and pressed it, to make a steadying pain. He walked slowly to London's tent, went in silently, and sat down on a box.

Mac looked at him under lowered eyelids. Only a shiny slit showed that he was awake. "How long've I been sleeping, Jim?"

"Just a little while. I don't think it's even noon yet, near noon."

"I dreamed a lot, but I'm rested. I think I'll get up now."

"Better get some more sleep if you can."

"What's the use? I'm rested now." He opened his eyes wide. "Lost the sandy feeling. You sleep hard when you're that tired. I dreamed commotion."

"Better go to sleep again."

"No." He sat up and stretched. "Anything happen while I was asleep? It's awful quiet out there."

"Plenty happened," Jim said. "Burke tried to kick London out, and London smashed him—nearly killed him, and—Christ! I forgot Burke." He ran to the door, and around the back to the tent, and looked toward the stand. Then he went into the tent again. "Somebody took him in," he said.

Mac was up now, and excited. "Tell me."

"Well, when the crowd saw the blood they went nuts, and London started 'em down to break the barricade."

Mac cried, "Didn't I tell you? They need blood. That works. That's what I told you. Well then—what?"

"They're down there now. God, Mac, you ought to of seen them. It was like all of them disappeared, and it was just one big—animal, going down the road. Just all one animal. I nearly was there. I wanted to go, and then I thought, 'You can't. You've got to use your head.' "

"Right!" said Mac. "People think a mob is wasteful, but I've seen plenty; and I tell you, a mob with something it wants to do is just about as efficient as trained soldiers, but tricky. They'll knock that barricade, but then what? They'll want to do something else before they cool off." And he went on, "That's right, what you said. It *is* a big animal. It's different from the men in it. And it's stronger than all the men put together. It doesn't want the same things men want—it's like Doc said —and we don't know what it'll do."

"It'll get that barricade," said Jim.

"That's not what I mean. The *animal* don't want the barricade. I don't know what it wants. Trouble is, guys that study people always think it's men, and it isn't men. It's a different kind of animal. It's as different from men as dogs are. Jim, it's swell when we can use it, but we don't know enough. When it gets started it might do anything." His face was alive and excited, and slightly fearful.

Jim said, "Listen, I think I hear——" He ran to the entrance. "Coming back," he cried. "It's different now. It's spread out now, not the same."

Mac stood beside him. The road was full of the returning men. London broke out ahead and trotted heavily toward them. And when he came near enough he yelled, "Get back in the tent. Get back in the tent."

"What's he mean?" Jim asked. But Mac pushed him inside the tent, untied the strings and dropped the flaps.

"He knows," Mac said. "Just keep quiet and let him handle it. No matter what happens, don't go out there."

They heard the rain of footsteps on the ground, and shouting voices. Then they saw London's squat black shadow on the canvas and heard him yell, "Now you guys cool off."

"We'll show 'im who's yellow bastards!"

London cried, "You're sore because we told you off. Now you go an' get a drink an' cool down. You just done fine, but you ain't a'gonna get my friend. He's your friend, too. I tell you he's been workin' for you till he's dead tired."

Mac and Jim, in the tent, could feel the thrust change, break up, lose itself in a hundred cries. "We know, London."

"Sure, but he called us yellow."

Mac's breath came out, heavily. "That was close, Jim. Jesus, that was close." London's square shadow still stood on the tent wall, but the many excited voices drifted and lost their impact.

London stretched the subject. "If any of you guys think I got canned peaches, you can come in and look."

"Hell, no, London. We never thought that."

"It was that son-of-a-bitch Burke."

"He's been workin' against you, London. I heard him."

"Well, you guys clear out, then. I got work to do." The shadow stayed still on the tent until the voices had dwindled until no crowd faced the tent. London lifted the flap and stepped tiredly inside.

"Thanks," said Mac. "You don't know how close it was any better than I do. You handled 'em, London. Oh, you handled 'em."

London said, "I was scared. You won't think no worse of me, Mac, for that. On the way back I caught myself wantin' to come an' kill you myself." He grinned. "I don't know why."

"Nobody does," said Mac. "But that's the way it is. Tell us what happened down the road."

"We ironed 'em out," said London. "We just rolled over 'em like they wasn't there. They give us the gas, an' some of the guys coughed an' cried, but, hell, them green cops didn't stand a chance. Some of 'em got away—I guess most of 'em did. But the rest of 'em got kicked to pieces like cheese. God, the guys was sore."

"Any shooting?"

"No. Too quick for 'em. They shot over us, thought we'd stop, I guess. But we come right on. Some cops like to shoot guys, but most of 'em don't, I guess. An' then we just rolled 'em out, an' tore down the barricade."

"Well, did the cars get out?"

"Hell, yes, eight of 'em went through, loaded with guys cuttin' hell loose."

"Kill any of the cops?" Mac demanded.

"Huh? Kill 'em? I don't know. I didn't look. Maybe we did. We might of. I bet machine-guns wouldn't of stopped us."

"That's swell," said Mac. "If we could turn on the heat like that when we wanted it, and turn it off when we were through, we'd have our God-damn revolution tomorrow, and all over tomorrow night. The guys got over it pretty quick."

"It was all that runnin' that did it," London said. "Damn near a mile. Time they got back, they was clear winded. I feel sick myself. I ain't used to runnin'."

"I know," said Mac. "It's not the running, so much, though. A thing like that gets you all messed up inside. I bet a lot of the guys are losing their beakfast right now."

London seemed suddenly to see Jim. He went over and banged him a clap on the back. "You pulled it, Jim. I was standin' up there after I cold-cocked Burke; I didn't know what the hell to do. An' them guys in the circle didn't know what to do, neither. They was all ready to get me, or anybody. An' I look out, and I seen you pointin', an' I know what to do with 'em."

Jim's face was alight with pleasure. "I'm not much use, with my bum shoulder. I was thinking what Mac said about a little blood setting the guys off. You remember saying that, Mac?"

"Sure I remember. But I'm not sure I would of thought of it out there. I don't know how you do it, Jim. Everybody loses their head except you. I heard about your old man; he wasn't a genius, all he knew was fight. I don't know where you learned to use your bean and keep clear."

"I've got to be some use," Jim said. "My father was like you say, but my mother was so cool she'd make you shiver."

London flexed his hand at his side, and then he looked in astonishment at his crushed knuckles. "Holy Christ! Look at that!"

"You sure smashed 'em," said Mac.

"I smashed 'em on that son-of-a-bitch Burke. How is he, Jim? Felt like I knocked his head clear off when I socked 'im."

Jim said, "I don't know how he is. Somebody took 'im off the stand."

"Guess I better see," said London. "Funny I never felt that hand till now."

"When you get mixed up with the animal, you never feel anything," said Mac.

"What animal?"

"Oh, it's just a kind of a joke. Be a good idea if you look at Burke. And see how the guys feel. They'll feel pretty rocky by now, I think."

London said, "I don't trust 'em no more. I can't tell what they'll do no more. I'm glad I wasn't back of that barricade."

Mac said, "Well, I'm glad you was in front of this tent. Jim an' me might be hangin' up on an apple tree by now."

"There was a minute there——" said London. He gathered the tent-flaps and tied them back. The sun did not enter the tent, it had passed its meridian. Mac and Jim watched London walk away, and then they faced each other again. Mac flopped down on the mattress. Jim looked at him until Mac said, "You accusing me of something?"

"No, I was just wondering—seems to

me now we've won a fight an' got our guys through we're more in danger of losing than ever. We came out here to do something, Mac. Have we messed up everything?"

Mac said sharply, "You think we're too important, and this little bang-up is too important. If the thing blew up right now it'd be worth it. A lot of the guys've been believing this crap about the noble American workingman, an' the partnership of capital and labor. A lot of 'em are straight now. They know how much capital thinks of 'em, and how quick capital would poison 'em like a bunch of ants. An' by Christ, we showed 'em two things—what they are, an' what they've got to do. And this last little ruckus showed 'em they could do it. Remember what the 'Frisco strike did to Sam? Well, all these guys'll get to be a little like Sam."

"But do you think they've got brains enough to see it?"

"Not brains, Jim. It don't take brains. After it's all over the thing'll go on working down inside of 'em. They'll know it without thinking it out."

"Well, what do you think's going to happen now?"

Mac rubbed his front teeth with a finger. "I guess they'll just have to steamroller us out of here, Jim. Might be this afternoon, might be tonight."

"Well, what do you think; had we better just fade, or put up a fight?"

"Fight, if we can make the guys do it," said Mac. "If they sneak off, they get a bad feeling out of it, but if they fight and get licked, well, they still fought; and it's worth doing."

Jim settled down on one knee. "Look, if they come through with guns they're going to kill a lot of our guys."

Mac's eyes grew slitted and cold. "We keep switching sides, Jim. Suppose they do kill some of our men? That helps our side. For every man they kill ten new ones come over to us. The news goes creeping around the country and men all over hear it and get mad. Guys that are just half-warm get hot, see? But if we sneak off and the word gets around, and men say, 'They didn't even put up a fight,' why all the working stiffs will be unsure of themselves. If we fight, an' the news gets around, other men in the same position'll fight too."

Jim put down the other knee and squatted on his heels. "I wanted to get the thing straight. But will the guys fight?"

"I don't know. Right now they won't. They're pretty sick. Maybe later. Maybe if we could throw 'em another chicken like Burke they would. Burke stepped on the third rail just in time, just when we needed him. Maybe somebody else'll spill a little blood for the cause."

Jim said, "Mac, if blood's all we need, I could pull off this bandage and start the hole bleeding."

"You're kind of funny, Jim," Mac said kindly. "You're so God-damn serious."

"I don' see anything funny."

"No. Remember the lady that was buying a dog? She asks, 'Are you sure he's a bloodhound?' The owner says, 'Sure he is. Bleed for the lady, Oscar.'"

Jim smiled thinly. Mac went on, "No, Jim, you're more use to the cause than a hundred of these guys."

"Well, a little loss of blood won't hurt me."

Mac stroked his lower lip nervously. "Jim," he said. "Did you ever see four or five dogs all fighting?"

"No."

"Well, if one of those dogs gets hurt or goes down, all the rest'll turn on him and kill him."

"So what?"

"So—men do that sometimes, too. I don't know why. It's kind of like Doc says to me one time, 'Men hate something in themselves.' "

"Doc was a nice guy, but he didn't get anywhere with his high-falutin ideas. His ideas didn't go anywhere, just around in a circle."

"All the same, I wish he was here. Your shoulder feel all right?"

"Sure. I'm not using it any more than I can help."

Mac got up. "Come on, let's look at it. Take off that coat." Jim worked the coat off. Mac pulled the plaster loose and carefully raised the bandage. "Looks pretty good. It's a little bit angry. I'll throw away a couple of layers of this gauze. I'll be glad when we get in town. You can get it taken care of. Now I'll put this clean part back." He pressed the plaster down in place and held it firmly until the body heat made it take hold.

"Maybe we'll find Doc in town," said Jim. "He talked awful funny just before he disappeared. Maybe he got disgusted, or scared, and beat it."

"Here, I'll help you with your coat. You can forget that. If Doc was goin' to get disgusted, he'd of got years ago. An' I've seen him under fire. He don't get scared."

London came in and stood quietly in the doorway. He looked serious and frightened. "I didn't kill 'im, but damn near. His jaw's busted terrible. I'm scared he'll die if he don't get a doctor."

"Well, we can ship him to town, but I don't think they'd take very good care of him in there."

London went on, "That woman of his is raisin' hell. Says she's goin' to have the whole bunch of us up for murder. Says the whole strike was just to get Burke."

Mac said, "It'd almost be worth it, at that. I never liked the bastard. I always thought he was the stoolpigeon. How do the guys feel?"

"They're just sittin' around, like you said. Look sick, like a bunch of kids that broke into a candy store."

"Sure," said Mac. "They used up the juice that should of lasted 'em about a week. We better get some food into 'em if we can. Maybe they'll sleep it off then. You're sure right, London. We need a doctor. How's the guy that hurt his ankle?"

"Well, he's raisin' merry hell too. Says it ain't set right, an' it hurts. An' he won't never be able to walk no more. All this howlin' around ain't helpin' the way the guys feel none."

"Yeah, an' there's Al," said Mac. "I wonder how Al is? We ought to go over an' see him. Think the guys you told to stay there stayed?"

London shrugged. "I don't know."

"Well, could we get half a dozen guys to go over with us?"

London said, "I don't think you'll get none of these guys to go no place. They just want to set there an' look at their feet."

"Well, by Christ, I'll go alone, then. Al's a good guy."

"I'll go with you, Mac," Jim broke in.

"No. You stay here."

London said, "I don't think there's nobody to bother you."

Mac begged, "Jim, I wish you'd stay. S'pose they got both of us? There'd be nobody here to go on. Stay here, Jim."

"I'm going. I've sat around here and nursed myself long enough. Why don't you stay and let me go?"

"All right, kid," Mac said resignedly. "We'll just be careful, and keep our eyes open. Try to keep the guys alive till we get back, London. Try to get a little of that beef and beans into 'em. They're sick of it, but it's food. We ought to be hearing something about those cars pretty soon."

London grunted, "I guess I'll just open me up a can of them peaches, an' some sardines. The guys said I had a flock of 'em, piled right up to the roof. I'll have some ready for you when you get back."

15

They walked out into the clear yellow sunshine. The camp looked bedraggled and grey in the clean light. A litter had accumulated since Burton was gone, bits of paper, strings, overalls hung on the guy-ropes of the tents. Mac and Jim walked out of the camp and across the surrounding field, to the edge of the orchard. At the line of trees Mac stopped. His eyes moved slowly across the horizontal fields of vision. "Look close, Jim," he advised. "It's probably a damn fool thing to go over alone. I know it isn't good sense." He studied the orchard. The long, sun-spotted aisles were silent. There was no movement. "It's so quiet. Makes me suspicious. It's too quiet." He reached to a limb and took down a small, misshapen apple the pickers had left. "God, that tastes good. I'd forgot about apples. Always forget what's so easy."

"I don't see anybody moving," said Jim. "Not a soul."

"Well look, we'll edge down in line with the trees. Anybody looking down a row won't see us, then." They stepped slowly in under the big apple trees. Their eyes moved restlessly about. They walked through shadows of branches and leaves, and the sun struck them with soft, warm blows.

Jim asked, "Mac, do you s'pose we could get a leave of absence some time and go where nobody knows us, and just sit down in an orchard?"

" 'Bout two hours of it, and you'd be raring to go again."

"I never had time to look at things, Mac, never. I never looked how leaves come out. I never looked at the way things happen. This morning there was a whole line of ants on the floor of the tent. I couldn't watch them. I was thinking about something else. Some time I'd like to sit all day and look at bugs, and never think of anything else."

"They'd drive you nuts," said Mac. "Men are bad enough, but bugs'd drive you nuts."

"Well, just once in a while you get that feeling—I never look at anything. I never take time to see anything. It's going to be over, and I won't know—even how an apple grows."

They moved on slowly. Mac's restless eyes roved about among the trees. "You can't see everything," he said. "I took a leave and went into the woods in Canada. Say, in a couple of days I came running out of there. I wanted trouble, I was hungry for a mess."

"Well, I'd like to try it sometime. The way old Dan talks about timber——"

"Damn it, Jim, you can't have everything! We've got something old Dan hasn't got. You can't have everything. In a few days we'll be back in town, and we'll be so damned anxious to get into another fuss we'll be biting our nails. You've got to take it easy till that shoulder heals. I'll take you to a flop-house where you can watch all the bugs you want. Keep back of the line of trees. You're standing out like a cow on a side-hill."

"It's nice out here," said Jim.

"It's too damn nice. I'm scared there's a trap someplace."

Through the trees they could see Anderson's little white house, and its picket fence, and the burning geraniums in the yard. "No one around," said Jim.

"Well, take it easy." At the last row Mac stopped again and let his eyes travel slowly across the open. The great black square on the ground, where the barn had been, still sent up a lazy, pungent smoke. The white tankhouse looked tall and lonely. "Looks O.K.," Mac said. "Let's go in the back way." He tried to open the picket gate quietly, but the latch clicked and the hinges growled. They walked up the short path to the porch with its yellowing passion vine. Mac knocked on the door.

A voice from inside called, "Who is it?"

"Is that you, Al?"

"Yeah."

"Are you alone?"

"Yeah. Who are you?"

"It's Mac."

"Oh, come on in, Mac. The door ain't locked."

They went into the kitchen. Al lay on his narrow bed against the wall. He seemed to have grown gaunt in the few days. The skin hung loosely on his face. "Hi, Mac. I thought nobody'd ever come. My old man went out early."

"We tried to get over before, Al. How's all the hurts?"

"They hurt plenty," said Al. "And when you're all alone they hurt worse. Who burned the barn, Mac?"

"Vigilantes. We're sorry as hell, Al. We had guards here, but they got a fast one pulled on 'em."

"My old man just raised hell all night, Mac. Talked all night. Give me hell about four times an hour, all night."

"We're damn sorry."

Al cleared one hand from the bed-clothes and scratched his cheek. "I'm still with you, Mac. But the old man wants to blast you. He went in this morning to get the sheriff to kick you off'n the place. Says you're trespassin', an' he wants you off. Says he's punished for listenin' to guys like you. Says I can go to hell if I string along with you. He was mad as a hornet, Mac."

"I was scared he would be, Al. Listen, we know you're with us, see? It don't do no good to make that old man any sorrier than he is. If it'd do any good, it'd

be different. You just pretend to come around to his side. We'll understand that, Al. You can keep in touch with us. I'm awfully sorry for your old man."

Al sighed deeply. "I was scared you'd think I doublecrossed you. If you know I ain't, I'll tell him t'hell with you."

"That's the stuff, Al. And we'll give you a boost in town too. Oh, say, Al, did Doc look in on you last night?"

"No. Why?"

"Well, he started over here before the fire, an' he ain't been back."

"Jesus! What do you think happened to him?"

"I'm scared they snatched the poor devil."

"They been pushing you all around, ain't they?"

"Yeah. But our guys got in some good licks this morning. But if your old man turns us in, I guess they'll roll over us tomorrow."

"Whole thing flops, huh, Mac?"

"That don't mean anything. We done what we came to do. The thing goes right on, Al. You just make peace an' pretend you ain't ever goin' to get burned no more." He listened. "Is that somebody coming?" He ran through the kitchen and into the front of the house, and looked out a window.

"It's my old man, I recognize his step," said Al.

Mac returned. "I wanted to see if anybody was with him. He's all alone. We could make a sneak, I guess. I'd rather tell him I'm sorry."

"You better not," Al advised. "He won't listen to nothing from you. He hates your guts."

There were steps on the porch and the door burst open. Anderson stood, surprised and glaring. "God damn it," he shouted. "You bastards get out of here. I've been and turned you in. The sheriff's goin' kick the whole smear of you off my land." His chest swelled with rage.

Mac said, "We just wanted to tell you we're sorry. We didn't burn the barn. Some of the boys from town did."

"What th' hell do I care who burned it? It's burned, the crop's burned. What do you damn bums know about it? I'll lose the place sure, now." His eyes watered with rage. "You bastards never owned nothing. You never planted trees an' seen 'em grow an' felt 'em with your hands. You never owned a thing, never went out an' touched your own apple trees with your hands. What do you know?"

"We never had a chance to own anything," Mac said. "We'd like to own something and plant trees."

Anderson ignored his words. "I listened to your promises. Look what happened. The whole crop's burned, there's paper coming due."

Mac asked, "How about the pointers?"

Anderson's hands settled slowly to his sides. A look of cold, merciless hatred came into his eyes. He said slowly, softly, "The kennel was—against—the barn."

Mac turned to Al and nodded. For a moment Al questioned with his eyes, and then he scowled. "What he says goes. You guys get the hell out, and don't never come back."

Anderson ran to the bed and stood in front of it. "I could shoot you men now," he said, "but the sheriff's goin' to do it for me, an' damn quick."

Mac touched Jim on the arm, and they went out and shut the door. They didn't bother to look around when they went out the gate. Mac set out so rapidly that Jim had to stretch his stride to keep up. The sun was cutting downward now, and the shadows of whole trees lay between the rows, and the wind was stirring in the branches, so that both trees and ground seemed to quiver nervously.

"It keeps you hopping, keeping the picture," Mac said. "You see a guy hurt, or somebody like Anderson smashed, or you see a cop ride down a Jew girl, an' you think, what the hell's the use of it. An' then you think of the millions starving, and it's all right again. It's worth it. But it keeps you jumping between pictures. Don't it ever get you, Jim?"

"Not very much. It isn't long ago I saw my mother die; seems years, but it wasn't long ago. She wouldn't speak to me, she just looked at me. She was hurt so bad she didn't even want a priest. I guess I got something burned out of me that night. I'm sorry for Anderson, but what the hell. If I can give up my whole life, he ought to be able to give up a barn."

"Well, to some of those guys property's more important than their lives."

Jim said, "Slow down, Mac. What's your hurry? I seem to get tired easy."

Mac did slow his steps a little. "I thought that's what he went to town for. I want to get back before anything happens. I don't know what this sheriff'll do, but he'll be happy as hell to split us up." They walked silently over the soft, dark earth, and the shadows flickered on them. At the clearing they slowed down. Mac said, "Well, nothing's happened yet, anyway."

The smoke rose slowly from the stoves. Jim asked, "Where do you s'pose all the guys are?"

"In sleeping off the drunk, I guess. It wouldn't be a bad idea if we got some sleep, too. Prob'ly be up all night."

London moved over and met them. "Everything all right?" Mac asked.

"Just the same."

"Well, I was right. Anderson's been in and asked the sheriff to kick us off."

"Well?"

"Well, we wait. Don't tell the guys about it."

"Maybe you was right about that," London said, "but you was sure wrong about what them guys would eat. They cleaned us out. There ain't a damn drop o' beans left. I saved you a couple of cans, over in my tent."

"Maybe we won't need anything more to eat," said Mac.

"How do you mean?"

"We prob'ly won't any of us be here tomorrow."

In the tent London pointed to the two food cans on the box. "D'you s'pose the sheriff'll try to kick us off?" he asked.

"Damn right. He won't let a chance like that go by."

"Well, will he come shootin', d'you suppose? Or will he give the guys a warnin'?"

Mac said, "Hell, I don't know. Where's all the men?"

"All under cover, asleep."

Mac said, "I heard a car. May be our guys coming back."

London cocked his head. "Too big," he said. "That's one of them big babies."

They ran outside. Up the road from Torgas a huge Mack dump-truck rolled. It had a steel bed and sides, supported by two sets of double tires. It pulled up in front of the camp and stopped. A man stood up in the steel bed, and in his hands he held a submachine-gun with a big cartridge cylinder behind the forward grip. The heads of other men showed above the truck sides. Strikers began to boil out of the tents.

The standing man shouted, "I'm sheriff o' this county. If there's anyone in authority I want to see him." The mob approached closer and looked curiously at the truck.

Mac said softly, "Careful, London. They may pop us off. They could do it now if they wanted to." They walked forward, to the edge of the road, and stopped; and the mob was lining the road now, too.

London said, "I'm the boss, mister."

"Well, I've got a trespass complaint. We've been fair to you men. We've asked you to go back to work, or, if you

wanted to strike, to do it peacefully. You've destroyed property and committed homicide. This morning you sent out men to destroy property. We had to shoot some of those men, and we caught the rest." He looked down at the men in the truck, and then up again. "Now we don't want any bloodshed, so we're going to let you out. You have all night tonight to get out. If you head straight for the county line, nobody'll bother you. But if this camp is here at daylight tomorrow, we're going through it."

The men stood silently and watched him. Mac whispered to London. London said, "Trespassin' don't give you no right to shoot guys."

"Maybe not, but resisting officers does. Now I'm talking fair with you, so you'll know what to expect. At daylight tomorrow a hundred men, in ten trucks like this, are coming out. Every man will have a gun, and we have three cases of Mills bombs. Some of you men who know can tell the others what a Mills bomb is. That's all. We're through fooling with you. You have till daylight to get out of the county. That's all." He turned forward. "Might as well drive along, Gus." He sank from sight behind the steel truck side. The wheels turned slowly, and gathered speed.

One of the strikers leaped into the shallow ditch and picked up a rock. And he stood holding it in his hand and looking at it as the truck rolled away. The men watched the truck go, and then they turned back into the camp.

London sighed. "Well, that sounds like orders. He didn't mean no funny business."

Mac said impatiently, "I'm hungry. I'm going to eat my beans." They followed him back into the tent. He gobbled his food quickly and hungrily. "Hope you got some, London."

"Me? Oh, sure. What we goin' to do now, Mac?"

"Fight," said Mac.

"Yeah, but if he brings the stuff he said, pineapples an' stuff, it ain't goin' to be no more fight than the stockyards."

"Bull," said Mac, and a little jet of chewed beans shot from his mouth. "If he had that stuff, he wouldn't need to tell us about it. He just hopes we'll get scattered so we can't put up a fight. If we move out tonight, they'll pick us off. They never do what they say."

London looked into Mac's face, hung on to his eyes. "Is that straight, Mac? You said I was on your side. Are you puttin' somethin' over?"

Mac looked away. "We got to fight," he said. "If we get out without a scrap ever'thing we've been through'll be wasted."

"Yeah, but if we fight, a lot of guys that ain't done no harm is goin' get shot."

Mac put his unfinished food down on the box. "Look," he said. "In a war a general knows he's going to lose men. Now this is a war. If we get run out o' here without a fight, it's losing ground." For a moment he covered his eyes with his hand. "London," he said. "It's a hell of a responsibility. I know what we should do; you're the boss; for Christ's sake, do what you want. Don't make me take all the blame."

London said plaintively, "Yeah, but you know about things. You think we ought to fight, really?"

"Yes, we ought."

"Well, hell then, we'll fight—that is, if we can get the guys to fight."

"I know," said Mac. "They may run out on us, every one of 'em. The ones that heard the sheriff will tell the others. They may turn on us and say we caused the trouble."

London said, "Some ways, I hope they clear out. Poor bastards, they don't know nothing. But like you say, if they're ever goin' to get clear, they got to take it now.

How about the hurt guys?" London went on, "Burke and old Dan, and the guy with the busted ankle?"

"Leave 'em," said Mac. "It's the only thing we can do. The county'll have to take care of 'em."

"I'm going to take a look around," London said. "I'm gettin' nervous as a cat."

"You ain't the only one," said Mac.

When he was gone, Jim glanced at Mac, and then began to eat the cold beans and strings of beef. "I wonder if they'll fight?" he asked. "D'you think they'd really let the guys through if they wanted to run?"

"Oh, the sheriff would. He'd be only too damn glad to get rid of 'em, but I don't trust the vigilante boys."

"They won't have anything to eat tonight, Mac. If they're scared already, there won't be any dinner to buck 'em up."

Mac scraped his can and set it down. "Jim," he said, "if I told you to do something, would you do it?"

"I don't know. What is it?"

"Well, the sun's going down pretty soon, and it'll be dark. They're going to lay for you and me, Jim. Don't make any mistake about that. They're going to want to get us, bad. I want you to get out, soon as it gets dark, get clear and go back to town."

"Why in hell should I do that?"

Mac's eyes slid over Jim's face and went to the ground again. "When I came out here, I thought I was hell on wheels. You're worth ten of me, Jim. I know that now. If anything happened to me, there's plenty of guys to take my place, but you've got a genius for the work. We can't spare you, Jim. If you was to get knocked off in a two-bit strike—well, it's bad economy."

"I don't believe it," said Jim. "Our guys are to be used, not saved. I couldn't run out. Y'said yourself this was a part of the whole thing. It's little, but it's important."

"I *want* you to go, Jim. You can't fight with that arm. You'd be no damn good here. You couldn't help at all."

Jim's face was rigid. "I won't go," he said. "I might be of some use here. You protect me all the time, Mac. And sometimes I get the feeling you're not protecting me for the Party, but for yourself."

Mac reddened with anger. "O.K., then. Get your can knocked off. I've told you what I think's the best thing. Be pigheaded, if you want. I can't sit still. I'm going out. You do anything you damn please." He went out angrily.

Jim looked up at the back wall of the tent. He could see the outline of the red sun on the canvas. His hand stole up and touched his hurt shoulder, and pressed it gently, all around, in a circle that narrowed to the wound. He winced a little as his exploring fingers neared the hurt. For a long time he sat quietly.

He heard a step in the door and looked around. Lisa stood there, and her baby was in her arms. Jim could see past her, where the line of old cars stood against the road; and on the other side of the road the sun was on the treetops, but in the rows the shade had come. Lisa looked in, with a bird-like interest. Her hair was damp, plastered against her head, and little, uneven finger-waves were pressed into it. The short blanket that covered her shoulders was draped and held to one side with a kind of coquetry. "I seen you was alone," she said. She went to the mattress and sat down and arranged her gingham dress neatly over her legs. "I heard guys say the cops'll throw bombs, an' kill us all," she said lightly.

Jim was puzzled. "It doesn't seem to scare you much."

"No. I ain't never been ascared o' things like that."

"The cops wouldn't hurt you," Jim said. "I don't believe they'll do all that. It's a bluff. Do you want anything?"

"I thought I'd come an' set. I like to— just set here."

Jim smiled. "You like me, don't you, Lisa?"

"Yes."

"I like you, too, Lisa."

"You he'ped me with the baby."

Jim asked, "How's old Dan? Did you take care of him?"

"He's all right. Just lays there mumblin'."

"Mac helped you more than I did."

"Yes, but he don't look at me—nice. I like t'hear you talk. You're just a young kid, but you talk nice."

"I talk too much, Lisa. Too much talk, not enough doing things. Look how the evening's coming. We'll light the lantern before long. You wouldn't like to sit here in the dark with me."

"I wouldn' care," she said quickly.

He looked into her eyes again, and his face grew pleased. "Did you ever notice, in the evening, Lisa, how you think of things that happened a long time ago— not even about things that matter? One time in town, when I was a little kid, the sun was going down, and there was a board fence. Well, a grey cat went up and sat on that fence for a moment, long-haired cat, and that cat turned gold for a minute, a gold cat."

"I like cats," Lisa agreed softly. "I had two cats onct, two of them."

"Look. The sun's nearly gone, Lisa. Tomorrow we'll be somewhere else. I wonder where? You'll be on the move, I guess. Maybe I'll be in jail. I've been in jail before."

London and Mac came quietly into the tent together. London looked down at the girl. "What you doing here, Lisa? You better get out. We got business." Lisa got up and clutched her blanket close. She looked sideways at Jim as she passed.

London said, "I don't know what's goin' on. There's about ten little meetin's out there, an' they don't want me at none o' them."

"Yeah, I know," Mac said. "The guys're scared. I don't know what they'll do, but they'll want to scram tonight." And then the conversation died. London and Mac sat down on boxes, facing Jim. They sat there while the sun went down and the tent grew a little dusky.

At last Jim said softly, "Even if the guys get out, it won't all be wasted. They worked together a little."

Mac roused himself. "Yeah, but we ought to make a last stand."

"How you goin' to get guys to fight when they want to run?" London demanded.

"I don't know. We can talk. We can try to make 'em fight talkin' to 'em."

"Talk don't do much good when they're scared."

"I know."

The silence fell again. They could hear the low talk of many voices outside, scattered voices that gradually drew together and made a babble like water. Mac said, "Got a match, London? Light the lantern."

"It ain't dark yet."

"Dark enough. Light it up. This God-damn half-light makes me nervous."

The shade screeched as London raised it, and screeched when he let it down.

Mac looked startled. "Something happened. What's wrong?"

"It's the men," said Jim. "They're quiet now. They've all stopped talking." The three men sat listening tensely. They heard footsteps coming closer. In the doorway the two short Italian men stood. Their teeth showed in self-conscious grins.

"C'n we come in?"

"Sure. Come on in, boys."

They stood in the tent like pupils preparing to recite. Each looked to the other to begin. One said, "The men out there—they want to call a meeting."

"Yeah? What for?"

The other answered quickly, "Those men say they vote the strike, they can vote again. They say, 'What's the use all the men get killed?' They say they can't strike no more." They were silent, waiting for London's answer.

London's eyes asked advice from Mac. "Of course you'll call a meeting," Mac said. "The men are the bosses. What they say goes." He looked up at the waiting emissaries. "Go out and tell the guys London calls a meeting in about half an hour, to vote whether we fight or run."

They looked at London for corroboration. He nodded his head slowly. "That's right," he said. "In a half hour. We do what the guys vote to do." The little men made foreign bows, and wheeled and left the tent.

Mac laughed loudly. "Why, that's fine," he said. "Why, that makes it better. I thought they might sneak out. But if they want to vote, that means they're still working together. Oh, that's fine. They can break up, if they do it by their own consent."

Jim asked, "But aren't you going to try to make them fight?"

"Oh, sure. We have to make plans about that. But if they won't fight, well anyway they don't just sneak off like dogs. It's more like a retreat, you see. It isn't just getting chased."

"What'll we do at the meeting?" London demanded.

"Well, let's see. It's just about dark now. You talk first, London. Tell 'em why they should fight, not run. Now I better not talk. They don't like me too well since I told 'em off this morning." His eyes moved to Jim. "You're it," he said. "Here's your chance. You do it. See if you can bring 'em around. Talk, Jim. Talk. It's the thing you've been wanting."

Jim's eyes shone with excitement.

"Mac," he cried, "I can pull off this bandage and get a flow of blood. That might stir 'em up."

Mac's eyes narrowed and he considered the thought. "No—" he decided. "Stir 'em up that way, an' they got to hit something quick. If you make 'em sit around, they'll go way down. No, just talk, Jim. Tell 'em straight what a strike means, how it's a little battle in a whole war. You can do it, Jim."

Jim sprang up. "You're damn right I can do it. I'm near choking, but I can do it." His face was transfigured. A furious light of energy seemed to shine from it.

They heard running footsteps. A young boy ran into the tent. "Out in the orchard," he cried. "There's a guy says he's a doctor. He's all hurt."

The three started up. "Where?"

"Over the other side. Been lyin' there all day, he says."

"How'd you find him?" Mac demanded.

"I heard 'im yell. He says come and tell you."

"Show us the way. Come on now, hurry up."

The boy turned and plunged out. Mac shouted, "London, bring the lantern." Mac and Jim ran side by side. The night was almost complete. Ahead, they saw the flying figure of the boy. Across the open space they tore. The boy reached the line of trees and plunged among them. They could hear him running ahead of them. They dashed into the dark shadow of the trees.

Suddenly Mac reached for Jim. "Jim! drop, for Christ's sake!" There was a roar, and two big holes of light. Mac had sprawled full length. He heard several sets of running footsteps. He looked toward Jim, but the flashes still burned on his retinas. Gradually he made Jim out. He was on his knees, his head down. "You sure got down quick, Jim."

Jim did not move. Mac scrambled over to him, on his knees. "Did you get hit, Jim?" The figure kneeled, and the face was against the ground. "Oh, Christ!" Mac put out his hand to lift the head. He cried out, and jerked his hand away, and wiped it on his trousers, for there was no face. He looked slowly around, over his shoulder.

The lantern bounced along toward him, lighting London's running legs. "Where are you?" London shouted.

Mac didn't answer. He sat back on his heels, sat very quietly. He looked at the figure, kneeling in the position of Moslem prayer.

London saw them at last. He came close, and stopped; and the lantern made a circle of light. "Oh," he said. He lowered the lantern and peered down. "Shot-gun?"

Mac nodded and stared at his sticky hand.

London looked at Mac, and shivered at his frozen face. Mac stood up, stiffly. He leaned over and picked Jim up and slung him over his shoulder, like a sack; and the dripping head hung down behind. He set off, stiff-legged, toward the camp. London walked beside him, carrying the lantern.

The clearing was full of curious men. They clustered around, until they saw the burden. And then they recoiled. Mac marched through them as though he did not see them. Across the clearing, past the stoves he marched, and the crowd followed silently behind him. He came to the platform. He deposited the figure under the handrail and leaped to the stand. He dragged Jim across the boards and leaned him against the corner post, and steadied him when he slipped sideways.

London handed the lantern up, and Mac set it carefully on the floor, beside the body, so that its light fell on the head. He stood up and faced the crowd. His hands gripped the rail. His eyes were wide and white. In front he could see the massed men, eyes shining in the lamplight. Behind the front row, the men were lumped and dark. Mac shivered. He moved his jaws to speak, and seemed to break the frozen jaws loose. His voice was high and monotonous. "This guy didn't want nothing for himself—" he began. His knuckles were white, where he grasped the rail. "Comrades! He didn't want nothing for himself——"

THE LIFE AND WORKS OF
JOHN STEINBECK

By BROM WEBER

THE LIFE and works of John Steinbeck are too protean to be encompassed by facile generalizations. Though unmistakably American in many respects, his ancestral roots, aesthetic affinities, and personal experience—even his reputation during the past two decades—nevertheless linked him inextricably with Europe. Neither his literary achievements nor his attitude to the role of the literary artist were characterized by steady development along clearcut lines. Steinbeck experimented freely with form, style, and substance; he conceived of his reader primarily as a member of a group, yet appealed to him as an individual conscience; he sought anonymity, but also involved himself directly in public affairs. To a very considerable extent, he was mercurial and unpredictable, thus puzzling, until his death in December 1968.

Steinbeck was born in the inland valley town of Salinas, California, on February 27, 1902, of German, Irish, and English ancestry. His paternal grandfather, whose original family name had been Grossteinbeck, emigrated to the United States in a roundabout way from Germany in the midnineteenth century. Before arriving in America, he married an American woman from Massachusetts in Jerusalem. Their son and the writer's father, John Ernst Steinbeck, was born in Florida and then lived for a time in Massachusetts. In 1874, he followed a traditional American pattern and moved West to California.

There, in Monterey County, John Ernst Steinbeck married Olive Hamilton, a schoolteacher, whose immigrant-Irish father had settled in California in 1851 as a rancher. Here our author was born. A flour-miller for some years, the elder Steinbeck ultimately became treasurer of Monterey County at Salinas, seat of the county government. As the writer asserted in 1952, countering the myth of his working-class origins, the family was middle-class and well-to-do rather than poor.

Although Steinbeck's first published book, *Cup of Gold* (1929), was a historical romance featuring an imagined seventeenth-century English adventurer, his subsequent works have contained a large amount of familial and personal experience. There is much family history in *To a God Unknown* (1933) and *East of Eden* (1952). The days of his youth in the Salinas Valley, bounded on both sides by mountain ranges which shut off the ocean on the west and the vast central California valley on the east, provided him with much of the material—

human, social, and environmental—that appeared in later works such as *The Long Valley* (1938). Most important, Steinbeck's boyhood adventures in fields, ranches, and adjacent foothills, as well as along the shores and promontories of the nearby Pacific, stimulated his sensitivity to the phenomena of nature and a love of the land.

In 1919 Steinbeck was graduated from Salinas High School, where he had been president of the senior class. His penchant for physical action found early expression in athletics. His formal education was supplemented by reading of the family's ample library, rich in English literature, where he grew familiar with two classic works that strongly influenced his later writing: Sir Thomas Malory's *Le Morte d'Arthur* and the King James Version of the Bible.

Like many young post–World War I writers dissatisfied with the genteel tradition in America, Steinbeck found the academic not to his taste. He was in irregular attendance as a student of English at Stanford University from 1920 to 1925, but departed without receiving a degree. He had enrolled in courses which interested him, however, including classical Greek and Roman literature, English literature, and elementary zoology. During these college years Steinbeck read assiduously in American and European literature, particularly the nineteenth-century English novelists and poets. He also delved into the works of modern writers such as James Branch Cabell, D. H. Lawrence, Robinson Jeffers, and Sherwood Anderson. In his spare time, Steinbeck wrote fiction and poetry for college publications and worked as a clerk and manual laborer.

Together with other young writers of the 1920s, Steinbeck was attracted to New York City, then as now the center of the American publishing industry and a haven for young, experimental writers.

After some disillusioning months during 1925 and 1926 as a construction laborer for one dollar an hour and as a reporter for the New York *American,* Steinbeck returned to California. For the next few years he lived in various parts of the state, including San Francisco and Lake Tahoe in the Sierra Nevada range. He earned his living as the caretaker of a High Sierra mountain lodge and subsequently as the employee of a fish hatchery. These were the years during which he wrote several works including *Cup of Gold.*

Cup of Gold appeared in 1929, the year of the stock market crash which introduced the great socioeconomic depression of the 1930s. Steinbeck evidently intended to write an ironic fable on the futility of the acquisitive materialism that had characterized the expansive, self-aggrandizing economy of the 1920s. But he turned back to the past for his time, characters, locales, and situations, making a seventeenth-century Welsh boy the central figure. Henry Morgan's dreams of success and love carry him through a career of piracy and high office that ends with a death beclouded by the knowledge that his worldly achievements have been valueless, his concept of success a petty fraud. Henry Morgan had been unable to accept the wisdom of Merlin, poet and visionary, who knows that dreams are only for children; men must reconcile themselves to the reality of failure, a noble fate in modern civilization.

Steinbeck's first novel was not an artistic success. The work of an imaginative and skilled young writer, it nevertheless is incoherent in its thematic and character development, oscillating uncertainly between a hatred of rapacity and inhumanity and an entranced enthusiasm for amoral blood-and-thunder melodrama. Reviewers of the novel pointed out the lack of unity in the style, which ranged between a rich baroque and the restrained, realistic idiom of modern American naturalism. Echoes of his vast reading appear profusely in references to the Arthurian myth of the Holy Grail, the story of the Trojan War, and the legend of Faust. Steinbeck was thus, at the beginning of his career, a poetic symbolist and moral allegorist, who sought to order his materials in mythic patterns derived from the classics. Many of his important, recurring, symbolic images and characters, such as the valley and the pious prostitute, made their first appearance in this youthful effort.

In 1930, a year after publication of *Cup of Gold,* Steinbeck married Carol Henning and established a home in Pacific Grove, a coastal city west of Salinas and south of San Francisco. The Steinbecks lived there until 1936, when they bought a ranch in Los Gatos, California. It was at Pacific Grove and the nearby waterfront town of Monterey that Steinbeck met many of the characters who appear in *Tortilla Flat* and *Cannery Row.*

Probably the most important literary association Steinbeck made during these years was with Edward Ricketts, a Chicagoan who first had settled in Pacific Grove and then moved to Monterey, where he died in an auto accident in 1948. Ricketts owned a commercial biological laboratory where he prepared biological slides and specimens to be used for study and dissection at educational and research institutions. Steinbeck's great admiration for Ricketts animates the affectionate memorial tribute introducing Steinbeck's *The Log from the Sea of Cortez* (1951). Ricketts seems to have had an enormous, joyous appetite for music, women, liquor, and adventure, as well as for philosophical musings on the nature of human existence and the cosmos. He appears as a character in Steinbeck's short story "The Snake," as well as

in three of Steinbeck's novels: *In Dubious Battle, Cannery Row,* and *Sweet Thursday.*

Steinbeck's mythopoeic temper grew more fruitful as he composed *To a God Unknown* (1933), a novel begun before *The Pastures of Heaven* (1932). In *To a God Unknown* the American experience of westward expansion and material prosperity is scrutinized in the light of Biblical and Western European mythology. Joseph Wayne and his brothers come to California from New England. Patriarchal, mystic, pagan, Joseph dominates his brothers and the Mexican Indians who also live in the fertile valley. He has a passionate attachment to the land, worshiping it sexually and finding messages in trees and rocks. This pantheistic bliss is interrupted when drought strikes the valley, and death overcomes its men, animals, and vegetation. Inspired by an old man living on a cliff overlooking the Pacific where he watches the sun's daily death and rejuvenates himself and the cosmos by ritual sacrifice of animals, Joseph offers himself as a sacrifice. By virtue of his suicide, the rains come and the dying valley is saved. *To a God Unknown* is one of Steinbeck's most powerful novels, sustained in tone and beautifully written. Its rhapsodic paean to nature as fertile mother and destructive force has an intensity that reminds one of Jean Giono's fervent prose.

The power that flows through *To a God Unknown* had apparently subsided in Steinbeck; *The Pastures of Heaven* is a relatively minor effort. The title is ironic, for the valley in which the inhabitants of "the pastures of heaven" reside is sterilized by their human frailties and life-destroying values. Consumed by petty dreams, desires, and weaknesses, they live lives that are haunted and destroyed, leaving behind a shambles of insanity, frustration, and shame. Unlike Joseph Wayne in *To a God Unknown,* none is possessed by the lyricism and passion of nature. Nature is hemmed in and devitalized by them; they are ignorant of the organic rhythms of life and death. But this death in life is presented by Steinbeck without significant depth.

The book's lack of success is immediately apparent when contrasted with Sherwood Anderson's *Winesburg, Ohio*, which *The Pastures of Heaven* resembles in structure as well as in the grotesque representation of the characters. Anderson's sketches are profoundly ironic because the flaws of his grotesque characters are the flaws of the narrator himself, whose compassion and horror are evoked not only by the inhabitants of Winesburg but also by a dim realization of his own tragic limitations. Steinbeck's irony, on the other hand, is gentle and diffused; his only explanation for the disorder found in the pastures of heaven is a curse alleged to have been laid upon an abandoned farm in this wretched Garden of Eden. Probably the book's greatest accomplishment is its treatment of men and events in the modern world, a development that also marks the stories Steinbeck wrote during the early 1930s and later collected in *The Long Valley* (1938).

Generally unknown as a writer until 1935, when *Tortilla Flat* was published, Steinbeck then received favorable critical attention and his book sold fairly well. In general, however, there is considerable disagreement about the meaning of the novel and its aesthetic achievement. The earliest critics felt that Steinbeck had delivered himself of a glorification of primitivism and bestiality as an alternative to the psychic and social terrors of modern civilization. He was charged with irresponsibility as a result. All critics have agreed, wisely in this writer's opinion, that it is a hilariously humorous work. But *Tortilla Flat,* though suffused with comedy and the joys of simple living, is at the same time a satire of American bourgeois values which had transformed the pastures of heaven into a spiritless community. The *paisanos* of *Tortilla Flat* turn defeat into temporary victory only by extending to their ridiculous extreme those values which have degraded them. Their parasitism is socially a logical development, so that Steinbeck's judgment of them—while amused and sympathetic—is yet a moral indictment of the *paisanos* in particular and American culture in general.

Those who had laughed at *Tortilla Flat* were sobered by the content of his next book and shocked by its tragic theme. *In Dubious Battle* (1936) relates the story of a migratory fruit-pickers' strike, under Communist leadership, in California's Central Valley. Steinbeck's style had been stripped to bare essentials. Rigorously, unsentimentally, limiting himself—except on the last few pages— to the point of view of one character whose experience traverses the novel, Steinbeck plunged more deeply into the maelstrom of revolutionary political action than almost any other American writer before or since. Steinbeck's sympathies lay with the dissident farm workers, but with remarkable artistic detachment he managed to view the strike situation as a microcosmic battleground of the warring elements in man.

The characters of *In Dubious Battle* were individualized with particularizing detail and their interaction enabled Steinbeck to explore the relationship between man and society which he later studied intellectually in *Sea of Cortez* (1941). Reduced to its broadest implications, *In Dubious Battle* demonstrated the inadequacy of man to control his individual and social fate so long as he was torn between the conflicting demands of reason and emotion and incapable of unifying himself. The gullible innocence of the strikers, the amoral anti-intellectualism of the Communists on the one hand and of the orchard owners on the other, and the detached intellectual perception of Doctor Burton exemplified the disunity of modern man in a time of crisis.

With *Of Mice and Men* (1937), Steinbeck became an important figure in the American literary firmament. Chosen by the Book of the Month Club as one of its widely distributed selections, the novel became a best seller and made Steinbeck a relatively prosperous man. Before the year's end, 150,000 copies had been sold. Shortly before the book's appearance, Steinbeck had apprehensively told his friend Lawrence Clark Powell that he hoped never to become a popular success: "A single best seller can ruin a writer forever." He stressed his preference for a consistently small audience of twenty thousand readers, whose support would enable him to live adequately and write to satisfy his own standards rather than those of a mass audience. But the book's success made popularity inevitable, as did his dramatization of the play presented on Broadway. The stage production was Steinbeck's first experiment with the drama and had been written in collaboration with the experienced popular playwright, George S. Kaufman. The script was picked as the best play of the 1937–1938 season by the New York Drama Critics Circle and the book was later filmed in Hollywood.

It was Steinbeck's original intention to write a play in the form of a novel when he undertook *Of Mice and Men*. The result was successful, each chapter opening with prose passages that serve to set the scene and then moving swiftly into dialogue rarely interrupted by narrative. As prose fiction, however, the work is thin in texture. Steinbeck's compassion for men socially and physically underprivileged is moving, but to a considerable extent the lyrical quality of his feeling is marred by an underlying sentimentality.

The depth and texture of *I[n Dubious] Battle* reappeared in *The Grapes [of Wrath]* (1939), which along with *Of Mice a[nd] Men* comprises the roster of books in which Steinbeck explored the life of migratory farm laborers in California. *The Grapes of Wrath* crystalized Steinbeck's position as a major American novelist. He had been working on the book for some time, incorporating observations first made of the California agricultural economy in 1936, and later supplemented with additional experience and research in the following years. Like Upton Sinclair's earlier *The Jungle,* which focused national attention on the meat-packing industry and resulted in regulatory Congressional legislation, *The Grapes of Wrath* was in great part a powerful muckraking document. It aroused national interest in the condition of migratory farm workers in California and helped stimulate a congressional investigation of labor camps.

The novel also brought Steinbeck extraordinary personal publicity, for he was discussed throughout the nation and both reviled and praised. The book itself was often denounced and sometimes publicly destroyed, all of which tended to increase its sales. In California, the Kern County Board of Supervisors banned the novel from the county's public and school libraries on the ground that it was "obscene and misleading propaganda." Subsequently, efforts were made to ban the book in all state-supported schools and libraries.

In March 1940, Steinbeck joined with his friend Ricketts on a marine expedition in the Gulf of California. The results of the voyage, scientific as well as philosophical, were published in 1941 in the collaboratively written volume, *Sea of Cortez.* Apart from several articles Steinbeck wrote and casual remarks he made in introductions, prefaces, and the like, *Sea of Cortez* contains the only systematic exposition of Steinbeck's ideas. Many of the concepts which have occupied critics of his work, including his theories of nonteleological thinking, collectivity, and cosmic unity, are set forth at length in *Sea of Cortez*. It is only fair to add that, to a considerable extent, the book only reflects his thoughts at the end of the 1930s and should not be used mechanically as a guide to the views underlying his later works, particularly those of the 1950s. Furthermore, as will be apparent to anyone who reads *Sea of Cortez*, Steinbeck—despite his attempt to establish a rationale for his novels and stories —is no more a rigorous philosopher than was Ernest Hemingway in *Death in the Afternoon*.

Steinbeck's other writing during the years of World War II represents the contribution of his reputation and journalistic skill to the cause of the United States and her Allies. At the request of the army air force, he wrote *Bombs Away* (1942), designed as an informative handbook that would acquaint the American people with the true facts about the conditions under which the various members of a bombing team were trained for their collective task.

Again at the request of a government agency, this time the Office of Strategic Services, Steinbeck wrote *The Moon Is Down* (1942), first as a novel and then as a play. It was also adapted into a film in Hollywood. *The Moon Is Down* was received with mixed attitudes both in the United States and abroad. In general, Steinbeck's anti-Fascist sentiments were approved. Reservations were expressed about the quality of the artistry and emotion displayed, some readers holding that the characters were simple abstractions devoid of human complexity regardless of whether they were Fascist or anti-Fascist.

In the late spring of 1943, Steinbeck embarked for Europe to report the war

as a correspondent for the New York *Herald-Tribune*. From June through December, Steinbeck sent back dispatches from England, Africa, and Italy. It was not until 1958 that these pieces were collected in *Once There Was a War*.

In 1941, Steinbeck and his first wife, Mrs. Carol Steinbeck, separated and a year later Mrs. Steinbeck obtained a divorce. Steinbeck was married for the second time in March 1943 to Miss Gwyn Conger of Los Angeles. Two sons, Steinbeck's only children, were born during the course of this marriage. After having lived in California since his birth there in 1902, he now crossed the continent and settled permanently in New York City.

Steinbeck's second marriage ended in divorce in 1948. In December 1950, he married Mrs. Elaine Scott, the former wife of stage and screen actor Zachary Scott. Steinbeck wrote affectionately about life with his family during their travels abroad and at their homes in New York's Manhattan and Sag Harbor, Long Island, where Steinbeck fished, sailed, and wrote. The locale and inhabitants of Sag Harbor furnished Steinbeck with details for his last novel, *The Winter of Our Discontent* (1961).

From 1945 to 1961, Steinbeck published eight novels. They differed greatly from each other in style, structure, and spirit. Most of them enjoyed great sales; some had appeared earlier in mass-circulation magazines, some were later converted into films. But though Steinbeck's work continued to attract a vast readership, it no longer brought him the critical acclaim that had greeted his fiction prior to World War II.

In general, it could be said that the critics were disappointed with the postwar fiction because in their opinion Steinbeck was no longer creating serious literature. A novel such as *The Pearl* (1947) was held to counsel defeatism and acceptance of the status quo; *East of*

Eden (1952) was charged with intellectual superficiality and moral confusion; *The Wayward Bus* (1947) was accused of sentimentalizing the primitive and cloaking itself in an aura of religiosity; *Cannery Row* (1945) and *Sweet Thursday* (1945) were regarded as potboiling exploitations of *Tortilla Flat* without the critical temper of that early novel. So pervasive was the critical dissatisfaction that it seemed to render critics and reviewers incapable of appreciating the high quality of Steinbeck's sustained satirio-comic achievement in *The Short Reign of Pippin IV* (1957).

Various explanations were advanced for Steinbeck's alleged failures. In leaving California in the 1940s, Steinbeck was said to have severed himself from the milieu and the people who had first awakened his creativity. His view of man as a biological entity had caused him to dehumanize his characters. His conceptions of morality were Victorian in origin and had left him ill-equipped to cope with the moral chaos of contemporary America. His reliance upon traditional forms of fiction, as well as upon traditional myths and symbols, had made it difficult for him to respond sensitively to fresh experience. The harshest charge of all concerned Steinbeck's allegedly positive attitude to the materialism and affluence which he regularly decried in his novels. It was said that his financial success had made him forget his former distaste for personal publicity and financial gain, so that as a writer he cooperated with editors, film producers, publishers, and literary agents and no longer wrote from deep need and conviction.

But the heart of the matter was that his last novel, *The Winter of Our Discontent* (1961), demonstrated that Steinbeck was more than aware of the price he may have had to pay for success. Indeed, the novel probed its protagonist's moral problems with greater emotional depth,

intellectual perspicuity, and stylistic richness than can be found in any novel Steinbeck had published since 1939. In *Travels with Charley* (1962), furthermore, Steinbeck admitted with admirable candor that he had lost touch with the realities of American life for the preceding quarter of a century. Traveling about over the country in the company of his dog Charley, Steinbeck began to wonder about the nature of communication. Can it be true, he asked himself: "A man who has no one to say anything to has no words as he has no need for words?"

Despite buffeting from critics, Steinbeck received many acknowledgements in the United States of his achievement as a creative artist and public figure. Early in his career, in 1935, he received the Gold Medal of the Commonwealth Club of San Francisco for *Tortilla Flat*. The Commonwealth Club's Gold Medal was awarded to him again the following year, after publication of *In Dubious Battle*. In January 1939, prior to publication of *The Grapes of Wrath,* he was elected to membership in the National Institute of Arts and Letters along with William Faulkner. In 1940, the periodical *Social Work Today* gave Steinbeck its first annual award designed to honor the individual who had most effectively interpreted unsatisfied social and economic need. In May, Steinbeck won the most famous of American literary awards, the Pulitzer Prize, for *The Grapes of Wrath*. During 1940, too, Steinbeck received praise from Mrs. Franklin D. Roosevelt —then touring migratory labor camps in California's San Joaquin Valley—for the accuracy and tone of *The Grapes of Wrath*. Later, that same year, in September, Steinbeck was a guest of President Franklin D. Roosevelt at the White House. Toward the close of the decade, in 1948, Steinbeck's continued prestige as an American writer resulted in his election to the American Academy of Arts and

Letters. Once again, Steinbeck's election occurred concurrently with that of William Faulkner.

During the early 1950s, when the American political scene was disturbed by violent clashes between liberalism and its opponents, Steinbeck became immersed in political activity. His parents traditionally had championed the Republican party; as he related in *Travels with Charley* (1962), his sisters in California vehemently supported the presidential aspirations of Republican Richard Nixon in 1960, despite Steinbeck's arguments in favor of John F. Kennedy. Steinbeck's involvement in politics became publicly known in 1952 during the presidential campaign of Adlai Stevenson, nominee of the Democratic party. Together with Herman Wouk, the popular novelist, Steinbeck issued an appeal for the American electorate to vote for Stevenson rather than for the Republican candidate, Dwight D. Eisenhower. He also joined ninety-two famous American authors, including Pearl Buck, John Hersey, and Carl Sandburg, who charged that American newspapers and magazines had been guilty of nationwide abuse of the written word for harming Stevenson's campaign by means of biased and inadequate news reporting.

Steinbeck was again a vigorous supporter of Adlai Stevenson during the 1956 presidential campaign. Steinbeck's most notable contribution was the preparation of speeches for Stevenson. Interviewed in Copenhagen in 1957 about the matter, Steinbeck said that he had undertaken the task because Stevenson, though a good writer, wrote with too much intellectual complexity to be easily understood by the masses of voters. In addition to writing speeches whose style and arguments would have a popular flair, Steinbeck declared that he had also contributed to the development of the political aims expostulated by Stevenson.

Despite Stevenson's failure to win the presidency in the campaigns of 1952 and 1956, Steinbeck joined Archibald MacLeish, Reinhold Niebuhr, and other national figures to urge in 1960 that the Democratic party nominate Stevenson for a third presidential effort instead of choosing John F. Kennedy, who was leading contender for the nomination.

Whereas prior to the mid-1940s Steinbeck's extensive travels abroad had been essentially private affairs with the exception of his wartime reporting, his subsequent travels frequently evoked international political repercussions. During the late summer and early fall of 1947, Steinbeck and Robert Capa, the photographer, traveled together to the U.S.S.R. for the New York *Herald-Tribune*. Steinbeck's dispatches were later collected into a volume, *Russian Journal* (1948), which was illustrated with Capa's photographs. In March 1948, extensive publicity was given to a notice in *Izvestia,* the important Russian newspaper, that charged Steinbeck with having written false reports. Two years later, Steinbeck was linked with André Gide, André Malraux, Upton Sinclair, and Jean-Paul Sartre by the Russian composer Dimitri Shostakovich, who charged them all with being "warmongers."

As Steinbeck's concern with international affairs increased, he spoke out more and more freely, even when abroad, on troubling international problems. In 1952, during a sojourn in Italy, he engaged in a dramatic newspaper debate with Italian Communists. He accused them of unwarranted attacks upon the moral character and background of young American soldiers serving in Europe. He also asserted that charges of American germ warfare in Korea were baseless, insisting that the only germs dropped by American airborne forces were the germs of truth contained in propaganda leaflets.

In the years following World War II, Steinbeck's works were frequently translated and discussed in Europe, especially those like *The Grapes of Wrath* and *Tortilla Flat* which offered an intimate view of American life, and those like *The Moon Is Down* which reflected a significant American attitude toward European life and problems. In those nations becoming aware that a vital American literature had been in process of creation during the 1920s and 1930s, Steinbeck's writing came to occupy a position of importance alongside that of Ernest Hemingway, William Faulkner, John Dos Passos, and Erskine Caldwell. Steinbeck's works were held up for consideration as revelations of American artistic maturity and innovation and were praised for their depth and achievement by distinguished literary critics.

As was the case with the work of his American contemporaries, Steinbeck's books became models for emulation and their influence can be discerned in the novels of various modern European writers.

In 1946 Steinbeck was awarded the Liberty Cross by King Haakon of Norway. In this way Norway honored Steinbeck for his portrayal in *The Moon Is Down* of the Norwegian resistance movement during the German occupation in World War II.

In 1962, at the age of sixty, John Steinbeck was awarded the Nobel Prize for Literature.

In July 1964, he was one of twenty-five American men and women who received the Medal of Freedom from President Lyndon B. Johnson. Established in 1945 to reward outstanding civilian achievements in World War II, the range of the Medal of Freedom had been extended in 1963 by President John F. Kennedy, so that it became an annual recognition by the White House of those who had made significant contributions to the quality of American life.

Questioned in 1963, five years before he died at the age of 66, about whether he preferred to be understood by readers during his lifetime or three thousand years later, Steinbeck unhesitatingly chose his contemporaries. That wish had already been granted. At the same time, Steinbeck insisted upon his character as an experimental writer. "No two novels of mine are alike," he said. There is little reason to doubt that Steinbeck's stories and novels will be read for many decades to come. The task facing literary historians and critics is the reevaluation of his works in order to determine to what extent, despite their varying contents and styles, they penetrated human experience with lasting compassion, depth, honesty, and aesthetic success.

Brom Weber is a professor of English at the University of California at Davis, not far from one of Steinbeck's favorite locales.

THE 1962 PRIZE

By KJELL STRÖMBERG

JOHN STEINBECK was the sixth American writer to be honored with a Nobel prize. He was proposed as early as the 1940s, at the same time as two other great American novelists, William Faulkner and Ernest Hemingway, both of whom were to win the award before Steinbeck (Faulkner in 1949, Hemingway in 1954). In 1954, various critics had maintained that although there was certainly no harm in honoring the American novel, especially as represented by William Faulkner and his fellow pioneer of the modern style John Dos Passos, but the generosity reached an excess when the Academy began to look for a new laureate in the same literary camp. Compared to the true innovator, Faulkner, for example, Hemingway was considered rather a brilliant reporter who used his talents to cover current events in fictional form.

Steinbeck's candidacy met with insistent opposition. Even so, from year to year his name was proposed by various supporters, some of them from the Academy itself. Finally in 1962, in spite of heavy competition, the day arrived. On October 25th the Swedish Academy decided to award the Nobel Prize for Literature to John Steinbeck "for his realistic as well as imaginative writings, distinguished by a sympathetic humor and a keen social perception."

No fewer than sixty candidates were considered that year, and the contest seemed to be wide open. For the preceding six years the prize had been won by writers from Latin or Slavic lands—the Spaniard Jiménez, the French writers Albert Camus and Saint-John Perse, the Italian Quasimodo, the Russian Boris Pasternak, and the Yugoslav Ivo Andrić. Considering the care the jury has always taken to give an equal chance to as many nations as possible, it seemed reasonable that, in 1962, English-language literature had a particular hold on the Academy's attentions, especially since fine writers were plentiful in both British and American ranks.

In England, Graham Greene, Aldous Huxley, and, in particular, Robert Graves, had been proposed for many years running. To these three the name of Lawrence Durrell had been added after the appearance of his *Alexandria Quartet*. This cycle of four novels caused critics everywhere—and particularly in Sweden, where critical language is normally a question of superlatives—to hail Durrell as the most remarkable novelist of his day.

In the United States there was an embarrassment of riches. If Steinbeck were preferred over a distinguished novelist like Dos Passos, or lyric poets like Ezra Pound, Robert Frost, and Carl Sandburg, it was doubtless not just for his socially oriented novels. These had been best sellers in the United States. However, he had also enjoyed an extremely favorable press in the Scandinavian countries ever since the publication in 1942 of a short novel, *The Moon Is Down,* a deeply felt homage to occupied Norway which was published simultaneously in Stockholm, London, and New York.

It was in 1943, the year following *The Moon Is Down,* that Steinbeck was first actually nominated for the Nobel Prize, preceding his two compatriots who would eventually win the Prize before him. As in the case of Hemingway, the task of preparing a report on Steinbeck fell to Per Hallström, the permanent secretary of the Academy, perhaps because Hallström, as a young engineer, had spent a few years in North America. Hallström had a high regard for *The Grapes of Wrath,* which he examined in detail in his report. He recognized the authenticity of the plot and the accuracy of the descriptions, which are often of a raw realism, but he found the psychology comparatively superficial and he noted a lack of "monumentality" in the general concept of the work. On the whole, the book impressed him as being "typically American," showing "the strength and extraordinary courage of a race of people who are still young."

Hallström was much less impressed by Steinbeck's first two great commercial successes, *Tortilla Flat* and *Of Mice and Men.* In the former, Hallström sought but could never find the fallen knights, still good lads, of Selma Lagerlöf, sidekicks of Gösta Berling naturalized as Americans. In the latter, he did not understand the symbolism and the sentimental ending displeased him. Nor was he particularly inclined to give very high marks to the romanticized reporting of the war in Norway in *The Moon Is Down,* which he described as a propagandistic book written on order, obvi-

ously without conviction. However, Hallström did admire the short stories collected under the title *The Long Valley,* especially the little masterpiece entitled "The Flight," the story of a young Mexican halfbreed who came into conflict with some white hoodlums. Hallström characterized this piece as "the artistic peak of Steinbeck's achievement to date." He concluded that Steinbeck was not yet ready for a Nobel Prize, but that his most recent works "perhaps give us reason to expect much from this writer in the future."

In 1949, Hallström wrote a second critique of Steinbeck's work in which he voiced disappointment, although he allowed that Steinbeck's many and diversified qualities might nevertheless justify maintaining a watchful attitude. Since 1949, Steinbeck had written a number of novels, all of them best sellers, but nothing, in the general opinion, comparable to his best work of the thirties. His novel *The Winter of Our Discontent,* according to Anders Österling who gave a radio broadcast on Steinbeck when he had finally been awarded the Prize, was one that convinced the Academy to abandon its policy of watching and waiting and put an end to their hesitation.

Among the leading newspapers in the United States which commented on the award of the Prize to Steinbeck, the New York *Herald-Tribune* was the only one to approve the choice without reservations. The prizewinner himself commented on both the Prize and his critics with great good humor and an unshakeable serenity.

"The Nobel Prize is a kind of comeback for me," he declared shortly after his arrival in Stockholm. Asked whether he considered himself worthy of it, he answered by giving a list of five or six fellow writers whom he considered at least equally qualified. They included Arthur Miller, Carl Sandburg, John Dos

Passos, Erskine Caldwell, Robert Frost, and Tennessee Williams. He added, "People never get what they deserve, they never deserve what they get. I received the Prize and naturally accepted it in a state of shock. It would have been ridiculous to refuse it."

Seated on the flowered dais with the five winners of the Nobel Prize for Science—all of them English or American —at the Concert Palace where the solemn awards ceremony is traditionally held, Steinbeck seemed very much at ease, smiling nonchalantly behind his closely cropped Van Dyke beard.

His acceptance speech concluded with the observation that "St. John the Apostle may well be paraphrased: In the end is the Word, and the Word is Man—and the Word is with Man."

Translated by Dale McAdoo